D1130050

Disciplines and Techniques of Systems Control

A Blaisdell Book in the Pure and Applied Sciences

Disciplines and Techniques of Systems Control

EDITED BY

JOHN PESCHON

BLAISDELL PUBLISHING COMPANY
A Division of Ginn and Company
NEW YORK · TORONTO · LONDON

First Edition, 1965

LIBRARY OF CONGRESS CATALOG CARD NUMBER: 64-10467

Preface

In 1954 Professor H. S. Tsien published a remarkable little book called "Engineering Cybernetics." His intention was to introduce the advanced student and the research engineer to concepts which shortly before had appeared in the specialized scientific press. Tsien's contribution was to select, among a wealth of articles, those that would have a major impact upon the science of automatic control, and to explain these in such a manner that the willing and studious engineer should not be discouraged. This is precisely the scope of the present text. Tsien gave an account of the new techniques that had become available to automate the routine decisions required to control complex processes involving primarily machines. The title "Engineering Cybernetics," which he chose in order to differentiate the subject matter from the somewhat narrower theory of automatic feedback control systems, would no longer be appropriate today. "Cybernetics" is now used to denote the study of information processes in biological systems as well as in certain machines deliberately designed to duplicate these information processes, and thus differs from the scope of Tsien's work. Our intention is to give an account of the main techniques available to automate—often by computer—the routine decisions required to improve the behavior of complex processes, which in general involve only machines, but which in certain cases may also comprise men. This is why "Systems Control" was preferred to the narrower "Automatic Control."

Since the subject under discussion has made substantial advances during the last few years, it was estimated that a single author would probably not be able to cover each subject with the required thoroughness. Contributions from several authors willing to explore one topic with sufficient detail were therefore requested. The obvious drawback of this scheme is that duplication and lack of uniformity cannot always be avoided, especially when some of the authors live in remote countries.

Contributions, not only from the United States, but also from Europe and from the Soviet Union, responded to this call. While the quality and originality of Soviet research had been recognized by some in the West for some time, the 1960 Congress of the International Federation of Automatic Control in Moscow persuaded many more of this fact. Directions in which the Soviets excel are Nonlinear Mechanics and the Theory of Optimum Control. Professors A. M. Letov and A. A. Feldbaum, both of the Institute of Automatics and Telemechanics, agreed to cover these two subjects. Academician Letov was the chairman of the 1960 IFAC congress, the proceedings of which still constitute a very complete report on the state of the art. These proceedings were instrumental in determining the structure of the present text and are extensively quoted in the bibliographies.

A glance at these proceedings suggests that the mathematical background of students familiar with the numerous texts of Automatic Control published in the 1950's is frequently exceeded. The present work attempts to introduce the reader to the mathematical terminology and to the concepts now required by the graduate student and the research engineer.

It is sometimes said that industrial development lags behind university research by seven years, part of which is spent by the engineer to master fundamental knowledge. Unless changes in the organization of industrial research take place, this incubation period will tend to increase rather than decrease. In support of this statement, it is pointed out that the first treatise on Dynamic Programming, the importance of which was only realized recently, had already been published in 1955; systematic industrial application, of course, is not yet envisaged. It is hoped that this text succeeds in reducing this lag by some small amount.

This then leads to a discussion on what advanced control systems look like now and will look like in a few years. It is safe to say that the second-order linear and even nonlinear single variable system, has become of limited interest, except for tutorial purposes and straightforward development work. The systems now in the design stage are complex, that is, of high order and with a multiplicity of inputs and outputs. The design criterion to be satisfied is no longer 20 percent overshoot in response to a step, but optimum behavior in a complex environment of which only a statistical description may be available. A concise statement of the subject might be "optimum control of complex processes." These processes would generally be physical, such as a catalytic cracking tower, but in an ever-increasing number of instances, the controllers will be connected to processes involving men as well as machines. "Man-machine" processes, for which the systems engineer or the operational analyst would normally be held responsible, fall into this category. It does not seem logical that the control engineer and the systems engineer both design independent control loops around a complex process, such as a production line, where there are obvious interactions between the operators and the production machines.

The material of this book comprises a fundamental part (Chapters I through VII) and an applications part (Chapters VIII through X).

In the Introduction, *Chapter I*, the classes of control systems that are now being designed or will soon be designed, are reviewed. Optimizing and adaptive systems are shown to be natural generalizations of classical closed loop feedback structures and not, as some of the earlier work suggests, classical feedback structures with clever protuberances.

In *Chapter II*, some of the modern mathematical tools required for the design of deterministic control systems are presented. The power of state space notation is impressed upon the reader.

In *Chapter III*, single variable feedback systems are briefly reviewed and several classes of multivariable systems are discussed in detail. Timesharing of control and computer components is introduced.

In *Chapter IV*, statistical design techniques and the problem of prediction are discussed.

In *Chapter V*, the classical nonlinear techniques (topological methods and describing function) are reviewed and certain aspects of the optimum n'th order contactor control are presented.

Detailed treatments of Liapunov's second method, the definitions of stability, the problem of quality of nonlinear systems, and the connection between Liapunov functions and optimal systems, are given in *Chapter VI*.

In *Chapter VII*, the optimal control of dynamic processes via dynamic programing and the principle of the maximum are discussed. These techniques are thereafter applied to the optimum control of a process affected by random disturbances.

Chapter VIII is the first of the application chapters. Here the very timely subject of inertial guidance is discussed.

Computer Process Control, that is the application of digital and analog computers to the optimum control of complex processes, is reviewed in *Chapter IX*. The economic and technical changes caused by the systematic utilization of computers to automate routine decision justify a uniform treatment of this vast and somewhat ill-defined subject.

In *Chapter X*, the reader is introduced to systems engineering which permits the design of computer-based systems around large-scale processes comprising men as well as machines.

We wish to express our sincere thanks to Miss Jean Stuart for her Russian-English translations, to Miss A. Bosseler for her secretarial help and to all the colleagues who helped in elucidating points of doubt.

J. PESCHON

Contents

CHAPTER VIII

REFERENCE STABILIZATION AND INERTIAL GUIDANCE SYSTEMS

Connie L. McClure

CHAPTER IX

COMPUTER PROCESS CONTROL

John Peschon Lucas Pun Stanford K. Mitter

CHAPTER X

SYSTEMS ENGINEERING: ITS PRINCIPLES, PRACTICES, AND PROSPECTS

Roy C. Amara

CHAPTER I

The State of the Art of Automatic Control

LUCAS PUN
JOHN PESCHON

CONTENTS

1. Automatic Control: The Subject Matter

As is the case with many fundamental discoveries, several people are credited with having developed the first automatic control system. England's inventor of the steam engine, James Watt, also patented a singularly ingenious device whereby the shaft speed of his steam engine was maintained constant regardless of load variations and boiler pressure. The fundamental principle was to make the amount of steam admitted to the cylinder proportional, not to the desired shaft speed, but to the difference between the desired and the actual shaft speeds.

During the latter part of the nineteenth century, such distinguished scientists as James Clerk Maxwell, Henri Poincaré, and Alexander Mikhailov Liapunov evolved the mathematical techniques whereby Watt's regulator as well as many kinds of modern automatic control systems could be analyzed.

In the nineteen thirties, the Bell Telephone Company was attempting to span the American continent with long distance telephone lines and, to this end, needed vacuum tube amplifiers of hitherto unknown quality. Various attempts failed to improve the vacuum tubes then available, and transcontinental telephony became possible only when H. Black incorporated the principle of feedback into conventional amplifier design. Black's monumental contribution was the key to the construction of the required high-quality amplifiers with the available low-quality components.

During World War II, several research teams, mostly in the United States and Great Britain, developed automatic computing machines under the sponsorship of the pertinent military agencies. Aiming guns and torpedoes with mathematical precision were to be the primary applications.

The unprecedented versatility of these machines was soon recognized and it was shown that almost any mathematical equation could be solved via computer; this in itself was a discovery of vast consequence, since the majority of the mathematical equations cannot be solved by conventional means because of their nonlinear or multidimensional character. The subsequent invention of new and powerful mathematical techniques—Monte Carlo Methods, Decision Theory, Dynamic Programing, etc.—tailored so as to exploit the potentialities of computers fully may even surpass this feat.

During the last decade, various complex military systems, such as the Continental Air Defense System, incorporating radars, computers, telecommunication networks, and conventional weapons, came into being. Rational methods to control the system constituents, which are spread over a whole continent, and to arrive at a smoothly working entity were urgently required. System engineering, which relies heavily on statistics, operations research, communication theory, etc., was developed to that end.

Since the mathematical techniques now employed by many mechanical engineers, mathematicians dealing with differential equations, amplifier designers, computer engineers, and system engineers are identical, and since the purpose of their activity is the same, namely, the rational improvement of the undesirable characteristics exhibited by given processes through addition of controllers or computers, the trend today is to teach automatic control in a unified manner to the students of the pertinent university departments and to have research carried out by teams comprising specialists in each of the stated disciplines. This trend towards unification, which is now taking place, gives automatic control the character of a science and not of an appendix to the various engineering curricula, as was previously the case.

In order to present some of the features of contemporary automatic control systems, we examine three representative systems of current interest.

1.1 Numerical Control. Numerical Control, or N.C., is the name given to those machine tools—lathes, milling machines, etc.—where the motion of the work head is controlled with extreme accuracy, not by a machinist, but by the binary information contained on a tape. The machining of complex parts at maximum milling speed and with uniform tolerances thus becomes possible. After a job order has been filled, the tape is stowed away and can be reused as often as the same part is reordered.

The cost of producing parts via N.C. may be as low as one-half the cost incurred by using conventional techniques. But the biggest advantage of N.C. may very well be not the reduction of cost, or the increase in accuracy, but the decrease in delivery time which can in certain cases be cut by a factor of 10.

The preparation of the tapes, which only a few years ago required great skill, can now be carried out by a digital computer which accepts the description of the part to be machined in clear English. This frequently eliminates the need for elaborate blueprints.

1.2 Traffic Control. In view of the extravagant cost of inter-city freeways, the optimal use of existing facilities by proper control of the traffic lights constitutes a problem of great economic importance. Research efforts are now slowly getting underway to develop systems where the number of cars waiting at each traffic light is continuously communicated to a central control computer which then generates that green-red sequence minimizing the average time the cars must wait at the intersections. The stated problem is of formidable complexity since the red-green sequence of a given light must be made to depend on the sequences adopted at nearby intersections. The now existing mathematical body appears inadequate in guiding the engineer toward a satisfactory computer program. Original techniques, not just extrapolations of present knowledge, are required.

1.3 Production Control. Production control systems are also of considerable economic importance and of great mathematical complexity. Let us assume that a production line is affected by a partial strike or that

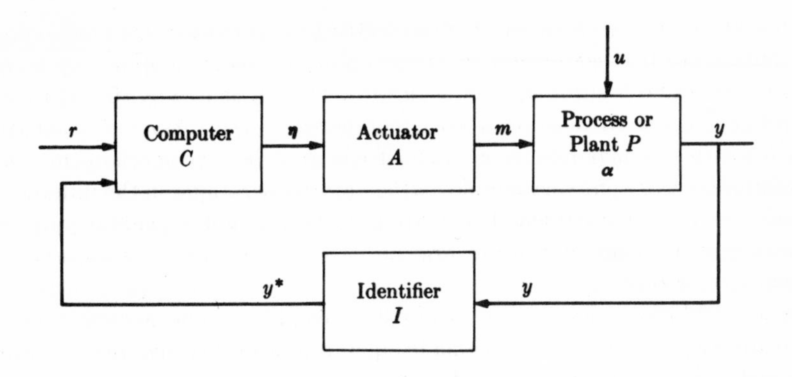

FIGURE 1. Conventional position control servomechanism.

the production process is perturbed by a heavy order. At the present time plant management copes with perturbations of this kind by issuing instructions which appear rational but certainly do not make optimum, that is, most economic use, of the available resources. Production control systems would take into consideration the exact nature of the perturbation as well as the state of the available production facilities and would either suggest to management what instructions should be issued or else would directly act upon the process at the pertinent locations. Steel mills comprising blast furnaces, open-hearth furnaces, annealing baths, and rolling mills, and controlled in accordance with these principles, are now being put into operation. The Program Evaluation and Reporting Technique (PERT) and the theory of business games [13]† are other significant examples of this general trend.

These production control systems, which should be viewed as the peaceful equivalents of certain military systems, such as the Continental Air Defense System, differ from conventional controls in that they include men as parts of the process to be controlled. This is why they are often referred to as man-machine systems.

Production processes have been optimized, mostly in the design stage, for at least two decades by means of *Operations Research.* The present trend is to program computers to solve such typical operations research problems not only during major plant reorganizations, but in a continuous or *on-line* fashion.

The control systems which are used in automatic machine-tools—see Section 1.1—are essentially conventional feed-back position control servomechanisms. These are usually represented by a "block diagram" as shown in Fig. 1.

† Numbers in brackets refer to the bibliography at the end of this chapter.

Here the plant P, which is either an electric or hydraulic motor positioning the cutter head, is connected to an actuator A, power amplifier or servo valve. The actual position $y(t)$ of the cutter-head is measured by the identifier I and the measured position $y^*(t)$ is compared to the *command input* $r(t)$ which a paper or magnetic tape reader feeds into the servomechanism. The computer C carries out very simple mathematical operations on the difference signal $r - y^*$ and instructs A accordingly. As C is not a general purpose digital or analog computer in the large majority of the cases, this constituent is also termed *controller*.

It is well known that under steady-state conditions and assuming ideal measuring apparatus I, y can be made equal to r, and this *regardless of plant parameter changes* α *and external disturbances* u provided that these are modest in size and that their variations are sufficiently slow. If the parameter changes or disturbances were very substantial, as is the case with certain airplane autopilots, the structure of Fig. 1 might not permit satisfactory performance and a so-called *adaptive* system would have to be used.

It is apparent that the traffic control system described in Section 1.2 is also a "feedback" process since the instructions issued by the central computer are based upon the number of cars waiting at each intersection. It would not be easy, however, to represent such a complex system by the simple block diagram of Fig. 1. We propose the structure shown in Fig. 2, which differs conceptually from Fig. 1 only in that the connecting lines are multiple; i.e., the single connection between actuator A and plant P would transmit an actuating *vector* $\mathbf{m}$ of components $m_1, m_2, \ldots, m_q$. In addition, the specific quantities r and y have been replaced by the much more general notions of "desired" and "actual" performance. In the literature adaptive and optimizing systems are usually represented by conventional block diagrams to which various *protuberances* have been added. These systems are thus perfectly accommodated by the general model of Fig. 2.

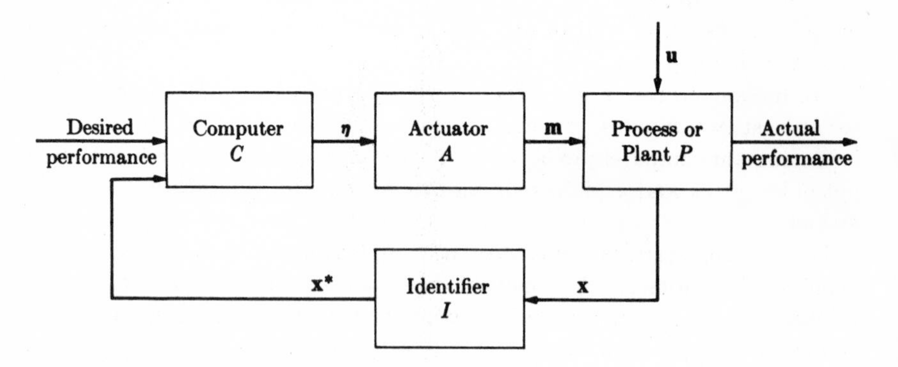

FIGURE 2. General model of a complex control system.

In the case of the traffic control system, P accounts for a city's traffic pattern at a stated time of the day. Weather conditions, events such as football games which attract an unusually high number of cars, accidents, etc., represent the disturbances $\mathbf{u}$. The ensemble of the traffic lights constitutes A. The identifier I consists of a set of counters which inform C of the number of cars waiting at the various intersections. The computer C in this particular case is no longer a simple device capable of only carrying out straightforward mathematical operations, but a general purpose digital computer. The actual performance might be the average time T during which all the cars are stopped, and the desired performance might be a statement to the effect that T should be *minimum*, that is, optimum and not just satisfactory. Further examples of such modern systems can be found in the bibliography [8, 9, 16, 18, 22, 23]. The required course material is discussed in Naslin [15].

2. Design Methodology of Automatic Control Systems

The synthesis of complex control systems as shown in Fig. 2 does not usually proceed in a straightforward manner, the reason being that we are not able as yet to evaluate such essential performance parameters as cost, reliability, . . . , *ab initio*. Our failure to understand precisely the complex interaction occurring in these systems, however, is no excuse for proceeding in a haphazard way. We list below the essential steps of a design methodology, which is certainly not unique, but, according to our experience, is of sufficient generality to accommodate most synthesis problems that we might be faced with.† Thus:

First step: Precise formulation of the objective, which is almost always economic rather than strictly technical.
Second step: Analysis of the process to be controlled.
Third step: Choice of adaptation or optimization techniques.
Fourth step: Choice of control components.
Fifth step: Evaluation and testing.

These five steps, which are linked by yes-no questions, are shown in the flow diagram of Fig. 3.

Having completed the first step, we might ask the question: "Can our initial objective be accomplished; in other words, does the estimated benefit exceed a prescribed amount N?" If the answer is "yes," we proceed. If the answer is "no," the objective must be reevaluated under a different set of boundary conditions. It frequently happens that these yes-no questions compel the designer to retrograde from an almost completed preliminary design to the very first steps. The extent to which such retrogressions are

† A slightly different methodology is presented in Chapter X.

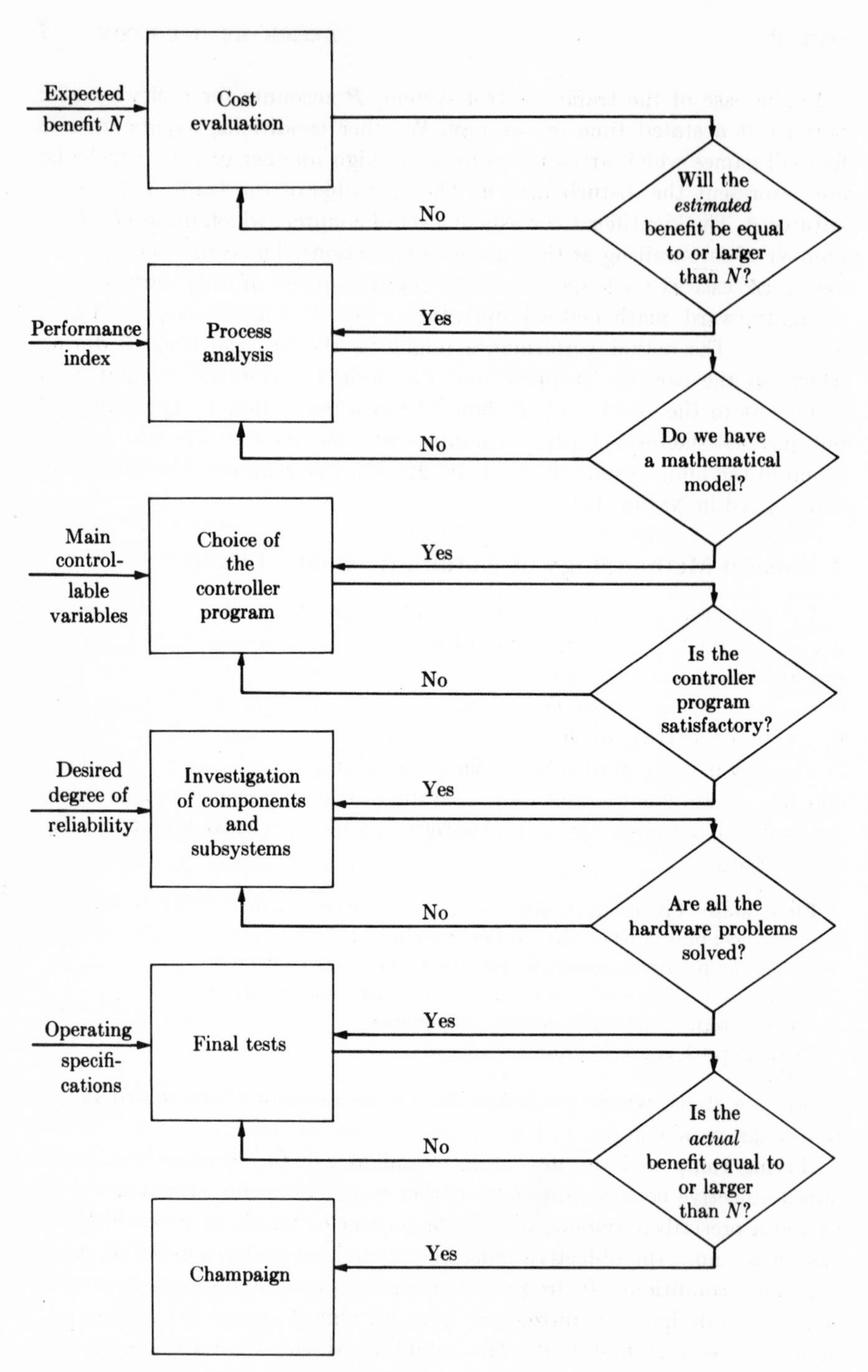

FIGURE 3. Flow diagram of the main steps to be followed in a design methodology.

rendered necessary depends on the designer's theoretical and technological ability, on the objective, and, of course, on the elaboration of analysis. This methodology holds for any complex design problem and is not limited to automatic control systems, though the terminology might become slightly different. The synthesis of complex systems, quite generally speaking, demands that many facets of the problem be examined. As in most engineering problems, the technical and economic requirements may be contradictory and an optimum† design, therefore, must take into account both factors.

While as yet we have not mastered precise methods for coordinating all these requirements in an optimum fashion in our specific field of interest, we anticipate that our improving knowledge of adaptive processes will suggest such methods.

As regards automatic control systems, the following points ought to be borne in mind.

The primary function of a control system is to *improve* in some way the characteristics of the process to be controlled. Control systems consequently *always* accomplish some form of adaptation or optimization. Since, on the other hand, any qualitative or quantitative improvement entails some expenditure, we must devote our attention to economic considerations at the outset.

The design of a satisfactory system demands that we have a sufficiently accurate *model* of the process to be controlled.

Certain *advanced* control systems referred to in the literature as optimizing, adaptive, learning, etc., do not require that all the parameters of the model be known accurately. While operating, such systems observe the response of the process and produce appropriate correcting signals on the basis of these observations. But regardless of how advanced the system is, we must always clearly define the essential inputs and outputs, the general relations between signals, and their effects upon the stated objective.

3. The Characteristics of the Process to be Controlled—Modeling and Identification

It is not necessary, generally speaking, that we know *all* the characteristics of the process we are asked to control. Those characteristics that we *must* know are dictated by the goal that we have set, that is by the objective. The design of a *minimum cost* power distribution system would require knowledge of all those factors influencing the price of the kw-hr, namely, the operating costs of the various power generating units, the cross sections of the transmission lines, etc. The design of a *maximum reliability* power distribution

† It is observed more and more frequently that precisely defined optimum designs tend to supersede a more or less vague compromise between the economic and technical requirements. Corresponding computational procedures are now explicitly used in certain system engineering problems. See, for example, Brown [4] and Dennis *et al.* [6].

system would require knowledge of an entirely different set of characteristics, perhaps a statistical description of the failure rates of certain types of transformers.

Classically, these process characteristics were determined once, namely during the design stage; today, in certain advanced systems, they are measured frequently so as to make an automatic adaptation or optimization possible. It is for this reason that accurate mathematical *modeling* has become such a pressing problem.

While modeling is carried out once during the design stage, identification of the process state is an on-line operation which permits the elaboration of adequate orders for adaptation and optimization. In some very recent systems, the structure of the identifier is not fixed, but is made to depend on the process state with the result that identification becomes more accurate; see Kalman [10] and Chang [5].

Process characteristics are categorized in Chapter III as principal process inputs, secondary process inputs, principal process outputs, secondary process outputs, states, disturbances, parameters, constraints, etc. While the difference between inputs and outputs is self-evident in most engineering situations, this is not so for inputs and parameters. Optimizing and adaptive systems have been differentiated from one another in that in the first case inputs, and in the second case parameters, are manipulated to act upon the system. We believe that a parameter which is externally altered inevitably becomes an input. This distinction, therefore, does not appear to be very rational.

3.1 Relations between Inputs and Outputs. If a process, see Fig. 4, is described by a set of linear, constant coefficient differential equations we often find it expedient to define *transfer functions* $p_{ij}(s)$ which relate some output $Y_i(s)$ to some input $M_j(s)$. If $m_j(t)$ is a quantity whose temporal behavior is given, then knowledge of $p_{ij}(s)$ yields the temporal behavior of $y_i(t)$. If, and this is frequently the case, we only have a statistical description of $m_j(t)$, then knowledge of $p_{ij}(s)$ provides us with a statistical description of $y_i(t)$. In the case of nonlinear or time-varying processes, $y_i(t)$ and $m_j(t)$

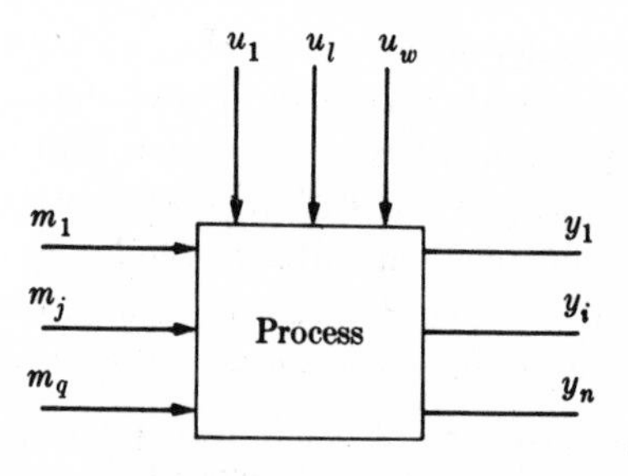

FIGURE 4. Representation of a complex process. The y_i, $i = 1, \ldots, n$, are process outputs. m_j, $j = 1, \ldots, q$, are process inputs. u_l, $l = 1, \ldots, w$, are disturbances.

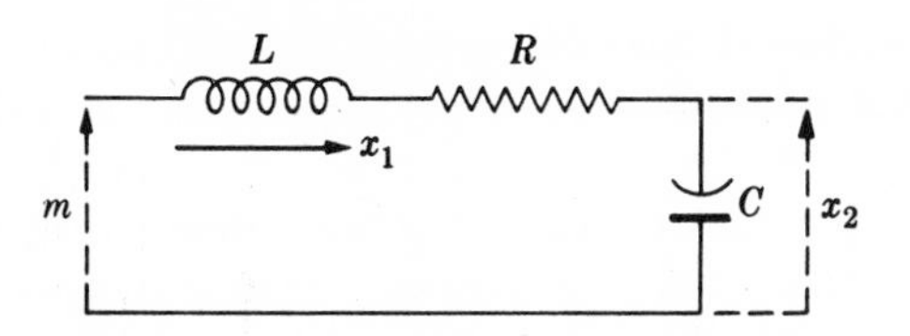

FIGURE 5. *RLC* circuit.

cannot generally be related in such a simple and straightforward manner. For a more detailed discussion of the ensuing problems, the reader is referred to Chapter V.

In addition to the inputs $m_j(t)$ upon which we will later on act to alter the state of the process, there are *disturbances* $u_l(t)$, $l = 1, \ldots, w$, by means of which the environment acts upon the process in a manner which is frequently not predictable. The effect upon $y_i(t)$ of $u_l(t)$ can be accounted for by another set of transfer functions $p_{u,il}(s)$.

Since, in the general case, we are considering a situation characterized by a multiplicity of inputs m_j, outputs y_i, and disturbances u_l, we find it convenient to use *matrix notation*. We agree to regard $\mathbf{m}$, $\mathbf{y}$, and $\mathbf{u}$ as vectors of components m_j, $j = 1, \ldots, q$; y_i, $i = 1, \ldots, n$; and u_l, $l = 1, \ldots, w$. In accordance with standard practice we differentiate vectors from scalars or matrices by *boldface type*.

We may also regard the transform $M_j(s)$, $Y_i(s)$, and $U_l(s)$ as components of the vectors $\mathbf{M}(s)$, $\mathbf{Y}(s)$, and $\mathbf{U}(s)$ and, in the linear case under discussion, relate these by the matrix equation

$$\mathbf{Y}(s) = P(s)\mathbf{M}(s) + P_u(s)\mathbf{U}(s) \tag{3.1}$$

where $P(s)$ has elements $p_{ij}(s)$ and $P_u(s)$ has elements $p_{u,il}(s)$.

3.2 The Concept of State and the Resulting Model. In the modern literature it is becoming more and more customary to describe a process (see Fig. 5) by a set of first-order linear or nonlinear differential equations of the form

$$\dot{x}_k = f_k(x_1, \ldots, x_v; m_1, \ldots, m_q) \quad (k = 1, \ldots, v) \tag{3.2}$$

or, using matrix notation

$$\dot{\mathbf{x}} = \mathbf{f}(\mathbf{x}, \mathbf{m}). \tag{3.3}$$

See Table I.

The variable x_k is termed a *state variable, phase,* or *coordinate*. The vector $\mathbf{x}$, which is called a state, or phase, or coordinate vector, may in a conventional analog process be so selected as to comprise as components the outputs—displacements, velocities, voltages, etc.—of all the energy storage elements. The vector $\mathbf{m}$, as before, accounts for the q external actions which permit us

TABLE I

Example	$n = 1; q = 1$	$n = 1; q > 1$	$n > 1; q > 1$
Block diagram	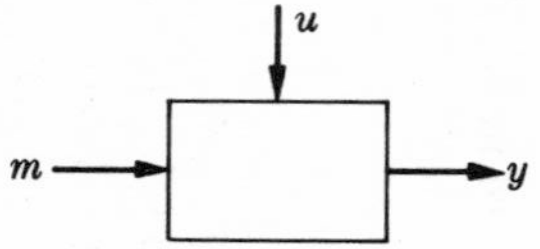	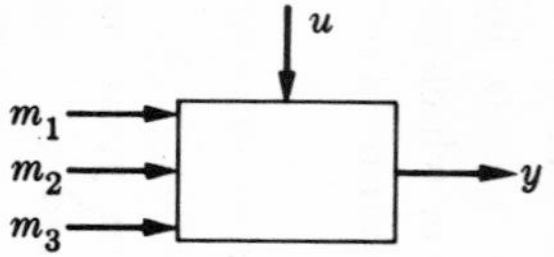	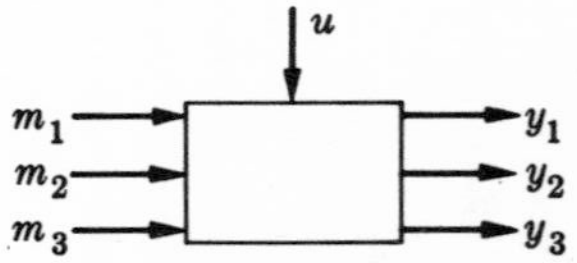
Hydroelectric power production	One turbine generator m = valve opening y = shaft speed u = generator load	Several interconnected turbine generators m_j = valve opening of the jth turbine y = frequency of the power system u = load of the power system	Interconnected power system m_j = valve opening of the jth turbine y_i = frequency of the interconnected system and power outputs of the individual power stations u = total system load
Chemical plant	Distillation column m = flow rate of raw material y = concentration of the main product u = concentration of raw material	Distillation column m_j = flow rate, pressure, temperature of raw material y = concentration of the main product u = concentration of raw material	Distillation column m_j = flow rate, pressure, temperature of raw material y_i = concentration of main and secondary products u = concentration of raw material

us to exert control over the *state* of the process.† The system output vector $\mathbf{y}$ of components $y_1, \ldots, y_n$ can almost always be related to the state $\mathbf{x}$ by an algebraic equation of the form

$$\mathbf{y} = \boldsymbol{\varphi}(\mathbf{x}). \tag{3.4}$$

Example. We consider the linear *RLC* circuit shown in Fig. 5. The outputs of the energy storage elements L and C are the current x_1 and the voltage x_2. Using the fundamental laws of circuit theory, we relate x_1 and x_2 to the voltage m by

$$\begin{aligned} \dot{x}_1 &= -\frac{R}{L}x_1 - \frac{1}{L}x_2 + \frac{1}{L}m \\ \dot{x}_2 &= \frac{1}{C}x_1. \end{aligned} \tag{3.5}$$

In this particular case, the generally nonlinear equation (3.3) simplifies to the linear matrix equation

$$\dot{\mathbf{x}} = A\mathbf{x} + B\mathbf{m} \tag{3.6}$$

where the elements of the two matrices A and B are pure numbers such as $\frac{R}{L}, \frac{1}{L}$, etc. Any output, perhaps the voltage drop across R, can be related to x_1 and x_2 by a linear algebraic equation of the form

$$\mathbf{y} = G\mathbf{x} \tag{3.7}$$

where the elements of G are also pure numbers.

Equations (3.3) indicate how the present state $\mathbf{x}(t)$, which we may agree to visualize as a point M of coordinates $x_1, \ldots, x_v$ in v-dimensional space, moves under the twofold influence of the existing transient regime and the instantaneous process input $\mathbf{m}(t)$ to an adjoining state $\mathbf{x} + \boldsymbol{\delta}\mathbf{x}$, which it reaches at the instant $t + \delta t$, δt being an arbitrarily small positive quantity. A much more detailed account of the properties of Eqs. (3.2) through (3.7) are to be found in Chapters II and V, in Zadeh [25], and in the numerous papers of R. E. Kalman and of R. Bellman.

Equations (3.2), (3.3), (3.4), (3.5), (3.6), and (3.7) hold for all times $t > 0$. It is sometimes convenient, for computational reasons, to observe the state $\mathbf{x}$ of the process at *discrete* and in general equally spaced "sampling" instants $t = l\Delta$, $l = 0, 1, 2, \ldots$, Δ = positive constant. Under those circumstances, (3.3) and (3.4) become *difference equations* of the form

$$\mathbf{x}[(l+1)\Delta] = \mathbf{f}[\mathbf{x}(l\Delta), \mathbf{m}(l\Delta)] \quad l = 0, 1, 2, \ldots \tag{3.8}$$

$$\mathbf{y}(l\Delta) = \boldsymbol{\varphi}[\mathbf{x}(l\Delta)] \tag{3.9}$$

† If there were disturbances u_l, they would be accounted for in exactly the same way that the m_j are accounted for. Equation (3.3) would then become

$$\dot{\mathbf{x}} = \mathbf{f}(\mathbf{x}, \mathbf{m}, \mathbf{u}).$$

where $\mathbf{x}[(l+1)\Delta]$ denotes the value of $\mathbf{x}$ at time $t = (l+1)\Delta$. Examples showing how Eqs. (3.8) and (3.9) can be obtained in simple cases are given in Chapter III, Sections 4 and 5. For the general case, the reader is referred to any mathematical text on difference equations.

Equations of the type (3.8) and (3.9) may not only be written for *continuous* processes which we agree to observe only at sampling instants $t = l\Delta$, but also serve to describe *discrete* processes, that is, processes whose state changes only at discrete intervals of time $t = l\Delta$. The digital computer is an example of this situation.

Equations of the type (3.8) and (3.9) can also be used to describe the behavior of sequential *binary networks* whose state changes at equally spaced discrete instants of time. The only difference now is that the conventional algebraic signs $+$, $-$, and $\cdot$ would have to be replaced by the symbols corresponding to the logical operations of "and," "or," "nor," etc., and that the x_i and m_j can only assume two values, for instance 0 and 1.

Certain types of random processes can also be accounted for by equations of the form (3.8) and (3.9), namely

$$\mathbf{X}[(l+1)\Delta] = \mathbf{f}[\mathbf{x}(l\Delta), \mathbf{m}(l\Delta)] \tag{3.10}$$

$$\mathbf{y}(l\Delta) = \boldsymbol{\varphi}[\mathbf{x}(l\Delta)]. \tag{3.11}$$

Here, $\mathbf{X}[(l+1)\Delta]$ denotes the *expected value* $E\{\mathbf{x}[(l+1)\Delta]\}$ of the state $\mathbf{x}$ at $t = (l \times 1)\Delta$ given $\mathbf{x}(l\Delta)$ and $\mathbf{m}(l\Delta)$. These *random parameter plants* which the reader should carefully distinguish from deterministic plants excited by *random signals* are expected to attract a great research effort in the future. Equations (3.10) and (3.11) appear to be ideally suited to account for a wide variety of system engineering problems; see Sections 1.2 and 1.3 of the present chapter. Processes of this kind are intimately related to what the statisticians call Markov processes [7].

It thus appears that the concept of *state* and the way one state is transformed into a subsequent state accommodate a variety of processes—continuous, discrete, sequential binary, probabilistic—and it will be seen in subsequent sections how *controlled* processes which we refer to as *systems* can also be described by a set of equations quite similar to those of the present section. As a result of the fascinating generality of this concept, the more conventional descriptions, Laplace transform, z-transform, are being used relatively less frequently, and it has become impossible to comprehend the modern literature without having a good grasp of the notion and properties of the *state*.

3.3 Some Practical Difficulties. It is important to note that while actuators and controllers are frequently discontinuous, conventional analog processes are always continuous† and consequently describable by differential

† The reason for this is that the outputs of energy storage elements, such as capacitors, cannot change abruptly, unless infinite amounts of energy are available.

rather than difference equations. This does not, however, preclude us from observing the process at discrete intervals of time and thus arriving at a description by difference equations, which is sometimes simpler though less informative in that events occurring between the discrete intervals of observation are ignored.

Mathematical descriptions of conventional processes may be the following:

(1) *Static*, that is, consist of algebraic equations, in the case of a steady-state regime. Here, all the derivatives $\dot{x}_k$ of Eq. (3.2) are zero.

(2) *Dynamic*, that is, consist of differential (or difference) equations in which time t is usually the independent variable. In certain seldom-encountered cases, t might be entirely missing from Eq. (3.2) and one of the x_k might assume the role of the independent variable.

In those cases where the process is linear, the relations between variables can, at least in theory, be determined with great accuracy and rigor. In practice, *modeling*—measurement of precise characteristics—of even linear plants may be very thorny because:

(1) All the significant coefficients of the process differential equations (3.1) or (3.2) must be known with good accuracy. This is frequently very difficult, especially for those coefficients associated with the higher order derivatives. It is also not unusual that the *order* v of the process is either unknown or else so high that a plausible low-order model must be determined.

(2) Measurements are invariably corrupted by noise and other disturbances.

(3) There are very few perfectly linear processes and a good measurement implies small excursions from the operating point. This then normally rules out the attractive "short-circuit" or "blocked-rotor" tests.

If the process is nonlinear, it is extremely difficult to arrive at an accurate and complete mathematical model. One may resort to Taylor, McLaurin, or orthogonal expansions, and arrive either by computation or experimentation at a description which is valid under certain conditions, perhaps in a finite region of the state space or for a specific class of inputs. The mathematical description of a process is considered with greater detail in Chapter II. Table II lists some typical models of conventional analog processes in the *static* and in the *dynamic* case. Though, for added simplicity, no disturbances are considered, it is apparent that the number of parameters α, a, b, or g which must be determined may indeed become very large.

4. The Problem of Control

Thus far, we have been concerned with the *characteristics* of the process P which are presumably unalterable. The fundamental reason why we take such trouble to design a control system consisting of the blocks A, I, and C around P, see Figs. 1 and 2, is that the *natural or uncontrolled behavior of P is not satisfactory*. It is well-known from elementary feedback amplifier theory that the addition of a feedback path from the load to the grid

Table II

Static Description for Continuous Deterministic Processes

	$n = 1; q = 1$	$n = 1; q > 1$	$n > 1; q > 1$	Observations
Linear process	$y = \alpha m$ $\alpha = \text{constant}$	$y = \sum_{j=1}^{q} \alpha_j m_j$	$y_i = \sum_{j=1}^{q} \alpha_{ij} m_j$ $i = 1, \ldots n$	Description by linear algebraic equations
Nonlinear (Transcendental) process	$y = \alpha_1 m + \alpha_2 m^2 + \cdots$ $+ \alpha_l m^l + \cdots$ $\alpha_l = \text{constant}$	$y = \alpha_{11} m_1 + \cdots + \alpha_{1l} {m_1}^l$ $+ \alpha_{21} m_2 + \cdots + \alpha_{2l} {m_2}^l$ $\cdot$ $\cdot$ $\cdot$ $+ \alpha_{q1} m_q + \cdots + \alpha_{ql} m^l$	$y_i = \sum_{j=1}^{q} \alpha_{ij,1} m_j + \cdots$ $+ \sum_{1}^{q} \alpha_{ij,l} {m_j}^l$ $i = 1, \ldots, n; l = 1, 2, \ldots$	Description by nonlinear algebraic equations

Dynamic Description for Continuous Deterministic Processes

	$n = 1; q = 1$	$n = 1; q > 1$	$n > 1; q > 1$	Observations
General nonlinear time-varying process	$\dot{\mathbf{x}} = \mathbf{f}(\mathbf{x}, m, t)$ $y = \varphi(\mathbf{x})$	$\dot{\mathbf{x}} = \mathbf{f}(\mathbf{x}, \mathbf{m}, t)$ $y = \varphi(\mathbf{x})$	$\dot{\mathbf{x}} = \mathbf{f}(\mathbf{x}, \mathbf{m}, t)$ $\mathbf{y} = \varphi(\mathbf{x})$	Modern description by a set of v first-order nonlinear time-varying differential equations in x_k, $k = 1, \ldots v$
	$F[y^{(v)}, \ldots, \dot{y}, y; t; m] = 0$	$F[y^{(v)}, \ldots, \dot{y}, y; t; m_1, \ldots, m_q] = 0$	Systems of n nonlinear time-varying differential equations in y_i, $i = 1, \ldots, n$; m_j, $j = 1, \ldots, q$ and t	Conventional description by nonlinear time-varying differential equations in y_i, $i = 1, \ldots, n$
Linear time-invariant process	$\dot{\mathbf{x}} = \mathbf{A}\mathbf{x} + \mathbf{B}m$ $y = G\mathbf{x}$ $a_{ij}, b_i, g_i = \text{constant}$	$\dot{\mathbf{x}} = A\mathbf{x} + B\mathbf{m}$ $y = G\mathbf{x}$ $a_{ij}, b_{ij}, g_i = \text{constant}$	$\dot{\mathbf{x}} = A\mathbf{x} + B\mathbf{m}$ $\mathbf{y} = G\mathbf{x}$ $a_{ij}, b_{ij}, g_{ij} = \text{constant}$	Modern description by v first-order constant coefficient differential equation in x_k, $k = 1, \ldots, v$
	$\sum_{k=1}^{v} \alpha_k y^{(k)} = m$ $\alpha_k = \text{constant}$	$\sum_{k=1}^{v} \alpha_k y^{(k)} = \sum_{j=1}^{q} \beta_j m_j$ $\alpha_k, \beta_j = \text{constant}$	System of n linear constant coefficient differential equations in y_i, $i = 1, \ldots, n$, and m_j, $j = 1, \ldots, q$	Conventional description by linear constant coefficient differential equations
	$Y(s) = P(s)M(s)$	$Y(s) = \sum_{j=1}^{q} p_j(s)M_j(s)$	$Y_i(s) = \sum_{j=1}^{q} p_{ij}(s)M_j(s)$ $i = 1, \ldots, n$	Conventional description by Laplace transform. No initial conditions are assumed to be present here

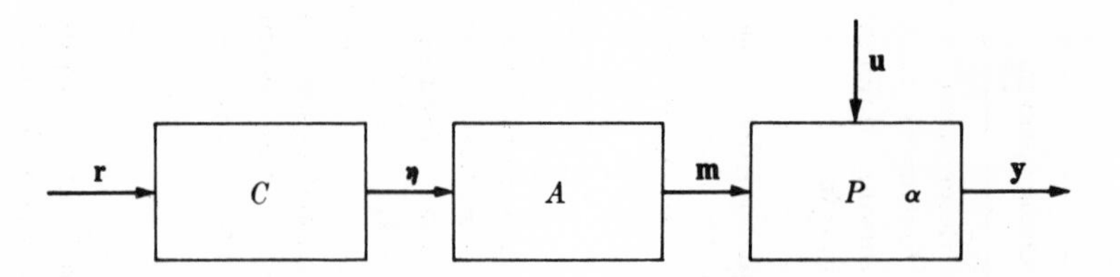

FIGURE 6. Open-loop system. **u** = external disturbances; **α** = internal parameter changes.

decreases distortion, sensitivity to parameter changes, noise, time constant, and gain, and alters both input and output impedances. Some relevant characteristics of the process, here a vacuum tube, have thus been improved. In what follows, it may not be too helpful to think in terms of *feedback paths*, because the processes under consideration are too complex and because there are many such paths, but rather to note how the process equations are altered when control is exerted and to observe how this effects such performance parameters as distortion, sensitivity, pole location, and many others.

4.1 Conventional Control Systems. Up to a decade ago, control systems were exclusively of either of the two types shown in Figs. 6 and 7.

We refer to the structure shown in Fig. 6 as an open-loop system. In response to external command signals **r**, the computer C which operates according to a fixed program or algorithm, produces a set of signals $\boldsymbol{\eta}$ which are the inputs of the actuator A. This actuator, which may comprise motors, valves, jacks, etc., drives the plant P. Open-loop systems are used when precise control of P is not essential.

The closed-loop structure of Fig. 7 is typical of the majority of the "feedback" systems in existence today. Here the computer, which still operates in accordance with a fixed algorithm, produces a set of signals $\boldsymbol{\eta}$ not only on the basis of the command input **r**, but also on the basis of the actual process state **x** as measured by the identification block I. Closed-loop

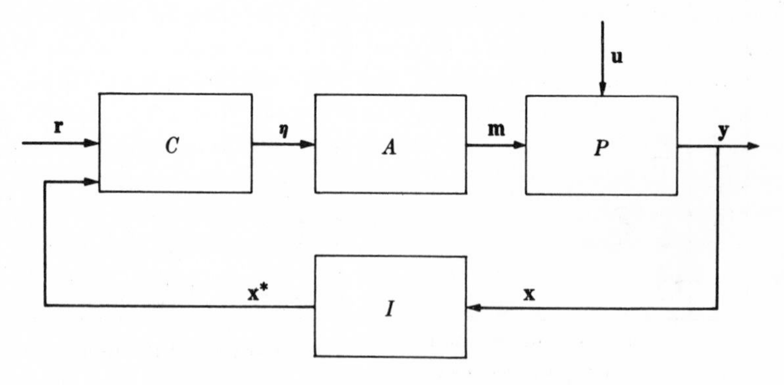

FIGURE 7. Closed-loop system.

structures are used when precise control of P in the presence of unknown external disturbance $\mathbf{u}$ and unknown internal parameter changes α is desired.

It is essential to note that we formulated an objective O—more satisfactory control of P—and added various constituents to P, namely I, C, and A, in order to meet this objective. In the case of a position control servomechanism, O would be as follows:

Under steady-state conditions, the plant output shall equal the command input r assumed to be a member of a stated class of time functions, perhaps a step or a ramp function.

It is clear that, in the design stage, the constituents I, C, and A are chosen in terms of the stated objective and in terms of the constraints exhibited by the process. This statement holds primarily for I and C since we generally do not have much freedom in the choice of A which is essentially a power amplifier.

It is customary to associate with each of the systems of Figs. 6 and 7 a scalar Ψ, termed *performance index*, which tells precisely to what extent O is satisfied under stated conditions of operation. With reference to the abovementioned position control servomechanism, Ψ might be defined as the maximum steady-state error $r - y$ in the presence of known disturbance $\mathbf{u}$ and parameter changes $\boldsymbol{\alpha}$. Frequently, Ψ is directly measured by the identifier I.

4.2 Adaptive Control Systems. In addition to the primary objective discussed in the previous section, we may wish to define a secondary, tertiary, etc., objective. Each of these objectives must be compatible. In the example quoted above, we may demand, and this is our second objective, that the transient response of the system shall meet certain specifications, for instance that the damping be critical.

If the environment in which the system operates is sufficiently stationary, satisfaction of the secondary objective is obtained by means of a proper choice of the values of the free parameters in C. In those cases where the environment is not sufficiently stationary, we have to add a secondary, tertiary, etc., loop whose functions are to *automatically* adjust the free controller parameters in such a way that the secondary, tertiary, etc., objectives be satisfied. It is important to note that these systems, which we call adaptive systems, are justified only if the perturbations are such such that the various objectives, assumed compatible, cannot be met unless the alterable system parameters, which are generally but not always located in C, are continuously and automatically adjusted. Perturbations, quite generally speaking, may consist of external disturbances $\mathbf{u}$, internal parameters changes $\boldsymbol{\alpha}$, or variations in the characteristics of the command input $\mathbf{r}$.

An adaptive system obtained from the conventional closed-loop system of Fig. 7 is shown in Fig. 8. Here, it may be assumed that, as a consequence of an unpredictable parameter change in P, the secondary objective, critical

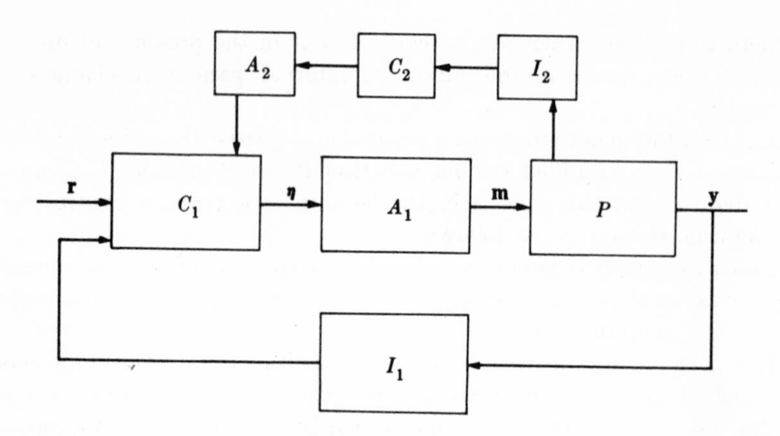

FIGURE 8. Adaptive system.

damping, cannot be met unless the gain of the controller C_1 is altered by the secondary loop which comprises the elements I_2, C_2, and A_2.

Identification, which previously was very simple, now requires fairly advanced measurement techniques. A possible way of finding the impulse response of the system $PI_1C_1A_1$ is to superimpose small-amplitude white noise upon r and to compute the cross-correlation function Φ_{ry}. This function, as is well known, equals the sought impulse response. The computer C_2 thereafter generates correcting signals in accordance with a fixed program and the actuator A_2 alters the gain of C_1 whenever the system damping fails to be critical. As before, the program of C_2 and the function of I_2 are chosen in the design stage in terms of the stated secondary objective.

In addition to the scalar Ψ_1, which measures how well the primary loop $PI_1C_1A_1$ performs its objective O_1, we associate a scalar Ψ_2 with the secondary loop $PI_2C_2A_2$ to measure how well the secondary objective O_2 is fulfilled.

There are cases where the identification block I_2 is not only or not at all connected to P. Because of the introductory nature of this chapter, we find it convenient to assume that I_2 is in fact connected to P and only to P.

For further examples of adaptive systems, the reader is referred to the bibliography [1, 9, 14, 16, 22, 23] and to Chapter IX.

4.3 Generalization of the Adaptive Concept. The conceptual similarity between the first and the second loop,† see Fig. 8, is called to the reader's attention. For both loops, we defined an objective O, a performance index Ψ, and we say to it that each of the objectives was automatically satisfied by means of the constituents I_1, C_1, A_1, I_2, C_2, and A_2.

† It is understood that although the *adaptive* structure represented in Fig. 8 exhibits two loops, adaptive systems are fundamentally different from the much simpler *multiloop* systems of which an account may be found in Chapter III.

There is no fundamental reason other than excessive system complexity why we could not define N mutually compatible objectives O_i and construct an adaptive system comprising N parallel loops. Each of these loops would contain in the general case an identification block I_i connected to P, a computer C_i, and an actuator A_i which would alter the adjustable parameters of the preceding loop in accordance with the computations carried out in C_i. A structure of this kind, which we agree to call an Nth degree adaptive system, is shown in Fig. 9. It is repeated that the free parameters altered by the A_i are *generally* located in the C_{i-1}, but may also be contained in the I_{i-1} or exceptionally in the A_{i-1}.

In accordance with the numbering system adopted here, a conventional control system, such as shown in Fig. 6 or Fig. 7, would be an *adaptive system of the first degree*. It is not customary in the literature to associate the qualificative "adaptive" with such systems. It is apparent, however, that the fundamental operations—identification, computation, actuation—of genuine

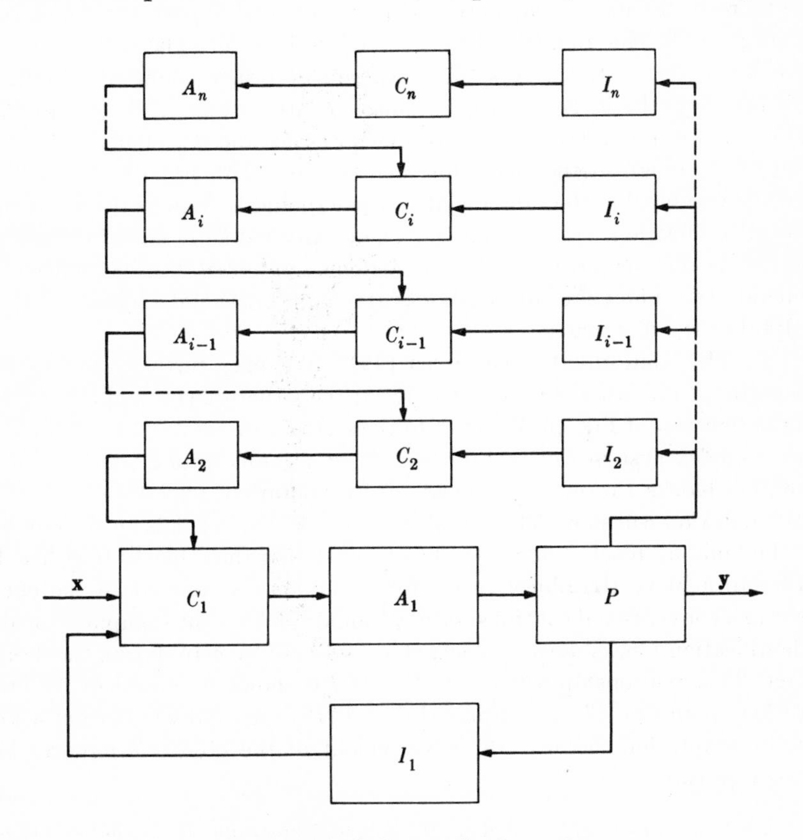

FIGURE 9. Nth degree adaptive system.

adaptive systems are already present in conventional systems though admittedly some might be overlooked because of their extreme simplicity. As a result of this observation we will refer in what follows to a conventional system as an adaptive system of the first degree and we will refer to the system of Fig. 8 as an adaptive system of the second degree.

In order to obtain an *Nth degree* adaptive system such as shown in Fig. 9, we need to define N mutually compatible objectives $O_1, O_2, \ldots, O_N$; for reasons of simplicity, we may collect these N individual objectives in a vector denoted by $\mathbf{O}$.

While in any advanced system the vector $\mathbf{O}$ may very well be defined rather loosely—we are quite frequently not able to give a precise mathematical description of what exactly we expect the system to do—the functions C and I, that is, the computation policy (cp) and the nature of the performance index (pi) must be carefully and accurately defined for each individual loop.

Progress consists of a sequence of experiments and hypotheses. An experiment gives the clue to a law; a hypothesis precisely formulates this law and prompts extrapolations. A second experiment either confirms or refuses this first hypothesis. As regards automatic control we have, in this section, formulated a hypothesis which accommodates advanced systems and which suggests a design methodology for such systems. This hypothesis which is further expanded in the subsequent sections should be viewed as an attempt toward unification. In order for it to be of any value, it must be *realistic*, that is, as close as possible to past experience; *universal*, that is, sufficiently general to accommodate all situations that might arise; and *adequate*, that is, helpful to the designer.

4.4 The Canonical Structures [19]. We may further simplify the diagrams of Fig. 6 and Fig. 7 and arrive at the structure (1a) and (1b) shown in the first row of Fig. 10. We refer to these structures as *canonical*† because any complex system can be represented by a configuration using the four building blocks Process, Identification, Computation, and Actuation, as a little reflexion will show. The complexity of a system depends on the number of the building blocks and on the links connecting these blocks together. In order to achieve the objective O—for example, a statement to the effect that in a conventional control system y should track r—the Computation and Identification blocks must be selected accordingly by man during the design stage. This relationship between O, C, and I is shown by means of the lines labeled cp and pi. The structures (1a) and (1b) are representative of a *first degree* adaptation, because the achievement of the objective requires but one cp-pi pair.

† The term "canonical" abounds in the technical literature. The reader should not attempt to find a tie between the canonical structures we are discussing here in connection with adaptive systems and the canonical structures of Chapter III.

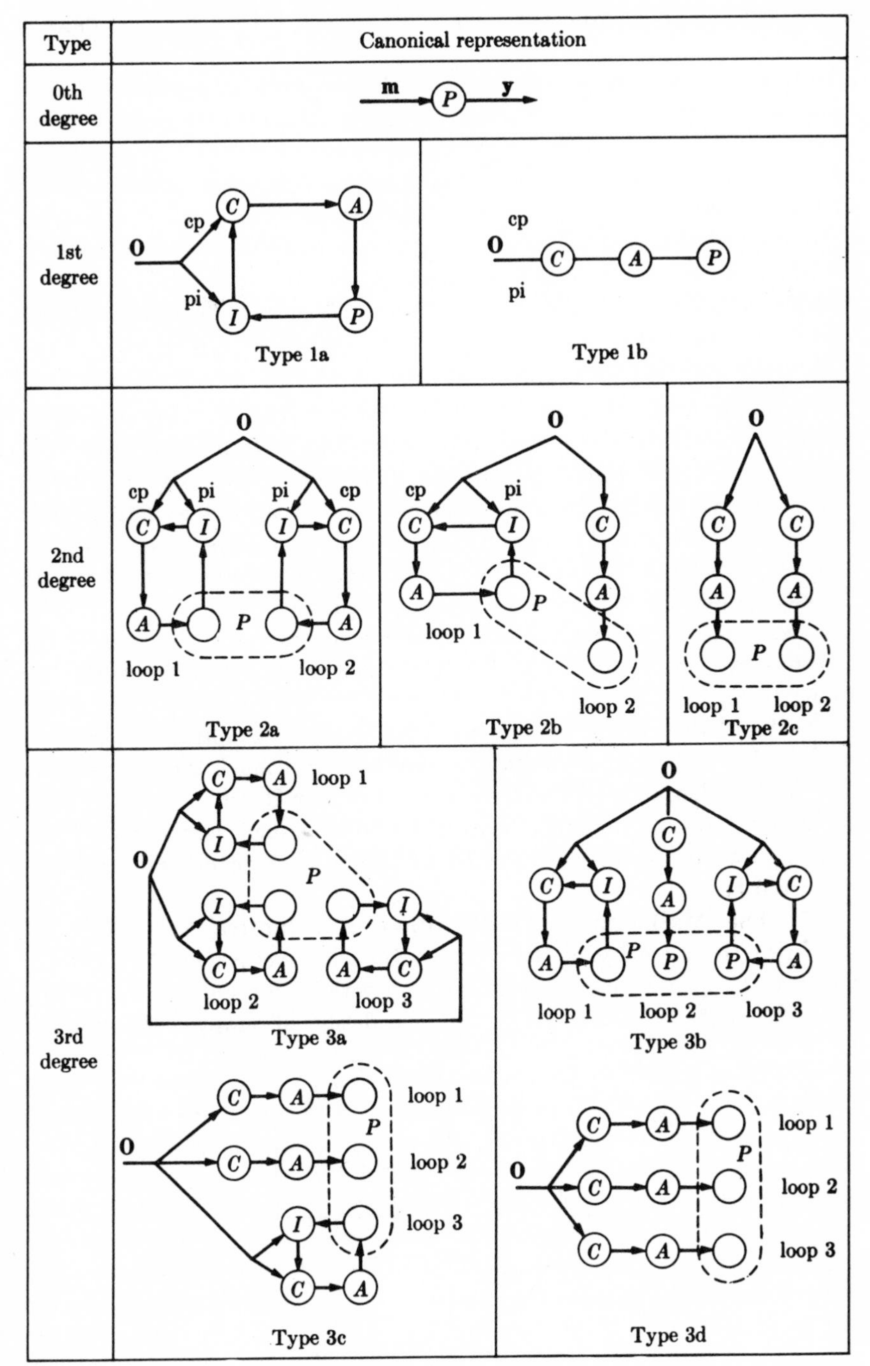

FIGURE 10. Canonical structures of systems characterized by various degrees of adaptation.

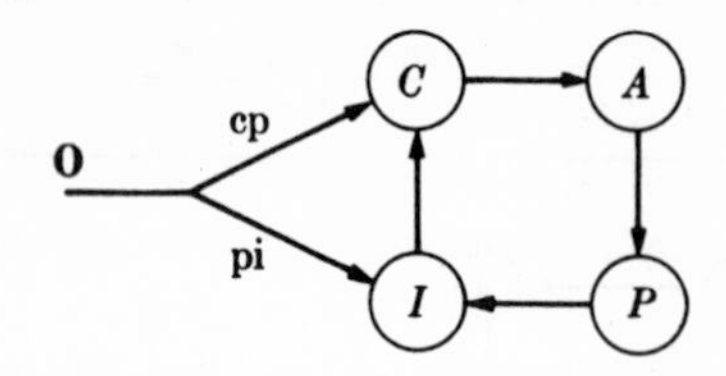

FIGURE 11. Canonical structure corresponding to the first-degree system shown in Fig. 8.

Starting from the canonical structures (1a) and (1b), it is easy to imagine adaptive systems of the second, third, . . . , degree. It is noteworthy that although in higher degree systems the basic adaptations may be carried out successively rather than simultaneously, they always lead to parallel topological structures. The reason for this is that the physical system to be adapted remains the same and the final objective **O** is only fulfilled after all the elementary adaptations have been accomplished.

As examples of application of the canonical structures, we consider the adaptive systems of Figs. 8 and 9. The resulting canonical structures are shown in Figs. 11 and 12.

The basic idea, which is to break down complex adaptive systems into manageable and familiar entities, is explored with much greater detail in [19], and further applications are given in Chapter II. In Section 4.7 it will be shown how certain other advanced systems, such as optimizing and learning systems, can be categorized by means of the canonical structures discussed here.

4.5 The Mathematical Description of Adaptive Systems. The design of the majority of the second-level adaptive systems in existence today was largely based on *intuitive* considerations. Since it was shown only very recently—see Tarjan [20]—that the design of adaptive systems can

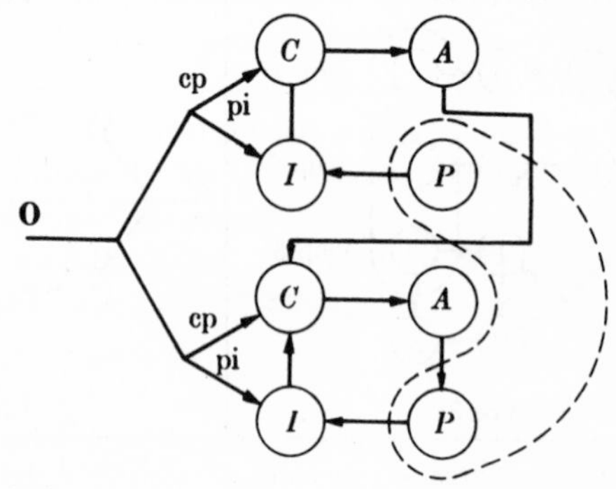

FIGURE 12. Canonical structure corresponding to the second-degree system shown in Fig. 9.

be made to lean upon known mathematical methods, little attention was devoted to the performance of the second loop. The time constants associated with the second loop were chosen to be so large compared to those of the first loop that the approximate analysis of the resulting system by conventional methods was justified.

We will now discuss a mathematical description which, in the form presented, accommodates simple but representative adaptive systems and which suggests other descriptions applicable to more complex systems. This discussion is largely based upon Tarjan [20]. The dynamic equations arrived at are usually nonlinear and the mathematical techniques treated in Chapters V and VI can be set to work to determine stability and performance. It is no longer necessary to assume that the time constants associated with the second loop are much larger than those of the first loop.

Before attacking second-degree adaptive structures, we stop to look at the mathematical description of a conventional feedback control system such as is shown in Fig. 7. We consider the process

$$\dot{\mathbf{x}} = \mathbf{f}(\mathbf{x}, \mathbf{m}, \mathbf{u}, \boldsymbol{\alpha}) \tag{4.1}$$

where the $\mathbf{u}$ and $\boldsymbol{\alpha}$ are unknown disturbances and parameter changes, and we propose to design a controller

$$\mathbf{m} = \mathbf{g}(\mathbf{x}, \mathbf{r}, \mathbf{p}_1) \tag{4.2}$$

where $\mathbf{p}_1$ is a vector composed of the adjustable parameters $p_{1,1}, p_{1,2} \cdots$ contained in C. Since in general the I and A blocks are not being altered externally, we find it convenient to include their dynamics into Eq. (4.1) and, for the purpose of this section, need to consider only the blocks P and C or their respective equations (4.1) and (4.2).

Elimination of the process input $\mathbf{m}$ between Eqs. (4.1) and (4.2) leads to

$$\dot{\mathbf{x}} = \mathbf{f}[\mathbf{x}, \mathbf{g}(\mathbf{x}, \mathbf{r}, \mathbf{p}_1), \mathbf{u}, \boldsymbol{\alpha}]. \tag{4.3}$$

The vast importance of (4.3) is stressed: this equation *adequately and fully accounts for the majority of the control systems realized thus far*. The similarity between Eqs. (3.3) and (4.3) is to be noted.

As pointed out in Section 4.3, a second-level adaptive system is one in which the adjustable parameters $\mathbf{p}_1$ of C_1 are altered in accordance with a *fixed* computation policy obeyed by C_2. Under fairly general assumptions, we may account for the dynamics of the second loop, which in addition to C_2 includes A_2 and I_2, by considering the state $\mathbf{p}_1^*$, which comprises the adjustable parameters $p_{1,1}, p_{1,2}, \ldots$, *and the outputs of the energy-storage elements of A_2 and I_2.*

The dynamic process taking place in the second loop can then be summarized by

$$\dot{\mathbf{p}}_1^* = \mathbf{g}_2(\mathbf{x}, \mathbf{p}_1^*, \mathbf{r}, \mathbf{p}_2). \tag{4.4}$$

Equations (4.3) together with (4.4) completely account for the motion of an adaptive system of the type shown in Fig. 8. In the case of a constant command input $\mathbf{r}$ and constant perturbations $\mathbf{u}$ and $\boldsymbol{\alpha}$, it is convenient to associate with Eqs. (4.3) and (4.4) the motion of a representative point M of coordinates $x_1, x_2, \ldots; p_{1,1}, p_{1,2}, \ldots$ starting from the initial state $\mathbf{x}(0)$, $\mathbf{p}_1^*(0)$ in the space $(\mathbf{x}, \mathbf{p}_1^*)$. The coordinates of the points at which the system may then settle are given by

$$O = \mathbf{f}[\mathbf{x}, \mathbf{g}(\mathbf{x}, \mathbf{r}, \mathbf{p}_1), \mathbf{u}, \boldsymbol{\alpha}]$$

$$O = \mathbf{g}_2(\mathbf{x}, \mathbf{p}_1^*, \mathbf{r}, \mathbf{p}_2). \tag{4.5}$$

We may now proceed to adaptive systems of the third degree by implementing a third loop whose function is to alter the adjustable parameters $\mathbf{p}_2$ of C_2. Using the same notation as before, we add to Eqs. (4.3) and (4.4) the equation

$$\dot{\mathbf{p}}_2^* = \mathbf{g}_3(\mathbf{x}, \mathbf{p}_2^*, \mathbf{r}, \mathbf{p}_3). \tag{4.6}$$

In exactly the same way, we may account for the general Nth degree adaptive system. It should be noted that Eqs. (4.3), (4.4), (4.5), and (4.6) are all of the continuous, deterministic type. In many representative adaptive systems, discrete and random variables are being considered; some of these equations, therefore, would have to be of the type discussed in Section 3.2—see Eqs. (3.8) and (3.10).

4.6 Adaptive, Optimum, Optimizing, and Learning Systems. During the past decade, a fair number of expressions were coined to designate *nonconventional* control systems. We list optimum, optimizing, optimalizing, adaptive, self-adaptive, self-adjusting, learning, self-organizing, self-improving, etc. Frequently, the same terms are used to designate different systems or else different terms to designate the same systems. This lack of unification clearly demands that a consistent set of expressions and definitions be found to permit all kinds of *advanced* systems to be analyzed and categorized in a more satisfactory manner. This, in conjunction with the canonic structures discussed previously, should not only shed light upon certain conventional problems, but, and this is even more important, should suggest new avenues of research.

The definitions to be presented now agree with most of the current literature on advanced systems. This, however, should not be accepted as a guarantee that these definitions will continue to hold: considerable progress is being accomplished at this time in automatic control, and ways of thinking are bound to change rapidly.

Among the long list of terms quoted above, we select optimum, adaptive, optimizing, and learning as essential headings. In order to briefly explain the rather vast conceptual difference between these four kinds of advanced systems, we refer to the structure shown in Fig. 8.

The primary objective O_1 is, as before, the steady-state equality between **y** and **r**. It may *in addition* be desired in a frequently encountered situation that, for random command $\mathbf{r}(t)$ presumed *nonstationary*, the rms error

$$\bar{\epsilon}^2 = \frac{1}{T} \int_0^T \sum_i (r_i - y_i)^2 \, dt \tag{4.7}$$

measured over a suitable averaging interval T be sufficiently small. This is objective O_2. To be more specific, we may assume that the stochastic characteristics of $\mathbf{r}(t)$ depend on the parameter β which assumes a finite number of discrete values $\beta_1, \beta_2, \ldots, \beta_k$ and that we do not know beforehand when the transitions from $\mathbf{r}(t, \beta_i)$ to $\mathbf{r}(t, \beta_j)$, $i \neq j$, occur.

Under these conditions, we qualify a system to be *optimum with respect to* O_2, if in the design stage the adjustable parameters p_1 of C_1 were chosen in such a way that Eq. (4.7) is minimized on the average under the varying input conditions defined above. Since the vector $\mathbf{p}_1$ is not altered in operation, there is no need to add the second loop of constituents I_2, C_2, and A_2.

An optimum system is hence a conventional system in which the adjustable parameters $\mathbf{p}_1$ and sometimes the entire controller structure are chosen once and for all so as to ensure optimum operation with respect to a stated objective and in the presence of a stated class of perturbations.

An *adaptive* system, on the other hand, is one in which the vector $\mathbf{p}_1$ is automatically adjusted *in operation* in such a way that Eq. (4.7) shall be sufficiently small. In order to attain this result, the constituents I_2, C_2, and A_2 of the second loop are required. The terms "self-adaptive" and "self-adjusting" are also used in the literature to designate systems of this kind.

Adaptive systems are hence characterized by the property that the adjustable parameters $\mathbf{p}_1$ and sometimes the entire controller structure are *automatically* altered so as to ensure *satisfactory* operation with respect to a stated objective and in the presence of a stated class of perturbations.

The adaptive system under discussion would deserve the qualificative of *optimizing* if the objective O_2, see Eq. (4.7), were automatically fulfilled, not only in a *satisfactory* manner, but in an *optimal* manner. The computer C_2 would be expected to perform a mechanized search in the parameter space $\mathbf{p}_1$ and ultimately determine *that* vector $\mathbf{p}_1$ which minimizes Eq. (4.7), assuming that the random command input $\mathbf{r}(t, \beta)$ has been stationary for a sufficiently long time to permit C_2 to complete its search. The term "optimalizing" is also used in the literature—see Tsien [24] and Truxal [22].

An *optimizing system* is hence a special adaptive system which automatically alters the adjustable parameters $\mathbf{p}_1$ and sometimes the entire controller structure so as ultimately to ensure *optimum* operation with respect to a stated objective and in the presence of a stated class of perturbations.

It is apparent from these definitions that adaptive and optimizing systems are not vastly different. If faced with a specific situation, one might occasionally find it difficult to decide if the system is optimizing or just adaptive.

The distinction between *learning systems* and adaptive or optimizing systems is much sharper. Learning systems have been attracting considerable attention, not only from engineers, but also from neurologists. The reason for this is that learning systems exhibit certain essential properties of the human brain.

It is not always apparent from the literature when a system deserves the qualificative "learning." Some of the resulting confusion may be due to the fact that the verb "to learn" has two different meanings, namely, "to gain knowledge" and "to acquire skill." Gaining knowledge may imply little more than a series of measurements, whereas acquiring skill constitutes a faculty which was not envisaged for technical systems until a very short time ago.

A fundamental property of a learning system is its ability to perform better as time progresses. It is for this reason that learning systems are also called "self-improving" or "self-organizing." In the case of the system of Fig. 8, learning might be implemented as follows: Suppose that optimum performance with respect to O_2 is accomplished for the parameter settings $\mathbf{p}_1^{(i)}$ when the input is $\mathbf{r}(t, \beta_i)$, $i = 1, 2, \ldots, k$. Corresponding to each β_i, the optimizing system previously discussed would ultimately settle on the vector $\mathbf{p}_1^{(i)}$, *but in each individual case, the search procedure carried out by* C_2 *would be the same*. In the learning system, the results of previous computations are stored in a *memory* which makes it unnecessary that the same lengthy process of attaining the optimum setting $\mathbf{p}_1^{(i)}$ must be repeated each time the command input $\mathbf{r}(t, \beta_i)$ is observed by I_2. The memory of this admittedly simple learning system would therefore ultimately consist of a table such that to each β_i there would correspond a $\mathbf{p}_1^{(i)}$.

If, as is the case in the example under consideration, the system does not deliberately generate test signals, learning is passive. The process of filling the memory with the required data could be speeded up by programing C_2 to inject suitable test signals $\mathbf{r}(t, \beta_i)$; learning in this case would be active.

A *learning system*—and this is a very general definition—is one which, if identical experiments are carried out, meets a stated objective more readily or more completely in late experiments than in early experiments.† It would not be sufficient to say that learning systems are characterized by the property that their performance increases as time progresses: this feature is already exhibited by conventional control systems which, if properly designed, progressively eliminate all initial error conditions. It is essential

† What exactly is meant by "more readily" or "more completely" must be stated in each case. For the example being considered here, "more readily" may mean more "rapidly."

that performance comparisons be carried out assuming identical perturbations.

Learning systems may also be differentiated from any of the other systems discussed in this section in that *the computer program or algorithm is not fixed*, but is made to vary in accordance with past failures and successes. This, of course, is never the case in conventional control systems.

An important feature of learning systems is that the complete computer C_2 is needed only until the memory, which is essentially a look-up table, has been filled with a sufficiently fine grid of instructions corresponding to the various perturbations that are expected to occur. After this task has been completed, the major portion of C_2 can be disconnected and turned over to other tasks. The memory which remains may have to be upgraded from time to time to account for slow process parameter changes.

The learning concept outlined here has not, as far as we know, been applied to any systems other than simple demonstration models [2]. However, we were told that in order to speed up certain iterative computations, ingenious computer programmers quite naturally instruct their machines to operate in accordance with the learning principles discussed above.

We are now entering upon an era where systems of great complexity will have to be designed; see, for example, the traffic and production controls of Sections 1.2 and 1.3. In some of these situations, the complexity of the process is such that the conventional design methodology does not allow us to arrive at a satisfactory system. The learning principles may very well permit detailed designs to be bypassed: a suitably programmed computer C_2 would slowly fill the memory of C_1 with the required control laws.

4.7 A Further Property of the Canonical Structures. In Section 4.3, we generalized the adaptive concept and examined how individual objectives O_i could be met automatically by addition of an adaptive loop comprising the constituents I_i, C_i, and A_i. In Section 4.4 we discussed the canonical structures which display with great clarity what the exact functions of each of these adaptive loops are.

It is apparent from what has been said in the previous section that any of the loops $I_iC_iA_i$ may be *adaptive*, *optimizing*, or *learning*. The implication of this is that a third degree system may be at the same time adaptive, optimizing, and learning depending on the program adopted for each of the three computers C_1, C_2, and C_3.

Therefore it is essential that we clearly specify in each individual case just how the objective O_i is met. Having done this, we might, in a particular case, come up with a system which is adaptive with respect to O_1, optimizing with respect to O_2, and learning with respect to O_3.

Furthermore it is essential to note that the improvement of performance observed in any of these systems is due to a *modification of the parameters* of one or several of the blocks C, I, or A. It is for this reason that we may now qualify any of the advanced systems discussed in the literature—adaptive, self-adjusting, optimizing, learning, self-organizing, self-improving—as possessing a *dynamic structure*.† Another important point is that none of these advanced systems contains loops other than those previously discussed, that is adaptive, optimizing, or learning.

A system having a dynamic structure may also be termed *autoevolutive* by analogy with certain biological or neuronic systems. It should be kept in mind, however, that there are significant differences between these two classes of systems: in the first, a process P which is unalterable and which therefore constitutes a *constraint* is given; this is generally not so in the case of biological or neuronic systems. In a control system, the block P acts upon the chain ICA and vice versa; in biological or neuronic systems, the separation between P on the one hand and ICA on the other hand cannot, generally speaking, be made easily.

Biologically speaking, the entire human being constitutes the controlled plant and the I, A, C, elements; i.e., the perceptive organs, the functional physiological organs, and the brain are parts of this plant. The whole automatically evolves in the environment, where the actions on the human being are perturbations. This concept of a *dynamic structure* can easily be extended to more general systems, e.g., the human society, the entirety of the living beings, the earth, the universe, etc. The interest of this concept is that it can be mathematically approached by the notion of state.

In spite of these differences, our understanding of neuronic and biological evolutive systems is expected to be helpful in the design of autoevolutive technical systems. We now begin to know how adaptation and learning can be built into a control system. This is not so for other "intelligent" operations or properties, such as association, transition, and distribution. Also, assuming the statistical nature of evolution, we need to know how certain technical criteria of quality, such as accuracy, can be connected to the notions of ultra-stability and homeo-stability which are characteristic of evolution.

The trend today in automatic control is to arrive at systems of ever increasing "intelligence." In order to accomplish this, we need to study exactly what intelligence is and how it is being used in the evolution of systems.

5. Analytical Methods in Automatic Control

In this section, we wish to review some of the analytical techniques pertaining to classical control systems (see Fig. 1) and next to outline those applicable to the analysis and design of advanced control systems such as

† The term *structure* is accepted here in a sufficiently general sense. By *dynamic structure* we understand that either the parameters characterizing the components C, I, or A, or the links between these components, or both, may vary. In simple cases, this amounts to a change of some of the elements in the transition matrix corresponding to the conventional closed-loop system.

are shown in Fig. 2. Many of these techniques will be presented or at least mentioned in the subsequent chapters of this book. It is clear, however, that space does not always permit extensive developments and that certain basic techniques are assumed to be already known.

In Section 3.3, we indicated that a process is mathematically described by a set of algebraic equations (static laws), or by a set of differential or possibly difference equations (dynamic laws); description by a set of linear or nonlinear differential equations is the most frequently encountered situation at this time.

Controlling a process signifies that, by means of additional constituents of the type A, C, and I, we alter the original equations in such a way as to render them more suitable for our purposes; see Eq. (4.3). This very simple statement has vast consequences: it explains the difference between *analysis*, a problem which has concerned mathematicians for centuries, and *synthesis*, which is what the engineer is called upon to accomplish. The addition of components presents the designer with the problem of predicting the essential characteristics of the controlled process, namely, stability and performance.

We shall now list the main types of constituents or *control elements* that might be incorporated into a modern system, and thereafter discuss the relevant mathematical techniques. It is clear that the character of this discussion will of necessity remain quite general and that many significant exceptions must be disregarded. The principal control elements are listed below:

1. Linear continuous elements
2. Nonlinear continuous elements
3. Linear discontinuous (sampled-data) elements
4. Quantizers or digital elements
5. Transport delays
6. Relays, contactors, or components with hard saturation.

Assuming first that the process is described by a set of linear, constant coefficient, differential equations such as (3.6), the introduction of 1 into the loop results in a linear system. Such systems were classically treated by Laplace transform methods [21]; state-space techniques (see Chapter II) are now extensively used in the literature. Stability and performance are determined by the location of the eigenvalues λ_i in the complex λ-plane.

Nonlinear continuous elements cause the system to be nonlinear; the analysis is in most cases extremely laborious. Topological methods (Poincaré's phase plane) are practically restricted to second-order systems; see Chapter V. The describing function, which is also presented in Chapter V, is still the most effective engineering tool to accommodate high-order nonlinear systems. Liapunov's second method (see Chapter VI), which was extensively developed in the Soviet Union during the last three decades, provides sufficient conditions of stability as well as an approximate measure of performance. In its present form, Liapunov's second method cannot as yet be regarded as an everyday engineering tool, but the generality of the concept is emphasized and solutions to numerous special problems have already been worked out.

The introduction of a digital computer into the loop leads to a mathematical description by difference equations, which, if linear, are almost as well known as linear differential equations. The z-transform [21], which is the discrete counterpart of the Laplace transform, may introduce some computational advantages, but is certainly not required. State-space techniques again turn out to be most effective, especially when the "infinitesimal width" approximation is no longer justified; see Chapter III. The problem of estimating performance and stability, as before, reduces to the search of the locations of the eigenvalues λ_i in the complex λ-plane.

Quantizers may turn up in continuous circuits, but are usually encountered in discrete (sampled-data) circuits. Since superposition holds approximately, but not quite exactly, the behavior in the case of large perturbations can be examined by purely linear techniques, whereas the motion in the vicinity of the equilibrium point requires the use of a nonlinear model, see Chapter V. The problem of predicting the existence of small amplitude limit cycles is very laborious because most systems contain not one, but several quantizers of different quantization grains.

Transport delays, which are never introduced on purpose but are inherent in certain types of control elements, lead to differential-difference equations; their study is of great computational complexity [24]. Systems containing transport delays were of more or less academic interest until high-performance loops were designed around chemical and nuclear reactors. There is considerable need for further research in this area.

Elements having a relay-type characteristic are inexpensive power amplifiers and, if properly controlled, lead to nonlinear systems which are piecewise linear and which achieve equilibrium in minimum time; see Chapters V, VI, and VII. In certain important cases, the *plant* P saturates very rapidly. Optimal, that is, minimum response time, control of such saturating processes can be achieved in exactly the same way that optimal control of conventional relay systems is accomplished; see Chapter V. Since process saturation invariably occurs in high-performance applications (aircraft, missiles), the problem of attaining optimal control is very pressing indeed. Second-order systems have been studied extensively by purely topological methods. Extensions to higher order systems proved to be very refractory and were not mastered until quite recently; see Chapter V. The extension to multivariable systems comprising several relays has not been made as yet.

If the process equations are nonlinear, the resulting system is usually nonlinear, and exact analysis generally becomes intractable. As a rule, we will say that the *heuristic methods*, describing function and nonlinear root locus (see Chapter V) are engineering tools par excellence whereas Liapunov's second method (see Chapter VI) is a mathematician's tool except for numerous special cases to which the solutions are available. Liapunov's second method was originally worked out for continuous nonlinear systems but has since been extended to discontinuous nonlinear systems [11].

Thus far, we have neglected to speak of the very important role played by statistics in automatic control. It is well known that a large number of systems are not normally subjected to deterministic command signals such as steps, but to random command signals of known statistical description; see Dennis *et al.* [6]. What is less well known is that certain processes that have not thus far concerned the control engineer can only be described by probabilistic *models*. The traffic and production control systems discussed in Sections 1.2 and 1.3 are examples of this situation. A comprehensive analysis of such models remains to be done.

While the importance of system *analysis* should not be underrated, and while we ought to appreciate that various powerful new analysis tools such as graph theory [12] and set theory have been developed, it remains nevertheless true that our fundamental problem is one of *synthesis*. We would naturally think that the complications resulting from the more refined process of synthesis exceed those of the primary process of analysis. This is frequently not so, since the requirement that we exert control in some prescribed fashion often leads to a considerable simplification, as was pointed out by Bellman [3]. The implementation of a linear system-input to system-output relation around a nonlinear plant may reduce to the trivial problem of finding suitable compensating networks to cancel the effect of the nonlinear plant parameters.

While computer-controlled processes (see Chapter II) in actual operation today are not very sophisticated and in some instances probably would not even justify the use of a general purpose computer, we are getting to the point where the only limitations imposed upon the designer will be those resulting from the process itself rather than from the control elements. The significance of this is that within that portion of the state space permitted by the process, motion is no longer constrained and a trajectory which is optimal in some stated fashion can be selected. Linear and nonlinear programming, the calculus of variations, dynamic programming, and the maximum principle are the analytic tools needed to implement the corresponding optimum controllers; see Chapters VI and VII. Another fact of equal significance, though less frequently mentioned, is that certain processes which thus far have been laboratory curiosities because their control proved to be too delicate, can in the future be set to work in industry. There appears to be little doubt that the availability of powerful and reliable computers has added a new dimension to the science of control and that many conventional processes may have to be rethought from the outset.

6. Directions for Research

In the subsequent chapters of this book and in the context of the material presented, many unsolved problems will be pointed out. Therefore, it is not the scope of the present section to compile a detailed directory of unsolved problems, but to suggest some general areas which in the authors' opinion demand original thinking. Although attempts to predict the future have frequently been proven wrong, it is expected that during the forthcoming decade, research in automatic control will focus on the following.

6.1 Advanced Systems. It is apparent from our description of automatic traffic control systems (see Section 1.2) that engineers are being asked to produce optimal designs around processes which are so *complex* that the now available mathematical apparatus is inadequate and that present design procedures can no longer be extrapolated. The task of ultimately arriving at an *optimum*, that is, most economic, system will be left to a computer which carries out rational experiments and plans its future actions on the basis of the outcome of these experiments. The similarity of the computer's behavior with that of man is to be noted.

6.2 The Integrated Control of Production and Other Economic Processes. In accordance with the control engineer's views, many production processes, as well as even larger economic entities, do not always behave satisfactorily if left to their own devices. It is expected that the mathematical description of such processes and the subsequent elaboration by computer of the pertinent stimuli will eventually produce systems which optimize a stated measure of quality, for instance, the annual profit. In the light of this, it is not surprising that some of the best-known control specialists are presently studying economic structures. The application of control concepts to certain other complex processes such as encountered in sociology, biology, and medicine may also be expected.

6.3 Development of New Processes. Many of the present production and transportation processes are not as economic as they could be if systematic use of modern computers and other control gear were made. More desirable processes, for instance, chemical reactions which evolve in minutes instead of hours, are rendered possible by the very fast control computers now available. The existence of these computers has brought about the situation where a thorough *rethinking* of many conventional processes—chemical, metallurgical, transportation, etc.—may very well be justified. Rethinking of conventional processes may have become desirable not only by the invention of the general purpose digital computer, but by several other recent developments, such as lasers and gyroscopes. Moreover it is safe to assume that even though presently available computers may not be sufficiently fast or reliable, or may be too expensive, these shortcomings will soon be corrected and the control engineer's long-range planning should be in terms of vastly better machines than those now available.

6.4 Applied Research. The last decade has produced a wealth of technical reports that have never been used to arrive at any useful equipment. We do not wish to state that an investigation is justified only to the extent that it provides the answer to a real life problem. But we believe that the application of the contents of some of these technical reports to specific real life situations would be a significant contribution, the difficulties of implementing a complex system being what they are. Computer process control (see Chapter IX) is a subject that has been dealt with at great length in the literature, but there are as yet few "closed-loop" systems. Those realizations that we know of are so simple that the inclusion of a full-sized computer into the loop may not even be justified technically. We would like to see demonstration models of realistic complexity where existing knowledge of dynamic programming, the maximum principle, certain aspects of Liapunov's second methods, etc., are being brought to bear.

Conversely, we believe that many branches of industry abound with unsolved theoretical problems which, as a result of inertia and ignorance, have not as yet been detected and precisely formulated. There might not be, after all, a single good reason today why iron is made in a blast furnace which is difficult to instrument and to control and which is essentially an enlarged version of the chemist's retort. Or, again, why must goods be transported in trains made up of individual cars which must be connected to other trains in switchyards, an expensive, time-consuming technique, hard on glassware and other fragile goods.

BIBLIOGRAPHY

1. Aseltine, J. A. *et al.*, "A survey of adaptive control systems," IRE Trans. on Automatic Control 102–108 (December, 1958).
2. Ashby, W. R., *Design for a Brain*, Wiley, 1952.
3. Bellman, R., "Directions of mathematical research in nonlinear circuit theory," IRE Trans. on Circuit Theory 542–553 (December, 1960).
4. Brown, R. R., A generalized computer procedure for the design of optimum systems," Trans. AIEE, Comm. and Electronics 285–293 (July, 1959).
5. Chang, S. S. L., "Adaptive Data Processing," Symposium on Optimizing and Self-Adaptive Systems Theory, Rome, April, 1962.
6. Dennis, J. B. *et al.*, "System synthesis with the aid of digital computers," Trans. AIEE, Comm. and Electronics 512–515 (November, 1959).
7. Feller, W., *An Introduction to Probability Theory and Its Applications*, Wiley, 1957, Volume 1, Chapters 5 and 16.
8. Goode, H. H., and Machol, R. E., *System Engineering*, McGraw-Hill, 1957, 551 pp.
9. Ivaknenko, A. G., "Sistemy avtomaticheskogo upravleniya s prisbosobleniyem kharakteristik"; translation in *Engineering Cybernetics*, Office of Technical Services, U.S. Department of Commerce, January, 1961, 406 pp.

10. Kalman, R. E., "The Variational Principle of Adaptation: Filters for Curve-Fitting," Symposium on Optimizing and Self-Adaptive Systems Theory, Rome, April, 1962.
11. Kalman, R. E., and Bertram, J. E., "Control system analysis and design via the 'second method of Liapunov'; II, Discrete time systems," J. Basic Eng. (June, 1960).
12. Kaufmann, A., "Quelques applications de la théorie des graphes," Informations Scientifiques, Cie des Machines Bull., 31 pp.
13. Kaufmann, A., Faure, R., and le Garff, A., *Les Jeux d'Entreprises*, Presses Universitaires de France, 1960, 126 pp.
14. Mishkin, E., and Braun, L., *Adaptive Control Systems*, McGraw-Hill, 1961, Chapter 3.
15. Naslin, P., "Mathematics in Theoretical and Applied Autonomics," *Mathematics for Physicists and Engineers*, OECD Report, February, 1961, pp. 189–207.
16. *Proceedings of the IFAC, Moscow*, 1960, edited by Coales, J. F., Fuller, A. T., and Raggazzini, J. R., Butterworths, 1961.
17. Proceedings of the IRE, 50th Anniversary Issue (May, 1962).
18. Proceedings of the IRE, Special Issue on Computers (January, 1961).
19. Pun, L., "Analysis of Optimizing Control Systems Using Fundamental Adaptation Concepts," Symposium on Optimizing and Self-Adaptive Systems Theory, Rome, 1962.
20. Tarjan, R., "Forms of Stability of Adaptive Control Systems," Symposium on Optimizing and Self-Adaptive Systems Theory, Rome, 1962.
21. Truxal, J. G., *Automatic Feedback Control System Synthesis*, McGraw-Hill, 1955, pp. 675.
22. Truxal, J. G., "Computers in automatic control systems," Proc. Inst. Radio Engrs. 305–312 (January, 1961).
23. Truxal, J. G., "Review of control developments," Proc. Inst. Radio Engrs. 781–787 (May, 1962).
24. Tsien, H. S., *Engineering Cybernetics*, McGraw-Hill, 1954, pp. 289.
25. Zadeh, L. A., "From circuit theory to system theory," Proc. Inst. Radio Engrs. 856–866 (May, 1962).

CHAPTER II

The Basic Mathematics of Automatic Control

EUGENE W. HENRY

CONTENTS

1. Introduction

The primary purpose of this chapter is to provide an introduction to the analysis and synthesis of systems in the state space. A qualitative discussion of differential equations and a brief summary of matrix notation and operations are included to provide proper orientation and background for the material in succeeding chapters.

The *state* of a dynamic system may be defined as a set of numbers, called *state variables*, which contain all information required about the past history of the system to permit calculation of the future behavior for all time when the inputs for future time and the system configuration are known. If the system behavior is described by an nth-order differential equation, it can be simulated on an analog computer with exactly n integrators. Then the set of integrator outputs is one proper definition of the state of the system. This is true because knowledge of all the integrator outputs at a given time (initial conditions) suffices to determine the solution for all time. It is convenient to arrange the n state variables into a column matrix or vector, and use a single symbol, $\mathbf{x}$, to represent the state of the system. With further use of matrix notation the nth-order differential equation of a system may be expressed as a single first-order matrix equation.

Although this description of differential equations is not a new mathematical technique [3],† it has been applied in control systems only in recent years. R. E. Kalman introduced state-space techniques in the design of saturating systems in 1955 [6]. Kalman and Bertram subsequently applied the method to the optimal synthesis of linear sampled-data systems with conventional sampling [8] and to the analysis of systems containing both discrete and continuous elements with arbitrary sampling [9]. Kalman and Koepcke employed state-space techniques and Dynamic Programing in the optimal synthesis of linear sampled-data systems using a generalized performance index [10]. These methods have been extended to include synthesis of systems with time-varying sampling and multiple inputs [4].

Matrix methods have proved invaluable in the design of multivariable control systems (see Chapter III). A combination of techniques from the theories of matrices, differential equations, and Dynamic Programing has yielded new methods of control system synthesis and promises to continue as a fertile field for further research.

2. Matrix Notation and Operations

2.1 Matrix Notation [2,5]. A matrix is a rectangular array of elements. The number of rows and columns of elements determines the size or order of the matrix. A matrix containing m rows and n columns of elements

† Numbers in brackets refer to the bibliography at the end of this chapter.

is called an $m \times n$, (read m by n) matrix. Matrices are denoted here by capital letters. The elements of the matrices are denoted by corresponding lower case letters having double subscripts, ij, which indicate the row and column, respectively, to which an element belongs. Thus, an $m \times n$ matrix A has the form

$$A = \begin{bmatrix} a_{11} & a_{12} & \cdots & a_{1n} \\ a_{21} & a_{22} & \cdots & a_{2n} \\ \cdot & \cdot & & \cdot \\ \cdot & \cdot & & \cdot \\ \cdot & \cdot & & \cdot \\ a_{m1} & a_{m2} & \cdots & a_{mn} \end{bmatrix} = [a_{ij}].$$

The elements a_{ij} are called scalars to distinguish them from matrices. These elements may be real numbers, complex numbers, or functions of real or complex variables.

A square matrix has the same number of rows as columns. The *determinant* of a square matrix is defined as the ordinary determinant of the elements which form the matrix. Several notations are in common use.

$$\text{determinant of } A = \det A = |A|.$$

A *minor* of an $n \times n$ determinant, denoted by M_{ij}, is the $(n-1) \times (n-1)$ determinant formed by crossing out the ith row and the jth column of the $n \times n$ determinant. A *cofactor* of a determinant, denoted by Δ_{ij}, is a signed minor defined in terms of the corresponding minor as

$$\text{cofactor } ij = \Delta_{ij} = (-1)^{i+j} M_{ij}.$$

2.2 Matrix Operations. The definitions of the basic operations involving matrices are presented here.

(a) *Multiplication of a Matrix by a Scalar.* Multiplication of an $m \times n$ matrix A by a scalar b is accomplished by multiplying each element in A by b. Thus,

$$bA = Ab = C \quad \text{where} \quad c_{ij} = ba_{ij} \quad i = 1, \ldots, m \quad j = 1, \ldots, n.$$

(b) *Addition of Matrices.* Two matrices, A and B, of the same size $(m \times n)$ are added by summing corresponding elements. Thus,

$$A + B = C \quad \text{where} \quad c_{ij} = a_{ij} + b_{ij} \quad i = 1, \ldots, m \quad j = 1, \ldots, n.$$

(c) *Multiplication of Matrices.* The product AB may be formed if the number of columns in A is equal to the number of rows in B. Such matrices are said to be conformable in the order stated. Then, if A is $m \times p$ and B is $p \times n$, the product AB yields an $m \times n$ matrix defined by

$$AB = C \quad \text{where} \quad c_{ij} = \sum_{k=1}^{p} a_{ik} b_{kj}.$$

$$i = 1, \ldots, m$$

$$j = 1, \ldots, n$$

Matrix multiplication is associative. That is, $(AB)C = A(BC)$. Matrix multiplication is also distributive with respect to addition. Thus, $A(B + C) = AB + AC$. Matrix multiplication is in general *not* commutative. That is, $AB \neq BA$ in general. The terms premultiplication and postmultiplication are used to denote the order of multiplication.

(d) *The Transpose Matrix.* The transpose of a matrix A, denoted as A^T, is a matrix formed by interchanging the rows and columns of A. Thus,

$$[a_{ij}]^T = [a_{ji}] = A^T.$$

(e) *The Adjoint Matrix.* The adjoint of a matrix A, denoted as Adj A, is a matrix formed by replacing each element in A by its cofactor and then taking the transpose of the result. Thus,

$$\text{Adj } A = [\Delta_{ij}]^T.$$

(f) *The Conjugate Matrix.* The conjugate of a matrix A, denoted as $\bar{A}$, is formed by replacing each element of A by its complex conjugate. Thus,

$$\overline{[a_{ij}]} = [\bar{a}_{ij}] = \bar{A}.$$

(g) *The Inverse Matrix.* The inverse of a square matrix A, denoted as A^{-1}, is defined as that matrix which when premultiplied or postmultiplied with A yields the unit or identity matrix (see Section 2.4). Thus,

$$AA^{-1} = A^{-1}A = I.$$

The inverse matrix may be found in terms of the original matrix as follows:

$$A^{-1} = \frac{\text{Adj } A}{|A|} = \frac{[\Delta_{ij}]^T}{\Delta}.$$

2.3 Some Properties of Matrices. Certain important and useful properties of matrices are presented here.

(a) *Equality.* Two matrices, A and B, are said to be *equal* if, and only if, they are of the same order and $a_{ij} = b_{ij}$ for all i and j.

(b) *Equivalence.* Two matrices, A and B, are *equivalent* if, and only if, nonsingular matrices P and Q exist such that $B = PAQ$.

(c) *Rank.* The rank of a matrix is defined as the size of the largest array in the matrix whose determinant does not vanish. The array is formed by deleting certain rows and columns from the matrix.

(d) *Inverse and Transpose of a Product.* The following useful properties are stated without proof:

$$(AB)^{-1} = B^{-1}A^{-1}$$
$$(AB)^T = B^T A^T.$$

(e) *Cayley Hamilton Theorem.* This important theorem states that a matrix satisfies its own characteristic equation. The characteristic equation of a matrix A is a polynomial in λ determined from the relationship $|A - \lambda I| = 0$.

2.4 Types of Matrices. Certain special types of matrices are defined here. The listing is in alphabetical order for reference.

(a) *Complex Matrix.* Elements are complex numbers.

(b) *Diagonal Matrix.* All off-diagonal elements are zero. That is, $a_{ij} = 0$ for $i \neq j$.

(c) *Hermitian Matrix.* The transpose is equal to the complex conjugate. That is, $A^T = \bar{A}$ or $a_{ij} = \bar{a}_{ij}$.

(d) *Orthogonal Matrix.* The transpose is equal to the inverse. That is, $A^T = A^{-1}$.

(e) *Positive Definite Matrix.* A real symmetric matrix A is *positive definite* if

$$\mathbf{x}^T A\mathbf{x} = \sum_{i,j=1}^{N} a_{ij}x_i x_j > 0$$

for all real nontrivial $\mathbf{x}$. A necessary and sufficient condition that the real symmetric matrix A be positive definite is that all the characteristic roots of A be positive.

(f) *Real Matrix.* Elements are real numbers.

(g) *Scalar Matrix.* This is a diagonal matrix whose diagonal elements are all equal. Thus $A = kI$.

(h) *Singular Matrix.* The determinant of the matrix is zero; no inverse exists. Thus, $\det A = 0$.

(i) *Symmetric Matrix.* This is a square matrix equal to its transpose. Thus, $A = A^T$ or $a_{ij} = a_{ji}$.

(j) *Unitary Matrix.* This matrix is both Hermitian and orthogonal. The transpose of the conjugate is equal to the inverse. $\bar{A}^T = A^{-1}$.

(k) *Unit Matrix, Identity Matrix.* This is a scalar matrix with $k = 1$. Thus, $a_{ij} = 0$ for $i \neq j$; $a_{ij} = 1$ for $i = j$. It is denoted by I.

(l) *Vector, Column Matrix, Row Matrix.* This matrix consists of only one row or one column.

(m) *Zero Matrix.* In this matrix all elements are zero. It is denoted by 0.

3. Differential Equations

The dynamic behavior of a system is described by one or more differential equations. The nature of these equations influences the approach to be taken in the analysis or synthesis of the system. Since there are excellent texts available on the general mathematical theory of differential equations [3], no detailed account will be given here. However, some basic definitions will be presented together with a discussion of relationships between differential equations and systems design.

A *differential equation* expresses a relationship among dependent variables and independent variables in terms of differentials or derivatives.

Differential equations involving only one independent variable are called *ordinary*.

A *partial* differential equation contains two or more independent variables and the associated partial derivatives.

In systems analysis and design the most common independent variable is time. If the system consists of a finite number of lumped elements, its performance may be described by a set of ordinary differential equations. A system containing distributed parameters has the space coordinates as well as time for its independent variables. In this case partial differential equations are necessary to describe the system behavior exactly. Since most systems encountered by the control engineer can be approximated satisfactorily by ordinary differential equations, we give no further consideration here to partial differential equations.

The *order* of a differential equation is the order of the highest derivative in the equation.

The *degree* of a differential equation is the power of the highest derivative when the equation is made rational and integral with respect to all the differential coefficients.

A differential equation is *linear* if the dependent variable and all of its derivatives occur to the first degree only. An equation which is not linear is called *nonlinear*.

An ordinary differential equation having time as the independent variable is called *time-varying* if the coefficients of any of the differential operators are functions of time. An equation with constant coefficients is called *stationary*. The term *autonomous* is applied to an equation which does not contain time explicitly.

A *solution* of an ordinary differential equation

$$F\left(x, \frac{dx}{dt}, \ldots, \frac{d^n x}{dt^n}, t\right) = 0 \tag{3.1}$$

is any function $x = f(t)$ which satisfies the equation identically in t. The *general solution* is one which involves exactly as many independent arbitrary constants as the order of the equation. A *particular solution* or *particular integral* is any solution obtained from the general solution by giving definite values to the constants. These constants are usually determined from a set of known initial conditions. Any solution which cannot be obtained from the general solution by assigning values to the constants is called a *singular solution*.

3.1 Solution of Differential Equations. Many methods exist for solving differential equations. Several techniques are also available for determining properties of system behavior without obtaining an explicit solution. The method to be used in solving a differential equation depends upon the nature of the equation itself. Boal and Steeg have presented in Chapter 3 of [12] a compilation of the most useful methods of solving differential equations. Further details of these methods are readily available elsewhere. We restrict ourselves here to some general remarks on equations and their solutions.

The nth-order linear differential equation with constant coefficients is probably most familiar to the engineer since many systems and networks can be represented or approximated by such an equation. A finite lumped RLC network with constant parameters, or a mechanical system consisting of a collection of masses, springs, and viscous damping mechanisms are examples of such systems. The solution of these equations is readily found by either classical or operational methods. The state-space methods described later in this chapter employ both techniques. Some of the important properties of linear stationary systems are the following.

(a) The nature of the force-free (autonomous in this case) response and the stability of the system are determined entirely by the roots of the characteristic equation.

(b) Superposition is valid. This property allows us to find a solution for an arbitrary periodic forcing function by expanding the function in a Fourier series and summing the response due to each term.

(c) Again, because superposition is valid, we may use convolution to find the response due to any forcing function, periodic or not.

(d) The steady-state output of a system subjected to a periodic forcing function is periodic of the same period, provided that the system's characteristic roots all have negative real parts. Furthermore, there are no frequencies present in the steady-state response which are not in the forcing term. The linear system can only change the amplitude and phase of each component frequency.

(e) Under conditions stated above, the steady-state response is independent of the system's initial conditions.

3.2 Linear Equation with Time-varying Coefficients [13]. Linear time-varying equations occur whenever some parameters in a system are functions of time. An example is the parametric amplifier in which a capacitance is made a periodic function of time. Since the equation is linear, superposition is still valid. Thus, the general solution of the force-free system is the sum of n linearly independent particular solutions. If the impulse response is known, the response due to any arbitrary excitation may be found from the superposition integral. The impulse response in this case is a function of the time at which the impulse is applied.

System stability may be affected by time-varying parameters. For example, a lightly damped series *RLC* circuit exhibits a decaying oscillatory natural response if the parameters are constant. If the capacitance is varied periodically at twice the natural frequency of the circuit, and with proper phase, the response will grow without bound. Since the phasing is a function of the initial conditions, we see that the nature of the system behavior may depend upon the initial conditions.

Although operational methods are not generally applicable to the solution of time-varying linear equations, certain special types of equations can be solved by appropriate methods such as the Laplace, Mellin, and Euler transforms. Other techniques include power series, continued fractions, variation of parameters, and direct solution by analog or digital computer. The adjoint method is of particular interest in the study of systems subjected to random signals, and in certain final-value problems [11].

3.3 Nonlinear Differential Equations. Nonlinear differential equations arise whenever a system contains, intentionally or unavoidably, some nonlinear component. The bang-bang servo is an example of a system which is intentionally nonlinear. Undesired or unavoidable nonlinearities usually result from imperfections such as saturation, dead zone, hysteresis, and backlash in the system components.

Nonlinearities may give rise to phenomena which are not exhibited by linear systems. For example, a force-free nonlinear system may exhibit a stable limit cycle, or oscillation of constant amplitude and frequency. A forced nonlinear system may exhibit a jump resonance or any one of several subharmonic responses. Jump resonance occurs, for example, in a lightly damped series *RLC* circuit containing an iron core inductor and sinusoidal excitation. This same circuit may exhibit several different subharmonic responses. That is, the frequency of the current may be any submultiple of the excitation voltage frequency. The initial conditions, the excitation amplitude and frequency, and the circuit parameters determine which particular subharmonic is generated.

The analysis of nonlinear systems is complicated by the fact that superposition is not valid. The nature of the response and the system stability may depend upon the amplitude of the excitation. For example, a control system with saturation may be stable for small step inputs, but may exhibit a sustained oscillation or limit cycle when subjected to a large step input.

A nonlinear system described by a second-order differential equation is readily studied by conventional phase plane techniques. Higher order systems may be analyzed in the frequency domain by means of the describing function. Liapunov's second method may be used to study system stability as discussed in Chapter VI.

3.4 Computer Solutions. Analog and digital computers are invaluable aids in the analysis of a complex system. If the system equations are put into the state-space notation of Eq. (4.1), the analog computer simulation may be obtained directly by defining the n state variables as outputs of n different integrators, and by forming the input to each integrator as some function of all the state variables as given by (4.1). Any or all of the state variables may then be observed and recorded in the simulated system. Sampled-data systems may also be analyzed on the analog computer by simulating the operations of the sample and hold devices. The digital computer is required for synthesis procedures employing the techniques of Dynamic Programing, or for adaptive systems which employ a large number of logical decisions. Again, state-space notation and matrix methods greatly facilitate computer programing. Sampled-data systems are readily studied by means of digital computations, especially if only the data at sampling instants are required. For systems with conventional sampling, the computer program may be written directly from the z-transforms. For other types of sampling the state-transition techniques lead directly to a computer program.

4. State-Space Representation of Systems

The behavior of most dynamic processes can be described or approximated by a set of ordinary differential equations of the form

$$\frac{dx_i}{dt} = F_i(x_1, x_2, \ldots, x_n, t), \quad i = 1, 2, \ldots, n \tag{4.1}$$

where the x_i and F_i are real functions of time. This representation is of particular interest to the control systems engineer because it leads directly to an analog computer simulation containing n integrators, where the integrator outputs can be viewed as linearly independent variables $x_1, x_2, \ldots, x_n$. Since the integrator whose output is x_i must by definition have dx_i/dt as its input, Eq. (4.1) indicates how the input of each integrator is formed as a function of all the integrator outputs and the time.

Although the description of system behavior by (4.1) is most convenient for analysis by computer simulation, the form is ordinarily too general to permit an analytical solution in terms of known functions. A more convenient form from the latter viewpoint is

$$\frac{dx_i}{dt} = \sum_{j=1}^{n} a_{ij}(t)x_j(t) + g_i(x_1, x_2, \ldots, x_n, t) + f_i(t) \tag{4.2}$$

$$i = 1, 2, \ldots, n$$

where the a_{ij} and f_i are real functions of time, and the g_i contain functions of the x_i of higher degree than the first. Equations (4.2) can be expressed compactly in matrix notation as

$$\frac{d\mathbf{x}(t)}{dt} = A(t)\mathbf{x}(t) + \mathbf{g}(x_1, x_2, \ldots, x_n, t) + \mathbf{f}(t) \tag{4.3}$$

where $A(t)$ is the $n \times n$ matrix of elements a_{ij}. The vector $\mathbf{x}(t)$ is called the *state* of the system, and its components $x_1, x_2, \ldots, x_n$ are the *state variables.* Note that the derivative of a vector or matrix is formed by taking the derivative of each element.

If in a particular system the vector $\mathbf{g}$ is identically zero, then the system is *linear*. That is, a linear system is described by the vector equation

$$\dot{\mathbf{x}}(t) = A(t)\mathbf{x}(t) + \mathbf{f}(t). \tag{4.4}$$

If A in Eq. (4.4) is a constant matrix, the system is linear with *constant coefficients*. It is this particular type of system that is readily solved by conventional operational methods such as the Laplace transform. If $\mathbf{f}(t)$ in Eqs. (4.3) and (4.4) is identically zero, then the system is *force-free*, and (4.4) is also called *homogeneous*. If the time does not appear explicitly in (4.3) and (4.4), the system is *autonomous*. Thus, in particular a linear, force-free system with constant coefficients is autonomous.

As an example of system behavior expressed in terms of state variables, consider the well-known van der Pol equation which describes a system with nonlinear damping:

$$\ddot{x} + \mu(x^2 - 1)\dot{x} + x = 0, \qquad \mu > 0. \tag{4.5}$$

If we define state variables x_1 and x_2 as $x_1 = x$, $x_2 = \dot{x}_1$, then Eq. (4.5) can be expressed as two first-order equations

$$\begin{aligned} \dot{x}_1 &= x_2 \\ \dot{x}_2 &= -x_1 + \mu x_2 - x_1{}^2 x_2. \end{aligned} \tag{4.6}$$

These equations are equivalent to the representation of Eq. (4.1). The representation in terms of Eq. (4.3) is

$$\dot{\mathbf{x}} = \begin{bmatrix} 0 & 1 \\ -1 & \mu \end{bmatrix}\mathbf{x} + \begin{bmatrix} 0 \\ -x_1{}^2 x_2 \end{bmatrix}. \tag{4.7}$$

Since the vector $\mathbf{f}(t)$ is identically zero, the system of Eq. (4.7) is force-free. The system is also autonomous.

An *equilibrium point* of a force-free system is a point in the state space where $\dot{\mathbf{x}} = 0$. In terms of the computer simulation, $\dot{\mathbf{x}} = 0$ implies that all integrator inputs are zero, so the system must remain at rest. An important problem in analysis is to determine the stability in the vicinity of the equilibrium points. Equation (4.6) has an equilibrium point at $\mathbf{x} = 0$. Its behavior in the vicinity of this point is described by $\dot{\mathbf{x}} = A\mathbf{x}$ where the

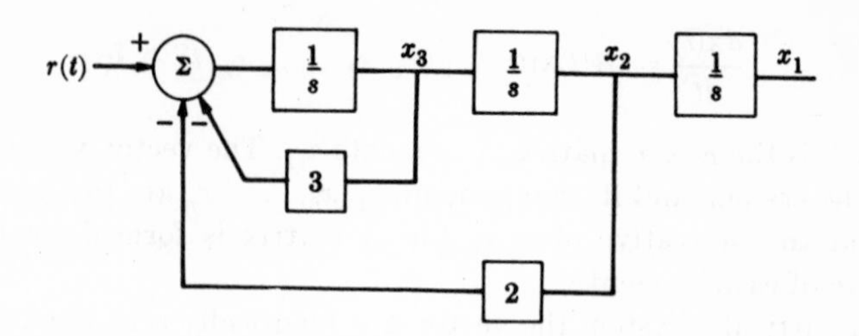

FIGURE 1. Analog simulation of Eq. (4.10).

A matrix of Eq. (4.7) contains all necessary information concerning stability.† If an equilibrium point occurs at a point in the state space other than the origin, it can be translated to the origin by a suitable change of variables so that investigation of an equation of the form $\dot{\mathbf{x}} = A\mathbf{x}$ will generally answer the question of stability in the region of an equilibrium point.

The investigation of stability and the correlation of the state-space method with conventional transform techniques provide a motivation for closer examination of the properties of Eq. (4.4). Consider now the linear system with constant coefficients described by

$$\dot{\mathbf{x}}(t) = A\mathbf{x}(t) + \mathbf{f}(t) \tag{4.8}$$

where A is a constant matrix. If the state variables, x_i, are taken as the outputs of integrators in an analog computer simulation, then the matrix A may be interpreted as the interconnection matrix or computer wiring diagram. The vector $\mathbf{f}(t)$ indicates the manner in which the forcing terms enter each integrator. For example, consider a system described by Eq. (4.8) with A and $\mathbf{f}(t)$ given by

$$A = \begin{bmatrix} 0 & 1 & 0 \\ 0 & 0 & 1 \\ 0 & -2 & -3 \end{bmatrix} \qquad \mathbf{f}(t) = \begin{bmatrix} 0 \\ 0 \\ r(t) \end{bmatrix}. \tag{4.9}$$

The corresponding set of three scalar equations is

$$\begin{aligned} \dot{x}_1 &= x_2 \\ \dot{x}_2 &= x_3 \\ \dot{x}_3 &= -2x_2 - 3x_3 + r(t). \end{aligned} \tag{4.10}$$

The analog simulation corresponding to Eq. (4.10) is shown in Fig. 1. Note that the simulation is written directly from inspection of (4.10), or equivalently, from inspection of the matrix A and of the vector $\mathbf{f}$ of Eq. (4.9).

† An exception occurs when the matrix A has one or more characteristic roots with zero real parts and no roots with positive real parts. In this instance stability is determined by the nonlinear terms.

Several approaches are available for solving Eq. (4.8). We will employ two different methods of solution here because each one sheds a different light on the behavior of the system. A solution in terms of a Taylor's series leads to an exponential state transition matrix while the classical approach leads to the determination of the free frequencies or eigenvalues.

4.1 Series Solution. Consider first the force-free linear system with constant coefficients described by

$$\dot{\mathbf{x}}(t) = A\mathbf{x}(t). \tag{4.11}$$

The initial state of the system is $\mathbf{x}(0)$, and we are to find the ensuing state $\mathbf{x}(t)$. Equivalently, we are given a set of initial conditions on the integrators for an analog computer simulation described by Eq. (4.11), and we are to find the subsequent output of each integrator. The solution will be found in terms of the power series expansion about the initial state. That is:

$$\begin{aligned} x(t) &= x(0) + t\dot{x}(0) + \frac{t^2}{2}\ddot{x}(0) + \cdots \\ &= \sum_{n=0}^{\infty} \frac{d^n\mathbf{x}(0)}{dt^n}\frac{t^n}{n!}. \end{aligned} \tag{4.12}$$

By repeated differentiation of (4.11) we obtain the relationship

$$\frac{d^n\mathbf{x}(t)}{dt^n} = A^n\mathbf{x}(t). \tag{4.13}$$

Substitution of Eq. (4.13) into (4.12) yields

$$\mathbf{x}(t) = \sum_{n=0}^{\infty} A^n\mathbf{x}(0)\frac{t^n}{n!} = \sum_{n=0}^{\infty} \frac{(At)^n}{n!}\mathbf{x}(0). \tag{4.14}$$

Now define the matrix $\Phi(t)$ by

$$\Phi(t) = I + At + \frac{(At)^2}{2!} + \cdots = e^{At}. \tag{4.15}$$

Then the solution given by Eq. (4.14) may be written as

$$\mathbf{x}(t) = \Phi(t)\mathbf{x}(0) = e^{At}\,\mathbf{x}(0). \tag{4.16}$$

The matrix $\Phi(t)$ is called the *state transition matrix* since it operates on the original state $\mathbf{x}(0)$ to yield the subsequent state $\mathbf{x}(t)$. Because of the exponential character of the state transition matrix as expressed in Eq. (4.15), it has the following useful properties:

$$\begin{aligned} \Phi(0) &= I \\ \Phi^{-1}(t) &= \Phi(-t) \\ \Phi(t_1 + t_2) &= \Phi(t_1)\Phi(t_2) \\ \Phi^n(t) &= \Phi(nt). \end{aligned} \tag{4.17}$$

Although the matrix $\Phi(t)$ can be calculated directly from the definition of (4.15), an alternative approach is suggested when Eq. (4.16) is written as the corresponding set of n scalar equations:

$$\begin{aligned} x_1(t) &= \varphi_{11}(t)x_1(0) + \cdots + \varphi_{1n}(t)x_n(0) \\ &\vdots \\ x_n(t) &= \varphi_{n1}(t)x_1(0) + \cdots + \varphi_{nn}(t)x_n(0). \end{aligned} \tag{4.18}$$

It is evident from Eq. (4.18) that $\varphi_{11}(t)$ may be obtained by setting $x_1(0) = 1$ and $x_i(0) = 0$ for $2 \leq i \leq n$. Then $\varphi_{11}(t)$ is equal to the output of integrator one when this integrator has unity initial condition and all other integrators have initial conditions of zero. In general,

$$\varphi_{ij}(t) = x_i(t)\Big|_{x_k(0)=0 \text{ all } k\neq j}^{x_j(0)=1} \tag{4.19}$$

The unit initial condition on the jth integrator may be thought of as arising from a unit impulse applied to the input of that integrator at time zero. Because of this the matrix $\Phi(t)$ is also called the system *impulsive response matrix*, and the conditions of Eq. (4.19) can be rephrased as

$\varphi_{ij}(t) =$ output of integrator i with a unit impulse applied to the input of integrator j at $t = 0$. $\mathbf{x}(0^-) = \mathbf{0}$; i.e., the system is initially at rest. (4.20)

Since the Laplace transform of the impulse response of an initially relaxed system is by definition a transfer function, $\varphi_{ij}(t)$ is also the inverse Laplace transform of the transfer function from the input of the jth integrator to the output of the ith integrator. Hence, conventional block diagram or signal flow graph techniques may be used to find the Laplace transform of $\Phi(t)$, from which the matrix $\Phi(t)$ is found by the inverse Laplace transformation.

4.2 Complete Solution. The complete solution of the vector equation for a linear system with constant coefficients will now be obtained by Laplace transform techniques. By definition, the Laplace transform of a matrix is obtained by transforming each element in the matrix. Then by taking the Laplace transform of the system equation

$$\dot{\mathbf{x}}(t) = A\mathbf{x}(t) + \mathbf{f}(t) \tag{4.21}$$

we obtain

$$s\mathbf{X}(s) - \mathbf{x}(0) = A\mathbf{X}(s) + \mathbf{F}(s). \tag{4.22}$$

The transformed state vector is written as

$$\mathbf{X}(s) = [Is - A]^{-1}\mathbf{x}(0) + [Is - A]^{-1}\mathbf{F}(s). \tag{4.23}$$

We have already shown that the solution to the force-free equation is given by (4.16). Therefore, we can assert by comparing Eq. (4.16) with (4.23) that

$$\mathscr{L}^{-1}\{[Is - A]^{-1}\} = e^{At} = \Phi(t) \tag{4.24}$$

where $\mathscr{L}^{-1}$ denotes the inverse Laplace transform. Note the similarity of this result to the corresponding scalar relationship

$$\mathscr{L}^{-1}\left(\frac{1}{s - a}\right) = e^{at}. \tag{4.25}$$

Using the result of Eq. (4.24) and the fact that multiplication in the s-domain corresponds to convolution in the time domain, we may write the complete solution of (4.21) as

$$\mathbf{x}(t) = \Phi(t)\mathbf{x}(0) + \Phi(t) * \mathbf{f}(t) \tag{4.26}$$

or

$$\mathbf{x}(t) = \Phi(t)\mathbf{x}(0) + \int_0^t \Phi(t - \tau(\mathbf{f})\tau)\, d\tau. \tag{4.27}$$

4.3 The Classical Method. The classical method for solving a linear differential equation with constant coefficients is to assume a solution of exponential form and substitute it into the equation. We now apply this method to the force-free vector equation (4.11). Assume that a solution is of the form

$$\mathbf{x}(t) = \mathbf{x}_0 e^{\lambda t} \tag{4.28}$$

where $\mathbf{x}_0$ is a constant vector, and λ is a scalar. Substitution of Eq. (4.28) into (4.11) yields

$$\lambda \mathbf{x}_0 e^{\lambda t} = A\mathbf{x}_0 e^{\lambda t}. \tag{4.29}$$

This may be written as

$$(A - \lambda I)\mathbf{x}_0 e^{\lambda t} = 0. \tag{4.30}$$

Since $e^{\lambda t} \neq 0$, we must have that

$$(A - \lambda I)\mathbf{x}_0 = 0. \tag{4.31}$$

Equation (4.31) represents a set of n homogeneous linear algebraic equations in terms of the n components of the state vector $\mathbf{x}_0$. These equations can have a nontrivial solution, i.e., other than $\mathbf{x}_0 = 0$, only if the determinant of the coefficient matrix vanishes. That is if

$$\det (A - \lambda I) = 0. \tag{4.32}$$

Equation (4.32) becomes an nth-degree polynomial in λ, called the *characteristic polynomial* or *characteristic equation* of the system. The roots of the characteristic polymonial are called *eigenvalues* of the system. Other terms used interchangeably with eigenvalues are *proper values, natural modes, free frequencies*, *characteristic roots*, and *characteristic values*. Since these eigenvalues are the roots of an nth-degree polynomial with real coefficients, the n values need not be distinct, and need not be real, although any complex root must be accompanied by its conjugate. The nature of these eigenvalues determines the force-free behavior of the system. We will consider first the important special case where all the eigenvalues are real and distinct. We will then discuss the more general condition in which repeated and complex roots are present.

4.4 Systems with Real Distinct Eigenvalues. If solution of Eq. (4.32) yields n real distinct values of λ, then each λ_i, $i = 1, \ldots, n$, when substituted back into (4.31), yields a corresponding vector $\mathbf{x}_{0i}$ having real components $x_{(0i)1}, \ldots, x_{(0i)n}$. The $\mathbf{x}_{0i}$ are called the *eigenvectors* of the system. It should be noted that since the determinant of the coefficient matrix in Eq. (4.31) is zero, the n-equations are linearly dependent. As a result each eigenvector is determined within an arbitrary scalar multiplier. A physical interpretation of the eigenvector is apparent from Eq. (4.28). We see that an eigenvector can be viewed as a certain set of initial conditions on the integrators of the system simulation which produces a force-free response consisting of a single time constant, $1/\lambda_i$. This same time constant is observed at the output of each integrator so that the system state at any time is simply a scalar multiple of the initial state. This property of the eigenvector to isolate its corresponding eigenvalue leads to the determination of a simulation of the canonical system which physically places this property in evidence. What we seek is a linear transformation of variables to a new system in which the eigenvalues are apparent, and the eigenvectors are mutually orthogonal. For each λ_i and its corresponding $\mathbf{x}_{0i}$ we have a relationship of the form given by Eq. (4.29) and repeated here:

$$\lambda_i \mathbf{x}_{0i} e^{\lambda_i t} = A \mathbf{x}_{0i} e^{\lambda_i t}. \tag{4.33}$$

Since $e^{\lambda_i t} \neq 0$, we may express Eq. (4.33) as

$$A\mathbf{x}_{0i} = \lambda_i \mathbf{x}_{0i}. \qquad i = 1, 2, \ldots, n \tag{4.34}$$

Now form the $n \times n$ matrix X by placing the n-eigenvectors side by side. Thus, the $\mathbf{x}_{0i}$ constitute the columns of X. We denote this symbolically by

$$X = [\mathbf{x}_{01}\ \mathbf{x}_{02} \cdots \mathbf{x}_{0n}]. \tag{4.35}$$

X is called the *modal matrix* of the system. It can readily be verified from Eqs. (4.34) and (4.35) that the matrix A operating on X gives the following result:

$$AX = [\lambda_1 \mathbf{x}_{01}\ \lambda_2 \mathbf{x}_{02} \cdots \lambda_n \mathbf{x}_{0n}]. \tag{4.36}$$

Because postmultiplication of a matrix B by a diagonal matrix D multiplies the ith column of B by d_{ii}, Eq. (4.36) may be expressed as

$$AX = X\begin{bmatrix} \lambda_1 & & & & 0 \\ & \lambda_2 & & & \\ & & \cdot & & \\ & & & \cdot & \\ & & & & \cdot \\ 0 & & & & \lambda_n \end{bmatrix}. \tag{4.37}$$

Since the eigenvectors are linearly independent, the columns of X are independent, and the inverse of X exists. We therefore obtain the following relation from Eq. (4.37):

$$X^{-1}AX = \begin{bmatrix} \lambda_1 & & & & 0 \\ & \lambda_2 & & & \\ & & \cdot & & \\ & & & \cdot & \\ & & & & \cdot \\ 0 & & & & \lambda_n \end{bmatrix} \equiv \Lambda. \tag{4.38}$$

A linear transformation of the general form $T^{-1}AT = B$ is called a *similarity transformation*. The determinant, the trace, and the characteristic polynomial of a matrix are invariant under a similarity transformation. Equation (4.38) shows that for a system with real distinct eigenvalues, a similarity transformation employing the modal matrix X yields a diagonal matrix Λ which displays the eigenvalues on its diagonal. We now define a new set of coordinates $\mathbf{y}$ in the state space by the transformation $\mathbf{x} = X\mathbf{y}$. In terms of $\mathbf{y}$, (4.11) becomes

$$X\dot{\mathbf{y}} = AX\mathbf{y} \tag{4.39}$$

which gives

$$\dot{\mathbf{y}} = X^{-1}AX\mathbf{y} = \Lambda\mathbf{y}. \tag{4.40}$$

The components of $\mathbf{y}$ are called the *normal coordinates* or *canonical variables* because the normal modes of the system are isolated when expressed in terms of these coordinates. Equation (4.40) relates in vector form n independent first-order differential equations of the form

$$\dot{y}_i = \lambda_i y_i. \qquad i = 1, 2, \ldots, n. \tag{4.41}$$

The solutions to these equations are simply

$$y_i(t) = y_i(0)e^{\lambda_i t}. \qquad i = 1, 2, \ldots, n. \tag{4.42}$$

Therefore, the solution of Eq. (4.40) may be expressed in matrix form as

$$\mathbf{y}(t) = \begin{bmatrix} e^{\lambda_1 t} & & & & \\ & e^{\lambda_2 t} & & & 0 \\ & & \cdot & & \\ & & & \cdot & \\ & & & & \cdot \\ & 0 & & & e^{\lambda_n t} \end{bmatrix}\mathbf{y}(0). \tag{4.43}$$

To find the solution in terms of the **x**-variables we substitute $\mathbf{x} = X\mathbf{y}$ into Eq. (4.43) and obtain

$$\mathbf{x}(t) = X \begin{bmatrix} e^{\lambda_1 t} & & & & 0 \\ & e^{\lambda_2 t} & & & \\ & & \cdot & & \\ & & & \cdot & \\ & & & & \cdot \\ 0 & & & & e^{\lambda_n t} \end{bmatrix} X^{-1}\mathbf{x}(0). \tag{4.44}$$

Comparison of Eqs. (4.16) and (4.44) shows that

$$X \begin{bmatrix} e^{\lambda_1 t} & & & & \\ & e^{\lambda_2 t} & & & 0 \\ & & \cdot & & \\ & & & \cdot & \\ & & & & \cdot \\ 0 & & & & e^{\lambda_n t} \end{bmatrix} X^{-1} = \Phi(t). \tag{4.45}$$

We have in Eq. (4.45) another way to calculate the state transition matrix. Transformation to the normal coordinate system simplifies many procedures of analysis and synthesis because of the simpler matrices involved.

Example. An example of a third-order system with real distinct eigenvalues will be given to clarify the preceding discussion. Consider a system described by the equation

$$\dot{\mathbf{x}} = A\mathbf{x} + \mathbf{f}(t) \tag{4.46}$$

where

$$A = \begin{bmatrix} 0 & 1 & 0 \\ -6 & -5 & 1 \\ 0 & 0 & -1 \end{bmatrix}, \qquad \mathbf{f}(t) = r(t)\begin{bmatrix} 0 \\ 0 \\ 1 \end{bmatrix}.$$

The corresponding simulation, found from inspection of Eq. (4.46), is shown in Fig. 2. If the time response in terms of the state **x** is the only result of interest, then determination of the state transition matrix $\Phi(t)$ by means of Eq. (4.20) is perhaps the most expedient course to take. The various transfer functions can

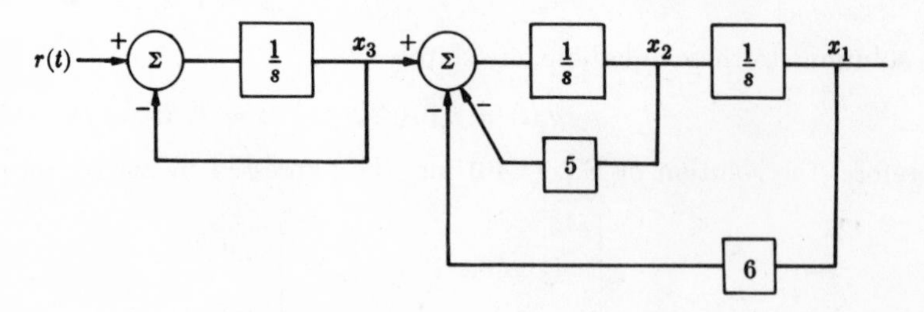

FIGURE 2. Analog simulation of Eq. (4.46).

quickly be found by conventional signal-flow graph analysis of Fig. 2. For example, $\varphi_{11}(s)$ is obtained by inspection as the transfer function from the input of integrator one to the output of the same integrator. The result is

$$\varphi_{11}(s) = \frac{\frac{1}{s}\left(1 + \frac{5}{s}\right)}{1 + \frac{5}{s} + \frac{6}{s^2}} = \frac{s + 5}{s^2 + 5s + 6} = \frac{s + 5.}{(s + 2)(s + 3)}. \tag{4.47}$$

The other elements are found in a similar manner so that the Laplace transform of the transition matrix is given by

$$\Phi(s) = \begin{bmatrix} \frac{s + 5}{(s + 2)(s + 3)} & \frac{1}{(s + 2)(s + 3)} & \frac{1}{(s + 1)(s + 2)(s + 3)} \\ \frac{-6}{(s + 2)(s + 3)} & \frac{s}{(s + 2)(s + 3)} & \frac{s}{(s + 1)(s + 2)(s + 3)} \\ 0 & 0 & \frac{1}{s + 1} \end{bmatrix}. \tag{4.48}$$

By performing the inverse Laplace transform of the $\Phi(s)$ matrix, we obtain the state transition matrix

$$\Phi(t) = \begin{bmatrix} (3e^{-2t} - 2e^{-3t}) & (e^{-2t} - e^{-3t}) & (\frac{1}{2}e^{-t} - e^{-2t} + \frac{1}{2}e^{-3t}) \\ (-6e^{-2t} + 6e^{-3t}) & (-2e^{-2t} + 3e^{-3t}) & (-\frac{1}{2}e^{-t} + 2e^{-2t} - \frac{3}{2}e^{-3t}) \\ 0 & 0 & e^{-t} \end{bmatrix}. \tag{4.49}$$

Note that $\Phi(0) = I$, as required by Eq. (4.17). The complete solution of Eq. (4.46) is then given by

$$\mathbf{x}(t) = \Phi(t)\mathbf{x}(0) + \Phi(t) * \mathbf{f}(t) \tag{4.50}$$

where $\Phi(t)$ is given by (4.49). Using the expression from (4.46) for $\mathbf{f}(t)$, the convolution in (4.50) may be written as

$$\Phi(t) * \mathbf{f}(t) = r(t) * \begin{bmatrix} \frac{1}{2}e^{-t} - e^{-2t} + \frac{1}{2}e^{-3t} \\ -\frac{1}{2}e^{-t} + 2e^{-2t} - \frac{3}{2}e^{-3t} \\ e^{-t} \end{bmatrix}. \tag{4.51}$$

The complexity of the state transition matrix, when expressed in the $\mathbf{x}$ coordinates motivates the following solution in terms of the normal coordinates. We first compute the characteristic polynomial by Eq. (4.32). For this problem we have

$$\begin{vmatrix} -\lambda & 1 & 0 \\ -6 & (-5 - \lambda) & 1 \\ 0 & 0 & (-1 - \lambda) \end{vmatrix} = 0 = (\lambda + 1)(\lambda + 2)(\lambda + 3). \tag{4.52}$$

The three eigenvalues, $\lambda_1 = -1$, $\lambda_2 = -2$, and $\lambda_3 = -3$, are real and distinct so we can determine three corresponding eigenvectors from Eq. (4.31). For example, to find $\mathbf{x}_{02}$ we insert $\lambda_2 = -2$ into the equations and obtain

$$\begin{aligned} 2x_{(02)1} + x_{(02)2} &= 0 \\ -6x_{(02)1} - 3x_{(02)2} + x_{(02)3} &= 0 \\ x_{(02)3} &= 0. \end{aligned} \tag{4.53}$$

Note that the equations are dependent as stated previously. Let us choose the first component of the eigenvector to be unity. Then the second component is determined from Eq. (4.53), and $\mathbf{x}_{02}$ becomes

$$\mathbf{x}_{02} = \begin{bmatrix} 1 \\ -2 \\ 0 \end{bmatrix}. \tag{4.54}$$

Applying the same method to the eigenvalues λ_1 and λ_3, we find their corresponding eigenvectors to be

$$\mathbf{x}_{01} = \begin{bmatrix} 1 \\ -1 \\ 2 \end{bmatrix} \quad \text{and} \quad \mathbf{x}_{03} = \begin{bmatrix} 1 \\ -3 \\ 0 \end{bmatrix}. \tag{4.55}$$

The modal matrix X is formed in accordance with Eq. (4.35) as

$$X = \begin{bmatrix} 1 & 1 & 1 \\ -1 & -2 & -3 \\ 2 & 0 & 0 \end{bmatrix}. \tag{4.56}$$

The inverse of the modal matrix is readily found to be

$$X^{-1} = \begin{bmatrix} 0 & 0 & \frac{1}{2} \\ 3 & 1 & -1 \\ -2 & -1 & \frac{1}{2} \end{bmatrix}. \tag{4.57}$$

It can be verified by direct calculation that the similarity transformation of A by the modal matrix yields the diagonal matrix Λ. That is,

$$X^{-1}AX = \begin{bmatrix} -1 & 0 & 0 \\ 0 & -2 & 0 \\ 0 & 0 & -3 \end{bmatrix} = \Lambda. \tag{4.58}$$

The system differential equation in terms of the normal coordinates $\mathbf{y}$ is then given by

$$\dot{\mathbf{y}} = \Lambda\mathbf{y} + X^{-1}\mathbf{f}(t) \tag{4.59}$$

where $\mathbf{x} = X\mathbf{y}$. Substituting from Eqs. (4.46), (4.57), and (4.58) into (4.59) we obtain

$$\dot{\mathbf{y}} = \begin{bmatrix} -1 & 0 & 0 \\ 0 & -2 & 0 \\ 0 & 0 & -3 \end{bmatrix} \mathbf{y} + r(t) \begin{bmatrix} \frac{1}{2} \\ -1 \\ \frac{1}{2} \end{bmatrix}. \tag{4.60}$$

The analog simulation corresponding to the normal coordinate system of Eq. (4.60) is shown in Fig. 3. The solution of (4.60) can now be written as

$$\mathbf{y}(t) = \begin{bmatrix} e^{-t} & 0 & 0 \\ 0 & e^{-2t} & 0 \\ 0 & 0 & e^{-3t} \end{bmatrix} \mathbf{y}(0) + r(t) * \begin{bmatrix} \frac{1}{2}e^{-t} \\ -e^{-2t} \\ \frac{1}{2}e^{-3t} \end{bmatrix}. \tag{4.61}$$

It can be verified that substitution of $\mathbf{x} = X\mathbf{y}$ into Eq. (4.61) yields (4.50) with the transition matrix and $\mathbf{f}(t)$ given by (4.49) and (4.51) respectively.

4.5 Systems with Complex Eigenvalues. Consider now the common situation in which the system exhibits one or more complex conjugate pairs of eigenvalues. If there are no repeated roots, then the mathematical formulation given for real distinct roots is still valid. However, the eigenvectors will now have complex elements. Therefore, diagonalization of a matrix having complex characteristic roots involves a similarity transformation with a modal matrix X having complex elements. The resulting diagonal matrix Λ exhibits the complex eigenvalues on its diagonal.

Even though there is nothing objectionable, from a purely mathematical viewpoint, about a matrix with complex elements, the lack of a physical representation of such a system in terms of a computer simulation leads us to seek a different form for Λ which, although not diagonal, does have real

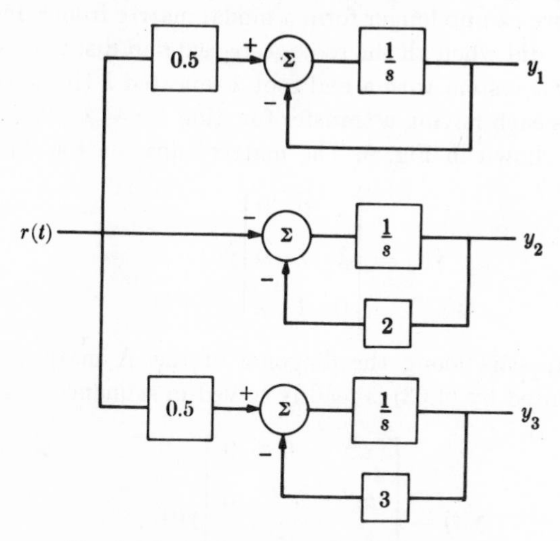

FIGURE 3. Analog simulation of Eq. (4.60).

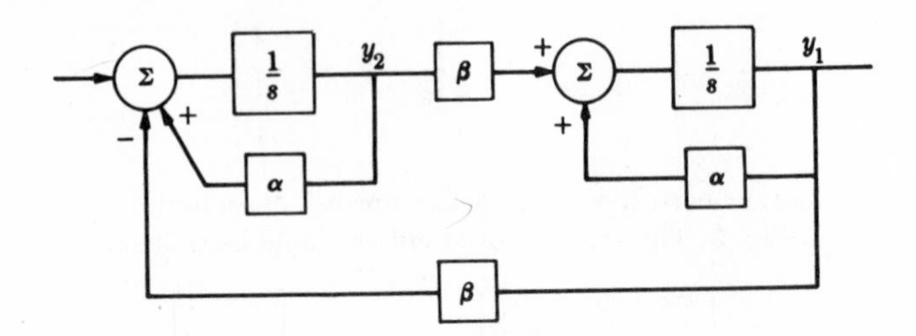

FIGURE 4. Canonical representation for complex roots.

elements and does isolate and clearly exhibit the eigenvalues. This canonic representation for one pair of eigenvalues $\alpha \pm j\beta$ is shown in Fig. 4. The matrix differential equation for this system is seen to be

$$\dot{\mathbf{y}} = \begin{bmatrix} \alpha & \beta \\ -\beta & \alpha \end{bmatrix} \mathbf{y}. \tag{4.62}$$

Note that this matrix satisfies our requirements: It has real elements; the real part of the root is displayed along the main diagonal, and the imaginary part is displayed on both sides of it. The relationship between the canonical variables and the actual system variables $\mathbf{x}$ is more readily determined by the transfer function method to be described later.

4.6 Systems with Repeated Eigenvalues. If an eigenvalue is repeated, that is, if the characteristic equation has a multiple root, then it is not generally possible to find independent eigenvectors for each root. This implies that we can no longer form a modal matrix from n independent eigenvectors as we did when all the roots were real and distinct. A canonical representation for a system with a real root λ repeated k times consists of k cascaded elements each having a transfer function $1/s - \lambda$. This representation for $k = 3$ is shown in Fig. 5. The matrix equation for this system is

$$\dot{\mathbf{y}}(t) = \begin{bmatrix} \lambda & 0 & 0 \\ 1 & \lambda & 0 \\ 0 & 1 & \lambda \end{bmatrix} \mathbf{y}(t). \tag{4.63}$$

The eigenvalue appears along the diagonal of the Λ matrix. The set of equations represented by (4.63) is readily solved in sequence to give

$$\mathbf{y}(t) = \begin{bmatrix} e^{\lambda t} & 0 & 0 \\ te^{\lambda t} & e^{\lambda t} & 0 \\ \frac{t^2}{2!}e^{\lambda t} & te^{\lambda t} & e^{\lambda t} \end{bmatrix} \mathbf{y}(0). \tag{4.64}$$

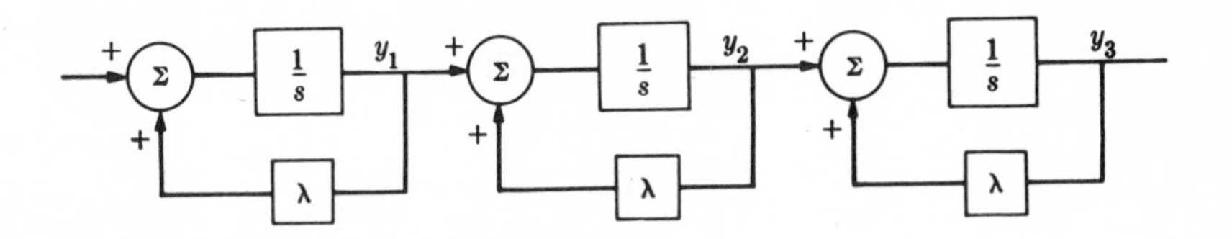

FIGURE 5. Canonical representation for repeated roots.

The solution may also be expressed as

$$\mathbf{y}(t) = \left(\mathbf{y}_{01} + \mathbf{y}_{02}t + \mathbf{y}_{03}\frac{t^2}{2!}\right)e^{\lambda t} \tag{4.65}$$

where

$$\mathbf{y}_{01} = \begin{bmatrix} y_1(0) \\ y_2(0) \\ y_3(0) \end{bmatrix} = \mathbf{y}(0), \quad y_{02} = \begin{bmatrix} 0 \\ y_1(0) \\ y_2(0) \end{bmatrix}, \quad \mathbf{y}_{03} = \begin{bmatrix} 0 \\ 0 \\ y_1(0) \end{bmatrix}. \tag{4.66}$$

Note that the initial conditions $\mathbf{y}(0)$ completely determine all the vectors $\mathbf{y}_{0i}$. Note also that $\mathbf{y}_{03}$ is an eigenvector since it isolates y_1. The general system having λ repeated k times has the solution

$$\mathbf{x}(t) = \sum_{n=1}^{k} \mathbf{x}_{0n} \frac{t^{n-1}}{(n-1)!} e^{\lambda t}. \tag{4.67}$$

To find a matrix X which transforms the original system into the canonical system, we may proceed as follows. Select initial conditions $\mathbf{x}(0) = \mathbf{x}_{01}$, and substitute these together with Eq. (4.67) into the system equation $\dot{\mathbf{x}} = A\mathbf{x}$. Solve for the remaining $\mathbf{x}_{0i}$ by equating powers of t in the resulting equations. Form the $k \times k$ matrix X with the vectors $\mathbf{x}_{0i}$ as its columns. Thus,

$$X = [\mathbf{x}_{01}\, \mathbf{x}_{02} \cdots \mathbf{x}_{0k}]. \tag{4.68}$$

Since $\mathbf{x}_{0k}$ is an eigenvector, it may also be found in the usual way as a partial check on the computation of the $\mathbf{x}_{0i}$. The relationship between the given system and the canonical system is then expressed by $\mathbf{x} = X\mathbf{y}$, and the canonical matrix of the form in Eq. (4.63) is found as $X^{-1}AX$. If the system contains other roots in addition to the multiple root, then Eqs. (4.65) and (4.67) are not the complete solutions, and $\mathbf{y}_{01}$ and $\mathbf{x}_{01}$ do not correspond to the initial conditions. However, the vectors $\mathbf{y}_{0i}$ and $\mathbf{x}_{0i}$ may still be found by substituting the solutions of Eq. (4.65) or (4.67) into the system differential equation and equating powers of t.

If a system has a repeated pair of complex conjugate eigenvalues, a canonical representation is the cascade connection of two canonical

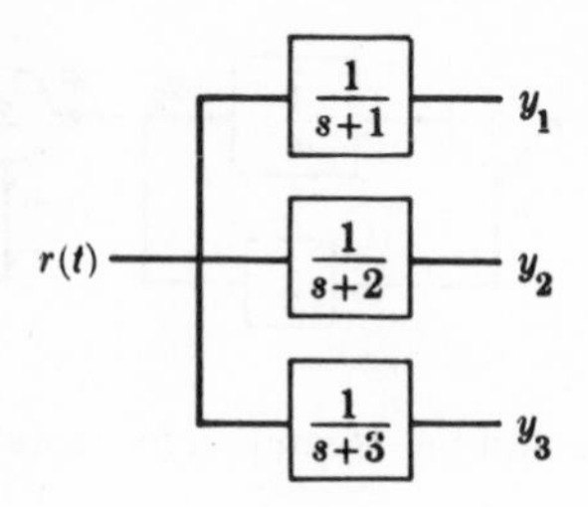

FIGURE 6. Canonical representation for example.

representations of a single complex pair. For a double root at $s = \alpha \pm j\beta$, the matrix Λ is

$$\Lambda = \begin{bmatrix} \alpha & \beta & 0 & 0 \\ -\beta & \alpha & 1 & 0 \\ 0 & 0 & \alpha & \beta \\ 0 & 0 & -\beta & \alpha \end{bmatrix}. \tag{4.69}$$

Methods presented thus far for determining the matrix X show the correlation between the classical procedure of solving differential equations and a corresponding approach in terms of matrices. An alternate and perhaps more straightforward technique employing transfer functions will now be discussed.

4.7 Analysis by Transfer Functions. The canonical representation of a system can be written by inspection after the eigenvalues have been determined explicitly. The eigenvalues are found by solving the characteristic equation of the system as determined from the A-matrix or from signal-flow graph analysis. Flow graph analysis also provides a general method for determining the matrix X which relates the x variables of the given system to the y-variables of the canonical representation by $\mathbf{x} = X\mathbf{y}$. The first step in this procedure is to define an input $r(t)$ in such a way that a nonzero transfer function exists between the input and each of the n state variables. In most cases the normal system input would be used. By expanding each of the n transfer functions in partial fractions we isolate the characteristic roots so that the expressions for each x-variable in terms of the y-variables may be written by inspection. These relationships define the matrix X.

Example. As an example of this procedure consider again the system shown in Fig. 2 and defined by Eq. (4.46). The transfer functions from the input to the three state variables are found by inspection to be

$$\frac{x_1}{r} = \frac{1}{(s+1)(s+2)(s+3)} = \frac{1/2}{s+1} - \frac{1}{s+2} + \frac{1/2}{s+3}$$

$$\frac{x_2}{r} = \frac{s}{(s+1)(s+2)(s+3)} = \frac{-1/2}{s+1} + \frac{2}{s+2} - \frac{-3/2}{s+3} \tag{4.70}$$

$$\frac{x_3}{r} = \frac{1}{s+1}.$$

If the canonical representation of the system is drawn as shown in Fig. 6, the corresponding transfer functions are

$$\begin{aligned} \frac{y_1}{r} &= \frac{1}{s+1} \\ \frac{y_2}{r} &= \frac{1}{s+2} \\ \frac{y_3}{r} &= \frac{1}{s+3}. \end{aligned} \tag{4.71}$$

By comparing Eqs. (4.70) and (4.71) we may immediately write the following relationships:

$$\begin{aligned} x_1 &= \tfrac{1}{2}y_1 - y_2 + \tfrac{1}{2}y_3 \\ x_2 &= -\tfrac{1}{2}y_1 + 2y_2 - \tfrac{3}{2}y_3 \\ x_3 &= y_1. \end{aligned} \tag{4.72}$$

These equations written in matrix notation become

$$\mathbf{x} = X\mathbf{y} = \begin{bmatrix} \frac{1}{2} & -1 & \frac{1}{2} \\ -\frac{1}{2} & 2 & -\frac{3}{2} \\ 1 & 0 & 0 \end{bmatrix} \mathbf{y}. \tag{4.73}$$

Although the matrix X of Eq. (4.73) is not identical to that of (4.56), it should be noted that each column of one matrix is a scalar multiple of the corresponding column in the other matrix. A comparison of Figs. 3 and 6 shows that the difference arises from the method used in connecting the input to the canonical simulation. It can be verified that a similarity transformation of A with the X of either Eq. (4.56) or (4.73) yields the same canonical form given by (4.58). The differential equation of the system of Fig. 3 is given by (4.60) while the equation for Fig. 6 is

$$\dot{\mathbf{y}} = \begin{bmatrix} -1 & 0 & 0 \\ 0 & -2 & 0 \\ 0 & 0 & -3 \end{bmatrix} \mathbf{y} + r(t) \begin{bmatrix} 1 \\ 1 \\ 1 \end{bmatrix}. \tag{4.74}$$

The only difference between (4.60) and (4.74) is in the forcing terms, as would be expected.

Example. As a final example of finding the canonical representation by the partial fraction expansion of transfer functions, consider a system whose over-all transfer function from input to output is given by

$$G(s) = \frac{s+5}{s^2(s+1)[(s+2)^2+1]}. \tag{4.75}$$

We seek a canonical representation yielding this over-all transfer function. No X matrix is needed since the internal structure of the system is not specified. Inspection of the characteristic equation shows a double root at $s = 0$, a real root at -1, and a complex conjugate pair at $-2 \pm j1$. Since there are five roots, a 5×5 Λ matrix will display the roots in canonical form. Therefore, Λ may be written at once as

$$\Lambda = \begin{bmatrix} 0 & 0 & 0 & 0 & 0 \\ 1 & 0 & 0 & 0 & 0 \\ 0 & 0 & -1 & 0 & 0 \\ 0 & 0 & 0 & -2 & 1 \\ 0 & 0 & 0 & -1 & -2 \end{bmatrix}. \tag{4.76}$$

To determine the proper combination of state variables to yield the transfer function of (4.75) we perform a partial fraction expansion which gives

$$G(s) = \frac{1}{s^2} - \frac{1.6}{s} + \frac{2}{s+1} - \frac{0.4s + 0.6}{(s+2)^2 + 1}. \tag{4.77}$$

The system simulation may now be written from inspection of Eqs. (4.76) and (4.77). The result is shown in Fig. 7. The system equation is

$$\dot{\mathbf{y}} = \Lambda \mathbf{y} + r(t)\mathbf{f} \tag{4.78}$$

where Λ is given by (4.76), and the vector for the forcing term has been chosen as seen from Fig. 7 to be

$$\mathbf{f} = \begin{bmatrix} 1 \\ 0 \\ 1 \\ 0 \\ 1 \end{bmatrix}. \tag{4.79}$$

The system output x can be written in terms of the state variables as

$$x = \boldsymbol{\alpha}^T \mathbf{y}, \quad \boldsymbol{\alpha}^T = [-1.6 \quad 1 \quad 2 \quad 0.2 \quad -0.4]. \tag{4.80}$$

Since there are two paths from y_4 to the output, the fourth component of $\boldsymbol{\alpha}^T$ is $-0.6 + (2)(0.4) = 0.2$.

4.8 A State-Space Method of Synthesis [4]. We present now an application of state transition techniques to the synthesis of a sampled-data system with periodically time-varying sampling. This type of sampling may occur when a single digital computer controls several different dynamic processes in a sequential manner. The sampling rate for any one process

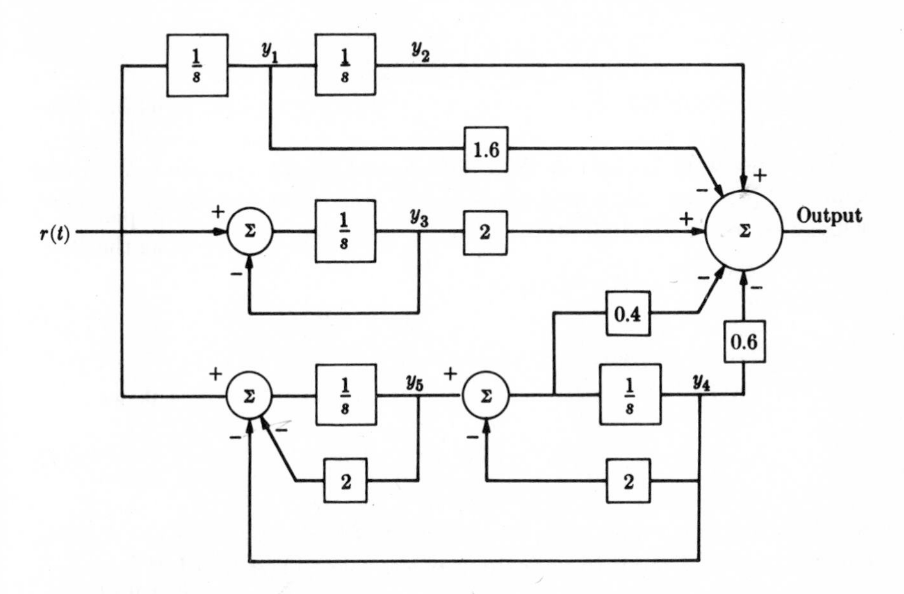

FIGURE 7. Simulation of Eq. (4.75).

may then be cyclic. The successive sampling periods are T_1, T_2, $T_3, \ldots,$ T_q, $T_1, \ldots$. This is also called multiple order sampling, of order q.

Suppose that the third-order plant shown in Fig. 8, of measurable state variables x_1, x_2, and x_3, is subjected to a piecewise constant input m with a cyclic sampling rate of order 2. Let $T_1 = 1$ and $T_2 = 2$. The control signal m is formed as a linear combination of the state variables:

$$m = \boldsymbol{\alpha}^T \mathbf{x}. \tag{4.81}$$

The vector $\boldsymbol{\alpha}$ is called the control vector. We are to find that $\boldsymbol{\alpha}$ which will cause any initial state of the system to be reduced to zero in the minimum number of sampling periods. Although z-transform methods are applicable

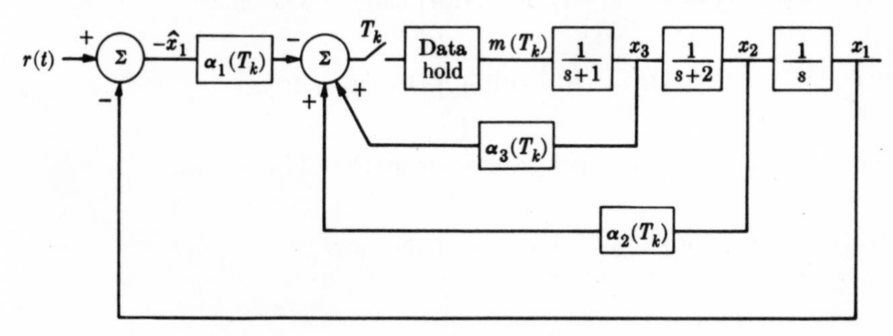

FIGURE 8. State feedback sampled-data system.

to such finite-settling time designs for conventional, i.e., constant rate, sampling, these methods are not readily adapted to the synthesis of systems with cyclic sampling. The state-space technique is applicable in either situation.

Since the input to the plant in most sampled-data systems is piecewise constant, it is convenient to define the step response vector $\mathbf{h}(t)$ as the state which results when a unit step

$$m(t) = \begin{cases} 1 & \text{for} \quad t > 0 \\ 0 & \text{for} \quad t < 0 \end{cases}$$

is applied to the initially relaxed plant at time zero. If $\mathbf{x}(0) = \mathbf{0}$, we have from Eq. (4.26) that

$$\mathbf{x}(t) = \int_0^t \Phi(\tau)\mathbf{f}(t - \tau)\, d\tau. \tag{4.82}$$

Since the input is a unit step, $\mathbf{f}(t - \tau) = \mathbf{f}^*$, $f_i^* =$ constant, $i = 1, \ldots, n$. The notation $\mathbf{f}^*$ is used to indicate that the control signal m is a unit step. It follows that

$$\mathbf{h}(t) = \int_0^t \Phi(\tau)\mathbf{f}^*\, d\tau. \tag{4.83}$$

It is known that the initial state of an nth-order plant can be reduced to zero in at most n sampling periods. For this particular problem we must find the proper vector $\boldsymbol{\alpha}$ such that $\mathbf{x}(T_1 + T_2 + T_1) = \mathbf{0}$. From Eq. (4.27) and for a piecewise constant control signal of arbitrary magnitude we have then that

$$\mathbf{x}(t) = \Phi(t)\mathbf{x}(0) + \int_0^t \Phi(t - \tau)m(\tau)\mathbf{f}^*\, d\tau. \tag{4.84}$$

Since $\Phi(t - \tau) = \Phi(t)\Phi(-\tau)$, Eq. (4.84) may be written as

$$\mathbf{x}(t) = \Phi(t)\left[\mathbf{x}(0) + \int_0^t m(\tau)\Phi(-\tau)\mathbf{f}^*\, d\tau\right]. \tag{4.85}$$

Since $\Phi(t) \neq 0$, and $m(\tau)$ is piecewise constant, we may write

$$\mathbf{x}(T_1 + T_2 + T_1) = \mathbf{0} = \mathbf{x}(0) + m_1 \int_0^{T_1} \Phi(-\tau)\mathbf{f}^*\, d\tau + m_2 \int_{T_1}^{T_1+T_2} \Phi(-\tau)\mathbf{f}^*\, d\tau + m_3 \int_{T_1+T_2}^{T_1+T_2+T_1} \Phi(-\tau)\mathbf{f}^*\, d\tau \tag{4.86}$$

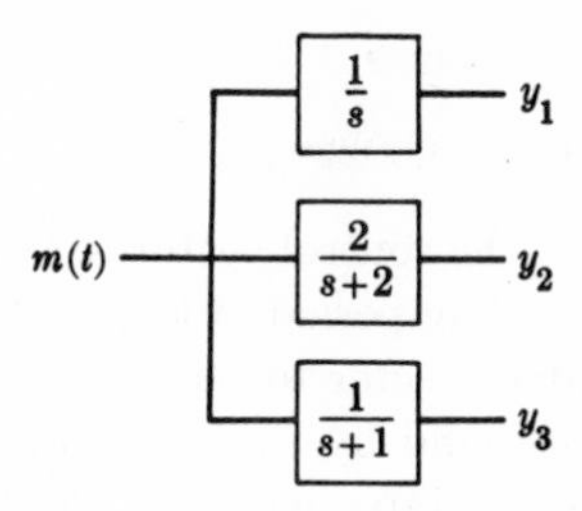

FIGURE 9. Normal form for plant.

where the m_i are constant over their respective sampling periods. By a suitable change of variables the integrals in (4.86) may be expressed in terms of the unit step vector of (4.83). Equation (4.86) then becomes

$$\mathbf{x}(0) = m_1\mathbf{h}(-T_1) + m_2[\mathbf{h}(-T_1 - T_2) - \mathbf{h}(-T_1)] \\ + m_3[\mathbf{h}(-T_1 - T_2 - T_1) - \mathbf{h}(-T_1 - T_2)]. \quad (4.87)$$

The vector equation (4.87) represents three scalar equations with three unknowns, m_1, m_2, and m_3. These equations can be solved for m_1 in terms of $\mathbf{x}(0)$ to yield the control vector $\boldsymbol{\alpha}(T_1)$. The argument T_1 indicates that this control vector is used at the beginning of a sampling period of duration T_1.

Although the solution of Eq. (4.87) can be obtained directly by using the unit step vector $\mathbf{h}(t)$ of the given plant, the solution is more readily obtained in terms of the canonical representation. This normal form is shown in Fig. 9. The factor 2 is included in the y_2 variable to simplify the step response vector which is found by inspection to be

$$\mathbf{h}(t) = \begin{bmatrix} t \\ 1 - e^{-2t} \\ 1 - e^{-t} \end{bmatrix}. \quad (4.88)$$

Substituting Eq. (4.88) into (4.87) and solving for m_1 by Cramer's rule, we obtain

$$m_1 = \frac{\begin{vmatrix} y_1(0) & -T_2 & -T_1 \\ y_2(0) & (1 - e^{2T_2})e^{2T_1} & (1 - e^{2T_1})e^{2(T_1+T_2)} \\ y_3(0) & (1 - e^{T_2})e^{T_1} & (1 - e^{T_1})e^{(T_1+T_2)} \end{vmatrix}}{\begin{vmatrix} -T_1 & -T_2 & -T_1 \\ (1 - e^{2T_1}) & (1 - e^{2T_2})e^{2T_1} & (1 - e^{2T_1})e^{2(T_1+T_2)} \\ (1 - e^{T_1}) & (1 - e^{T_2})e^{T_1} & (1 - e^{T_1})e^{(T_1+T_2)} \end{vmatrix}}. \quad (4.89)$$

With $T_1 = 1$ and $T_2 = 2$ (4.89) becomes

$$m(T_1) = -1.34y_1(0) - 0.00226y_2(0) + 0.206y_3(0). \tag{4.90}$$

The coefficients in Eq. (4.90) form the control vector to be used in the normal system at the beginning of a sampling period of length T_1. This is indicated by the argument of m. The control vector to be used at the beginning of a sampling period of length T_2 is found by cyclic permutation of the T_i in Eq. (4.89). In this case we simply interchange T_1 and T_2. The result is

$$m(T_2) = -0.695y_1 - 0.000314y_2 + 0.0636y_3. \tag{4.91}$$

To obtain the control vectors of the original system we must find the matrix X which relates the x and y variables by $\mathbf{x} = X\mathbf{y}$. Using the transfer function method we obtain the following equations from inspection of Fig. 8:

$$\begin{aligned}\frac{x_1}{m} &= \frac{1}{s(s+1)(s+2)} = \frac{0.5}{s} - \frac{1}{s+1} + \frac{0.5}{s+2}\\ \frac{x_2}{m} &= \frac{1}{(s+1)(s+2)} = \frac{1}{s+1} - \frac{1}{s+2}\\ \frac{x_3}{m} &= \frac{1}{s+1}.\end{aligned} \tag{4.92}$$

From Eq. (4.92) and Fig. 9 we see that

$$\begin{aligned}x_1 &= 0.5y_1 + 0.25y_2 - y_3\\ x_2 &= -0.5y_2 + y_3\\ x_3 &= y_3.\end{aligned} \tag{4.93}$$

Therefore, the matrix X and its inverse are

$$X = \begin{bmatrix} 0.5 & 0.25 & -1 \\ 0 & -0.5 & 1 \\ 0 & 0 & 1 \end{bmatrix} \qquad X^{-1} = \begin{bmatrix} 2 & 1 & 1 \\ 0 & -2 & 2 \\ 0 & 0 & 1 \end{bmatrix}. \tag{4.94}$$

The control vector in terms of the original system is then given by

$$\boldsymbol{\alpha}^T(T_k) = \boldsymbol{\alpha}_y{}^T(T_k)X^{-1} \tag{4.95}$$

where the vectors $\boldsymbol{\alpha}_y{}^T(T_k)$ are the coefficients of Eqs. (4.90) and (4.91). We obtain finally from (4.90), (4.91), (4.94), and (4.95):

$$\begin{aligned}\boldsymbol{\alpha}^T(T_1) &= [-2.68 - 1.336 - 1.139]\\ \boldsymbol{\alpha}^T(T_2) &= [-1.39 - 0.694 - 0.632].\end{aligned} \tag{4.96}$$

Equations (4.96) are the solutions to the problem. We see that cyclic sampling gives rise to periodically varying control coefficients, if a finite-settling time

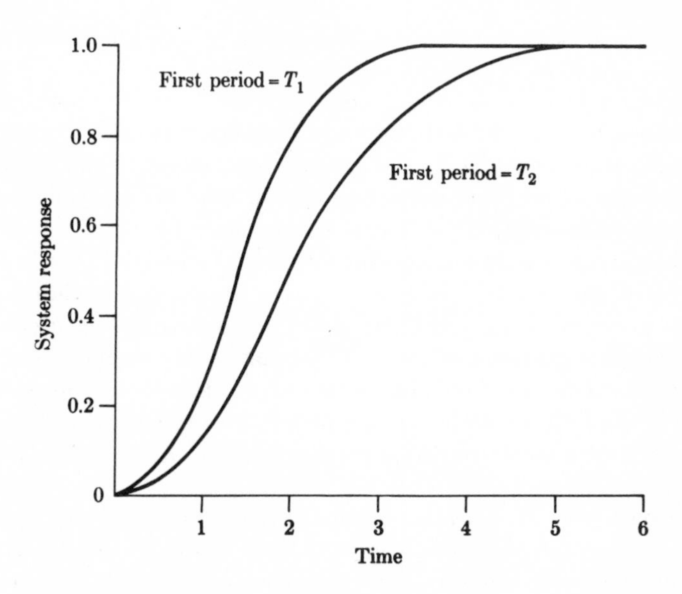

FIGURE 10. Unit step responses of sampled-data system.

design is required. In general, if there are q different sampling periods before the pattern repeats, (order q sampling), there will be q corresponding control vectors obtained by q cyclic permutations of the T_i in Eq. (4.89).

A step function input $r(t)$ may be applied to the system shown in Fig. 8 by introducing the change in variables

$$\hat{x}_1 = x_1 - r. \tag{4.97}$$

The system will now exhibit finite-settling time zero-ripple response to a step input. Since it is time-varying, the response depends upon the time at which the step is applied. The step responses for the example are shown in Fig. 10. Note that while each response settles in exactly three sampling periods, the total settling times are different because $T_1 + T_2 + T_1 = 4$ while $T_2 + T_1 + T_2 = 5$.

5. Conclusion

The state-space techniques presented in this chapter embody a fructiferous combination of mathematical methods and physical models for the analysis and synthesis of dynamic processes. A set of first-order ordinary differential equations written in matrix notation describes the system behavior. A correspondence between the state vector and a set of integrator outputs in an analog computer model allows physical interpretation of mathematical properties and transformations in terms of computer simulations. In linear systems a transformation to normal coordinates isolates the natural modes and yields a simple model which facilitates computations.

State-space analysis of a sampled-data system containing both discrete and continuous elements leads directly to a combination analog-digital model in which the state variables are outputs of delay elements and integrators [4,9]. State transition equations, written for an arbitrary sampling pattern, may be programmed directly on a digital computer.

This chapter gives only an introduction to the state-space methods and the associated physical models. Further developments and applications are given in the references. R. E. Kalman has initiated a general theory of linear control systems in state-space notation by applying the techniques of linear algebra, differential equations, and matrices to define such properties as observability and controllability [7]. Kalman also uses the same mathematical framework to solve the linear least-square smoothing and prediction problem of Wiener.

Zadeh and Desoer have written the first textbook devoted entirely to the state space approach [14]. This comprehensive work includes linear, nonlinear, time-invariant, time-varying, continuous, and discrete systems.

A concise presentation of transformations in dynamical systems is given in Chapter II of R. Bellman's book on *Adaptive Control Processes* [1]. Bellman also discusses applications in dynamic programing, and stochastic and adaptive control processes.

State-space analysis allows the control engineer to effectively combine the theories of differential equations, matrices, linear algebra, signal-flow graphs, the Laplace transformation, and analog and digital computation in studying the behavior and stability of dynamic processes.

BIBLIOGRAPHY

1. Bellman, R., *Adaptive Control Processes: A Guided Tour*, Princeton, 1961.
2. Bellman, R., *Introduction to Matrix Analysis*, McGraw-Hill, 1960.
3. Coddington, E. A., and Levinson, N., *Theory of Ordinary Differential Equations*, McGraw-Hill, 1955.
4. Henry, E. W., "Logical Scheduling of a Multiplexed Digital Controller," Stanford Electronics Laboratory, Stanford, California, Tech. Rept. No. 2106–1, July 11, 1960.
5. Hildebrand, F. B., *Methods of Applied Mathematics*, Prentice-Hall, 1952.
6. Kalman, R. E., "Analysis and design principles of second and higher order saturating servomechanisms," AIEE Trans. **74**, Part II, Applications and Industry, 294–310 (November, 1955).
7. Kalman, R. E., "On the General Theory of Control Systems," *Proceedings of the IFAC, Moscow, 1960*, Butterworths, 1961, pp. 481–492.

8. Kalman, R. E., and Bertram, J. E., "General synthesis procedure for computer control of single-loop and multiloop linear systems, an optimum sampling system," AIEE Trans. **77,** Part II, Applications and Industry, 602–609 (January, 1959).
9. Kalman, R. E., and Bertram, J. E., "A unified approach to the theory of sampling systems," J. Franklin Inst. **267,** 405–435 (May, 1959).
10. Kalman, R. E., and Koepcke, R. W., "Optimal synthesis of linear sampling control systems using generalized performance indexes," Trans. ASME **80,** 1820–1826 (November, 1958).
11. Laning, J. H., and Battin, R. H., *Random Processes in Automatic Control,* McGraw-Hill, 1956.
12. Seifert, William W., and Steeg, Carl W., Jr., *Control Systems Engineering,* McGraw-Hill, 1960.
13. Stoker, J. J., *Nonlinear Vibrations in Mechanical and Electrical Systems,* Interscience, 1950.
14. Zadeh, L. A., and Desoer, C. A., *Linear System Theory—The State Space Approach,* McGraw-Hill, 1963.

CHAPTER III

Multivariable and Timeshared Systems

JOHN PESCHON

CONTENTS

1. Introduction

Automatic feedback control systems are described in a large number of textbooks and are taught in most universities. The structure usually considered is that of a single variable system where the output y is compared to the desired output r and where the error $r - y$ is amplified in order to force y to approach r. In general, all components are assumed to be linear and stationary. The Laplace transform is then used to relate system output to desired system output by the familiar expression:

$$\frac{Y(s)}{R(s)} = \frac{kG(s)}{1 + kG(s)} \qquad (k = \text{constant}) \qquad (1.1)$$

This single-variable structure is too simple to accommodate the complex situations now frequently encountered. Therefore we wish to discuss a model where n outputs y_i are to be made equal to as many desired outputs r_i. Some of the fundamental problems of single variable systems, for example, stability, become considerably more complex and can no longer be resolved well by the Nyquist criterion and the root locus technique.

We furthermore believe that the transform description has been overused frequently and has caused computational and conceptual errors as a result of its *apparent* simplicity. There is no doubt that such concepts as poles and zeros, typical of Laplace transform notation, are very meaningful and should be maintained. But the fundamental system description by differential equations is more direct, and we shall show that it frequently yields answers with hardly any computational effort and suggests structures which the Laplace transform tends to disguise. Differential equations, incidentally, were used by Maxwell [17]† in what is probably the first mathematical analysis of feedback control systems.

In addition to continuous multivariable systems, we consider structures where a dynamic component is timeshared among several channels. In view of the fact that these systems are very recent, there is little practical experience available, and it may be that the user will be disappointed. Even so, we introduce the reader to the mathematical description of such systems in the belief that the approach toward the solution of this fairly complex problem is useful, and applicable to related classes of problems such as finite width sampled-data systems or timeshared analog computers, which are now being produced for the rapidly expanding computer control field.

2. The Single-Variable Feedback Control System

Single-variable feedback control systems are described in a large number of modern texts on automatic control. We will only briefly consider the

† Numbers in brackets refer to the bibliography at the end of this chapter.

subject in order to present the framework for multivariable systems. For a detailed treatment of single-variable systems, we recommend Tsien [28] and Truxal [27].

2.1 The Mathematical Description. We consider a physical process and assume that this process is mathematically described by an ordinary differential equation of the form

$$P_1(\ldots, \ddot{y}, \dot{y}, y; b) = 0. \tag{2.1}$$

We say that this process has one output y and one input b. Even as simple a process as a triode has several outputs, i.e., plate voltage, plate current, etc., and several inputs, i.e., grid voltage, plate bias, etc. Quite frequently, it is convenient to consider only one output, either because there exists a fixed relation between this output and all the others, or because these other outputs are of no interest to us. Also, we frequently maintain all the inputs fixed, except one, and we alter the one output of interest y by acting upon the one input b.

A control system consists of a set of electronic and electromechanical components whose function is to force y to behave in some prescribed manner,† generally

$$y(t) = r(t), \tag{2.2}$$

The function r is indifferently called *desired output*, *system input*, or *command input* and is distinct from the *process* input b. It is moreover not possible to realize Eq. (2.2) for *any* $r(t)$. What we generally can achieve by an appropriate choice of the electronic and electromechanical components is that

(1) $$\lim_{t\to\infty} y(t) = r \qquad \begin{pmatrix} r = 0 & \text{for} & t < 0 \\ r = \tilde{r} = \text{constant} & \text{for} & t > 0 \end{pmatrix} \tag{2.3}$$

and

(2) $$\Psi(\epsilon) = \text{minimum} \tag{2.4}$$

where $\epsilon = r - y$ and where $\Psi(\epsilon)$ is the performance function.

Two performance functions of frequent usage are

$$\Psi(\epsilon) = \int_0^\infty \epsilon^2\, dt \qquad (r = \tilde{r} = \text{constant})$$

and

$$\Psi(\epsilon) = \lim_{T\to\infty} \frac{1}{2T} \int_{-T}^{T} \epsilon^2\, dt.$$

† There are notable exceptions to this formulation; it is sometimes desired to render the system output $y(t)$ equal to the predicted input $r(t + \tau)$, $\tau > 0$.

In the latter case, $r(t)$ is a stationary random function of known power spectrum.

The process input b is usually connected to an electromechanical component, amplidyne, hydraulic valve, etc., which, we assume, can be described by a linear constant coefficient ordinary differential equation† relating actuator output b to actuator input

$$P_2(\ldots, \ddot{b}, \dot{b}, b; m) = 0. \tag{2.5}$$

Since a particular process input b usually requires a particular actuator, we often find it convenient to lump the process and the actuator together in one block, termed plant, which is described by one single differential equation

$$P(\ldots, \ddot{y}, \dot{y}, y) = m. \tag{2.6}$$

Although this is not a necessary restriction, we assume that Eq. (2.6) is stable unless stated otherwise.

Example. We consider the process (2.1a) and the actuator (2.5a)

$$a_2\ddot{y} + a_1\dot{y} + a_0y = b \tag{2.1a}$$

$$\alpha_1\dot{b} + \alpha_0 b = m \tag{2.5a}$$

and we obtain the plant

$$p_3\dddot{y} + p_2\ddot{y} + p_1\dot{y} + p_0y = m \tag{2.6a}$$

where

$$p_0 = \alpha_0 a_0 \qquad p_2 = \alpha_1 a_1 + \alpha_0 a_2$$

$$p_1 = \alpha_1 a_0 + \alpha_0 a_1 \qquad p_3 = \alpha_1 a_2.$$

The controller, which is frequently a purely electronic component, relates the system input r and the plant output y and some of its derivatives $\dot{y}, \ddot{y}, \ldots$ to the actuator input m. Because of the ease with which electronic components can be adjusted, we usually act upon the free parameters $c_0, c_1, \ldots$ included in the controller to satisfy Eq. (2.4). This controller, we assume, is described by a linear integro-differential equation

$$S\left(\ldots, \ddot{y}, \dot{y}, y, \int_{-\infty}^{t} y\,dt; c_0, c_1, \ldots; r, \int_{-\infty}^{t} r\,dt\right) = m. \tag{2.7}$$

We may now eliminate m between Eqs. (2.6) and (2.7) and obtain a linear differential equation which relates the system output y to the system input r

$$K(\ldots, \ddot{y}, \dot{y}, y; c_0, c_1, \ldots; r) = 0. \tag{2.8}$$

In control system theory, we usually wish to satisfy Eq. (2.3). This then requires:

† In this chapter, we consider exclusively systems describable by ordinary linear differential equations whose coefficients are not functions of time. For the sake of brevity, we frequently qualify a system as linear, meaning that it is described by a constant coefficient ordinary differential equation.

(1) that Eq. (2.8) be *stable*, i.e., that none of its eigenvalues be such that $\text{Re}\,\lambda \geqslant 0$;

(2) that under steady-state conditions, characterized by $\ldots, \ddot{y} = \dot{y} = 0, y = r$.

2.2 The Preferred Structure. Returning to the plant (2.6a), we select m such that

$$m = w_{-1} \int_{-\infty}^{t} (r - y)\, dt + w_0 y + w_1 \dot{y} + w_2 \ddot{y} \qquad (w_{-1}, w_0, w_1, w_2 = \text{constants}). \tag{2.9}$$

We next eliminate m between Eqs. (2.6a) and (2.9) to obtain the closed-loop system equation

$$p_3 y^{(4)} + (p_2 - w_2) y^{(3)} + (p_1 - w_1)\ddot{y} + (p_0 - w_0)\dot{y} + w_{-1} y = w_{-1} r. \tag{2.10}$$

Equation (2.10) is of utmost importance in our study because the majority of modern single variable linear systems are described precisely by an equation of this type. We recall some of its properties to the reader's attention.

(1) The controller (2.9) is chosen in such a manner that the closed-loop system equation (2.10) contains enough adjustable parameters w_{-1}, w_0, w_1, w_2 to control the location of *all* the eigenvalues λ in the complex λ-plane.

(2) Assuming that Eq. (2.10) is stable, the steady-state or obvious solution is

$$\lim_{t \to \infty} y = \tilde{r}. \qquad (\tilde{r} = \text{constant}) \tag{2.3}$$

(3) The plant is of third order and the closed-loop system is of fourth order. It was necessary to include one additional integration into the controller network in order to satisfy Eq. (2.3).† The reader may convince himself that this requirement could be met *exactly* without the introduction of an integrator, provided the plant parameters were not subject to gradual changes. Since, in practice, this generally cannot be guaranteed, we retain Eq. (2.9) as the only valid engineering solution to our problem.

(4) If the plant is such that $p_0 = 0$, no further integration is required in the controller network. This special case is of considerable practical importance because position control servomechanisms always have plants of this type.

(5) The successive output derivatives or state variables‡ $\dot{y}, \ddot{y}, \ldots$ are frequently available for a direct measurement and need not be obtained from y by differentiation. In those cases where the $y, \dot{y}, \ldots$, are not measurable, they may frequently be obtained by means of a linear transformation carried out on certain measurable internal plant states $x_1, x_2, \ldots$, as discussed in Chapter II.

If an analog computer simulation were made, these derivatives would be the outputs of the integrators, as shown in Fig. 1.

† It is sometimes not necessary to fulfill (2.3) *exactly*. In such a case, it may be advantageous to replace the integrator by a sufficiently large gain in the forward loop.

‡ The successive output derivatives $\dot{y}, \ddot{y}, \ldots$, in conjunction with y qualify as state variables, as explained in Chapter II.

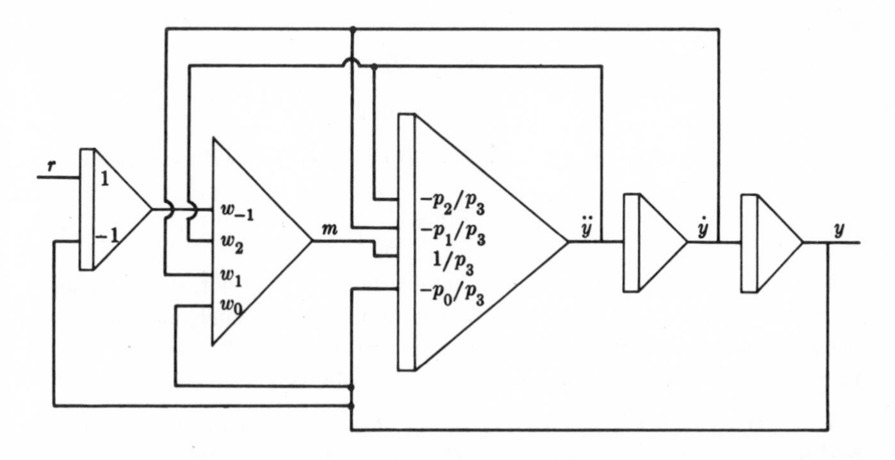

FIGURE 1. Analog computer simulation of Eq. (2.10). The symbols ⧐ and ▷ denote integrators and summing amplifiers, respectively. For added simplicity, no sign inversion is assumed to take place.

(6) If, as is customary in linear system analysis, the Laplace transforms of system input and system output, $R(s)$ and $Y(s)$, are related by the so-called *over-all transfer function*,

$$K(s) = \frac{Y(s)}{R(s)} = \frac{w_{-1}}{p_3 s^4 + (p_2 - w_2)s^3 + (p_1 - w_1)s^2 + (p_0 - w_0)s + w_{-1}} \tag{2.11}$$

then $K(s)$ is constrained to have only poles and no zeros.

By virtue of its extraordinary flexibility and the fact that frequently no differentiation at all is required, we generally prefer this *multiple parallel loop structure* to all others, in particular to those that rely on series compensation. We refer to it as the *preferred structure*.

If the fixed structure (2.10) is optimized in accordance with the rms criterion (2.4), or some other related criterion, then all the eigenvalues λ_i are specified and system synthesis can be completed by calculating the settings of the adjustable parameters $w_{-1}, w_0, w_1, \ldots$.

If this is not so, the designer will have to find out first which locations of the λ_i are desirable, considering the operating conditions and hardware constraints imposed upon the system.

An elegant procedure whereby the coefficients $\ldots, p_3, p_2 - w_2, p_1 - w_1, \ldots,$ are related to what is usually understood as suitable temporal behavior is described in Naslin [21].

2.3 Response. We consider the linear differential equation:

$$\sum_{i=0}^{u} a_i y^{(i)} = r(t) \qquad (a_0 \neq 0) \tag{2.12}$$

and the forcing function

$$r(t) = \begin{cases} 0 & \text{for } t < 0 \\ \tilde{r} = \text{constant} & \text{for } t > 0. \end{cases} \tag{2.13}$$

If the u eigenvalues λ_i are such that Re $\lambda_i < 0$, $(i = 1, \ldots, u)$, then

$$\lim_{t \to \infty} y(t) = \frac{\tilde{r}}{a_0}. \tag{2.14}$$

It is of great practical interest to have a measure of how fast $y(t)$ responds to $\tilde{r}$ under a given set of circumstances. A number of such measures have been proposed, but none has been universally adopted. We will, for the purpose of this chapter, define a measure as follows:

DEFINITION. *Let* $\lambda^{(0)}$ *be that eigenvalue of* (2.12) *which has the least negative real part. The* **response time**† τ *is then related to* Re $\lambda^{(0)}$ *by*

$$\tau = \frac{-1}{\text{Re } \lambda^{(0)}}. \tag{2.15}$$

The implication is evidently that the transient $Ce^{\lambda^{(0)}t}$ takes longest time to vanish. The reader is cautioned against blindly trusting this measure since two systems having the same eigenvalues may react quite differently as will be discussed in Section 2.5. τ should be viewed as a rough measure of the time scale in which the system operates.

2.4 The Block Diagram. We assume that the reader is familiar with the Laplace transform and has already been exposed to the *block-diagram* representation, which indicates (1) how the constituents (plant, actuator, controller) of a system are physically interconnected, and (2) what mathematical relation exists between the component input and output.

The engineer who is used to this representation may derive useful information at a glance. We wish to emphasize, however, that the fundamental description of a dynamic system is its differential equation and that the Laplace transform and the related block diagram are useful aids which should be handled with circumspection since they hide certain fundamental phenomena, as will be briefly shown in the subsequent sections.

We recall the block-diagram representation by considering a second-order servomechanism where

$$\ddot{y} + \dot{y} = m \tag{2.16}$$

and

$$-c_1\dot{y} - y + r = m. \tag{2.17}$$

Hence

$$\ddot{y} + (c_1 + 1)\dot{y} + y = r. \tag{2.18}$$

The corresponding block diagram is shown in Fig. 2.

† The terms *dominant time constant* and *delay time* are also used in the literature.

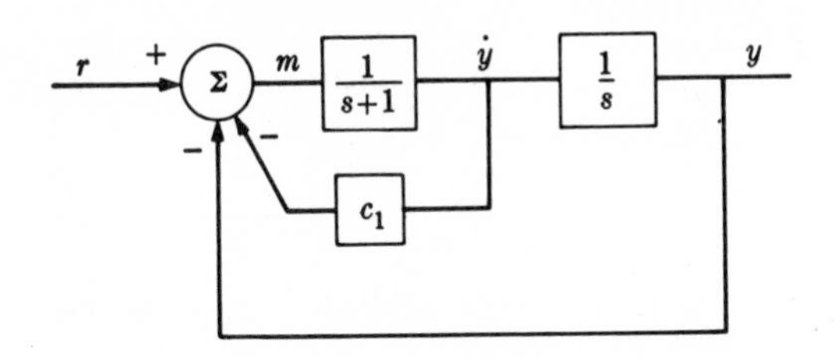

FIGURE 2. Block diagram of a second-order servomechanism.

2.5 Series and Parallel Controllers. We recall that the eigenvalues of the closed-loop system (2.10) depend on the free parameters $w_{-1}, w_0, w_1, \ldots$, which indicate how much of each of the variables y, $\dot{y}$, ..., is returned to the controller. We sometimes act upon the eigenvalues of the closed-loop system by relating the plant input m to the error $r - y = \epsilon$ by an integro-differential equation which includes the free parameters $\ldots, \beta_{-1}, \beta_0, \beta_1, \ldots$. Thus

$$D(\epsilon, \dot{\epsilon}, \ldots; m, \dot{m}, \ldots; \ldots, \beta_{-1}, \beta_0, \beta_1, \ldots) = 0. \qquad (2.19)$$

We eliminate m between Eqs. (2.6) and (2.19) and obtain

$$K(\ldots, \ddot{y}, \dot{y}, y; \ldots, \beta_{-1}, \beta_0, \beta_1, \ldots; \ldots, \ddot{r}, \dot{r}, r) = 0. \qquad (2.20)$$

Example. We consider the plant (2.16) and we relate m to

$$\epsilon = r - y$$

by

$$\beta_0(r - y) + \beta_1(\dot{r} - \dot{y}) = \beta_{-1}m \qquad (2.19a)$$

and obtain the closed-loop system equation

$$y + \left(1 + \frac{\beta_1}{\beta_{-1}}\right)\dot{y} + \frac{\beta_0}{\beta_{-1}}y = \frac{\beta_0}{\beta_{-1}}r + \frac{\beta_1}{\beta_{-1}}\dot{r}. \qquad (2.20a)$$

We observe that the eigenvalues of Eq. (2.20a) are identical with those of (2.18) if

$$\frac{\beta_1}{\beta_{-1}} = c_1$$

$$\frac{\beta_0}{\beta_{-1}} = 1$$

but that for a given system input $r(t)$, the output corresponding to (2.18) will differ from that of (2.20a) because the network (2.19a) has in fact changed the system input from r to $r + c_1\dot{r}$. In the first case, we say that a *parallel controller C* is used; in the second case we have a *series controller D*. The terminology "parallel" and "series" *compensation* is also used in the literature.

The reason for this vocabulary becomes clear if we compare the block diagram shown in Figs. 2 and 3.

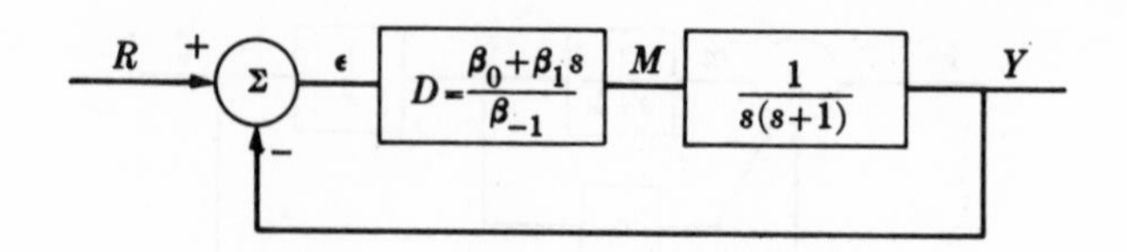

FIGURE 3. Block diagram of a servomechanism using a series controller $D(s)$.

2.6 Design for Specified Transfer Function. The problem of designing a linear control system around a given and unalterable linear plant may be approached from two distinct directions. We may start out by selecting a structure which, we know from experience, provides us with a sound engineering solution, but which is subject to certain constraints. This is precisely what we did in Section 2.2 when discussing the preferred structure. As an alternative and seemingly more attractive approach to the synthesis problem, we may start out by specifying a stable $K(s)$ subject to the only additional constraint that it be expressible as a rational function of s, and thereafter determine the required compensating networks $C(s)$ or $D(s)$, which is always possible.† From the obvious relations

$$K = \frac{Y(s)}{R(s)} \frac{DP}{1 + DP} \tag{2.21}$$

and

$$K = \frac{P}{1 + CP} \tag{2.22}$$

we derive

$$\eta = \frac{M(s)}{\epsilon(s)} = \frac{K}{P(1 - K)} \tag{2.23}$$

and

$$C = \frac{R(s) - \epsilon(s)}{Y(s)} = \frac{P - K}{PK}\,. \tag{2.24}$$

Although the linear networks (2.23) and (2.24) can always be synthesized, we should specify K so as to arrive at a sound engineering solution. By this we mean that:

(1) The required D and C networks should remain simple.

(2) Differentiating networks,‡ which amplify noise, should be avoided as much as possible.

† It is understood that the synthesis of C or D may require the use of active components. Therefore we are not restricted by the physical realizability conditions of passive network synthesis.

‡ We shall use the term "differentiating network" quite generally to designate an electronic or electromechanical component which, by actual differentiation, produces the derivatives $y^{(i)}$ or $r^{(i)}$. We do not include components, such as tachometers, which measure certain output derivatives directly.

(3) Plant saturation should not occur for the class of system inputs expected under normal operating conditions.

As an illustration of constraint (1), we use the plant (2.16) to compute the networks D_1 and D_2 required by two almost identical system transfer functions K_1 and K_2, namely

$$K_1 = \frac{1}{s^2 + s + 1} \tag{2.25}$$

$$K_2 = \frac{1}{s^2 + 1.1s + 1} . \tag{2.26}$$

Equation (2.23) yields

$$D_1 = 1 \tag{2.27}$$

$$D_2 = \frac{s + 1}{s + 1.1} . \tag{2.28}$$

It would probably be difficult to justify the use of D_2, which makes the system third-order, since almost identical performance is obtained with the second-order system (2.25).

It is not apparent from K_2, Eq. (2.26), that the closed loop is of the third order. However, this becomes clear when we recall that the forward controller D_2 introduces one additional energy storage element or state. The reader may further satisfy himself that, in this particular case, K_2 *alone* does not provide sufficient information to write out the system integro-differential equation, which is

$$\dddot{y} + 2.1\ddot{y} + 2.1\dot{y} + y = r + \dot{r}. \tag{2.29}$$

As an illustration of constraint (2), the reader may verify that the parallel network C required by

$$K = \frac{s + 2}{s^2 + 2s + 2} \tag{2.30}$$

is

$$C = -s^2 + \frac{2}{s + 2} .$$

This would not be considered sound engineering because it makes it necessary to produce the nonavailable second output derivative $\ddot{y}$.

Finally, with regard to constraint (3), we point out that the requirement $K(s) = 1$ clearly causes the plant input m to become unbounded for any nonconstant system input, and this regardless of the type of compensation used.

Hence the seemingly attractive approach of specifying K without carefully considering how simple D or C networks combine with a fixed and stable plant is treacherous, not because physical realizability conditions cannot be met, but because the resulting design may not be sound. In Section 2.8, we consider a situation where this approach produces an unstable design although a stable K was specified.

2.7 Design for Specified Disturbance Response. Feedforward. One of the fundamental reasons for using feedback systems is to minimize the effect of disturbances U entering into the forward loop. The reader may verify, for example, that in the steady state the system output y is not at all affected by constant disturbances if the forward loop contains at least one integration to the left of the disturbance.

Furthermore it is possible, by using *both* series and parallel compensation, to design a system transfer function "K" to an input R and a different transfer function "K_u" to a disturbance U, which might enter the plant at the location shown in Fig. 4; see Lang and Ham [16].

We write by inspection

$$Y = \frac{DP}{1 + DPC} R + \frac{P'}{1 + DPC} U = KR + K_u U. \tag{2.31}$$

We solve for D and C

$$D = \frac{K}{P''K_u} \tag{2.32}$$

$$C = \frac{1}{K}\left(1 - \frac{K_u}{P'}\right). \tag{2.33}$$

This procedure of course does not guarantee that the controller (2.32) and (2.33) represent a sound engineering solution.

An entirely different and, in general, more effective procedure to cancel out the effects of disturbances is to use *feedforward*. If a disturbance is measurable, then its effect upon the system can be computed, at least approximately, and suitable compensating signals can be generated by a special controller D', as shown by the dotted loop of Fig. 4.

Feedforward is really a very old trick to cancel out the effects of disturbances *before* they have altered the output Y; in many dc generators, the load current (which as far as the control engineer is concerned constitutes a disturbance) is made to flow through special *compensating* windings and thus

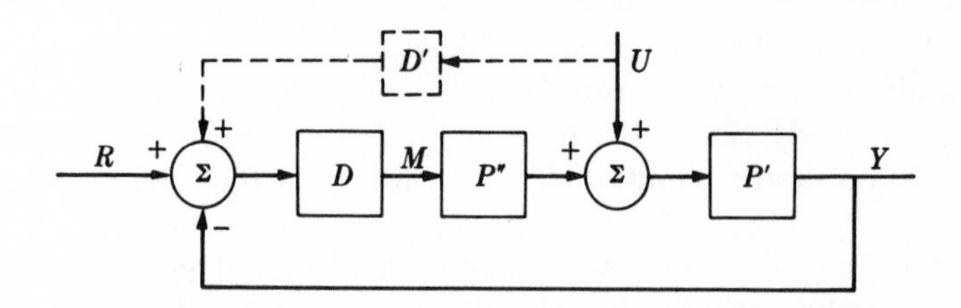

FIGURE 4. Disturbance U affecting the plant $P = P'P''$.

maintains the output voltage Y approximately constant in the presence of load variations. Slight errors in the amount of compensation used are thereafter eliminated by the main feedback loop.

Since, in the general case, the relation between Y and U is nonlinear and therefore cannot be implemented easily with conventional controllers, feedforward was usually not included in control systems before the introduction of digital and analog control computers capable of producing the required compensating signals.

2.8 The Control of Unstable Plants. So far we have assumed that the plants we are called upon to control are stable. If this is not the case, we can synthesize a stable over-all transfer function K, provided this does not require the *exact* cancellation of the unstable plant poles, because it is impossible to measure the *exact* location of these poles and to design networks which are perfectly accurate. If the plant is unstable, parallel compensation is usually superior to series compensation and often constitutes the only way to achieve a stable K.

Example. We consider the hypothetical unstable plant

$$P = \frac{1}{s(1 - s)} \tag{2.34}$$

and we wish to achieve

$$K = \frac{2}{s^2 + 2s + 2}. \tag{2.35}$$

We use Eq. (2.23) to determine D

$$D = \frac{2(1 - s)}{2 + s}. \tag{2.36}$$

The network which we actually synthesize is D_β

$$D_\beta = \frac{2(\beta_1 + \beta_2 s)}{2 + s} \tag{2.37}$$

where β_1 and β_2 are nearly 1 and -1, respectively. The resulting over-all transfer function

$$K = \frac{2(\beta_1 + \beta_2 s)}{-s^3 - s^2 + 2s(1 + \beta_2) + 2\beta_1} \tag{2.38}$$

is clearly unstable. It is most expedient here to return to the fundamental description by differential equations

$$-\ddot{y} + \dot{y} = m \tag{2.34a}$$

and

$$\ddot{y} + 2\dot{y} + 2y = 2r \tag{2.35a}$$

and to seek a compensating network

$$m = c_0 y + c_1 \dot{y} + c_0^* r. \tag{2.39}$$

We eliminate m between Eqs. (2.34a) and (2.39) to obtain

$$-\ddot{y} + (1 - c_1)\dot{y} - c_0 y = c_0{}^* r \tag{2.40}$$

which is identical with the desired differential equation (2.35a) if

$$c_0 = 2,\ c_0{}^* = -2;\ c_1 = 3.$$

The resulting control system is stable.

2.9 Additional Mathematical Descriptions. The control systems considered thus far have been described by ordinary linear integro-differential equations of the general form (2.20), or by the Laplace transform thereof. Other descriptions, which may prove less laborious in many instances, are state equations of which A. I. Lur'e's canonical form is a particularly useful special case.

When using the state equations, we relate the outputs or state variables x_i, $i = 1, \ldots, u$, of all the "u" energy storage elements contained in the system to each other and to external forcing functions, such as r. This yields a system of "u" first-order differential equations of the form:

$$x_i = \sum_{j=1}^{u} a_{ij} x_j + b_i r \qquad \left.\begin{matrix} a_{ij} \\ b_i \end{matrix}\right\} = \text{constant} \tag{2.41}$$

or equivalently

$$\dot{\mathbf{x}} = A\mathbf{x} + \mathbf{B}r \tag{2.42}$$

where the $\mathbf{x}$ and $\mathbf{B}$ are vectors and where A is a $u \times u$ matrix whose elements a_{ij} can be obtained easily from Eq. (2.20).

The concept of the state has been known at least since Poincaré, but many recent authors, mostly in the United States and in the Soviet Union, have considerably extended this concept and applied it to the solution of many problems in automatic control.

State-space techniques are presented in Chapter II and in Kalman *et al.* [12–14]. Sections 4 and 5 of this present chapter make use of such techniques to solve a problem which formulation (2.20) probably could not have accommodated.

Lur'e's "canonic form" is applicable to single variable systems that may or may not contain a (single) nonlinear component. This form is termed "canonic" because a matrix similar to the A-matrix of Eq. (2.42) is rendered normal or diagonal by means of a suitable transformation of the state variables. One advantage of this description is that the plant eigenvalues λ_i become the (diagonal) elements of the new matrix after the transformation has been performed.

Lur'e's canonic form is presented in Chapter VI in connection with Liapunov's "second method."

While the full advantages of these descriptions and techniques generally do not appear as long as one is concerned with purely linear time-invariant systems, they definitely should belong to the repertoire of skills of the modern control engineer.

2.10 Conclusion. In this section on single variable systems, we have discussed several ways of synthesizing feedback control systems around a given linear plant. We have, in particular, observed that it is frequently possible to specify a desired system response $K(s)$ and to compute the required series (D) or parallel (C) controllers. We then proceeded to show by way of examples that this method sometimes yields answers which may be mathematically correct, but are not sound solutions to an engineering problem. The preferred structure, i.e., a parallel multiloop compensation structure which generally requires the use of one additional integrator, always provides us with a sound design without requiring the use of block diagram, and Laplace transform techniques at all. Although some years ago the specialized literature hardly mentioned the differential and state equation, there is a definite tendency today to prefer this fundamental problem description to the less direct and oftentimes misleading transform techniques.

3. Multivariable Systems

The great majority of the papers published on the theory of automatic control are concerned with processes in which one output y is related to one input m. In those cases where the process has many inputs and many outputs, the classical design procedure is to select input-output pairs (m_i, y_i) and to design conventional single variable feedback systems neglecting the interaction or couplings which might exist between y_i and m_j, $j \neq i$.

It was realized during the last two decades that consideration of these plant interactions leads to the design of higher performance feedback control systems. Much of the work done by Bode [4] *et al.* before World War II in connection with complex feedback amplifiers was directly applicable.

In addition to achieving higher performance, i.e., shorter response times, it was soon discovered that some output y_i could be made independent of some input r_j, $j \neq i$. In the United States, Boksenbom and Hood [5] synthesized a noninteracting jet engine controller. Their paper is summarized in Tsien's *Engineering Cybernetics* [28]. Ergin and Ling [7] thereafter designed a noninteracting boiler control in which a change in the pressure setpoint r_p has no influence on the water level y_L and where a change in the desired water level r_L similarly does not alter the boiler pressure y_p. Chatterjee [6] gives a very clear description of the synthesis of a noninteracting boiler control and of a noninteracting density and level control by means of commercially available PID-process controllers. We recommend this paper as an excellent introduction to linear multivariable control systems. Jeffrey [11] considers the stability of a restricted class of linear multivariable control systems and extends his analysis to plants containing time delays. Mitchell and Webb [20] present a theoretical and experimental analysis of a two-variable system and discuss the beneficial effects of multivariable compensation on performance.

In the Soviet Union, complex multiloop structures were studied as early as 1940 by Luzin, who formulated the conditions under which some coordinate y_i of a set of differential equations is independent of some forcing function $f_j(t)$. Using the Russian terminology, one would say that y_i is *invariant* with respect to $f_j(t)$ which might be a system input or a disturbance. Assuming that a complex structure is described by a set of linear differential equations

$$A\mathbf{Y}(s) = \mathbf{F}(s) \tag{3.1}$$

where A is a square nonsingular matrix of elements $a_{ij}(s)$, the condition of invariance of Y_i with respect to F_j is obviously that the minor

$$\Delta_{ji}(s) \equiv 0. \tag{3.2}$$

For readily available translations of recent Russian contributions, the reader is referred to the work of Petrov [23] and Kulebakin [15].

It is apparent that although the Russian and the U.S. authors use the term invariance and noninteracting control, respectively, both are concerned with the same problem. Clearly, if $\Delta_{ji} \equiv 0$, $j \neq i$, for all other i and j, the resulting invariant structure is noninteracting.

In the literature concerned with the control of coupled or multivariable plants, the synthesis of noninteracting controllers has probably received more attention than other aspects of this complex and frequently encountered design problem. The natural extension to sampled-data systems has been made [22]. The fact that a change of one of the system inputs r_i disturbs only part of the process is a real practical advantage. The fact that noninteracting control breaks a complex dynamic system down into several isolated and

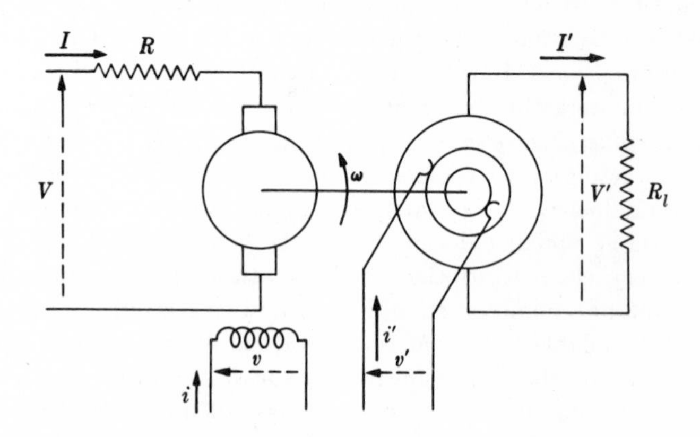

FIGURE 5. Simplified model of a dc to ac rotary converter.

simpler systems will probably prove to be most valuable in the present and future attempts to optimize complex structures. It is understood that for the performance criteria and the constraints that one usually selects, a noninteracting system is generally not quite as good as an optimum coupled system, but has the advantage of being more easily tractable at this time.

3.1 Multivariable Plants—An Example. In order to familiarize the reader with *multivariable* plants, we consider a simplified model of a rotating dc to ac converter, as shown in Fig. 5.

We study the influence of the *inputs* v, v', V on the outputs ω and V' in the vicinity of the normal operating point designated by the symbol (*). The various differential equations describing the operation of this converter have previously been normalized.† See Table I.

TABLE I

Value	*Significance*	*Value*	*Significance*
$V^* = 1.2$	dc armature voltage	$V'^* = 1.0$	rms generator voltage
$I^* = 1.0$	dc armature current	$I'^* = 1.0$	rms load current
$v^* = 1.0$	Field voltage	$v'^* = 1.0$	Field voltage
$i^* = 1.0$	Field current	$i'^* = 1.0$	Field current
$T^* = i^*I^* = 1.0$	Motor torque	$T'^* = \dfrac{V'^{*2}}{R_l\omega^*} = 1.0$	Generator torque
$\omega^* = 1.0$	Angular shaft velocity and frequency		

The only nonnegligible system parameters are given in Table II.

† Normalization is almost mandatory as soon as the process or system under consideration has more than two or three variables, especially when these variables do not have the same physical dimensions or when the numbers which measure their ranges of variation are unwieldy.

Suppose that a circuit is described by

$$10^{-3}\frac{d\bar{I}}{dt} + 10^3\bar{I} = \bar{V}^3 \qquad 0 \leqslant \bar{V} \leqslant 15.$$

We seek to utilize the new variables I, t, and V which are related to $\bar{I}$, $\bar{t}$, and $\bar{V}$ by

$$I = a\bar{I}; \qquad t = b\bar{t}; \qquad V = c\bar{V}.$$

TABLE II

Value	*Significance*	*Value*	*Significance*
$R = 0.2$	Armature resistance	$R_l = 1.0$	Load resistance
$r = 1.0$	Field resistance	$r' = 1.0$	Field resistance
$J = 1.0$	Inertia of both rotors	$l' = 0.5$	Field inductance

It follows from the elementary theory of rotating machines that

$$J\frac{d\omega}{dt} - iI + \frac{V'^2}{\omega} = 0 \tag{3.3}$$

$$I = \frac{V - i\omega}{0.2} \tag{3.4}$$

$$v = i \tag{3.5}$$

$$0.5\frac{di'}{dt} + i' = v' \tag{3.6}$$

$$V' = i'\omega. \tag{3.7}$$

One could eliminate i, I, and i' from this set of five equations and arrive at a set of two nonlinear differential equations relating the outputs ω, V' to the inputs v, v', V. We prefer to first *linearize* Eq. (3.3) through (3.7) about the operating point by performing appropriate Taylor expansions and by defining increments y_1, y_2 and m_1, m_2, m_3 such that:

$$\begin{aligned} y_1 &= \omega - \omega^* & m_1 &= v - v^* \\ y_2 &= V' - V'^* & m_2 &= v' - v'^* \\ & & m_3 &= V - V^*. \end{aligned} \tag{3.8}$$

We first determine c such that the range of $\bar{V}$ is (0,1) instead of (0,15), i.e., $c = \frac{1}{15}$. We next rewrite the original circuit equation

$$3375\ 10^{-3}\frac{b}{a}\frac{dI}{dt} + \frac{3375\ 10^3}{a}I = V^3.$$

By letting $a = 3375\ 10^3$ and $b = 10^6$, we obtain

$$\frac{dI}{dt} + I = V \qquad (0 \leqslant V \leqslant 1)$$

which can be manipulated with much greater ease than the original equation.

It is clear that in general only a *limited* number of variables or parameters can be normalized *independently*, the remainder being uniquely determined by the coefficients $a, b, c, \ldots$.

The incremental generator torque contained in Eq. (3.3) would thus become

$$T' - T'^* = -\frac{V'^{*2}}{\omega^{*2}}(\omega - \omega^*) + 2\frac{V'^*}{\omega^*}(V' - V'^*) = -y_1 + 2y_2. \quad (3.9)$$

The reader may verify that the linearized converter is described by the second-order system

$$\begin{aligned} \frac{dy_1}{dt} + 4y_1 + 2y_2 &= -4m_1 + 5m_3 \\ -\frac{dy_1}{dt} - 2y_1 + \frac{dy_2}{dt} + 2y_2 &= 2m_2. \end{aligned} \quad (3.10)$$

It is often more convenient to use Laplace transform rather than differential equation notation in the theory of multivariable systems. State-space notation has been used in the literature, and will be considered in Section 3.10 in connection with the preferred structure. The difficulty which arises is that the number u of state variables (u being the order of the system) is in no way related to the number of input or output variables.

The transformed equations

$$\begin{aligned} (s + 4)Y_1 + 2Y_2 &= y_1(0) - 4M_1 + 5M_3 \\ -(s + 2)Y_1 + (s + 2)Y_2 &= -y_1(0) + y_2(0) + 2M_2 \end{aligned} \quad (3.11)$$

are usually written in the form

$$\mathbf{Y} = G\mathbf{y}(0) + P\mathbf{M} \quad (3.12)$$

where the matrices G and P have elements

$$G = \begin{bmatrix} \dfrac{s+4}{(s+2)(s+6)} & \dfrac{-2}{(s+2)(s+6)} \\ \dfrac{-2}{(s+2)(s+6)} & \dfrac{s+4}{(s+2)(s+6)} \end{bmatrix} \quad (3.13)$$

$$P = \begin{bmatrix} \dfrac{-4}{s+6} & \dfrac{-4}{(s+2)(s+6)} & \dfrac{5}{s+6} \\ \dfrac{-4}{s+6} & \dfrac{2(s+4)}{(s+2)(s+6)} & \dfrac{5}{s+6} \end{bmatrix}. \quad (3.14)$$

Equation (3.12) entirely defines the outputs $y_1(t)$ and $y_2(t)$ of the linearized converter for any known initial conditions and inputs. It is often of importance to know the *steady-state* effects that constant inputs $\tilde{m}_1$, $\tilde{m}_2$, $\tilde{m}_3$ have upon the plant. These are conveniently obtained from

$$\lim_{t\to\infty} \mathbf{y}(t) = \lim_{s\to 0} P\tilde{\mathbf{m}} = P_0\tilde{\mathbf{m}} \quad (3.15)$$

where P_0 is derived from P by letting $s = 0$. Thus

$$P_0 = \begin{bmatrix} -\frac{2}{3} & -\frac{1}{3} & \frac{5}{6} \\ -\frac{2}{3} & \frac{2}{3} & \frac{5}{6} \end{bmatrix}. \tag{3.16}$$

3.2 Multivariable Plants.† The results of Section 3.1 will now be generalized. We speak of a linear, time-invariant, multivariable plant whenever "q" inputs m_j are related to "n" outputs y_i by a set of n-coupled linear, constant-coefficient differential equations such as (3.10). Neglecting initial conditions, we relate the Laplace transform $Y_i(s)$ to the Laplace transform $M_j(s)$ by the *transfer elements* $p_{ij}(s)$. We furthermore define the $n \times q$ *plant transfer matrix* P, composed of elements $p_{ij}(s)$, and the $n \times n$ matrices $G_0, G_1, \ldots$, which indicate the effect of initial conditions $\mathbf{y}(0)$, $\dot{\mathbf{y}}(0), \ldots$, i.e.,

$$\mathbf{Y} = P\mathbf{M} + G_0\mathbf{y}(0) + G_1\dot{\mathbf{y}}(0) + \cdots. \tag{3.17}$$

For the purpose of this section, it is usually of no interest to consider the effects of initial conditions $\mathbf{y}(0), \dot{\mathbf{y}}(0), \ldots$. We therefore exclusively use P to describe a multivariable plant and recall that the matrices $G_0, G_1, \ldots$, can generally‡ be derived from P.

We next consider the relations which exist between the number of inputs q and the number of outputs n.

DEFINITION. *Among all the possible outputs of a plant, we define as* **principal outputs** *those* (n) *which we wish to control, as* **secondary outputs** *those which we do not wish to control, as* **linearly dependent outputs** *those which are related to one or more of the principal or secondary outputs by a linear differential equation.*

Example. In the example of Section 3.1, V' and ω are principal outputs, the winding temperatures of either of the machines are secondary outputs, and I' is a linearly dependent output, since $I' = (V'/R_l)$. The significance of this is that V' and I' cannot be controlled *independently*.

It is clear that for a given plant, the distinction between principal and secondary outputs is made in terms of the particular control problem that we are asked to solve. Their number is in no way related to the number u of energy-storage elements (or states) of the plant.

THEOREM. *If the n outputs are not linearly dependent, then the number of inputs q must be such that $q \geqslant n$.*

† Some authors [8, 24] use the terms "multipole" and "complex multiloop" instead of "multivariable." It appears, however, that the less ambiguous term "multivariable" is now preferred.

‡ For an exception, see Eqs. (2.26) and (2.29).

We assume that $q = n - 1$. Under these conditions, we can eliminate all $n - 1$ inputs from any of the n-equations (3.17) and thus express one output wholly as a linear combination of all the others. We therefore require that $q \geqslant n$.

Example. For the two-output plant of Section 3.1, we need a minimum of two inputs, for example v and v'. The remaining input, V, is not required for control, and hence may be used for optimization purposes. One might for instance seek to implement a relation between V and (v, v') such that operating efficiency is maximized. It follows then that there are several classes of inputs, namely:

DEFINITION. *Principal inputs are those n inputs selected to control the n principal outputs. Secondary inputs are those* $(q - n)$ *inputs which are not required to control the principal outputs.*

Among the secondary inputs, we list those that are used for optimization, those that are kept constant, and those that in a particular problem are left unattended. These latter are often termed *disturbance inputs*, since they may fluctuate freely. As an example of a disturbance input, we mention the temperature of the room containing the dc to ac converter of Section 3.1. Room-temperature fluctuations alter the principal outputs as a consequence of the changes in resistances R, r, R_l, r'.

THEOREM. *Let P be the square plant transfer matrix corresponding to an n principal input —n principal output situation. If* det $P \equiv 0$, *then at least one of the outputs is* **linearly related** *and only at most* $(n - 1)$ *outputs can be controlled independently with the n-inputs.*

This theorem is a direct consequence of an important result of the algebra of determinants: A determinant is zero if and only if at least two rows or at least two columns are *proportional*. Now if two or more rows are proportional, then two or more outputs are, according to our definition, linearly related. The reader may satisfy himself that the same statement holds if two columns are proportional. In either case, only $n - 1$ inputs are now required since there are only $(n - 1)$ principal outputs left.

Assuming that n principal inputs have been selected and that det $P \neq 0$, we associate each principal input m_i with a principal output y_i. Although it is generally possible in a multivariable plant to change *any* of the outputs by acting on *any* of the inputs, certain input-output pairs are more appropriate than others. In the example of Section 3.1, we would associate V' with v' rather than with V or v. In most engineering problems, there is little doubt as to which output ought to be associated with which input.

If this were not so, one might rearrange the P_0-matrix in such a way as to maximize the elements $p_{0,ii}$ of the principal diagonal, assuming that normalization with respect to the allowed operating range of both the input and output variables has previously been carried out. Suppose, for instance, that the following steady-state relation between the unnormalized variables $\bar{y}_1$ and $\bar{m}_1$, $\bar{m}_2$ has been measured:

$$\bar{y}_1 = \bar{m}_1 + 0.1\bar{m}_2 \tag{3.18}$$

and that the operating ranges β_1, γ_1, γ_2 of these variables are, respectively,

$$\beta_1 = 1; \quad \gamma_1 = 0.1; \quad \gamma_2 = 15.$$

We rewrite Eq. (3.18)

$$\frac{\bar{y}_1}{\beta_1} = \frac{\gamma_1}{\beta_1}\frac{\bar{m}_1}{\gamma_1} + 0.1\,\frac{\gamma_2}{\beta_1}\frac{\bar{m}_2}{\gamma_2} \tag{3.19}$$

and define the normalized variables

$$y_1 = \frac{\bar{y}_1}{\beta_1}; \quad m_1 = \frac{\bar{m}_1}{\gamma_1}; \quad m_2 = \frac{\bar{m}_2}{\gamma_2}$$

which, as a result of engineering considerations, can only vary in the range (0, 1).

Equation (3.19) then becomes

$$y_1 = 0.1m_1 + 1.5m_2. \tag{3.20}$$

It is apparent from Eq. (3.20) that y_1 should be controlled by m_2 and not by m_1 as (3.18) might have suggested.

3.3 The Canonical Forms.† In Section 3.1 we have constructed the linear model of a multivariable plant and obtained, as a final result, the elements p_{ij} of the $n \times q$ P-matrix (3.14). If the outputs are related to the inputs by

$$\mathbf{Y} = P\mathbf{M} \tag{3.17}$$

we say that the plant is given in the *P-canonical form*.

In some problems, it may be more convenient to write a different relation between the inputs and outputs of the *same* plant as is pointed out by M. D. Mesarovic [18, 19]. We may, for example, write that

$$\begin{aligned} Y_i &= f_i M_i + f_i \sum_{\substack{j=1 \\ j \neq i}}^{n} v_{ij} Y_j \\ f_i &= f_i(s); \quad v_{ij} = v_{ij}(s) \end{aligned} \tag{3.21}$$

provided the number of inputs equals the number of outputs. Form (3.21) is known as the V-canonical form. In a two-variable situation, we write

$$\begin{aligned} Y_1 &= f_1(M_1 + v_{12}Y_2) \\ Y_2 &= f_2(M_2 + v_{21}Y_1). \end{aligned} \tag{3.22}$$

† Certain authors [8] use the term "canonical form" to designate a particular closed-loop multivariable structure. In this chapter, the term "canonical form" always refers to the way we relate the input and output variables of the same structure.

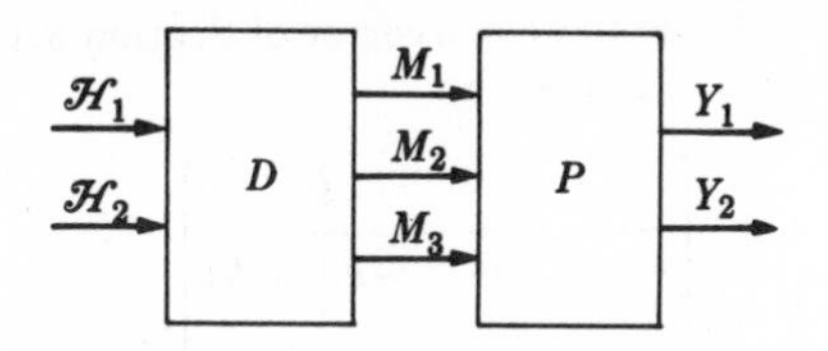

FIGURE 6. Open-loop multivariable control structure.

Here, the coefficients f_1, f_2, v_{12}, v_{21} are *uniquely* related to the coefficients p_{11}, p_{12}, p_{21}, p_{22} of the P-canonical form by

$$\begin{aligned} f_1 &= \frac{p_{11}p_{22} - p_{12}p_{21}}{p_{22}} \quad v_{12} = \frac{p_{12}}{p_{11}p_{22} - p_{12}p_{21}} \\ f_2 &= \frac{p_{11}p_{22} - p_{12}p_{21}}{p_{11}} \quad v_{21} = \frac{p_{21}}{p_{11}p_{22} - p_{12}p_{21}} \end{aligned} \tag{3.23}$$

provided P is nonsingular.

3.4 Open-loop Control. We consider the arrangement of Fig. 6 and we seek to design a series controller D such that the plant outputs Y_i are related to the controller inputs $\mathscr{H}_i$, $(i = 1, \ldots, n)$, by a *specified* transfer matrix K^* such that

$$\mathbf{Y} = K^*\mathscr{H}, \quad k_{ij}^* = k_{ij}^*(s) \tag{3.24}$$

in the absence of initial conditions. We assume that none of the plant outputs are linearly related and that P is stable. Since

$$\mathbf{M} = D\mathscr{H} \quad d_{ij} = d_{ij}(s) \tag{3.25}$$

it follows that

$$\mathbf{Y} = PD\mathscr{H} \tag{3.26}$$

and that

$$PD = K^*. \tag{3.27}$$

The matrices P and D must clearly be *compatible*, that is, D must be a $q \times n$ matrix if P is $n \times q$. If the principal inputs m_i, $(i = 1, \ldots, n)$, have been singled out, then P is an $(n \times n)$ matrix and D is explicitly and uniquely† obtained as

$$D = P^{-1}K^*. \tag{3.28}$$

In theory, we may specify any arbitrary stable K^* and derive D from Eq. (3.28). In practice, this procedure leads to the use of differentiating networks, which we avoid by carefully specifying the k^*_{ij}. At this stage, we just indicate that differentiating networks remain reasonably simple if the poles of the k^*_{ij} are made to coincide with the characteristic roots of the plant.

† If $q > n$, the required D is not unique.

Example. We consider the dc to ac converter of Section 3.1 and assume that v and v' are principal inputs. Hence

$$P = \begin{bmatrix} \dfrac{-4}{s+6} & \dfrac{-4}{(s+2)(s+6)} \\[2ex] \dfrac{-4}{s+6} & \dfrac{2(s+4)}{(s+2)(s+6)} \end{bmatrix}. \tag{3.29}$$

We wish to design D such that

(1) in the steady state

$$y_1 = \tilde{\eta}_1$$
$$y_2 = \tilde{\eta}_2$$
$$(\tilde{\eta}_1, \tilde{\eta}_2 = \text{constants});$$

(2) any transient of η_i does not effect y_j, $i \neq j$;

(3) K^* have eigenvalues -2 and -6.

Matrix (3.30) summarizes these requirements:

$$K^* = \begin{bmatrix} \dfrac{12}{(s+2)(s+6)} & 0 \\[2ex] 0 & \dfrac{12}{(s+2)(s+6)} \end{bmatrix}. \tag{3.30}$$

It follows from Eq. (3.28) that

$$D = \begin{bmatrix} -\dfrac{3(s+4)}{(s+2)(s+6)} & \dfrac{-6}{(s+2)(s+6)} \\[2ex] \dfrac{-6}{s+6} & \dfrac{6}{s+6} \end{bmatrix}. \tag{3.31}$$

We note that this particular design has achieved *decoupling* or noninteraction, i.e., the given multivariable structure (3.29) has in fact been reduced to two single variable structures (3.30).

By assuming that it was possible to specify the matrix K^*, we have arrived at an explicit solution of the series controller D. The drawback of this method is (1) the controller D may not be easily implemented from commercially available hardware, and (2) losing sight of how the d_{ij} and p_{ij} combine to form k^*_{jj}, we may specify an unreasonable K^*. H. K. Chatterjee [6] explicitly relates the k^*_{jj} to the controller and plant elements in the case of a noninteracting design. Denoting by det P the determinant of the plant matrix and by $|P_{ij}|$ the cofactor of the term p_{ij}, he shows that

$$k_{jj}^* = d_{jj} \frac{\det P}{|P_{jj}|} \tag{3.32}$$

and

$$\frac{d_{\alpha j}}{d_{jj}} = \frac{|P_{j\alpha}|}{|P_{jj}|}. \qquad (\alpha, j = 1, \ldots, n) \tag{3.33}$$

Equation (3.32) clearly indicates the constraints on k^*_{jj} imposed by available controllers. In order to prove Eqs. (3.32) and (3.33), we demand that the $n(n - 1)$ cross terms k^*_{ij}, $i \neq j$ be zero. This then leads to n-sets of $(n - 1)$ equations of the form

$$k^*_{ij} = \sum_{\alpha=1}^{n} p_{i\alpha} d_{\alpha j} = 0 \qquad \begin{cases} i = 1, \ldots, n \\ i \neq j \\ j = \text{fixed.} \end{cases} \tag{3.34}$$

By allowing j to take the values $1, \ldots, n$, we obtain n sets of the form (3.34). In order to find a nontrivial solution to (3.34), we seek to express the cross terms $d_{\alpha j}$, $\alpha \neq j$ as functions of the diagonal term d_{jj}. Thus

$$d\alpha j = d_{jj} \frac{|P_{j\alpha}|}{|P_{jj}|} . \tag{3.33}$$

We next prove Eq. (3.32) by starting from

$$k^*_{jj} = \sum_{\alpha=1}^{n} p_{j\alpha} d_{\alpha j} \tag{3.35}$$

and use (3.33) to express all the cross terms $d_{\alpha j}$, $\alpha \neq j$, as functions of d_{jj}. Thus

$$\begin{aligned} k^*_{jj} &= p_{jj} d_{jj} + \sum_{\substack{\alpha=1 \\ \alpha \neq j}}^{n} p_{j\alpha} d_{jj} \frac{|P_{j\alpha}|}{|P_{jj}|} \\ &= d_{jj} \frac{\det P}{|P_{jj}|} . \end{aligned} \tag{3.32}$$

3.5 Closed-loop Control. We now seek to implement a structure which exhibits the classical advantages of *feedback*, namely perfect steady-state accuracy, insensitivity to external disturbances and plant parameter changes, shortened response time, etc. As in single-variable systems, this can be done with series and/or parallel compensation. This is shown in Fig. 7, which represents the type of multivariable feedback systems we consider

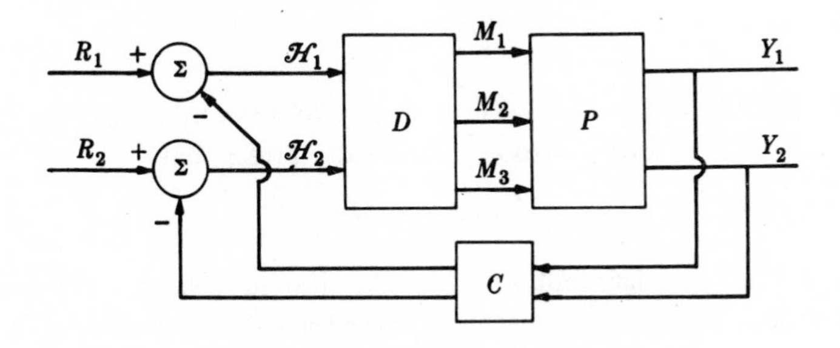

FIGURE 7. Multivariable feedback structure for $n = 2$, $q = 3$.

almost exclusively throughout this chapter. It is understood that the matrices P, C, and D of elements $p_{ij}(s)$, $c_{ij}(s)$, $d_{ij}(s)$ must be compatible, i.e., if P is $n \times q$, D must be $q \times n$, and C must be $n \times n$. We always assume that there are as many system inputs R_i as there are plant outputs Y_j.†

We establish the closed-loop system equations, in the absence of initial conditions

$$\begin{aligned} \mathbf{Y} &= P\mathbf{M} \\ \mathbf{M} &= D\mathscr{H} \\ \mathscr{H} &= \mathbf{R} - C\mathbf{Y}. \end{aligned} \tag{3.36}$$

We eliminate $\mathbf{M}$ and $\mathscr{H}$ and relate plant output $\mathbf{Y}$ to system input $\mathbf{R}$

$$\mathbf{Y} = (I + PDC)^{-1}PD\mathbf{R} \tag{3.37}$$

provided $(I + PDC)$ is not a singular matrix. We recall that Eq. (3.37) is a *compatible* matrix equation since PD is $n \times n$. Assuming furthermore that the closed loop system is stable, we specify the *over-all transfer matrix* K such that

$$\mathbf{Y} = K\mathbf{R} \tag{3.38}$$

where

$$K = (I + PDC)^{-1}PD. \tag{3.39}$$

3.6 Steady-state Accuracy. Since we usually require that

$$\lim_{t\to\infty} y_i = \tilde{r}_i \qquad \begin{matrix} (\tilde{r}_i = \text{constant}) \\ (i = 1, \ldots, n) \end{matrix} \tag{3.40}$$

we wish to determine in this section which constraints should be imposed upon the compensating networks C or D such that Eq. (3.40) is satisfied. It is clear that K must be stable and that the elements k_{ij} must be such that

$$K_0 = I \tag{3.41}$$

where K_0 is the steady-state over-all transfer matrix of elements

$$k_{0,ij} = k_{ij}(s)\,\big|_{s=0}. \tag{3.42}$$

Condition (3.42) can be realized in a variety of ways by proper design of either C or D. For *sensitivity reasons*, we usually prefer that

$$C_0 = C(s)\,\big|_{s=0} = I. \tag{3.43}$$

The reader may satisfy himself that the desired result (3.41) can be obtained with a compensating matrix C other than that specified by (3.43),

† Some authors, in particular Freeman [8], discuss structures where the number of system inputs exceeds the number of system outputs.

provided that the plant elements $p_{ij,0}$ are not subject to parameter changes.† We consider this, in general, an unacceptable engineering solution. If Eqs. (3.41) and (3.43) hold, then the steady-state forward transfer matrix $K_0^* = P_0 D_0$ must be such that

$$I + K_0^* = K_0^* \tag{3.44}$$

as can be derived easily from (3.39). Equation (3.44) places no constraints upon the elements k^*_{ij}, $j \neq i$, but stipulates that

$$\lim_{s \to 0} k^*_{ii}(s) = \infty. \qquad (i = 1, \ldots, n) \tag{3.45}$$

We now summarize these results.

THEOREM. *A sufficient condition to achieve zero steady-state error is that $C_0 = I$ and that the forward transfer matrix $K^* = PD$ contain at least one integration in each of its "n" diagonal elements k^*_{ii}. If in addition it cannot be ascertained that the elements $p_{0,ij}$, $i \neq j$ are free from parameter changes, then this condition is also necessary.*

We next examine the constraints placed upon P and D in order for Eq. (3.45) to hold. Since

$$\lim_{is \to 0} k^*_{ii}(s) = \lim_{s \to 0} \sum_{\alpha=1}^{n} p_{i\alpha}\, d_{\alpha i} = \infty \tag{3.46}$$

we require that at least one of the terms $p_{i\alpha} d_{\alpha i}$ entering into the n-sums (3.46) contain one or several integrations. It then suffices to ensure that each row of P *or* each column of D contain the factor $1/s$ at least once and that this factor is not canceled out when the products $p_{i\alpha} d_{\alpha i}$ are formed.

Example. We consider the stable multivariable control system of Fig. 8, where $C = D = I$, and where

$$P = \begin{bmatrix} \frac{1}{s} & -1 \\ \frac{1}{s} & \frac{1}{s^2} \end{bmatrix}. \tag{3.47}$$

We obtain by inspection

$$k^*_{11}(s) = \frac{1}{s}$$

$$k^*_{22}(s) = \frac{1}{s^2} \tag{3.48}$$

and conclude that the closed-loop system of Fig. 8 satisfies the steady-state accuracy condition (3.40).

† In the single variable case, Eq. (3.40) could be satisfied by selecting c_0 such that $c_0 = \dfrac{p_0 - 1}{p_0}$. Straightforward sensitivity analysis shows that the desired result (3.40) is strongly dependent on variations in p_0, especially if p_0 is not many times larger than 1. Similar results can be worked out for multivariable systems.

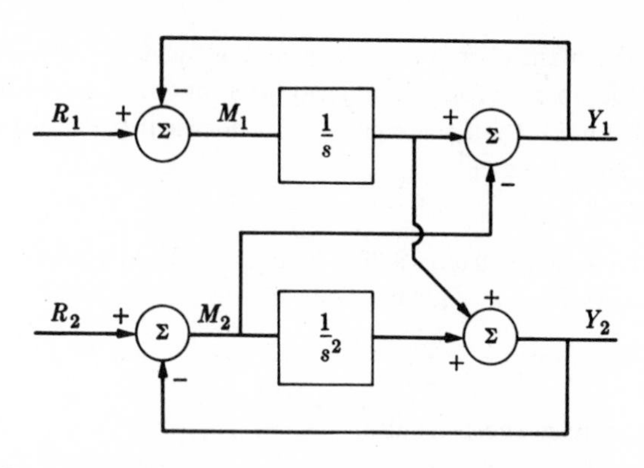

FIGURE 8. Example of closed-loop multivariable system.

3.7 Particular Cases. Equation (3.39) allows us to determine C or D so as to satisfy K. Thus

$$C = K^{-1} - (PD)^{-1}$$
$$D = P^{-1}K(I - CK)^{-1} \tag{3.49}$$

where (3.49) supposes the existence of P^{-1}. If $q > n$ we first determine the required forward transfer matrix:

$$K^* = PD = K(I - CK)^{-1} \tag{3.50}$$

and then synthesize D, which in this case is no longer *unique*.

We frequently assume that either of the matrices C or D reduces to the identity matrix I, since a specified K can be realized at least in theory by a suitable C *or* D matrix. We thus arrive at the two important particular cases, namely parallel compensation ($D = I$) and series compensation ($C = I$). If we maintain the structure of Fig. 7, parallel compensation is realizable only if $q = n$. The resulting design equations are then

$$D = I: \quad C = K^{-1} - P^{-1} \tag{3.51}$$
$$C = I: \quad D = P^{-1}K(I - K)^{-1}. \tag{3.52}$$

As in single variable systems, we usually prefer parallel compensation which does not introduce noise as easily when the required derivatives $\dot{y}_i, \ddot{y}_i, \ldots, (i = 1, \ldots, n)$ are directly available and need not be implemented by special derivative networks.

3.8 Noninteracting Control. It is often desired that under transient conditions $y_i(t)$ remain independent of $r_j(t)$, $i \neq j$. This particular design is termed *noninteracting* or *decoupled* and requires that $K(s)$ be a diagonal matrix. In the case of series compensation, Eq. (3.52) can be used to determine D such that K is diagonal and such that each of the n-channels has the proper transient response.

However, there is a quicker way to arrive at a decoupled structure.

THEOREM. *Let K^* designate the forward transfer matrix PD and let $C = I$. A necessary and sufficient condition for* **noninteraction** *is that K^* is a diagonal matrix of elements ${k^*}_{jj}$, $(j = 1, \ldots, n)$. If so, the closed-loop transfer matrix K is diagonal and has elements*

$$k_{jj} = \frac{{k^*}_{jj}}{1 + {k^*}_{jj}}. \tag{3.53}$$

We prove this theorem by assuming that K is noninteracting, i.e.,

$$k_{ij} = 0 \qquad (i \neq j) \tag{3.54}$$

and by demonstrating that K^* must then be noninteracting. By virtue of

$$(I + K^*)K = K^*$$

we explicitly obtain K^*

$$K^* = K(I - K)^{-1} \tag{3.55}$$

where the *diagonal* matrix $(I - K)^{-1}$ has elements

$$\frac{1}{1 - k_{jj}}.$$

Therefore

$$k^*_{ij} \begin{cases} = 0 & i \neq j \\ = \dfrac{k_{jj}}{1 - k_{jj}} & i = j \end{cases} \tag{3.56}$$

and

$$k_{jj} = \frac{{k^*}_{jj}}{1 + {k^*}_{jj}}. \tag{3.57}$$

If parallel compensation is used, it is often more convenient to express the plant equations in terms of the V-canonical form (3.21). We write for the closed loop system

$$Y_i = f_i M_i + f_i \sum_{\substack{j=1 \\ j \neq i}}^{n} v_{ij} Y_j \tag{3.21}$$

$$M_i = R_i - \sum_{j=1}^{n} c_{ij} Y_j. \tag{3.58}$$

Hence

$$Y_i = f_i \left[R_i - \sum_{j=1}^{n} c_{ij} Y_j + \sum_{\substack{j=i \\ j \neq i}}^{n} v_{ij} Y_j \right]. \tag{3.59}$$

We satisfy the requirement for noninteraction by selecting the c_{ij}, $j \neq i$ such that

$$c_{ij} = v_{ij} \tag{3.60}$$

and *then* obtain the desired relation between Y_i and R_i

$$Y_i = f_i(R_i - c_{ii} Y_i)$$

or

$$Y_i = \frac{f_i}{1 + f_i c_{ii}} R_i. \qquad (i = 1, \ldots, n) \quad (3.61)$$

Example. We consider the dc to ac converter of Sections 3.1 and 3.4. We include two integrators $4/s$ into each channel in order to satisfy Eq. (3.40).

1. *Series Compensation.* Using the decoupling network (3.31) preceded by the integrating network

$$\begin{bmatrix} \frac{4}{s} & 0 \\ 0 & \frac{4}{s} \end{bmatrix} \qquad (3.62)$$

we obtain the open-loop transfer matrix

$$K^* = \begin{bmatrix} \frac{48}{s(s+2)(s+6)} & 0 \\ 0 & \frac{48}{s(s+2)(s+6)} \end{bmatrix}. \qquad (3.63)$$

As a result of Eq. (3.57), we have

$$K = \begin{bmatrix} \frac{48}{s^3 + 8s^2 + 12s + 48} & 0 \\ 0 & \frac{48}{s^3 + 8s^2 + 12s + 48} \end{bmatrix}. \qquad (3.64)$$

In this particular design, the transient responses of both channels are identical. This is a consequence of our choice of Eq. (3.63). As a general rule, the various k_{ii} may be entirely different although we usually select K^* in such a way that D remains reasonably simple.

2. *Parallel Compensation.* We first obtain the V-canonical form of the plant (3.29) from (3.23)

$$f_1 = -\frac{4}{s+4} \qquad v_{12} = \frac{1}{2}$$

$$f_2 = \frac{2}{s+2} \qquad v_{21} = \frac{s+2}{2}. \qquad (3.65)$$

We next precede P by an integrating network as shown in Fig. 9.

The new V-canonical form $(\bar{f}_1, \bar{f}_2, \bar{v}_{12}, \bar{v}_{21})$, which relates $\mathbf{Y}$ to $\mathscr{H}$, is written by inspection

$$\bar{f}_1 = -\frac{4\alpha_1}{s(s+4)} \qquad \bar{v}_{12} = \frac{s}{2\alpha_1}$$

$$\bar{f}_2 = \frac{2\alpha_2}{s(s+2)} \qquad \bar{v}_{21} = \frac{s(s+2)}{2\alpha_2}. \qquad (3.66)$$

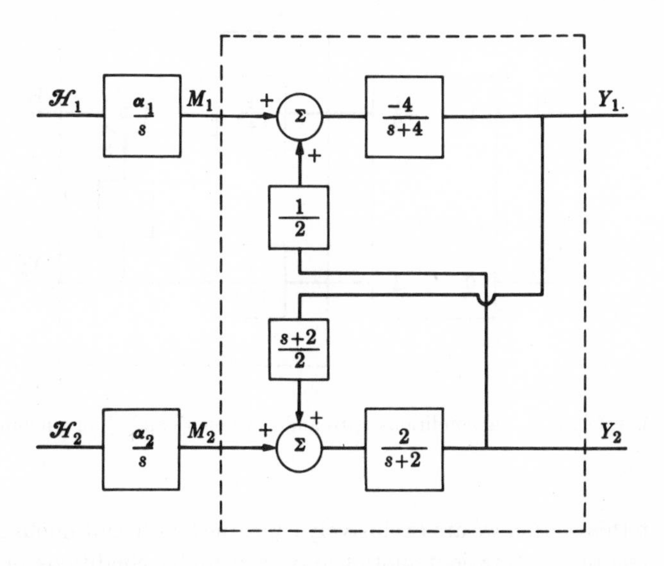

FIGURE 9. Canonical form of plant P which is preceded by an integrating network.

Assuming for simplicity that $c_{ii} = 1$, $(i = 1, 2)$ (see Section 3.6), we obtain the closed-loop transfer matrix K from Eq. (3.61)

$$K = \begin{bmatrix} \dfrac{-4\alpha_1}{s^2 + 4s - 4\alpha_1} & 0 \\ 0 & \dfrac{2\alpha_2}{s^2 + 2s + 2\alpha_2} \end{bmatrix}. \tag{3.67}$$

For acceptable transient response, we may select $\alpha_1 = -2$, $\alpha_2 = 1$, and obtain the remaining unknowns of the parallel compensating network from Eq. (3.60)

$$\begin{aligned} c_{12} &= -\frac{s}{4} \\ c_{21} &= \frac{s(s + 2)}{2}. \end{aligned} \tag{3.68}$$

The Effects of Initial Conditions. We have seen that with a properly designed controller, either series or parallel, the transient motion of a system input r_i did not propagate to the system output y_j, $j \neq i$. The question then arises whether the initial condition $x_k(0)$ of the kth energy storage element influences the transient motion $y_j(t)$. Recalling that the transfer matrix of a decoupled structure breaks down into n isolated transfer functions [see, for example, Eqs. (3.30) and (3.61)], we might conclude erroneously that some initial condition $x_k(0)$ will affect only one of the system outputs, say $y_j(t)$.

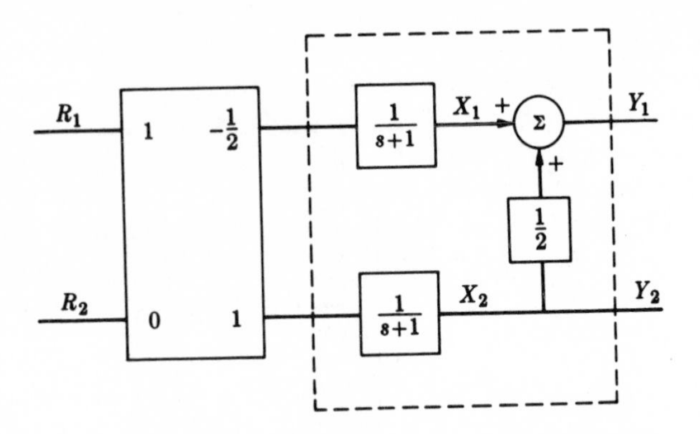

FIGURE 10. Effect of initial conditions $x_1(0)$ and $x_2(0)$ on Y_1 and Y_2 in a noninteracting structure.

Since in this section we are exclusively concerned with continuous systems, the analysis of the transient motion observed under conditions of startup are of purely academic interest to us. Let it suffice to say that some initial condition $x_k(0)$ may, but will not always, affect more than one of the system outputs. Although a mathematical proof of this property can be obtained, we advise the reader to consider the *noninteracting* structure of Fig. 10 and to satisfy himself that the initial state $x_2(0)$ does propagate to both output terminals. A glance at Fig. 10 indeed indicates that it must be so, in spite of the fact that a careless way of writing the system equations may hide this. The best way to avoid mistakes is to first relate the state variables $X_1(s)$ and $X_2(s)$ to $R_1(s)$, $R_2(s)$, $x_1(0)$, $x_2(0)$, and then to express $Y_1(s)$ and $Y_2(s)$ as functions of $R_1(s)$, $R_2(s)$, $x_1(0)$, $x_2(0)$. The correct result is

$$Y_1(s) = \frac{x_1(0)}{s+1} + \frac{\frac{1}{2}x_2(0)}{s+1} + \frac{R_1(s)}{s+1}$$

$$Y_2(s) = \frac{x_2(0)}{s+1} + \frac{R_2(s)}{s+1}.$$

3.9 Design for Specified Disturbance Response. As in single variable systems (Section 2.7), it is possible to independently specify the system response K and the disturbance response K_u to disturbances U entering into the forward loop. Using the same arguments and the same notation as in Section 2.7, it follows

$$\mathbf{Y} = P\mathbf{M} + P'\mathbf{U}. \tag{3.69}$$

By inspection we write that

$$\begin{aligned}\mathbf{Y} &= (I + PDC)^{-1}PD\mathbf{R} + (I + PDC)^{-1}P'\mathbf{U} \\ &= K\mathbf{R} + K_u\mathbf{U}.\end{aligned} \tag{3.70}$$

If **M** and **U** are n-vectors, the compensating matrices C and D can be uniquely determined in terms of K and K_u. If this is not the case, the solutions C and D are generally not unique.

The effects of measurable disturbances can also be minimized by the use of feedforward as discussed in Section 2.7.

3.10 Eigenvalues of Multivariable Systems and Multivariable Plants. In this chapter, we consider physical processes which are mathematically described by a set of ordinary, linear, time-invariant, integro-differential equations such as

$$\varphi_i(\ldots, \ddot{y}_1, \dot{y}_1; \ldots, \ddot{y}_n, \dot{y}_n, y_n) = \psi_i(\ldots, \ddot{m}_1, \dot{m}_1, m_1; \ldots, \ddot{m}_q, \dot{m}_q, m_q)$$
$$q \geqslant n. \qquad (i = 1, \ldots, n) \quad (3.71)$$

We usually find it convenient to take the Laplace transform of the n-equations (3.71). In the absence of all initial conditions, these equations are

$$A\mathbf{Y} = B\mathbf{M} \quad (3.72)$$

where the a_{il} and the b_{ik} $(i, l = 1, \ldots, n;\ k = 1, \ldots, q)$ are polynomials in s. As an example of this, the reader is referred to Eqs. (3.10) and (3.11).

The eigenvalues or characteristic roots $\lambda_1, \lambda_2, \lambda_u$ of Eq. (3.72) are of extreme importance since they determine stability and give a measure of the response. We state without proof that these eigenvalues are the roots of the polynomial

$$\det \begin{bmatrix} a_{11}(\lambda) \cdots a_{1n}(\lambda) \\ a_{n1}(\lambda) \cdots a_{nn}(\lambda) \end{bmatrix} = \det a_{il}(\lambda) = 0 \quad (3.73)$$

where

$$a_{il}(\lambda) = a_{il}(s) \big|_{s=\lambda}$$

The number u of eigenvalues is equal to the order of the polynomial (3.73) and depends in no way on the indices n and q.

Frequently the plant or system is described by

$$\mathbf{Y} = P\mathbf{M} \quad (3.74)$$

or

$$\mathbf{Y} = K\mathbf{R} \quad (3.75)$$

where P is an $n \times q$ and where K is an $n \times n$ matrix. Since Eq. (3.75) is a particular case of (3.74), we consider only (3.74) and assume $q > n$.

In order to determine these eigenvalues, we analyze the mechanism whereby (3.74) was obtained from the fundamental formulation (3.72), namely

$$\mathbf{Y} = A^{-1}B\mathbf{M} = \frac{\hat{A}}{\det\,[a_{il}(s)]} B\mathbf{M} \quad (3.76)$$

where the $\hat{A}$ matrix of elements $\hat{a}_{il}$ is the adjoint of A. An arbitrary output

Y_i is then related to an arbitrary input M_k by

$$Y_i = \frac{\sum_{l=1}^{n} \hat{a}_{il} b_{lk}}{\det [a_{il}(s)]} M_k = p_{ik} M_k. \tag{3.77}$$

Recalling that the $\hat{a}_{il}$ and the b_{lk} are *polynomials* in s, we conclude that the denominator polynomial of each p_{ik} is precisely det $[a_i(s)]$, unless one or more of the roots of det $[a_{il}(s)]$ are canceled out by $\sum_{l=1}^{n} \hat{a}_{il} b_{lk}$. In practice, therefore, we directly obtain the characteristic equation (3.73) by setting the highest order denominator present in the P-matrix equal to zero.

Example. We consider the problem of Section 3.1 and we determine the eigenvalues from Eqs. (3.10) and (3.14). Equation (3.10) yields the characteristic determinant immediately

$$\det \begin{bmatrix} \lambda + 4 & 2 \\ -(\lambda + 2) & \lambda + 2 \end{bmatrix} = (\lambda + 2)(\lambda + 6) = 0. \tag{3.78}$$

Turning now to Eq. (3.14), we select the highest order denominator, i.e., the denominator of p_{12} or of p_{22}, which is precisely the characteristic equation (3.78).

3.11 Stability of Noninteracting Control Systems. We consider the closed-loop system

$$A\mathbf{Y} = \mathbf{R}$$

where A is a nonsingular square matrix of elements $a_{ij}(s,\varphi_\beta)$, the φ_β being those controller parameters which we can adjust to make A a diagonal matrix, i.e., to achieve decoupling. Let the $\varphi_\beta{}^*$ be those values of the φ_β which cause noninteraction, i.e.,

$$a_{ij} \equiv 0. \qquad \begin{cases} i \neq j \\ i, j = 1, \ldots, n \end{cases}$$

It appears that the original characteristic equation det $A = 0$ has been broken down into "n" characteristic equations of the form

$$a_{ii} = 0. \qquad (i = 1, \ldots, n)$$

On the basis of this, we might conclude that a necessary and sufficient condition for the noninteracting system to be stable is that all the roots of the "n" equations

$$a_{ii} = 0$$

have negative real parts.

In practice, we cannot adjust the parameters φ_β so that the a_{ij}, $i \neq j$ are exactly zero. Consequently, there is always some coupling left. There are cases where the imperfect cancellation of the a_{ij} causes the almost noninteracting system to be unstable. Therefore it is necessary to ascertain that the roots of $\det A = 0$ all have negative real parts for those variations of the φ_β around the $\varphi_\beta{}^*$ that one might reasonably expect to occur. If, and this is generally the case, small variations of the φ_β do not cause instability, then the characteristic equation of the ith channel is approximately $a_{ii} = 0$.

Example. We consider the hypothetical system

$$A = \begin{bmatrix} s+1 & \varphi_1(s^2+2s+1) \\ \varphi_2 s & s+1 \end{bmatrix}.$$

Clearly, if

$$\varphi_1 = \varphi_1{}^* = 0 \quad \text{and} \quad \varphi_2 = \varphi_2{}^* = 0$$

the eigenvalue corresponding to each of the two channels is -1. In order that the characteristic equation

$$-\varphi_1\varphi_2 s^3 + (1 - 2\varphi_1\varphi_2)s^2 + (2 - \varphi_1\varphi_2)s + 1 = 0$$

of the almost uncoupled system may be stable, we demand that

$$(1) \qquad \varphi_1\varphi_2 \leqslant 0$$

$$(2) \qquad (1 - \varphi_1\varphi_2)^2 > 0.$$

We conclude from condition (1) that the noninteracting structure will probably be unstable, since small parameter changes may cause $\varphi_1\varphi_2$ to become negative.

This problem of stability has been dealt with in detail by some of the Russian authors [23]. Let us just indicate quite generally, that although the roots of all the a_{ii} have negative real part, instability may occur when the order of $\prod_{i=1}^{n} a_{ii}$ is lower than the order of $\det A$, i.e., when one or more of the cross terms is of higher order than the diagonal term in the same row.

3.12 The Preferred Structure. We wish to show in this section that the attractive preferred structure of single variable systems (Section 2.2) can be extended to multivariable systems. The procedure does not require the use of Laplace transform techniques and always yields a sound engineering solution. Moreover it maintains the original plant description, which is often simpler than the P-matrix might lead us to believe. In support of this last statement we compare Eqs. (3.10) and (3.14), assuming $V = \text{constant}$, i.e., $m_3 = 0$

$$\begin{aligned} \dot{y}_1 + 4y_1 \qquad\quad + 2y_2 &= -4m_1 \\ -\dot{y}_1 - 2y_1 + \dot{y}_2 + 2y_2 &= 2m_2 \end{aligned} \tag{3.10a}$$

and

$$P = \begin{bmatrix} \dfrac{-4}{s+6} & \dfrac{-4}{(s+2)(s+6)} \\[2ex] \dfrac{-4}{s+6} & \dfrac{2(s+4)}{(s+2)(s+6)} \end{bmatrix}. \tag{3.29}$$

We state without proof that if all the y_i and m_i are principal outputs and principal inputs, respectively, then the plant equation can generally be written as

$$A^{(0)}\mathbf{y} + A^{(1)}\mathbf{y} + \cdots + A^{(h)}\mathbf{y}^{(h)} = \mathbf{m}. \tag{3.79}$$

The matrices $A^{(\alpha)}$ are n by n and have elements $a_{ij}^{(\alpha)}$ which are real constants. The order u of the differential system (3.79) is at most hn. In the case of (3.10a), the matrices $A^{(0)}$ and $A^{(1)}$ are

$$A^{(0)} = \begin{bmatrix} -1 & -\frac{1}{2} \\ -1 & 1 \end{bmatrix} \quad A^{(1)} = \begin{bmatrix} -\frac{1}{4} & 0 \\ -\frac{1}{2} & \frac{1}{2} \end{bmatrix}. \tag{3.80}$$

We next seek a controller network such that

$$\mathbf{m} = W^{(-1)} \int_{-\infty}^{t} (\mathbf{r} - \mathbf{y})\, dt + W^{(0)}\mathbf{y} + W^{(1)}\dot{\mathbf{y}} + \cdots + W^{(h)}\ddot{y}^{(h)} \tag{3.81}$$

where the matrices $W^{(\beta)}$, $\beta = -1, 0, \ldots, h$ are $n \times n$, where $W^{(-1)}$ is diagonal,† and where the elements $w_{ij}^{(\beta)}$ are real constants.

We eliminate $\mathbf{m}$ between Eqs. (3.79) and (3.81) and obtain the closed-loop system differential equation

$$W^{(-1)}\mathbf{y} + (A^{(0)} - W^{(0)})\dot{\mathbf{y}} + \cdots + (A^{(h)} - W^{(h)})\mathbf{y}^{(h+1)} = W^{(-1)}\mathbf{r}. \tag{3.82}$$

System (3.82), which is at most of order $n(h + 1)$, contains enough adjustable parameters $w_{ij}^{(\beta)}$ to force all the roots of

$$\det [W^{(-1)} + (A^{(0)} - W^{(0)})\lambda + \cdots + (A^{(h)} - W^{(h)})\lambda^{h+1}] = 0 \tag{3.83}$$

to have the desired locations in the complex λ-plane. The intricate dependence of suitable temporal behavior on the values of the coefficients of Eq. (3.83) is explored in Naslin [21] for certain simple multivariable systems.

If Eq. (3.82) is stable, the obvious solution is such that

$$\lim_{t \to \infty} \mathbf{y}(t) = \tilde{\mathbf{r}}. \qquad (\tilde{\mathbf{r}}_i = \text{constant})$$

The controller network of each channel is connected to all of the *nh-plant states*, as shown in Fig. 11 for the situation $n = 2$, $h = 2$.

This control system can evidently be rendered noninteracting and a suitable channel response can be synthesized by an appropriate choice of the adjustable parameters $w_{ij}^{(\beta)}$.

Example. We consider the plant (3.10a) and seek to determine a controller (3.81) so as to obtain a noninteracting structure of acceptable channel response.

† This is not a necessary restriction, though little is gained by giving W^{-1} a more general form.

Thus

$$w_{11}^{(-1)}y_1 + (-1 - w_{11}^{(0)})\dot{y}_1 + (-\tfrac{1}{2} - w_{12}^{(0)})\dot{y}_2 + (-\tfrac{1}{4} - w_{11}^{(1)})\ddot{y}_1 - w_{12}^{(1)}\ddot{y}_2 = w_{11}^{(-1)}r_1$$

$$w_{22}^{(-1)}y_2 + (-1 - w_{21}^{(0)})\dot{y}_1 + (1 - w_{22}^{(0)})\dot{y}_2 + (-\tfrac{1}{2} - w_{21}^{(1)})\ddot{y}_1 + (\tfrac{1}{2} - w_{22}^{(1)})\ddot{y}_2 = w_{22}^{(-1)}r_2. \quad (3.84)$$

Noninteraction requires that

$$w_{12}^{(0)} = -\tfrac{1}{2} \qquad w_{21}^{(0)} = -1$$
$$w_{12}^{(1)} = 0 \qquad w_{21}^{(1)} = -\tfrac{1}{2}. \quad (3.85)$$

We may now obtain the channel responses (3.67) by letting

$$w_{11}^{(-1)} = 8 \qquad w_{22}^{(-1)} = 2$$
$$w_{11}^{(0)} = -5 \qquad w_{22}^{(0)} = -1$$
$$w_{11}^{(1)} = -\tfrac{5}{4} \qquad w_{22}^{(1)} = -\tfrac{1}{2}.$$

The reason why the feedback coefficients are different from those found in Section 3.8 is that a different control configuration is used.

If, as is frequently the case, one or more of the $a_{ii}^{(0)}$ are zero, some simplification may result, since these channels then already contain an integration. This fact becomes immediately apparent if the set of n-equations (3.82) is written out in terms of the unknown coefficients $w_{ij}^{(\beta)}$.

3.13 Nonlinear Multivariable Systems [18, 23]. The dynamic analysis of low-order single variable nonlinear control systems cannot at the present time be undertaken in any straightforward manner. The problem of stability, for example, is incomparably more difficult than in the linear case because nonlinear systems may be stable or unstable depending on initial conditions.

In this section we only consider the possibility of designing noninteracting nonlinear systems. The important problem of ascertaining whether such systems are stable is not touched upon. We further restrict ourselves to plants expressed in the V-canonical form and to parallel compensation.

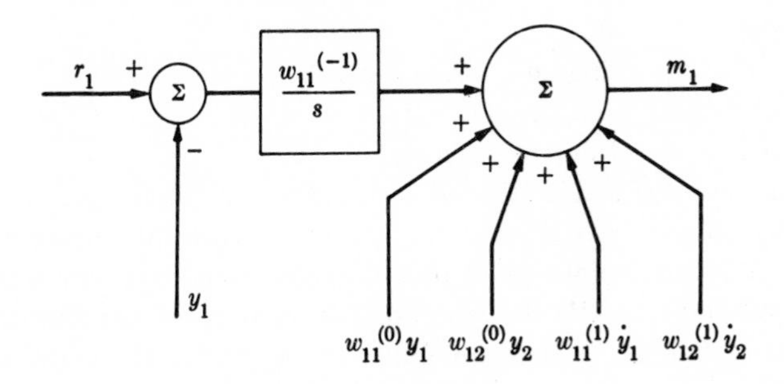

FIGURE 11. Controller network of the first channel, $n = 2$, $h = 2$.

Certain other classes of invariant nonlinear systems are described by Petrov [23].

We consider a set of n-nonlinear integro-differential equations

$$\varphi_i(\ldots, \ddot{y}_i, \dot{y}_i, y_i) = F_i(\ldots, \dot{m}_i, m_i; \ldots, \dot{y}_l, y_l)$$
$$(i = 1, \ldots, n) \quad (l = 1, \ldots, n; l \neq i) \quad (3.86)$$

and we use a controller network such that

$$m_i = C_i(r_i; \ldots, \dot{y}_j, y_j). \quad (j = 1, \ldots, n) \quad (3.87)$$

Hence

$$\varphi_i(\cdots \ddot{y}_i, \dot{y}_i, y_i) = F_i\left[\cdots \frac{d}{dt} C_i(r_i; \ldots, \dot{y}_j, y_j), \right.$$
$$\left. C_i(r_i; \ldots, \dot{y}_j, y_j), \ldots, \dot{y}_l, y_l\right] \quad (3.88)$$

If the nonlinear functions F_i are such that all the $\ldots, \dot{y}_l, y_l, (l = 1, \ldots, n; l \neq i)$ can be canceled out by the functions C_i, then the closed-loop system (3.88) is noninteracting. However, this is frequently not possible

Example.

$$\varphi_1(\cdots \dot{y}_1, y_1) = m_1 + y_2^3 \quad (3.89a)$$
$$\varphi_2(\cdots \dot{y}_2, y_2) = m_2^3 + y_1. \quad (3.89b)$$

The output y_2 can be made to disappear from Eq. (3.89a) if

$$m_1 = C_1^*(r_1; \ldots, \dot{y}_1, y_1) - y_2^3 = C_1(r_1; \ldots, \dot{y}_1, y_1; \ldots, \dot{y}_2, y_2). \quad (3.90)$$

The output y_1 can also be made to disappear from (3.89b) and a desired relation between y and r_2 can be obtained by use of the nonlinear network

$$m_2 = \sqrt[3]{r_2 - y_1 + C_2^*(\cdots \dot{y}_2, y_2)}.$$

3.14 Multivariable Relay Systems. Single-variable relay systems are said to be optimum if the equilibrium state is reached in minimum time.† The problem of designing a controller which reverses the relay at precisely the right instants was solved over twenty years ago in the case of a second-order linear plant. Extensions were recently made to certain linear plants of arbitrary order u.

The problem of designing an optimal controller in the case of multivariable systems is attracting considerable attention at this time. The nonlinear system under consideration is shown in Fig. 12.

From its knowledge of the desired constant output $\tilde{\mathbf{r}} = \{\tilde{r}_1, \ldots, \tilde{r}_n\}$ and the actual system state $\mathbf{x}(t) = \{x_1, \ldots, x_u\}$, the controller is required to produce the relay coil voltages $\sigma_1(t), \ldots, \sigma_n(t)$ such that an equilibrium $\mathbf{y} = \tilde{\mathbf{r}}$, $\tilde{\mathbf{r}} =$ constant, is achieved in minimum time. It is important to note that the goal here is not to realize noninteraction during the transient.

† For further detail, see Chapters V and VII.

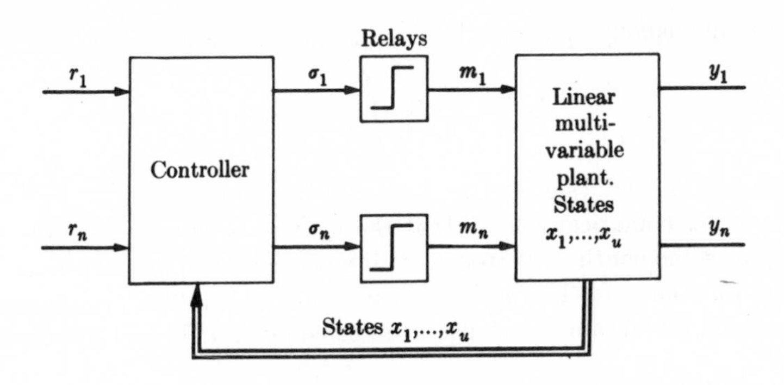

FIGURE 12. Optimum multivariable relay system. The multivariable plant is linear and the relays have neither hysteresis nor dead time.

Since this problem has not yet been solved in the general case and since we know how to design optimum single-variable relay systems, the obvious way to circumvent the difficulty is to first render the plant noninteracting and then design n optimum single-variable controllers, each of which accommodates one of the now independent channels. It is known, however, that the optimum multivariable controller, generally speaking, accomplishes equilibrium in a shorter time and with fewer switchings than n independent controllers would. A four-state, two-variable plant, for instance, can be brought to rest, in certain cases, in at most three switchings, whereas the two independent second-order plants would require a total of four switchings.†

The most promising approach toward the optimum control of multivariable relay systems appears to be Pontriagin's maximum principle (see Chapter VII). If the required number of switchings were known, then the exact times at which switching should occur could also be found by means of a straightforward extension of the material contained in Chapter V, Section 4.3.

3.15 Statistical Design Principles. Requirement (3.40) which we repeat here

$$\lim_{t\to\infty} y_i = \tilde{r}_i \qquad (\tilde{r}_i = \text{constant}) \quad (i = 1, \ldots, n)$$

may not be sufficiently exacting, since it gives no indication on the transient behavior. If the system is called upon to respond to nonconstant inputs $r_i(t)$ of which we only have a statistical description, it is customary to determine the over-all transfer matrix $K(s)$ in such a way that some function of the error $\boldsymbol{\epsilon} = \mathbf{r} - \mathbf{y}$ is minimized *on the average*. In single-variable control

† We define the number of switchings to be equal to the number of times the relay output is positive plus the number of times the relay output is negative. In accordance with this definition, the optimum second-order single-variable relay system requires at most two switchings to reach equilibrium.

systems, one usually optimizes the mean squared error

$$\bar{\epsilon}^2 = \lim_{T \to \infty} \frac{1}{2T} \int_{-T}^{T} (r - y)^2 \, dt. \tag{3.91}$$

See Truxal [27] and Tsien [28].

This is mathematically feasible if the system is linear and if the power spectrum of the continuous stochastic input r is known and expressible as a rational function of s. The problem of minimizing Eq. (3.91) in the presence of noise and disturbances has also been considered in Truxal [27] and Tsien [28].

These statistical design techniques have gone through two stages of development.

1. We assume that the system structure is *fixed* and that the system transfer function $K = (Y/R)$ is known except for a limited number of adjustable parameters φ_α. The optimum φ_α are then determined by seeking the minimum of ϵ^2 (φ_α), i.e., by setting

$$\frac{\partial}{\partial \varphi_\alpha} \bar{\epsilon}^2 (\varphi_\alpha) = 0 \tag{3.92}$$

for each of the φ_α.

2. We assume that the plant P is known and we wish to synthesize the optimum *physically realizable* system structure K, that is, find C and D. This problem formulation leads to the Wiener-Hopf integral equation, the solution of which is well known [27].

Both of these problem formulations have been extended to the theory of linear time-invariant multivariable systems. Since there are now n errors $\epsilon_i(t)$, it has become customary to minimize the *sum* of their mean squares

$$\sum_{i=1}^{n} \overline{(r_i - y_i)^2} \tag{3.93}$$

assuming that the auto- and cross-correlation functions of all the $r_i(t)$ are known and that the related power spectra are expressible as rational functions of s.

Colomb and Usdin [9] have worked out a technique whereby the adjustable parameters φ_α of the otherwise fixed system transfer matrix K are optimized. Amara [1, 2] arrived at an explicit description of a physically realizable structure K and solved the corresponding set of Wiener-Hopf integral equations, using matrix techniques throughout.

4. The Timesharing of Control System Components

4.1 Multivariable Timeshared Systems [29]. In practice, we frequently encounter situations where two or more similar control systems are located side by side. As a representative example, we might consider a

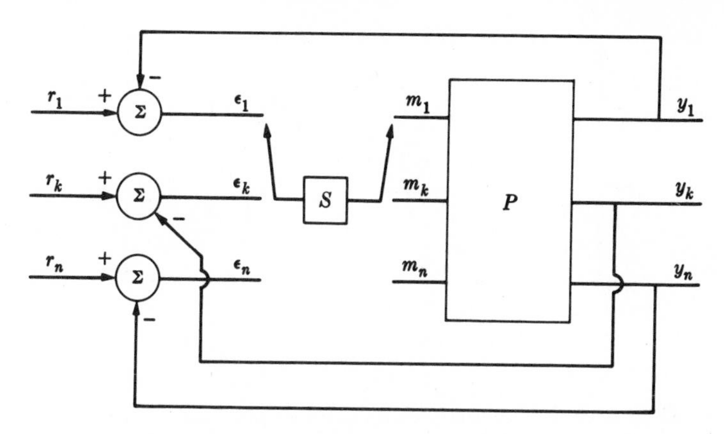

FIGURE 13. Multivariable timeshared system. P, multivariable process presumed linear and stationary; S, shared component presumed linear and stationary; r_i, $i = 1, \ldots, n$, command input or desired output; y_i, $i = 1, \ldots, n$, actual output; m_i, $i = 1, \ldots, n$, process input; ϵ_i, $i = 1, \ldots, n$, error $r_i - y_i$.

programmed contouring machine where the motion of the cutter is controlled by three similar position control servo-mechanisms.

Since in general the loop components have a much shorter response time than the over-all system, savings in cost and bulk may in certain cases be realized if some of these components, for instance, servo valves and transducers, are shared between two or more control loops. In this section, we only consider timesharing arrangements where a linear component S is sequentially commutated around n linear control loops. For added simplicity, we assume that the duration of the commutation cycle is normalized to one second and that S is connected to each of the loops during an equal time $\Delta = 1/n$.

The very timely problem of timesharing digital computers [10] among several processes is also accommodated by the analysis techniques to be presented. The multiplexing of digital computers is even easier to account for since the computer can be programmed to *issue instructions only to that loop to which it is actually connected*. The timesharing of telecommunication networks, on the other hand, is not included here.

We simultaneously consider the general multivariable model of Fig. 13 and the example problem of Fig. 14.

The state-space techniques described in Chapter I and II permit an exact analysis of the n-channel linear timeshared system of Fig. 13. Certain important results, such as stability or system response $\mathbf{y}$ to a given excitation $\mathbf{r}$ are obtained with relative ease by combining state space and z-transform techniques. The systems considered in this section are related to sampled-data systems using switches which remain closed during a nonnegligible fraction

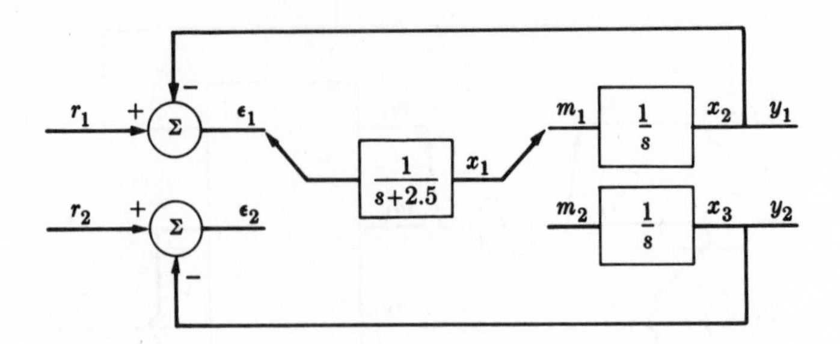

FIGURE 14. Timeshared system of example problem.

of the sampling period. The analysis techniques presented here are immediately applicable to such "finite width" sampled-data systems.

It is important to note that at any particular time, Figs. 13 and 14 reduce to single-loop feedback structures. Thus, for $l < t < l + \frac{1}{2}$, where l is any positive integer, Fig. 14 simplifies to Fig. 15.

4.2 State Equations Corresponding to the Interval $\Delta = 1/n$. For simplicity, we start our calculations at time $t = 0$ when the first loop is closed. The system state is then described by the vector $\mathbf{x}(t)$ whose components can be chosen rather arbitrarily provided their number is equal to the number "u" of energy storage elements of the *complete* system. We may thus select the states x_1, x_2, and x_3 as the outputs of S and of the two integrators, respectively.

Denoting by $\mathbf{X}(s)$ the Laplace transform of $\mathbf{x}(t)$, it follows from elementary feedback theory that

$$X_1(s) = R_1(s)\frac{s}{(s+\frac{1}{2})(s+2)} + x_1(0)\frac{s}{(s+\frac{1}{2})(s+2)} - x_2(0)\frac{1}{(s+\frac{1}{2})(s+2)}$$

$$X_2(s) = R_1(s)\frac{1}{(s+\frac{1}{2})(s+2)} + x_1(0)\frac{1}{(s+\frac{1}{2})(s+2)} + x_2(0)\frac{s+2.5}{(s+\frac{1}{2})(s+2)}$$

$$X_3(s) = \frac{x_3(0)}{s}. \tag{4.1}$$

The set of equations (4.1) is expressed concisely as a single matrix equation, also applicable to the general system of Fig. 13

$$\mathbf{X}(s) = \mathbf{\Phi}_1(s)\mathbf{x}(0) + \mathbf{H}_1(s)R_1(s) \tag{4.2}$$

where the subscript 1 recalls that the first loop is closed. $\mathbf{\Phi}_1$ is a $u \times u$ matrix of elements $\phi_{1,ij}$ and $\mathbf{H}_1$ is a vector of components $H_{1,i}$.

Taking the inverse Laplace transform of Eq. (4.2), we obtain that

$$\mathbf{x}(t) = \varphi_1(t)\mathbf{x}(0) + \mathbf{h}_1(t) * r_1(t) \tag{4.3}$$

where the symbol * denotes convolution and where

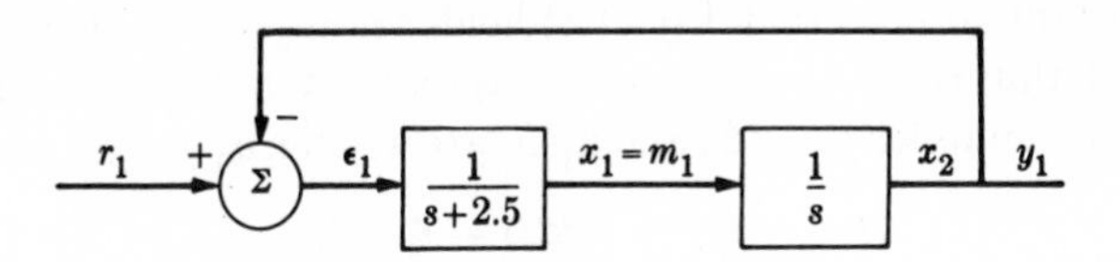

FIGURE 15. Reduction of Fig. 14 valid for $l < t < l + \frac{1}{2}$.

$$\varphi_1(t) = \mathscr{L}^{-1}\{\Phi_1(s)\}$$

and

$$\mathbf{h}_1(t) = \mathscr{L}^{-1}\{\mathbf{H}_1(s)\}. \tag{4.4}$$

In order to evade the troublesome integral equation (4.3), we assume that the $R_i(s)$ are step functions whose amplitude $\tilde{r}_i$ is allowed to change only at integer times "l." Thus, $r_i(l)$ signifies that the ith input line carries a step of amplitude $\tilde{r}_i$ during the interval $l < t < l + 1$. Under these conditions, Eq. (4.3) simplifies to

$$\mathbf{x}(t) = \varphi_1(t)\mathbf{x}(0) + \mathbf{g}_1(t)\tilde{r}_1(0) \tag{4.5}$$

where any component $g_{1,i}(t)$ is obtained from $h_{1,i}$ by

$$g_{1,i}(t) = \mathscr{L}^{-1}\left\{\frac{H_{1,i}(s)}{s}\right\}. \tag{4.6}$$

The reader may verify that the matrices $\varphi_1(t)$ and $\mathbf{g}_1(t)$ corresponding to the example-problem are

$$\varphi_1(t) = \begin{bmatrix} -\frac{1}{3}e^{-t/2} + \frac{4}{3}e^{-2t} & -\frac{2}{3}e^{-t/2} + \frac{2}{3}e^{-2t} & 0 \\ \frac{2}{3}e^{-t/2} - \frac{2}{3}e^{-2t} & \frac{1}{3}e^{-t/2} - \frac{1}{3}e^{-2t} & 0 \\ 0 & 0 & 1 \end{bmatrix}$$

$$\mathbf{g}_1(t) = \begin{bmatrix} \frac{2}{3}e^{-t/2} - \frac{2}{3}e^{-2t} \\ 1 - \frac{4}{3}e^{-t/2} + \frac{1}{3}e^{-2t} \\ 0 \end{bmatrix}. \tag{4.7}$$

At the end of the first interval, that is, at $t = \Delta$, Eq. (4.5) becomes

$$\mathbf{x}(\Delta) = \varphi_1(\Delta)\mathbf{x}(0) + \mathbf{g}_1(\Delta)\tilde{r}_1(0). \tag{4.8}$$

Thus, for the example-problem, Δ equals $\frac{1}{2}$, so that

$$\varphi_1(\Delta) = \begin{bmatrix} 0.232 & -0.273 & 0 \\ 0.273 & 0.916 & 0 \\ 0 & 0 & 1 \end{bmatrix} \quad \mathbf{g}_1(\Delta) = \begin{bmatrix} 0.273 \\ 0.084 \\ 0 \end{bmatrix}. \tag{4.7a}$$

It is important to note that Eq. (4.8) holds for any time interval $l < t < l + \Delta$. We will thus relate the state $\mathbf{x}(l + \Delta)$ to the state $\mathbf{x}(l)$ by means of Eq. (4.9), where, for simplicity, $\varphi_1(\Delta)$ and $\mathbf{g}_1(\Delta)$ are written φ_1 and $\mathbf{g}_1$, respectively

$$\mathbf{x}(l + \Delta) = \varphi_1 \mathbf{x}(l) + \mathbf{g}_1 \tilde{r}_1(l). \tag{4.9}$$

4.3 State Equations Corresponding to the Interval $n\Delta = 1$ second. The reader realizes that the state $\mathbf{x}(l + k\Delta)$ can be related to the state $\mathbf{x}[l + (k - 1)\Delta]$ in exactly the same manner that the state $\mathbf{x}(l + \Delta)$ was related to the state $\mathbf{x}(l)$. It will be recalled that we shall concern ourselves with the state $\mathbf{x}(l + k\Delta)$ at the time when the commutator switches to the channel labeled $k + 1$. Hence

$$\mathbf{x}(l + k\Delta) = \varphi_k \mathbf{x}[l + (k - 1)\Delta] + \mathbf{g}_k \tilde{r}_k(l). \tag{4.10}$$

It is clear that the matrices φ_k and $\mathbf{g}_k$ are different from the matrices φ_1 and $\mathbf{g}_1$. Thus, in the case of the example-problem

$$\varphi_2 = \begin{bmatrix} 0.232 & 0 & -0.273 \\ 0 & 1 & 0 \\ 0.273 & 0 & 0.916 \end{bmatrix} \quad \mathbf{g}_2 = \begin{bmatrix} 0.273 \\ 0 \\ 0.084 \end{bmatrix}. \tag{4.7b}$$

In order to sweep a complete cycle, one would write "n" equations of the form (4.8) or (4.9). Having done this, one would eliminate the intermediate states $\mathbf{x}(l + k\Delta)$, $k \neq n$, and relate $\mathbf{x}(l + 1)$ to $\mathbf{x}(l)$.

We obtain from elementary matrix theory

$$\begin{aligned} \mathbf{x}(l + 1) = (\varphi_n \varphi_{n-1} \cdots \varphi_2 \varphi_1)\mathbf{x}(l) &+ \mathbf{g}_n \tilde{r}_n(l) \\ &+ \varphi_n \mathbf{g}_{n-1} \tilde{r}_{n-1}(l) + \cdots + (\varphi_n \varphi_{n-1} \cdots \varphi_3 \varphi_2)\mathbf{g}_1 \tilde{r}_1(l) \end{aligned} \tag{4.11}$$

For convenience, let

$$(\varphi_n \varphi_{n-1} \cdots \varphi_2 \varphi_1) \triangleq \varphi$$

$$(\varphi_n \varphi_{n-1} \cdots \varphi_{k+1})\mathbf{g}_k \triangleq \mathbf{\Gamma}_k.$$

Hence

$$\mathbf{x}(l + 1) = \varphi \mathbf{x}(l) + \mathbf{\Gamma}_1 \tilde{\mathbf{r}}_1(l) + \cdots + \mathbf{\Gamma}_n \tilde{\mathbf{r}}_n(l). \tag{4.12}$$

In the case of the example-problem, one would have

$$\varphi = \begin{bmatrix} 0.054 & -0.0633 & -0.273 \\ 0.273 & 0.916 & 0 \\ 0.0633 & -0.0742 & 0.916 \end{bmatrix} \quad \mathbf{\Gamma}_1 = \begin{bmatrix} 0.0633 \\ 0.084 \\ 0.0742 \end{bmatrix} \quad \mathbf{\Gamma}_2 = \begin{bmatrix} 0.273 \\ 0 \\ 0.084 \end{bmatrix}.$$

Placing side by side the "n" vectors $\mathbf{\Gamma}_k$ one may form a $u \times n$ matrix Γ with the result that Eq. (4.12) simplifies to

$$\mathbf{x}(l + 1) = \varphi \mathbf{x}(l) + \Gamma \tilde{\mathbf{r}}(l). \tag{4.13}$$

Matrices φ and Γ are termed the *system transition* and the *system distribution* matrix. In the particular case of the example, Γ would become

$$\Gamma = \begin{bmatrix} 0.0633 & 0.273 \\ 0.084 & 0 \\ 0.0742 & 0.084 \end{bmatrix}. \tag{4.14}$$

4.4 Introduction of the z-Transform. Equation (4.13) constitutes in fact a set of linear difference equations. This suggests that z-transform techniques are applicable and may lead to results that are concise and easily interpreted by the control engineer.

Recalling that the z-transform of the discrete time function $x_k(l)$ is

$$X_k(z) = \sum_{l=0}^{\infty} x_k(l) z^{-l} \tag{4.15}$$

we transform Eq. (4.13) into

$$(zI - \varphi)\mathbf{X}(z) = z\mathbf{x}(0) + \Gamma\tilde{\mathbf{R}}(z) \tag{4.16}$$

where I is the identity matrix.

4.5 Conclusions. Equation (4.16) entirely resolves the linear square-wave commutation problem, under the sole assumption that the forcing vector $\mathbf{r}$ varies in discrete steps at integer times. It holds approximately if $\mathbf{r}$ varies slowly in a one-second interval. By returning to Eq. (4.3), the reader will also realize that the timesharing problem could be explicitly solved along similar lines for *any explicitly known forcing vector*.

We often prefer to know the system output $\mathbf{Y}(z)$, rather than $\mathbf{X}(z)$, in terms of $\tilde{\mathbf{R}}(z)$. This is achieved quite simply by recalling that $\mathbf{y}$ can always be related to $\mathbf{x}$ through an $n \times u$ matrix G whose elements are constants

$$\mathbf{y}(t) = G\mathbf{x}(t). \tag{4.17}$$

In the case of the example-problem, G is written by inspection

$$G = \begin{bmatrix} 0 & 1 & 0 \\ 0 & 0 & 1 \end{bmatrix}.$$

Since the elements of G are pure numbers, it follows that

$$\mathbf{Y}(z) = G\mathbf{X}(z) \tag{4.18}$$

with the result that the following input-output equation can be simply derived from (4.16)

$$\mathbf{Y}(z) = G(zI - \varphi)^{-1}z\mathbf{x}(0) + G(zI - \varphi)^{-1}\Gamma\tilde{\mathbf{R}}(z). \tag{4.19}$$

Since the transfer matrix $G(zI - \varphi)^{-1}\Gamma$ generally does not reduce to a diagonal matrix, timesharing causes the system to exhibit cross coupling or interaction.

The problem of stability and the related question of performance would at first glance appear to be quite difficult. The introduction of the z-transform, however, reduces this problem to a study of the zeros of the *characteristic determinant* $\det[zI - \varphi]$. The system is stable if and only if all the zeros of the characteristic equation

$$\det[zI - \varphi] = 0$$

are located inside the unit circle.

Also, the inverse transform of $\mathbf{Y}(z)$ in Eq. (4.19) yields the system outputs at integer sampling times $0, 1, 2, \ldots, l$. By cyclic permutation of the n matrices entering into φ, the system outputs at *intermediate* sampling times can be obtained. Thus, for $\varphi = \varphi_1\varphi_n\varphi_{n-1}\cdots\varphi_3\varphi_2$, Eq. (4.19) would yield values of the y_i corresponding to the times $\Delta, 1 + \Delta, \ldots, l + \Delta$.

5. The Timesharing of Computer Components†

As an application of the material of Section 4, we make use of timesharing techniques to reduce the number of computer components required to carry out a particular computation. Certain digital computer components have been shared for a considerable time. This technique, however, is quite recent for the linear computing components of analog machines. We propose to show that all those operational amplifiers required for integration purposes can be replaced by one operational amplifier which is sequentially switched around the computing setup. The integrating capacitors are maintained to store the results of successive computations.

To illustrate the technique, we consider the forced linear second-order differential equation

$$\begin{aligned} \dot{x}_1 &= -k_1x_1 - k_1x_2 \\ \dot{x}_2 &= k_2x_1 - k_2r. \end{aligned} \qquad (k_1, k_2\text{: positive constants}) \quad (5.1)$$

To solve Eq. (5.1), we use the conventional continuous setup of Fig. 16 where

$$\frac{1}{R_1C_1} = \frac{1}{R_1'C_1} = k_1; \quad \frac{1}{R_2C_2} = \frac{1}{R_2'C_2} = k_2.$$

5.1 Implementation of Timesharing. As in Section 4, we normalize the switching cycle to one second and we sequentially commutate the operational amplifier S used for integrating purposes around the setup, taking *one* input at a time. With reference to Fig. 16, we have four integrator inputs $r, -x_1, x_2, x_1$ and thus would allocate $\Delta = \frac{1}{4}$ second to each elementary

† This particular problem has not been treated in any detail in the literature. Anatrol [3] and Rawdin [26] were found to be the only references concerned with the timesharing of analog computer components.

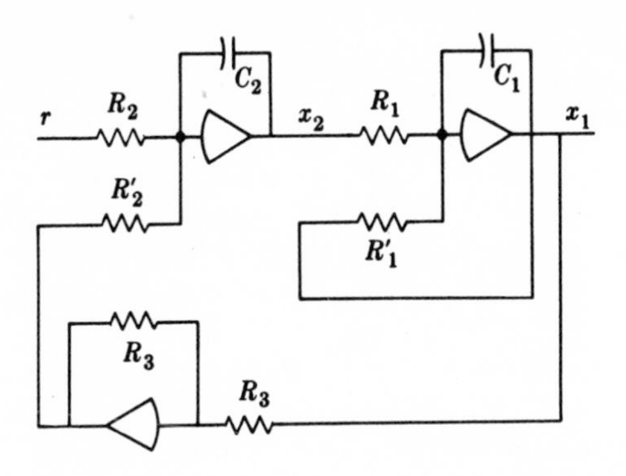

FIGURE 16. Conventional analog computer setup to solve Eq. (5.1).

computation within the cycle. Since integration of each of the four inputs is performed during Δ seconds only, we must correspondingly increase the integrator gains, i.e., k_1 becomes k_1/Δ. The computing networks formed during a complete cycle $l < t < l + 1$ (l = positive integer) are shown in Fig. 17.† The gains are now chosen such that

$$\frac{1}{R_1{}^*C_1{}^*} = \frac{1}{R_1{}'^*C_1{}^*} = \frac{k_1}{\Delta}; \quad \frac{1}{R_2{}^*C_2{}^*} = \frac{1}{R_2{}'^*C_2{}^*} = \frac{k_2}{\Delta}$$

5.2 The Mathematical Description. We assume that the capacitors $C_1{}^*$ and $C_2{}^*$ are perfect and that the resistors $R_1{}^*$, $R_1{}'^*$, $R_2{}^*$, $R_2{}'^*$, and R_3 are so large that the voltages stored on the capacitors do not appreciably drop. Under these conditions, we obtain for $l < t < l + \Delta$:

$$x_1{}^*(l + \Delta) = x_1{}^*(l) \tag{5.2}$$

$$x_2{}^*(l + \Delta) = -\frac{k_2}{\Delta}\int_l^{l+\Delta} r^*\,dt + x_2{}^*(l). \tag{5.3}$$

If, during the interval $(l < t < l + 1)$, the function r^* is constant and equal to $\tilde{r}^*(l)$, Eq. (5.3) simplifies to

$$x_2{}^*(l + \Delta) = -k_2\tilde{r}^*(l) + x_2{}^*(l). \tag{5.4}$$

We now summarize the changes that occurred during the interval $(l < t < l + \Delta)$ by

$$\mathbf{x}^*(l + \Delta) = \varphi_1\mathbf{x}^*(l) + \mathbf{\Gamma}_1\tilde{r}^*(l) \tag{5.5}$$

† In the subsequent discussion, we distinguish the variables and parameters of the continuous setup from those of the shared setup by starring the latter ones.

where

$$\varphi_1 = \begin{bmatrix} 1 & 0 \\ 0 & 1 \end{bmatrix} \mathbf{\Gamma}_1 = \begin{bmatrix} 0 \\ -k_2 \end{bmatrix}. \tag{5.6}$$

The reader may verify that the system transition and the system distribution matrices corresponding to the three succeeding intervals of duration Δ are

$$\begin{aligned} \varphi_2 &= \begin{bmatrix} 1 & 0 \\ k_2 & 1 \end{bmatrix} \quad \mathbf{\Gamma}_2 = \begin{bmatrix} 0 \\ 0 \end{bmatrix} \\ \varphi_3 &= \begin{bmatrix} 1 & -k_1 \\ 0 & 1 \end{bmatrix} \mathbf{\Gamma}_3 = \begin{bmatrix} 0 \\ 0 \end{bmatrix} \\ \varphi_4 &= \begin{bmatrix} e^{-k_1} & 0 \\ 0 & 1 \end{bmatrix} \mathbf{\Gamma}_4 = \begin{bmatrix} 0 \\ 0 \end{bmatrix}. \end{aligned} \tag{5.7}$$

We next combine Eqs. (5.6) and (5.7) as indicated in Section 4.3 and relate $\mathbf{x}^*(l+1)$ to $\mathbf{x}^*(l)$ and $\tilde{r}^*(l)$ by

$$\begin{aligned} \mathbf{x}^*(l+1) &= \varphi_4\varphi_3\varphi_2\varphi_1\mathbf{x}^*(l) + \varphi_4\varphi_3\varphi_2\mathbf{\Gamma}_1\tilde{r}^*(l) \\ &= \varphi\mathbf{x}^*(l) + \mathbf{\Gamma}\tilde{r}^*(l) \end{aligned} \tag{5.8}$$

where

$$\varphi = \begin{bmatrix} e^{-k_1}(1 - k_1k_2) & -k_1e^{-k_1} \\ k_2 & 1 \end{bmatrix} \mathbf{\Gamma} = \begin{bmatrix} k_1k_2e^{-k_1} \\ -k_2 \end{bmatrix}. \tag{5.9}$$

The z-transform of difference equation (5.8) is obtained as

$$(zI - \varphi)\mathbf{X}^*(z) = z\mathbf{x}^*(0) + \mathbf{\Gamma}\tilde{R}^*(z) \tag{5.10}$$

which completely describes the timeshared computer of Fig. 17 at integer times l.

5.3 Comparison with a Continuous Computer Solution. We consider the *sampled* characteristic equation

$$\det\,[zI - \varphi] = z^2 - z[1 + e^{-k_1}(1 - k_1k_2)] + e^{-k_1} = 0 \tag{5.11}$$

and compare the *envelope* of any transient motion of the shared system (5.10) to the transient motion of the continuous system (5.1). This envelope is of the form

$$x_1^{(E)}(t) = Ce^{-\beta^* t}\cos\,(\omega^* t - \theta^*) \tag{5.12}$$

where C and θ^* depend on the initial state $\mathbf{x}^*(0)$. The logarithmic decrement β^* and the angular frequency ω^* are related to k_1 and k_2 by†

† See, for example, the conversion table of Ragazzini and Franklin [25], p. 317.

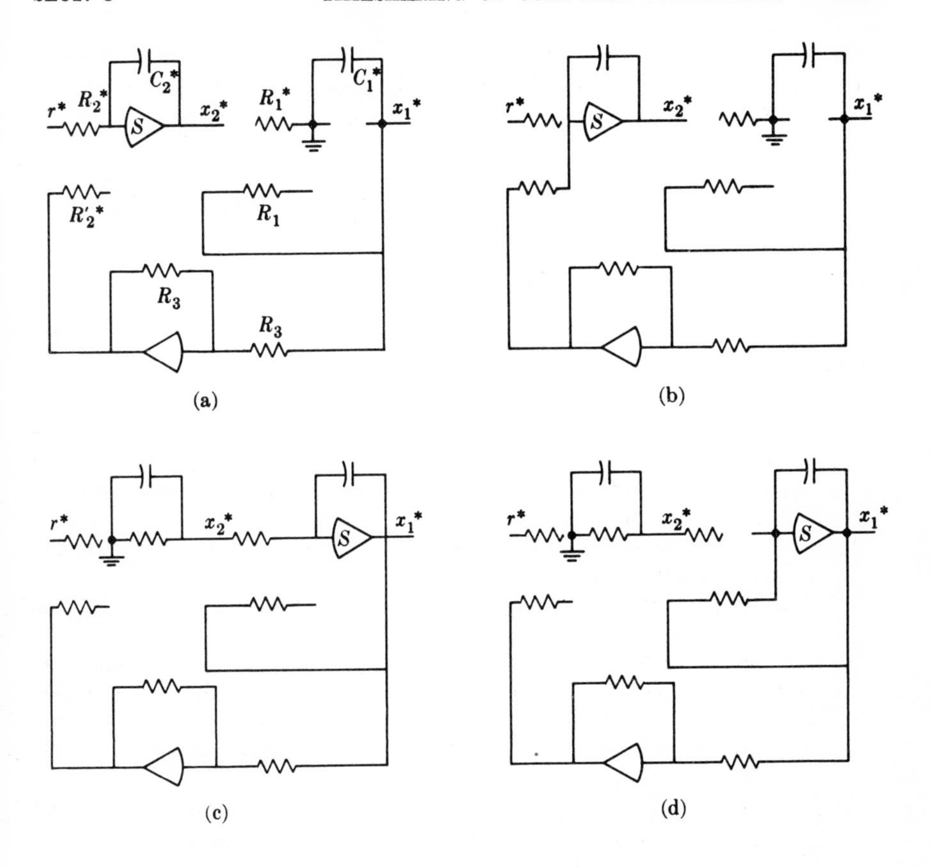

FIGURE 17. Computing networks sequentially formed during a one-second cycle. (a) $l < t < l + \Delta$; (b) $l + \Delta < t < l + 2\Delta$; (c) $l + 2\Delta < t < l + 3\Delta$; (d) $l + 3\Delta < t < l + 1$.

$$\beta^* = \frac{k_1}{2} \tag{5.13}$$

$$\omega^* = \cos^{-1}\left[\frac{e^{-(k_1/2)}(1 - k_1k_2) + e^{k_1/2}}{2}\right]. \tag{5.14}$$

The parameters β and ω of the continuous system (5.1) are

$$\beta = \frac{k_1}{2} \tag{5.15}$$

$$\omega = \sqrt{k_1k_2 - \frac{k_1^2}{4}}. \tag{5.16}$$

The logarithmic decrements β and β^* are seen to be identical. Moreover, if k_1 and k_2 are small compared to unity, which means that the motion varies slowly in a one-second time interval, ω^* becomes approximately

$$\omega^* \approx \sqrt{k_1 k_2 - \frac{k_1^2}{4}}. \qquad (k_1, k_2, \ll 1) \quad (5.17)$$

BIBLIOGRAPHY

1. Amara, R. C., "Application of matrix methods to the linear least squares synthesis of multivariable systems," J. Franklin Inst. **268,** 1–16 (1959).
2. Amara, R. C., "Hybrid Multivariable Control Systems," *Proceedings of the IFAC, Moscow, 1960*, Butterworths, 1961.
3. Anatrol, Publication No. 5117, 1961. The De Havilland Aircraft Company Limited, Hatfield, England.
4. Bode, W. H., *Network Analysis and Feedback Amplifier Design*, D. Van Nostrand, 1955.
5. Boksenbom, A. S., and Hood, R., "General Algebraic Method applied to Control Analysis of Complex Engine Types," NACA Tech. Rept. 980, Washington, D.C., April, 1949.
6. Chatterjee, H. K., "Multivariable Process Control," *Proceedings of the IFAC, Moscow, 1960*, Butterworths, 1961.
7. Ergin, E. I., and Ling, C., "Development of a Noninteracting Controller for Boilers," *Proceedings of the IFAC, Moscow, 1960*, Butterworths, 1961.
8. Freeman, H., "A synthesis method for multipole control systems," Trans. AIEE **76,** Part II (1957).
9. Golomb, M., and Usdin, E., "A theory of multidimensional servo systems," J. Franklin Inst. **253,** 29–57 (1952).
10. Henry, E. W., "Logical Scheduling of a Multiplexed Digital Controller," Stanford Electronics Laboratories, Standford University, Stanford, California, Tech. Rept. No 2106–1, July 11, 1960.
11. Jeffrey, A., "The Stability of Interacting Control Systems," *Proceedings of the IFAC, Moscow, 1960*, Butterworths, 1961.
12. Kalman, R. E., and Bertram, J. E., "General synthesis procedure for computer control of single and multiloop linear systems," Trans. AIEE **77,** Part II, 602–609 (1958).
13. Kalman, R. E., and Koepcke, R. W., "Optimal Synthesis of Linear Sampling Control Systems Using Generalized Performance Indexes," ASME Paper No. 58-IRD-6, 1958.
14. Kalman, R. E., "On the General Theory of Control Systems," *Proceedings of the IFAC, Moscow, 1960*, Butterworths, 1961.
15. Kulebakin, V. S., "The Theory of Invariance of Regulating and Control Systems," *Proceedings of the IFAC, Moscow, 1960*, Butterworths, 1961.

16. Lang, G., and Ham, J. M., "Conditional feedback systems—a new approach to feedback control," AIEE Trans. **74,** Part II, 152–158 (1955).
17. Maxwell, J. C., "On governors," Proc. Roy. Soc. London **16,** 270–283 (1867).
18. Mesarovic, M. D., *The Control of Multivariable Systems*, Wiley, 1960.
19. Mesarovic, M. D., "Control of Multivariable Systems," *Proceedings of the IFAC, Moscow, 1960*, Butterworths, 1961. This is a summary of [18].
20. Mitchell, D. S., and Webb, C. R., "A Study of Interaction in a Multiloop Control System," *Proceedings of the IFAC, Moscow 1960*, Butterworths, 1961.
21. Naslin, P., "Nouveau critère d'amortissement," Automatisme **V,** 229–243 (June, 1960).
22. Nishida, F., "Synthesis of Multivariable Control Systems by Means of Sampled Data Compensations," *Proceedings of the IFAC, Moscow, 1960*, Butterworths, 1961.
23. Petrov, B. N., "The Invariance Principle and the Conditions for Its Application During the Calculation of Linear and Nonlinear Systems," *Proceedings of the IFAC, Moscow, 1960*, Butterworths, 1961.
24. Povejsil, D. J., and Fuchs, A. M., "A method for the preliminary synthesis of a complex multiloop Control system," Trans. AIEE **74,** Part II, 129–134 (1955).
25. Ragazzini, J. R., and Franklin, G. F., *Sampled Data Control Systems*, McGraw-Hill, 1958.
26. Rawdin, E., "Time multiplexing as applied to analog computation", IRE Trans. on Electronic Computers (1959).
27. Truxal, J. G., *Automatic Feedback Control System Synthesis*, McGraw-Hill, 1955.
28. Tsien, H. S., *Engineering Cybernetics*, McGraw-Hill, 1954, pp. 53–69.
29. Peschon, J., and Horton, W. W., "On timesharing of control system components," IRE Trans. on Automatic Control 33–38 (July, 1962).

CHAPTER IV

Optimum Stochastic Control

LEONARD G. SHAW

CONTENTS

The design of an automatic control system often requires the analysis of random phenomena. It is not surprising to encounter randomness in control problems since a controller is essentially a device which compensates for unexpected changes in reference signals and unexpected changes in the plant whose outputs are being controlled. A control system design procedure which takes account of random or stochastic phenomena will have the same basic subdivisions as a deterministic design. In stochastic problems, however, instead of aiming for good transient response for a class of inputs, such as step and ramp functions, we can anticipate random inputs by looking for controllers which will produce some kind of good *average* performance for a class of random inputs and random plant variations.

In order to evaluate average performance, we must choose a performance criterion, such as integral squared error, and then compare the performance of various controllers in terms of this criterion. The physical significance of probability statements is related to average measurements, where operations are averaged over the results of many trials of a stochastic experiment. Therefore, system performance in a random environment must be measured in terms of statistical averages which weight the randomly occurring situations according to a probability law. The choice of a particular statistical description for the environment limits the analysis to a class of signals such as is done in a deterministic problem by the choice of a set of test signals like steps and ramps.

This chapter will review some of the basic relations of mathematical statistics and then it will present some of the main results in the theory of optimum stochastic filtering and control. The emphasis here will be on squared error types of performance criteria and on linear filters and controllers.

1. Review of Mathematical Statistics

The mathematical techniques employed in the study of random variables and random processes may be unfamiliar to the control engineer, but an appreciation of some of these ideas is necessary for an understanding of the performance of control systems in random environments. This section will review some of the relevant mathematics. The reader should not expect such a short survey to be a substitute for more authoritative and more complete presentations available in the many excellent texts which are available.† The main purpose here is to define the terminology and notation to be used in the following sections.

We will begin with numerical valued scalar random variables. A random variable may be thought of as the outcome of an experiment, e.g., the

† Numbers in brackets refer to the bibliography at the end of this chapter. Introductory references: Parzen [20], Feller [8], Cramer [4]; advanced: Cramer [5], Loeve [18], Doob [7]; Cramer [5] is especially good for the properties and use of Gaussian variables.

measurement of the height of a person from a specified population. In this example the height of one person is a *sample value*, and the set of all possible heights is a *sample description space*. Random variables will be denoted by capital letters, X, Y, . . . , and their sample values will be denoted by lower case forms of the same letters, x, y, ...

The sample description space of a scalar or one-dimensional random variable may be any set of points or any set of intervals on the real line from $-\infty$ to ∞. The *distribution function* $F_X(x)$ is one representation of the probabilistic information describing the random variable X. It is defined by

$$F_X(x) = \text{Prob}\,(X \leqslant x). \tag{1.1}$$

(We will not attempt to define or discuss the significance of the *probability of an event* or the *probability measure of a set*.) It is easy to see that

$$\text{Prob}\,(b < X \leqslant a) = F_X(a) - F_X(b).$$

$$\lim_{x\to\infty} F_X(x) = 1, \tag{1.2}$$

and

$$\lim_{x\to-\infty} F_X(x) = 0$$

where the last two relations require the further conventional choice that all probabilities are nonnegative and that the probability of a certain event is 1.

The information in $F_X(x)$ is also contained in its derivative, the *probability density function* $p_X(x)$,

$$p_X(x) = \frac{d}{dx} F_X(x). \tag{1.3}$$

(Constant terms are lost in differentiation, but by Eq. (1.2) F_X can have no undetermined constant component.) In these terms

$$\text{Prob}\,(b < X \leqslant a) = \int_b^a p_X(x)\,dx$$

and

$$\int_{-\infty}^{\infty} p_X(x)\,dx = 1. \tag{1.4}$$

When a discussion involves only one random variable, it is customary to simplify $F_X(x)$ to $F(x)$ and $p_X(x)$ to $p(x)$, letting the argument of the function denote the random variable to which it refers.

In most problems the ultimate interest is in the evaluation of probabilities of events, or mean values (see the following), so that we use density functions only in terms of their integrals. For this reason, as well as our assumption that the reader has an engineering background, we will represent the derivative of a step discontinuity in F_X by a $\delta(x)$ (impulse function) term in $p_X(x)$. When the sample description space of X consists of a finite or denumerable set of points, then p_X consists of a weighted sum of impulse functions, and integrals involving such a density function become sums.

The value of probability theory in engineering is that it allows us to make statements about the "average" behavior of random phenomena. The term *average* generally will be reserved for the time average of a function of time. The term used for a probabilisitc "average" is the *mean value* or *expected value*. We will talk about the expected value of a random variable, or, more generally, the expected value of a function of a random variable. The expected value of $g(X)$ is written as

$$E[g(X)] = \int_{-\infty}^{\infty} g(x)p_X(x)\,dx. \tag{1.5}$$

The expected values of integral powers of a random variable are especially important and are called the *moments* of the random variable. The nth moment of X is

$$E(X^n) = \int_{-\infty}^{\infty} x^n p_X(x)\,dx. \tag{1.6}$$

Also, the first moment is called the *mean value of* X and the second moment is called the *mean square value of* X. The *variance of* X is defined as the *second central moment*, i.e.

$$\text{Var}\,(X) = E[X - E(X)]^2. \tag{1.7}$$

It should be noted that the definition of the expectation operator in Eq. (1.5) implies that this operator is linear such that

$$E[ag(X) + bh(X)] = aE[g(X)] + bE[h(X)]. \tag{1.8}$$

1.1 Joint Descriptions of Several Random Variables. Many interesting problems involve several random variables. All of the previous ways of characterizing a single random variable can be generalized for the study of a set of several variables. In addition, new probabilistic functions can be defined when we have more than one random variable.

The joint distribution function of n random variables $X_1, X_2, \ldots, X_n$ is

$$F_{X_1,\ldots,X_n}(x_1, \ldots, x_n) = \text{Prob}\,(X_1 \leqslant x_1, \text{ and } X_2 \leqslant x_2 \text{ and } \ldots, X_n \leqslant x_n). \tag{1.9}$$

Similarly, the joint density function is

$$p_{X_1,\ldots,X_n}(x_1, \ldots, x_n) = \frac{\partial^n F_{X_1,\ldots,X_n}(x_1, \ldots, x_n)}{\partial x_1\,\partial x_2 \cdots \partial x_n}. \tag{1.10}$$

It is helpful to think of the X_i as the rectangular coordinates of an n-dimensional random vector. From this point of view, the integral

$$\int_{b_1}^{a_1}\int_{b_2}^{a_2}\cdots\int_{b_n}^{a_n} p_{X_1,\ldots,X_n}(x_1,\ldots,x_n)\,dx_1\,dx_2\cdots dx_n \tag{1.11}$$

is the probability that the vector will lie in the region of n-dimensional space which is enclosed by the plane boundaries described by $b_i < X_i \leqslant a_i$ for $i = 1, 2, \ldots, n$.

Marginal distributions and densities arise when we are interested in only m of a set of n random variables where $m < n$. The marginal density of m random variables, say X_1 to X_m, is defined as

$$p_{X_1,\ldots,X_m}(x_1,\ldots,x_m) = \int_{-\infty}^{\infty}\cdots\int_{-\infty}^{\infty} p_{X_1,\ldots,X_n}(x_1,\ldots,x_n)\,dx_{m+1}\cdots dx_n. \tag{1.12}$$

That is, the joint density of all n variables is averaged with respect to those variables which are not of specific interest.

Of particular engineering importance is the problem of finding the density of m random variables when the remaining $(n - m)$ variables have been observed. This density function is called the *conditional* density function of $X_1, \ldots, X_m$ *given* the observed values of $X_{m+1}, \ldots, X_n$ and is defined by

$$p_{X_1,\ldots,X_m \mid X_{m+1},\ldots,X_n}(x_1,\ldots,x_m \mid x_{m+1},\ldots,x_n) = \frac{p_{X_1,\ldots,X_n}(x_1,\ldots,x_n)}{p_{X_{m+1},\ldots,X_n}(x_{m+1},\ldots,x_n)}. \tag{1.13}$$

For Eq. (1.13) to be meaningful the denominator of the right side must not vanish, but such a condition is not likely to be of interest since any set of values of $X_{m+1}, \ldots, X_n$ for which the denominator vanishes has a zero probability of being observed.

Equation (1.13) can also be interpreted as showing that the joint density of n random variables is the product of the joint density of $(n - m)$ of them and the conditional density of the other m given observations of the first $(n - m)$. This decomposition is useful for studying expected values of functions of several random variables. The basic definition of the *expectation of a function of several variables* is a natural extension of that for a function of a single variable, namely

$$E[g(X_1,\ldots,X_n)] = \int_{-\infty}^{\infty}\cdots\int_{-\infty}^{\infty} g(x_1,\ldots,x_n)\,p_{X_1,\ldots,X_n}(x_1,\ldots,x_n)\,dx_1\cdots dx_n. \tag{1.14}$$

Using Eq. (1.13) we can decompose the expectation of (1.14) into

$$E[g(X_1, \ldots, X_n)] = E\{E[g(X_1, \ldots, X_n) \mid X_{m+1}, \ldots, X_n]\}. \quad (1.15)$$

The innermost expectation on the right side of Eq. (1.15) is called a *conditional expectation* and is evaluated by using the conditional density function. The conditional expectation is especially important in the applications which follow below.

1.2 Statistical Independence. Two random variables are intuitively judged to be independent when knowledge of the value of one tells us nothing about the value of the other. In symbols, X_1 and X_2 are said to be independent if and only if

$$p_{X_1 \mid X_2}(x_1 \mid x_2) = p_{X_1}(x_1). \quad (1.16)$$

From Eq. (1.13) it is apparent that equivalent conditions for independence of these two random variables are

$$p_{X_1, X_2}(x_1, x_2) = p_{X_1}(x_1) p_{X_2}(x_2) \quad (1.17)$$

or

$$E[g(X_1)h(X_2)] = E[g(X_1)]E[h(X_2)] \quad (1.18)$$

for all functions g and h.

Sums of independent random variables are very important. Random variables which can be thought of as sums of many independent random variables appear frequently in physical problems because a macroscopic event which we observe is often describable as the sum of a large number of independent microscopic events. The noise voltage between two points on a piece of metal is the sum of the voltages due to the independent motion of a large number of electrons within the metal.

The density function of the sum of two random variables can be found in terms of their joint density from the basic definitions. The result is that if $X_3 = X_1 + X_2$ then

$$p_{X_3}(x_3) = \int_{-\infty}^{\infty} p_{X_1, X_2}(x_3 - x_2, x_2)\, dx_2. \quad (1.19)$$

If X_1 and X_2 are independent then the integral in Eq. (1.19) becomes a convolution of the two individual density functions. For any X_1 and X_2 it is true that

$$E(X_1 + X_2) = E(X_1) + E(X_2). \quad (1.20)$$

But if X_1 and X_2 are independent, Eq. (1.17) can be used to show that

$$\mathrm{Var}\,(X_1 + X_2) = \mathrm{Var}\,(X_1) + \mathrm{Var}\,(X_2). \quad (1.21)$$

When we discuss particular probability density functions it will be seen that sums of many independent random variables have some other nice properties.

1.3 Correlation. Correlation is a property of two random variables which is similar to, but different from independence. The correlation between two random variables X_1 and X_2 is defined as

$$\rho_{X_1, X_2} = \frac{\text{Cov}\,(X_1, X_2)}{\sqrt{\text{Var}\,(X_1)\,\text{Var}\,(X_2)}} \tag{1.22}$$

where Cov stands for the *covariance* defined as

$$\text{Cov}\,(X_1, X_2) = E\{[X_1 - E(X_1)][X_2 - E(X_2)]\} = E[X_1 X_2] - E[X_1]E[X_2]. \tag{1.23}$$

The correlation coefficient ρ can take on values between plus and minus 1 and the variables are said to be uncorrelated when their correlation coefficient vanishes. It is apparent that independence implies lack of correlation. However, if the variables are uncorrelated, Eq. (1.18) is known to be satisfied *only* for the particular functions $g(X_1) = X_1 - E(X_1)$ and $h(X_2) = X_2 - E(X_2)$. Thus uncorrelated random variables are not necessarily statistically independent.

1.4 Gaussian Random Variables. Thus far we have examined the definitions and some of the properties of probability distribution and density functions and the expected value of a function of random variables. There is an endless variety of possible probability distributions which satisfy Eq. (1.2), but a few particular ones are especially important. The most important distribution is the *Gaussian* or *normal distribution* which arises frequently in physical problems, is relatively easy to manipulate mathematically, and has been studied in great detail by statisticians.

The Gaussian density function for a single random variable X is given by

$$p_X(x) = \frac{1}{\sqrt{2\pi\sigma^2}} \exp\left[-\frac{(x-m)^2}{2\sigma^2}\right] \tag{1.24}$$

where $E(X) = m$ and $\text{Var}\,(X) = \sigma^2$. Equation (1.24) shows that a Gaussian distribution is completely determined by its first two moments—a situation which does not generally apply to other distributions. The fact that many observed random variables appear to have a Gaussian distribution is explained in terms of the previously mentioned summing of independent microscopic effects. This explanation is called the *Central Limit Theorem* and it states that a *sum of independent random variables* will itself be a random variable whose density function will approach a Gaussian one as the number of variables being summed approaches infinity. A proof of this theorem requires the additional assumption of fairly weak restrictions on the distributions of the variables being summed.

Several random variables are said to have a joint Gaussian distribution if their joint density function is of the form

$$p_{X_1,\ldots,X_n}(x_1,\ldots,x_n) = \frac{1}{(2\pi)^{n/2}\,|K|^{1/2}} \exp\left[-\frac{1}{2}\sum_{j,i=1}^{n}(x_j - m_j)k^{ji}(x_i - m_i)\right] \tag{1.25}$$

where

$$m_j = E(X_j); \quad \text{and} \quad k_{ji} = \operatorname{Cov}(X_j, X_i)$$

and k^{ji} is the j, i element of the inverse of the matrix K whose elements are k_{ji}. Notice that an n-dimensional Gaussian density is completely described by n first-order moments and $[n(n-1)]/2$ second-order moments, or a total of $[n(n+1)]/2$ numbers. The central limit theorem also has a multidimensional form. If we think of a multidimensional joint distribution as describing the properties of the coordinates of an n-dimensional vector, then a sum of a large number of independent random vectors will approach a Gaussian vector as the number of summands increases.

The following is a list of some of the many nice properties possessed by Gaussian variables and vectors.

1. If several random variables have a joint Gaussian distribution then their sum is also a Gaussian variable. If the summands are independent then the variance of the sum is the sum of the variances. Moreover, any linear combination of such Gaussian variables is Gaussian.
2. The conditional distribution of some of a set of jointly Gaussian variables, conditioned on observation of the rest, is also Gaussian.
3. The conditional expectation of one out of a set of jointly Gaussian variables, conditioned on observations of the rest, is a linear function of the observations.
4. There is a unique set of Gaussian variables corresponding to mean values m_1 and covariances k_{ij}; $i, j = 1, 2, \ldots, n$.
5. A sum of many independent random variables (vectors) is a variable (vector) with an approximately Gaussian distribution (joint distribution).

1.5 Random Processes and Sequences. Many random physical phenomena such as noise voltages and wind gust velocities can be described as random time functions. These random functions are classified as either sequences or processes. A *random* or *stochastic sequence* is a set of random variables X_i where the index i may take on all integer values from minus to plus infinity. This kind of sequence can be characterized by its joint density functions.

$$p_{X_i, X_j, \ldots, X_m}(x_i, x_j, \ldots, x_m) \tag{1.26}$$

for all possible sets of variables chosen from the sequence. Since the variables X_i are labeled with integers there is an implicit ordering which can naturally be associated with the flow of time. Thus X_i can be thought of as $X(t_i)$ where t_i represents i seconds after some arbitrary time origin. The time nature of a random sequence is emphasized by writing a typical joint density function like that of expression (1.26) as

$$p_X(x_i, x_j, \ldots, x_m; t_i, t_j, \ldots, t_m). \tag{1.27}$$

The complexity of the description of an infinity of random variables can be reduced in many useful cases in which the random sequence can be shown to satisfy certain additional restrictions. One such restriction is that of *stationarity*. A random sequence is said to be *stationary of order k* if all of its joint density functions of k random variables $X_i, X_j, \ldots, X_m$ have the property

$$p_X(x_i, x_j, \ldots, x_m; t_i, t_j, \ldots, t_m) = p_X(x_i, x_j, \ldots, x_m; t_{i+k}, \ldots, t_{m+k}). \tag{1.28}$$

Equation (1.28) expresses the fact that the joint density function is independent of an arbitrary time origin, and depends only on the amount of time separating the variables. A sequence which is stationary of all orders is said to be *strictly stationary*.

A sequence whose variables have Gaussian joint densities of all orders is called a *Gaussian sequence*. Recalling the observation that a Gaussian joint density is completely specified by the means and covariances of the jointly distributed variables, it is clear that if these means and covariances are independent of a time origin then the sequence is strictly stationary. We will see that in many applications the only properties of a sequence which are of interest are its means and covariances so that even if the sequence is not Gaussian we would benefit from having these quantities be independent of time. A sequence with these properties is said to be *wide sense stationary* and it will have a time-independent mean and a covariance function $\text{Cov}(X_i, X_j)$ which depends on i and j only as $(i - j)$. Second-order stationarity implies, but is stronger than, wide sense stationarity.

Another nice class of sequences is the set of stationary sequences which are ergodic. A stationarity sequence is termed *ergodic* if its time averages are equal to its ensemble averages. In symbols, ergodicity implies

$$\begin{aligned} &E[g(X_i, X_j, \ldots, X_m)] \\ &= \int_{-\infty}^{\infty} g(x_i, x_j, \ldots, x_m) p_X(x_i, x_j, \ldots, x_m; t_i, t_j, \ldots, t_m)\, dx_i\, dx_j \cdots dx_m \qquad (1.29) \\ &= \lim_{N\to\infty} \frac{1}{2N+1} \sum_{k=-N}^{N} g(X_{i+k}, X_{j+k}, \ldots, X_{m+k}). \end{aligned}$$

We could also speak of the order of ergodicity in terms of the number of random variables appearing in Eq. (1.29). Since the summation is independent of time, it is clear that a sequence *must* be stationary of order k if it is to be ergodic of order k. Some of the special significance of ergodicity lies in the fact that a single sample of an ergodic sequence can be used to estimate the statistical properties of the sequence.

1.6 Random Processes. A random or stochastic *process* is much like a random sequence, but differs from the latter in that a process $X(t)$ defines a random variable for each real number t, rather than for integral values of t. It is tempting to think of a random process as the limiting case of a random sequence for which the time between random variables is made to approach zero. This kind of limiting operation cannot generate all random processes, since there is a larger infinity of real numbers than of integers, but it will be an adequate definition of random processes for our purposes.

Random processes are subject to the same kinds of classification as were listed for sequences, e.g., stationary, wide sense stationary, Gaussian, ergodic. With the exception of "ergodic," all of these terms were defined for sequences as conditions on the joint density functions of the variables defined by the sequence $X(t)$ as various values were assigned to the parameter t. These definitions are extended to include processes by letting t take on noninteger values. An *ergodic process* is one which satisfies

$$E[g(X(t))] = \lim_{T\to\infty} \frac{1}{2T} \int_{-T}^{T} g[X(t)]\, dt. \tag{1.30}$$

Equation (1.30) parallels the ergodicity condition for sequences with a time averaging integral replacing the sum in Eq. (1.29).

1.7 Power Spectral Density and Autocovariance. The engineer is particularly interested in spectral or frequency distribution properties of time waves because of the availability of linear system design techniques which utilize spectral decompositions. It is not generally possible to apply the familiar Fourier series or integral analysis to a random process. However, we can define a *power spectral density* which describes how the *power* in a random wave is distributed with respect to frequency. The power spectral density $\Phi(\omega)$ of a time wave is defined by saying that its integral over any radian frequency range is 2π times the wave's mean square value in that frequency band. A wave's mean square value in a band is the mean square value of the response of a band-pass filter which has the given time wave as its input when the filter has a unity transfer function over the given range of frequencies and zero response to other frequencies.

There is a natural correspondence between this power spectral density and the time variation of the wave which it describes. A time function whose amplitude varies rapidly in time will have a power spectral density which has substantial area at high frequencies. A time domain representation of the fluctuation characteristics of a process is given by its *autocovariance* (often called autocorrelation) function $R(\tau)$.† For a stationary process $R(\tau)$ is defined as

$$R(\tau) = E[X(t)X(t+\tau)]. \tag{1.31}$$

† Note that $R(\tau)$ as defined is not truly a covariance function if the process is not zero mean: and even if the process is zero mean $R(\tau)$ is not a *correlation* function since it is generally *not* true that $R(\tau)$ will satisfy the normalization $R(0) = 1$.

If $X(t)$ is wide sense ergodic, then by definition

$$R(\tau) = \lim_{T\to\infty} \frac{1}{2T} \int_{-T}^{T} X(t)X(t+\tau)\,dt. \tag{1.32}$$

Since $R(\tau)$ and $\Phi(\omega)$ are a transform pair we can write

$$\Phi(\omega) = \int_{-\infty}^{\infty} R(\tau)\, e^{-j\omega\tau}\, dt \tag{1.33}$$

and

$$R(\tau) = \int_{-\infty}^{\infty} \Phi(\omega)\, e^{j\omega\tau}\, \frac{d\omega}{2\pi}.$$

There is not a one-to-one correspondence between a time function and a power spectral density-autocorrelation pair. As the name "power" might suggest, these descriptions of a random process are insensitive to the phase relations among the various frequency components. Thus many different time waves may have the same power spectral density.

In the following sections of this chapter the performance of filter and control systems in random environments is analyzed using the statistical terms and relations which have been enumerated here.

2. Minimum Loss Function Designs

A discussion of optimum control systems presupposes the definition of a quantitative measure of performance. If the system is attempting to keep a set of output variables at the same values as the respective members of a set of reference signals, then the errors between output and reference signals can be used to measure system performance. A loss function combines these errors to form a single number which reflects the relative importance of errors in various variables, and the relative importance of different size errors. For example, if $y_1(t)$ and $y_2(t)$ are outputs whose respective references are $r_1(t)$ and $r_2(t)$, then

$$2[y_1(t) - r_1(t)]^2 + [y_2(t) - r_2(t)]^2$$

is an instantaneous loss function which weights errors in the first component more than errors in the second, and which emphasizes big errors.

If the outputs and references are random processes then it makes sense to define a loss function which involves statistical averaging. A large body of knowledge has been developed concerning optimum systems when some of the pertinent variables are random and the loss function is an expectation. Often the computational complexity obscures the essential features of these problems. We will try to expose the fundamental statistical aspects with a minimum of complex detail.

Optimum estimation appears in many guises in control literature and has very simple cases which reveal many properties of the more general forms of the problem. One such problem considers trying to find the best estimate of a random variable Z given the value of a dependent variable X. If one were tracking a satellite, X might be a noisy observation of its present angular position $\theta(t)$, i.e.,

$$X = \theta(t) + N$$

where N is a random noise variable. The desired variable Z might be chosen to be $\theta(t + \tau)$, the satellite's position τ seconds in the future. If the satellite were known to have a constant angular velocity ω, then

$$Z = X - N + \omega\tau. \tag{2.1}$$

However, the unknown position $\theta(t)$ and N are random variables so that Eq. (2.1) cannot be used to evaluate Z exactly. We will assume that N is a zero mean random variable with variance σ^2, and then we can talk about trying to make a good estimate of Z.

This problem is not strictly speaking a control problem since there is no fixed plant whose dynamics constrain the estimate. We will later discuss similar, true control problems such as directing an antenna with inertia, motor time constants, etc., at the satellite. However, the present kind of unconstrained estimation problem is often encountered by control engineers, and sometimes an optimum controller can be decomposed into an optimum estimator followed by an optimum deterministic controller (Section 5).

A performance criterion must be chosen in order to judge the relative effectiveness of various satellite position estimators. We will start by using the commonest criterion of good estimation, namely the mean square error. This criterion averages the square of the difference between the estimate $\hat{Z}$ and the actual value Z over the ensemble of all possible combinations of X and Z. The loss for any $\hat{Z}$ is

$$L = E[(Z - \hat{Z})^2].$$

Evaluation of the expectation requires the use of the joint density function of X and Z. Using conditional densities we could write L as

$$L = E\{E[(Z - \hat{Z})^2 \mid X]\} \tag{2.2}$$

where the inner expectation is the mean square error considering all values of Z and $\hat{Z}$ for a given value of X.

A good estimate is one which minimizes L, but if the conditional expectation is minimized for each value of X its average over all values of X will also be a minimum. Remember that $\hat{Z}$ is to be based on the observed value of X; it is $\hat{Z}(X)$ and it is a deterministic constant $\hat{z}(x)$ once X is known to have the value x. The plan is then to choose the constant $\hat{z}(x)$ to minimize

$$\int_{-\infty}^{\infty} [z - \hat{z}(x)]^2 p_{Z\mid X}(z \mid x)\, dz.$$

The minimization is easy to carry out after the variable of integration is changed to w where $w = z - E(Z \mid x)$. We then have

$$E[(Z - \hat{Z})^2 \mid X \mid = \int_{-\infty}^{\infty} [w + E(Z \mid x) - \hat{z}]^2 p_{Z\mid X}[w + E(Z \mid x)]\, dw.$$

The integral simplifies to

$$E[(Z - \hat{Z})^2 \mid X] = \int_{-\infty}^{\infty} w^2 p_{Z\mid X}[w + E(Z \mid x)]\, dw + [E(Z \mid x) - \hat{z}]^2$$

due to the fact that w is a zero mean random variable. The value of $\hat{z}$ which minimizes the mean square error is clearly

$$\hat{z}(x) = E(Z \mid x). \tag{2.3}$$

This formal result states that if we knew the conditional probability law $p_{Z\mid X}(z \mid x)$, its mean would be the best estimate.

The information assumed to be given in the satellite estimation problem is sufficient to compute the required density $p_{Z\mid X}$. From Eq. (1.13)

$$p_{Z\mid X}(z \mid x) = p_{X\mid Z}(x \mid z) p_Z(z)/p_X(x), \tag{2.4}$$

where

$$p_X(x) = \int_{-\infty}^{\infty} p_{X\mid Z}(x \mid z) p_Z(z)\, dz.$$

The statistical independence of $\theta(t)$ and N can be used to show that

$$p_{X\mid Z}(x \mid z) = p_N(x - z + \omega\tau) \quad \text{and} \quad p_Z(z) = p_\theta(z - \omega\tau).$$

Thus the mean of the density defined in (2.4) can be evaluated for any specified p_N and p_θ. For example, Gaussian N and θ yield X and Z which are jointly Gaussian.

In the case when Z and X are jointly distributed Gaussian variables, the conditional density $p_{Z\mid X}$ is also Gaussian with a mean given by

$$E[Z \mid x] = E(Z) + \frac{\sigma_Z}{\sigma_X} \rho [x - E(X)] \tag{2.5}$$

where $\sigma_X{}^2$ and $\sigma_Z{}^2$ are the variances of X and Z and ρ is their correlation coefficient. Thus if the joint distribution of Gaussian Z and X is known, the best mean square estimate is given directly by Eq. (2.5). We will refer later to the fact that

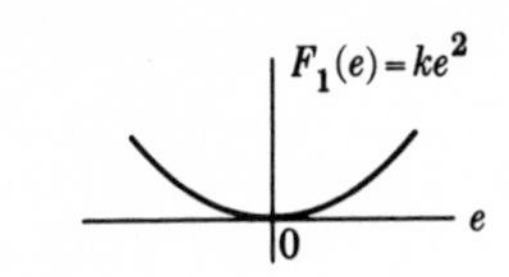

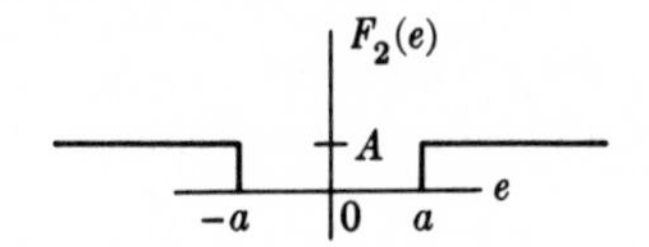

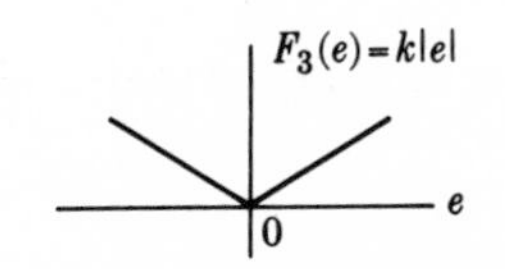

FIGURE 1. Typical error functions.

Eqs. (2.4) and (2.5) show that the best mean square estimate is a *linear* function of the observation x, plus some constant which can be determined in advance of the observation.

2.1 Other Loss Functions. The conditional mean has been shown to be an estimate which minimizes the expected value of the square of the error. We can also show that this estimator is often best for minimizing the expected value of many other functions $F(e)$ of the error. This class of functions consists of those which are symmetrical about $e = 0$ and are nondecreasing as $|e|$ increases. See Fig. 1. The best mean square estimator, the conditional mean, is also best for this class of $F(e)$ functions if the conditional density of Z given X is *symmetrical* for all X and either

(1) $F(e)$ is also a convex function of e; or
(2) the conditional density is also unimodal.

A *convex* function is one which satisfies

$$F(e + a) + F(e - a) \geqslant 2F(e). \tag{2.6}$$

That is, all points on a line segment connecting two points on the $F(e)$ curve will be on or above the curve. $F(e) = e^2$ is an example of a convex function.

A *unimodal* function is one which has only one relative maximum point. It is easy to see that if a density function has even symmetry about some point and is unimodal, then the mode, or maximum point, is the symmetry point. In this case the mode will also be the mean value of the random variable which is described by the density. A Gaussian conditional density function is an example of a symmetrical and unimodal one.

There are several methods of proving these results [2, 19, 24]. We will follow the approach of Lorens and Viterbi [19] which begins by writing the symmetrical condition density as

$$p_{Z|X}(z \mid x) = g[z - S(x), x] = g[S(x) - z, x] \tag{2.7}$$

where $S(x)$ is the symmetry point which may be a function of the conditioning variable x. The conditional expectation to be minimized is then

$$L(\hat{z}) = \int_{-\infty}^{\infty} F(z - \hat{z})g(z - S, x)\, dz. \tag{2.8}$$

If we let $\hat{z}$ be $(S + u)$, an estimate displaced u units from the symmetry point, then Eq. (2.8) becomes

$$L(S + u) = \int_{-\infty}^{\infty} F(z - S - u)g(z - S, x)\, dz. \tag{2.9}$$

The variable of integration in Eq. (2.9) can be changed to $z' = 2S - z$ so that

$$L(S + u) = \int_{-\infty}^{\infty} F[z' - (S - u)]g(z' - S, x)\, dz' \tag{2.10}$$

where use has also been made of the symmetries of the functions F and g.

A comparison of Eqs. (2.9) and (2.10) shows that

$$L(S + u) = L(S - u) \tag{2.11}$$

so that $\hat{z} = S$ is a stationary point of $L(\hat{z})$ which either minimizes or maximizes the average loss. We will use separate arguments for proving that $\hat{z} = S$ provides a minimizing optimum in each of the two cases.

Case 1. Convex $F(e)$. From Eq. (2.8) we can write L in terms of a new variable of integration $z' = (z - S)$ as

$$L(\hat{z}) = \int_{-\infty}^{\infty} F(z' + S - \hat{z})g(z', x)\, dz'. \tag{2.12}$$

The symmetry of F allows the integral to be rewritten as

$$L(\hat{z}) = \int_{0}^{\infty} [F(z' + S - \hat{z}) + F(z' - S + \hat{z})]g(z', x)\, dz' \tag{2.13}$$

and the convexity of F [Eq. (2.6)] implies that

$$L(\hat{z}) \geqslant \int_0^\infty 2F(z')g(z', x)\,dz' = L(S). \tag{2.14}$$

The proof for Case 1 is complete.

Case 2. *Unimodal* $p_{Z \mid X}$. The unimodal assumption means that the conditional density has only one hump (which must be at the point of symmetry). Thus if $z > S$ then

$$p_{Z \mid X}(z - u \mid x) \geqslant p_{Z \mid X}(z + u \mid x); \text{ for } 0 < u < z - S \tag{2.15}$$

or

$$g(z - u, x) \geqslant g(z + u); \text{ for } z > 0 \text{ and } 0 < u < z.$$

The property of F being monotonically nondecreasing in the magnitude of its argument implies

$$F'(z) \geqslant 0 \text{ for } z \geqslant 0. \tag{2.16}$$

(If $F'(z)$ is undefined, consider F as a limit of F_i which are everywhere differentiable.) The inequalities of Eqs. (2.15) and (2.16) allow us to complete the proof by showing that the mean loss using S as an estimate is no greater than the mean loss using any other estimate, i.e.

$$D \triangleq L(\hat{z}) - L(S) \geqslant 0. \tag{2.17}$$

Referring once more to Eq. (2.8) we change the variable of integration to $z' = (z - \hat{z})$ with the result

$$L(\hat{z}) = \int_{-\infty}^{\infty} F(z')g(z' + \hat{z} - S, x)\,dz'. \tag{2.18}$$

We will make the reasonable assumption that $L(\hat{z})$ is bounded for values of x which have nonzero probabilities, with the implication that as $|z'|$ approaches infinity the behavior of $F(z')$ is constrained so that

$$\lim_{|z'| \to \infty} F(z')g(z' + \hat{z} - S, x) = 0. \tag{2.19}$$

The difference D is evaluated by an integration by parts which uses the inequalities and limits stated above.

$$D = \int_{-\infty}^{\infty} F(z)[g(z + \hat{z} - S, x) - g(z, x)]\,dz. \tag{2.20}$$

Invoking the symmetry of F we get

$$D = \int_0^\infty F(z)[g(z + \hat{z} - S, x) + g(z - \hat{z} + S, x) - 2g(z, x)]\,dz \tag{2.21}$$

$$\triangleq \int_0^\infty F(z)G(z, \hat{z}, x, S)\,dz.$$

Integrating by parts

$$D = F(z)\int_0^z G(u, \hat{z}, x, S)\, du \Big|_{z=0}^{\infty} - \int_0^{\infty} F'(z) \int_0^z G(u, \hat{z}, x, S)\, du\, dz. \tag{2.22}$$

Making use of symmetry

$$\int_0^z G(u, \hat{z}, x, S)\, du = \left[\int_{-z}^{S-\hat{z}-z} + \int_{S-\hat{z}-z}^{S-\hat{z}} + \int_{S-\hat{z}}^{z}\right] g(u + \hat{z} - S, x)\, du$$
$$+ \left[-\int_{-z}^{0} - \int_{0}^{z-S+\hat{z}} - \int_{z-S+\hat{z}}^{z}\right] g(u, x)\, du. \tag{2.23}$$

In the six integrals on the right side of Eq. (2.23) the second and third cancel, respectively, with the fourth and fifth. By changing variables in the first and last we get

$$D = \int_0^{\hat{z}-S} F(z)[g(z + u, x) - g(z - u, x)]\, du \Big|_{z=0}^{z=\infty}$$
$$- \int_0^{\infty} F'(z) \int_0^{\hat{z}-S} [g(z + u, x) - g(z - u, x)]\, du\, dz. \tag{2.24}$$

The first term in Eq. (2.24) is zero at the lower limit by the symmetry of g and at the upper limit due to Eq. (2.19). The second term in Eq. (2.24) is positive since $F'(z) \geqslant 0$ and the inner integrand is negative over the range of integration if $z > S$ due to Eq. (2.15). The inner integrand is also negative for $z < S$ since we have shown in the preceding that $L(\hat{z})$ is symmetrical about $\hat{z} = S$.

We have shown that $D \geqslant 0$ for the assumptions of Case 2, so that the symmetry point of the conditional density is a minimizing estimate.

2.2 Properties of the Conditional Mean. Before leaving this discussion of the wide variety of problems for which the conditional mean of a random variable is its best estimate, it is worthwhile to consider some of the other properties of this quantity. Its mean value with respect to all possible sets of observations is the mean value of the desired random variable, i.e.,

$$E[E(Z \mid X)] = E(Z).$$

Equality of the mean of a random variable and the mean of its estimate is the defining property of an *unbiased* estimate. Thus the conditional mean is an unbiased estimate. The mean square value of the error resulting from use of this estimate, or the variance, since the error has a zero mean, takes on a simple form.

$$E[(Z - \hat{Z})^2] = E[(Z - E[Z \mid X])^2] = E\{E[(Z - E[Z \mid X])^2 \mid X]\}$$
$$= E(Z^2) - E(\hat{Z}^2). \tag{2.25}$$

2.3 Summary. This section on optimum estimates has presented a derivation of the result that the best estimate of a random variable is often the mean of its conditional probability distribution *given* the observation. The best estimator is then a device which knows enough about the statistics of the observation and desired variable so it can produce the conditional mean for each possible observation. The next section restates the optimum estimation problem in a less general way, but in a way which leads to design procedures which require less prior information about the random behavior of the desired variable and the observation.

Up to this point, the available data have consisted of a single observation. However, the formal derivations never made any use of the nature of X. It was never a variable of differentiation or integration. Therefore, we can easily extend the conclusions concerning the conditional mean to the general case where the conditioning data are a finite or denumerable set of numbers, or even a continuum of values. Despite the great generality of these results it is difficult to make direct use of them since at this time little is known about relating the symmetry of the conditional density of a random variable to the class of data which makes up the conditioning information.

3. Linear Mean Square Error Filtering

Considerable study has been devoted to the problem of trying to generate conditional mean value estimates, but a great many results in optimum estimation theory have been developed for the more specialized problem of optimum *linear* estimation. The constraint to linear estimators means that if $\hat{z}(x)$ is a linear estimate of Z based on the observation x then

$$\hat{z}(ax_1 + bx_2) = a\hat{z}(x_1) + b\hat{z}(x_2) \tag{3.1}$$

for any constants a and b. The mathematician is interested in linear estimation because it yields interesting results, and the engineer likes this approach because he is experienced in analyzing and synthesizing linear systems.

We could use the formal results of Section 2 for minimum loss function design if we knew the conditional density of the desired random variable given any observation. Now we are trying to find optimum linear estimates without knowing the conditional density. In ignorance of the probabilities we must be more specific about the estimator function. This section presents a study of problems in minimum mean square error linear estimation, beginning with the case of a finite number of observations. We will find that the optimum linear estimator will require prior knowledge of only the means and covariances of the observations and the desired variable.

Let $\chi = x_1, x_2, \ldots, x_N$ be the set of observations. The best linear estimate $\hat{z}$ is then of the form

$$\hat{z}(\chi) = \sum_{i=1}^{N} a_i x_i \tag{3.2}$$

and it minimizes

$$L(\hat{Z}) = E[(Z - \hat{Z})^2]. \tag{3.3}$$

This expression can be minimized with respect to the a_i by setting its derivatives with respect to each of the a_i equal to zero and solving the resulting N simultaneous equations.

$$-E\left[2\left(Z - \sum_{i=1}^{N} a_i X_i\right) X_j\right] = 0; \quad j = 1, 2, \ldots, N \tag{3.4}$$

or

$$E(ZX_j) = \sum_{i=1}^{N} a_i E(X_i X_j).$$

The second derivative of L with respect to a_j is always positive (namely, $+2E[X_j^2]$) so that the a_i determined from Eq. (3.4) are minimizing values.

The expectation of a product of random variables, as found in Eq. (3.4), is called their *product moment*. Recall that the definition of *covariance* involves a product moment, namely

$$\text{Cov}\,(X_1, X_2) = E(X_1 X_2) - E(X_1)E(X_2).$$

It is common to call a product moment a covariance because linear estimation problems usually deal with zero random variables where the two terms are indeed synonymous. Extension of zero mean results to cases of known, nonzero mean values is usually just a matter of increased computational complexity.

We, too, will assume all random variables are zero mean, and we will define $E(X_i X_j)$ as the *auto*-covariance function of the observations, and $E(ZX_i)$ as the *cross*-covariance function of the desired random variable and the set of observations. The optimization equations (3.4) express the cross-covariance in terms of a linear combination of autocovariances. The coefficients in this representation are the same ones to be used in combining the observations into an optimum estimate. For finite N the a_i can be found from the N simultaneous covariance equations—if the covariances are known. We must know at least this much about the statistical relationships among the observations and between them and the desired random variable. It should be recognized that knowledge of the covariances (and means) is, in general, less than knowledge of the conditional density function of the desired variable, given the data.

Later on we shall make use of the interesting result that the product moment of an optimum† linear estimate and the error resulting from its use

† *Optimum* will henceforth mean in the minimum mean square error sense.

is zero. Statisticians call this error the *residual*, and they describe two random variables with zero product moment as being *orthogonal*. For the present case of a finite number of observations, orthogonality of the optimum linear estimate and its residual follows readily from the optimization equation.

$$E[\hat{Z}(\hat{Z} - Z)] = E\left[\sum_i a_i X_i \left(\sum_j a_j X_j - Z\right)\right]. \tag{3.5}$$

Bringing the expectation inside of the first summation we get

$$E[\hat{Z}(\hat{Z} - Z)] = \sum_i a_i E\left[\sum_j a_j X_i X_j - X_i Z\right] \tag{3.6}$$

The last expression vanishes since the expectation on the right equals zero for the optimum set of a_i.

3.1 Gaussian Random Variables. The ubiquitous Gaussian distribution plays an important role in linear estimation theory as well as in describing the probability laws of many physical random variables. In the section on conditional mean estimators we saw that the conditional distribution of one of two jointly Gaussian random variables, conditioned on the other one, is also a Gaussian distribution. In that case the conditional mean was proportional to the observed value of the conditioning variable, if the two variables had zero mean values [Eq. (2.5)]. That is, the minimum mean square error estimate of one of two jointly Gaussian zero mean variables, based on observing the other one, is a *linear* function of the observation. Therefore, for this all Gaussian problem, the best *linear* estimate is the best of *all possible* estimates—including nonlinear ones! Moreover, the conditional Gaussian density is symmetrical and unimodal so that this best linear estimate for the squared error loss function is best for the whole class of loss functions described in Section 2.

The equivalence of the best linear estimate and the best unrestricted estimate is maintained when the estimate is conditioned on the observation of *many* jointly Gaussian variables. To see this, we must examine the joint Gaussian density function

$$p_{X_1, X_2, \ldots, X_N}(x_1, x_2, \ldots, x_N)$$

of N *zero mean* random variables [see Eq. (1.25)]

$$p_{X_1, X_2, \ldots, X_N} = \frac{1}{(2\pi)^{N/2}\,|K|^{1/2}} \exp\left[-\frac{1}{2\,|K|} \sum_{j,i=1}^{N} K_{ji} x_j x_i\right] \tag{3.7}$$

where K is the covariance matrix with elements

$$k_{ij} = E(X_i X_j)$$

and cofactors K_{ij}. The conditional density of x_1 given all of the other x's can be found from Eq. (1.13) and matrix manipulations, with the result

$$p(x_1 \mid x_2, \ldots, x_N) = \frac{1}{[(2\pi |K|)/K_{11})]^{1/2}} \exp\left[-\frac{K_{11}}{2|K|}\left(x_1 + \sum_{j=2}^{N} \frac{K_{1j}}{K_{11}} x_j\right)^2\right] \tag{3.8}$$

Note that the conditional mean, as in the bivariate case discussed above, is a linear combination of the observations

$$E(X_1 \mid x_2, \ldots, x_N) = -\sum_{j=2}^{N} \frac{K_{1j}}{K_{11}} x_j. \tag{3.9}$$

Thus the conditional mean which is the best of all estimates coincides with the best linear estimate.

Restriction to Gaussian variables permits some elaboration on the previous result that an optimum linear estimate and its error, or residual, are orthogonal. Linear combinations of Gaussian variables are Gaussian, so that the estimate and its residual are also Gaussian. If all of the X_i have zero means, then $\hat{X}_1$ and $(\hat{X}_1 - X)$ will also be zero mean. Thus the orthogonality of these variables implies that they are uncorrelated and, for these Gaussian variables, independent.

These special results for estimating Gaussian variables form the basis for an interesting approach to synthesizing optimum linear estimators developed by R. E. Kalman. Kalman's method will be described after commenting on optimum linear estimation based on infinite sets of data and surveying the various design techniques which have followed from Wiener's pioneering work.

3.2 Infinite Sets of Observations. The optimum linear estimate for a finite number of observations becomes increasingly cumbersome to find as N grows. The method of solving for the best estimate must be modified if we want to let N become infinite. In order to formulate the problem it is necessary to find a way of expressing the statistical properties of an infinite set of data. For problems of engineering significance the observations may be members of a random sequence related to the desired variable (a denumerable set of data), or the observation may consist of a segment of a random process (a continuum of data). In these descriptions the infinite sets of random variables are indexed by the time parameter.

When the data consist of a continuous observation of a random process, say $X(t)$ for $t_1 < t < t_2$, a general linear operator on the data is a linear *functional* which can be represented by an integral of the form

$$\hat{z} = \int_{t_1}^{t_2} a(t)x(t)\,dt. \tag{3.10}$$

The distinction between a function and a functional should be carefully noted. A sum of $a_i x_i$ is a linear *function* of the x_i which gives a number $\hat{z}$ for each observed set of x_i *values*. The integral of $a(t)x(t)$ is a linear *functional* which gives a number $\hat{z}$ for each observed *function* $x(t)$.

The best estimate of Z is by definition that $\hat{Z}$ which minimizes

$$E[(Z - \hat{Z})^2]. \tag{3.11}$$

Substitution of the integral expression for Z changes the optimization problem to one of choosing $a(t)$ so as to minimize

$$E\left[\left(Z - \int_{t_1}^{t_2} a(t)X(t)\,dt\right)^2\right]. \tag{3.12}$$

(A treatment of the infinite summation form of $\hat{Z}$ would parallel the present discussion.) When only a finite set of data was used, differential calculus sufficed for finding the best set of a_i. Here we could find the optimum function $a(t)$ either by the methods of variational calculus [17, Chapter 14] or by the more general argument which follows [21].

Let h be any linear functional of $x(t)$ on the interval $t_1 < t < t_2$ which might be represented by the integral

$$h = \int_{t_1}^{t_2} w(t)x(t)\,dt. \tag{3.13}$$

Comparing h with $\hat{z}$, the *best* linear functional of $x(t)$, it is clear that

$$E[(z - \hat{z})^2] \leqslant E[(h - z)^2]. \tag{3.14}$$

(See footnote explaining new notation.†)
The right side of Eq. (3.14) can be rewritten as

$$\begin{aligned} E[(h - z)^2] &= E[(h - \hat{z} + \hat{z} - z)^2] \\ &= E[(h - \hat{z})^2] + E[(\hat{z} - z)^2] + 2E[(h - \hat{z})(\hat{z} - z)]. \end{aligned} \tag{3.15}$$

Combination of Eqs. (3.14) and (3.15) yields

$$0 \leqslant E[(h - \hat{z})^2] + 2E[(h - \hat{z})(\hat{z} - z)]. \tag{3.16}$$

At this point we make a substitution for the general functional h such that

$$h = \hat{z} + bh_1E[h_1(\hat{z} - z)] \tag{3.17}$$

where b is a real number, h_1 is any other linear functional on $x(t)$ for $t_1 < t < t_2$, and the expectation of $h_1(\hat{z} - z)$ will also be a real number.

† We have been representing random variables and processes by upper case letters Z, $X(t)$, . . . , and their sample values by lower case letters z, $x(t)$, ... The expectation operator E always has had upper case letters in its argument. Integral evaluations of expectations always have been written in terms of lower case letters. At this point we will institute the typographical simplicity of using lower case letters for both a random variable or process *and* its sample values. The context should make it clear which interpretation is intended.

Equation (3.16) then becomes

$$0 \leqslant \{E[h_1(\hat{z} - z)]\}^2[b^2E(h_1^2) + 2b]. \tag{3.18}$$

The squared expectation in Eq. (3.18) is nonnegative, but if b has a value such that

$$-\frac{2}{E(h_1^2)} < b < 0 \tag{3.19}$$

then the inequality will be violated. To prevent this situation the squared expectation must vanish. Thus Eq. (3.14) has the strong implication

$$E[h_1(\hat{z} - z)] = 0 \tag{3.20}$$

i.e., the residual must be orthogonal to any linear functional on the data. In particular, the linear functional $\hat{z}$ must satisfy the equation

$$E[\hat{z}(\hat{z} - z)] = 0 \tag{3.21}$$

which expresses the orthogonality of the best estimate and its error.

We have shown that Eq. (3.20) is a *necessary* condition on the best estimate $\hat{z}$. It is also a sufficient condition since in Eq. (3.15) we could let h_1 be the difference of linear functionals $(h - \hat{z})$. With this substitution the cross term vanishes and

$$E[(\hat{z} - z)^2] = E[(h - z)^2] - E[(h - \hat{z})^2] \leq E[(h - z)^2]. \tag{3.22}$$

An integral equation for $a(t)$ can be found by substituting the integral definitions for h_1 and $\hat{z}$ into Eq. (3.20) and interchanging the integration and expectation operations, namely

$$\int_{t_1}^{t_2} w(t)\left\{\int_{t_1}^{t_2} a(\tau)E[x(t)x(\tau)]\,d\tau - E[x(t)z]\right\} dt = 0. \tag{3.23}$$

Since every linear functional must be orthogonal to $(\hat{z} - z)$, Eq. (3.22) must hold for every $w(t)$. A necessary and sufficient condition for this general orthogonality is that $a(t)$ satisfy

$$\int_{t_1}^{t_2} a(\tau)E[x(t)x(\tau)]\,dt = E[x(t)z] \quad \text{for all } t_1 < t < t_2. \tag{3.24}$$

This same sort of derivation could have been used for finding the conditions for the minimum mean square error linear operator on finite data, and it is easy also to modify the present arguments for a denumerable amount of data. The so-called Wiener-Hopf equation (3.24) involves a finite or infinite sum, respectively, for these discrete data problems.

3.3 Covariance Functions. The expectations which appear in the integral Eq. (3.24) will be with us quite often and so the following definitions are convenient.

$$R_{XX}(t, \tau) = E[x(t)x(\tau)]$$
$$R_{XZ}(t) = E[x(t)z]. \tag{3.25}$$

Most often the desired random variable being estimated, Z, is the value of a random process $Z(\eta)$ which is related to $X(t)$. In such cases

$$R_{XZ}(t, \eta) = E[x(t)z(\eta)]. \tag{3.26}$$

In engineering literature R_{XX} is called the "autocorrelation" function of $X(t)$, but we prefer the term auto-covariance function (see page 133). From the same point of view, R_{XZ} is the cross-covariance function.

With the aid of these definitions the optimum linear operation is defined by

$$R_{XZ}(t, \eta) = \int_{t_1}^{t_2} a(\tau) R_{XX}(t, \tau)\, d\tau; \quad \text{for } t_1 < t < t_2. \tag{3.27}$$

When compared with the definition of the optimum linear estimate, the Wiener-Hopf equation (3.27) states that the best linear operation on the data is the same as the linear operation which takes the auto-covariance of the data into the cross-variance of the data process with the desired variable. The problem now is to find the function $a(\tau)$ which satisfies Eq. (3.27).

The most obvious way to solve for $a(\tau)$ is to try to solve the Wiener-Hopf integral equation directly. However, another fruitful approach is to try to find the most general, abstract linear representation of the cross-covariance in terms of the auto-covariance [21–23]. A third approach we will consider in detail uses the orthogonality relation of Eq. (3.20) to build up an iterative linear estimator for finite or denumerable data. This iterative approach is extended to continuous data by considering it as a limiting case of denumerable data.

3.4 Spectral Factorization. Many different special problems have been studied in which the specializations allow the Wiener-Hopf equation to be solved. For instance, if the limits of integration are minus and plus infinity and the random processes are stationary, then Eq. (3.27) becomes the convolution integral

$$R_{XZ}(t - \eta) = \int_{-\infty}^{\infty} a(\tau) R_{XX}(t - \tau)\, dt = \int_{-\infty}^{\infty} a(t - \tau) R_{XX}(\tau)\, d\tau. \tag{3.28}$$

This equation must be satisfied for all values of t. Therefore it is easy to find $a(\tau)$ by first taking the Fourier integral transform of both sides of Eq. (3.28) with the familiar result

$$\Phi_{XZ}(\omega) e^{-j\omega\eta} = A(\omega) \Phi_{XX}(\omega) \tag{3.29}$$

where Φ_{XX} is the power spectral density of the process $X(t)$ and Φ_{XZ} is the cross-spectral density of $X(t)$ with the process $Z(t)$. Equation (3.29) can be solved for $A(\omega)$ and the inverse Fourier transform can be applied to get

$$a(t) = \int_{-\infty}^{\infty} \frac{\Phi_{XZ}(\omega)}{\Phi_{XX}(\omega)} e^{j\omega(t-\eta)} \frac{d\omega}{2\pi}. \tag{3.30}$$

The $a(t)$ of Eq. (3.30) is the optimum weighting function for linear estimation of $Z(\eta)$ based on the observation of $X(t)$ when the linear operation is expressed in terms of the integral of Eq. (3.10) with $t_1 = -\infty$ and $t_2 = \infty$. It is not surprising then to find that $a(t)$ is a function of η, the time at which the Z process value is desired.

Prediction of the value of a random process is usually desired continuously in time. That is, we feed $X(t)$ into a linear system whose output is always desired to be the prediction of Z at a time γ seconds in the future. If T is taken as the present time then $\gamma = \eta - T$. We have chosen X and Z to be a stationary process so that the best linear operator for a fixed γ should not be a function of time. The output of a general linear, time-invariant operator can be written as the convolution integral

$$y(T) = \int_{-\infty}^{\infty} h(T - \tau)x(\tau)\, dt \tag{3.31}$$

where $h(T - \tau)$ is the output at time T resulting from a unit impulse input at time τ. Comparing Eqs. (3.10) and (3.31) we can identify $a(\tau)$ as $h(T - \tau)$ with a resulting optimum linear estimation of $Z(T + \gamma)$ written as

$$\hat{z}(T + \gamma) = \int_{-\infty}^{\infty} h(T - \tau)x(\tau)\, d\tau. \tag{3.32}$$

However, this definition of $h(T - t)$ in terms of Eq. (3.30) may result in a linear predictor which is not physically realizable in the sense that the estimate formed in Eq. (3.32) may, in general, make use of *future* values of $x(\tau)$, when $\tau > T$. Wiener filter theory for stationary processes makes use of transform methods to solve the integral equation and get realizable filters.

A filter which uses only past input values can be assured by restricting the range of integration to values of t less than T, the time at which the estimate is being made

$$\hat{z}(T + \gamma) = \int_{-\infty}^{T} h(T - \tau)x(\tau)\, d\tau. \tag{3.33}$$

An equivalent condition consists of integrating over-all values of t but requiring $h(t)$ to be zero for negative arguments. The spectral factorization technique for getting realizable impulse responses begins by extending the domain of the power spectral density functions to include complex arguments $\omega = -js$ where s may be any complex number [17]. Then

$$S_{XX}(s) = \Phi_{XX}(\omega)\big|_{\omega=-js} \tag{3.34}$$

and if $S_{XX}(s)$ is rational in s it is factored into the form

$$S_{XX}(s) = S_{XX}^{+}(s) S_{XX}^{-}(s) \tag{3.35}$$

so that $S_{XX}^{+}(s)$ has all of its poles and zeros in the left half of the complex s-plane and $S_{XX}^{-}(s)$ has all of its poles and zeros in the right half-plane. It follows that $S_{XX}^{+}(s) = S_{XX}^{-}(-s)$.

Using the foregoing notation, the best system function for filtering and predicting γ seconds into the future is

$$H_{OPT}(\omega)\big|_{\omega=-js} = G_{OPT}(s) = \frac{1}{S_{XX}^{+}(s)}\left[\frac{S_{XZ}(s)e^{\gamma s}}{S_{XX}^{-}(s)}\right]_{+} \tag{3.36}$$

The subscript + in Eq. (3.36) assumes that the quantity in the brackets can be written as

$$A(s) = A_{+}(s) + A_{-}(s) \tag{3.37}$$

where the inverse Laplace transform of A_{+} exists only for $t > 0$ and that of A_{-} exists only for $t < 0$. A_{+} is then the sum of the terms in the partial fraction expansion of A which have poles in the left half-plane.

If the impulse response given by Eq. (3.30) is realizable, then the minimum mean square error is expressible as

$$\int_{-j\infty}^{j\infty} \frac{ds}{2\pi j}\left[S_{ZZ}(s) - \frac{S_{XZ}(s)S_{ZX}(s)}{S_{ZZ}(s)}\right]. \tag{3.38}$$

Otherwise there is an additional mean square error of

$$\int_{-j\infty}^{j\infty} \frac{ds}{2\pi j}\left[\frac{S_{XZ}(s)e^{\gamma s}}{S_{XX}^{-}(s)}\right]_{-}. \tag{3.39}$$

3.5 An Interesting Example. This quick review of standard results is presented for future comparison with other points of view on optimum linear filtering. A simple example will help emphasize the steps necessary for getting the optimum impulse response. We will find the best filter and predictor of $Z(T + \gamma)$ from an observation of $Z(t)$ plus independent noise $N(t)$ over the interval $-\infty < t < T$.

The respective autocovariance functions are chosen to be

$$R_{ZZ}(\tau) = e^{-a|\tau|} \quad \text{and} \quad R_{NN}(\tau) = \frac{K}{b}\, e^{-b|\tau|}. \tag{3.40}$$

Each of these random processes could be generated as the output of a suitable low pass RC filter whose input would be a "white" process with auto-covariance.

$$R_{ii}(\tau) = \delta(\tau)\sigma_i^2. \tag{3.41}$$

The power spectral densities corresponding to R_{ZZ} and R_{NN} are, in terms of the variable s.

$$S_{ZZ}(s) = \frac{2a}{a^2 - s^2} \quad \text{and} \quad S_{NN}(s) \frac{2K}{b^2 - s^2}. \tag{3.42}$$

The independence of signal and noise means that

$$S_{XX} = S_{ZZ} + S_{NN}. \tag{3.43}$$

Substitution and factorization yield

$$S_{XX}^{+}(s)S_{XX}^{-}(s) = \frac{K_1(K_2 + s)}{(a + s)(b + s)} \frac{K_1(K_2 - s)}{(a - s)(b - s)} \tag{3.44}$$

where

$$K_1^2 = 2a + 2K \quad \text{and} \quad K_2^2 = \frac{ab^2 + Ka^2}{a + K}.$$

After the factors of Eq. (3.44) are substituted into (3.36), a Laplace inversion gives the result

$$h_{OPT}(t) = \frac{a(b + a)e^{-a\gamma}}{(a + K)(K_2 + a)} \{[be^{-K_2 t} - K_2 e^{-K_2 t}]u(t) + \delta(t)\} \tag{3.45}$$

where $u(t)$ and $\delta(t)$ are the unit step and unit impulse functions, respectively.

The filter of Eq. (3.45) is especially interesting in the case when there is no noise, $K = 0$. As K approaches zero, K_2 approaches b and the predictor becomes

$$h_{OPT}(t) = e^{-a\gamma}\, \delta(t). \tag{3.46}$$

This predictor has all past observations of the signal process available, but its best prediction is merely a constant multiplier times the present observation! A signal random process which has this prediction property is known as a (wide sense) Markoff process. Moreover, if one asks what kinds of auto-covariance functions can a Markoff random process possess, the conclusion is Doob's theorem [7] that $R_{ZZ}(\tau)$ must be of the form $Ce^{-a|\tau|}$.

One proof of Doob's theorem argues that if the best realizable predictor for a process at time T is $K\,\delta(t - T)$, then the Wiener-Hopf equation says

$$R_{ZZ}(T + \gamma - t) = \int_{-\infty}^{T} K\,\delta(T - \tau)R_{ZZ}(\tau - t)\,d\tau = KR_{ZZ}(T - t). \tag{3.47}$$

When Eq. (3.47) is examined for the case of $t = T$, it is seen that

$$R_{ZZ}(T + \gamma - t) = \frac{R_{ZZ}(\gamma)}{R_{ZZ}(0)} R_{ZZ}(T - t). \tag{3.48}$$

If a new function $\phi(\tau)$ is defined as

$$\frac{R_{ZZ}(\tau)}{R_{ZZ}(0)} = \phi(\tau)$$

then Eq. (3.48) implies that

$$\phi(\beta + \gamma) = \phi(\gamma)\phi(\beta). \tag{3.49}$$

It can be shown [20, p. 263] that $\phi(\tau) = e^{-a|\tau|}$ is the only continuous and even function which has the property of Eq. (3.49). The proof is complete now because all autocovariance functions of stationary processes are even, and most interesting stationary processes have continuous auto-covariance functions.† Section 4 on Feedback Filters will expand the Markoff process definition to vector-valued random processes and will take advantage of their unique estimation properties.

3.6 Gaussian Processes. Infinite sets of observations possess special properties similar to those of finite sets when all joint densities are Gaussian. The best linear estimate of a Gaussian variable based on an infinite set of jointly distributed Gaussian variables is the best of all possible estimates. (Recall again that *best* is being used to mean in the minimum mean square sense.) In the finite case we demonstrated that the conditional mean of one of a set of jointly Gaussian variables was linear in the observations of the other variables, i.e.,

$$E(Z \mid x_1, x_2, \ldots, x_N) = \sum_i^N a_{iN} x_i. \tag{3.50}$$

Double subscript notation is necessary on the a_{iN} since the weighting of one observation may depend on which other observations are available. This argument can be extended to denumerably infinite sets by letting N approach infinity.

The conditional mean of Z is the best mean square estimate of Z and it follows that as N approaches infinity

$$E[Z - E(Z \mid x_1, x_2, \ldots, x_N)]^2 < \infty. \tag{3.51}$$

An increase in the N of expression (3.51) cannot increase the value of the mean square error, since more data cannot lead to a worse estimate, on the average. Thus the sequence of conditional means converges in a mean square sense. Any finite set of Gaussian variables has a linear conditional mean, and the convergence of the sequence assures that the conditional mean exists in the limit as N approaches infinity. This limiting conditional mean must also be linear in the observations x_i.

We can also argue that the conditional mean is linear in the data when the observation is a segment of a Gaussian random *process*. For a large class of

† $R(\tau)$ for a stationary process is continuous for all τ if it is continuous at $\tau = 0$.

processes, the values of the process at some denumerable set of times which are dense in the time interval (e.g., all rational times in the interval) completely specify the process. The values of a Gaussian process at these times will be Gaussian random variables. We have just seen that the conditional mean of Z given the values of a denumerable set of jointly Gaussian variables is linear in the observed values of these variables. A linear functional of the form

$$\int_{t_1}^{t_2} a(\tau)x(\tau)\,d\tau \tag{3.52}$$

is general enough to form the proper linear combination of the values of $x(\tau)$ at these denumerable times. Thus, even observations of a Gaussian *process* are best processed by a linear operation when the aim is to estimate a correlated Gaussian random variable.

3.7 Non-Gaussian Processes. The general formulation of the optimum mean square linear estimation problem led to the Wiener-Hopf equation which involved the observed data only in terms of covariance functions. These covariance functions are only partial descriptions of the random data, and can be computed from the knowledge of only the second-order joint densities of the process. In general, second-order joint densities are not a complete process description, but in the special case of Gaussian processes all higher order densities are expressible in terms of second-order ones. [Refer to Eq. (1.26) in which the general multivariable Gaussian density function is defined in terms of a *covariance* matrix.]

If observations of a non-Gaussian sequence or process $X(t)$ are to be used for estimating a random variable $Z(\eta)$, the best linear operation on the data can be found by assuming that $X(t)$ is Gaussian with the same auto-covariance function and cross-covariance with $Z(\eta)$. This apparently trivial subterfuge is justifiable since the Wiener-Hopf equation is independent of higher order joint densities. The advantage to be gained is that when searching for the best linear operation on $X(t)$, the second-order equivalent Gaussian processes X_g and Z_g can be used to advantage. The best linear estimator operating on $X_g(t)$ will be the best of all estimators of $Z_g(\eta)$, i.e., it will generate the conditional mean of $Z_g(\eta)$. The orthogonality of $\hat{Z}$ and $[\hat{Z}(X_g) - Z_g]$,

$$E\{\hat{Z}[\hat{Z}(X_g) - Z_g]\} = 0 \tag{3.53}$$

implies that the estimate and the equivalent Gaussian residual are *independent* Gaussian random variables.

3.8 Recapitulation. Under the heading of minimum loss function systems we looked at problems of minimizing the expected value of a function of the error between a random variable and an estimate of it. We showed how the best estimate for a squared error loss function was best for a whole class of loss functions when the conditional probability density of the desired random variable (given the observed data) satisfied some symmetry conditions.

The Gaussian sequence and process were introduced and it was shown that the search for the optimum estimate of a correlated Gaussian variable based on the observation of such a sequence or process could take advantage of the loss function generalization theorem.

The general minimum mean square error estimate turned out to be the conditional mean of the desired random variable given the observations. In order to get a solution which might require less prior information, and which might be easier to implement, we looked for the best *linear* estimate. Restriction of the allowable operations on the data to the class of linear operations led to many special results, such as orthogonality of the best estimate and its error, and the nice property that for Gaussian observations and desired variable the conditional mean is linear in the observations.

It should be reiterated that this section has dealt with optimum estimation—not truly a control problem since there has been no fixed system to be driven. We will ultimately have something to say about optimum control problems, but it must be preceded by a further discussion of estimation.

A multitude of variations on the optimum estimation problem, linear and nonlinear, have been considered and solved. Zadeh [28] supplies a good survey and bibliography of this field.

One quite general development is due to Kalman and includes cases where the data is discrete or continuous, stationary or nonstationary, and of an amount which is finite, infinite, or growing. In addition, this work, which forms the basis for the rest of this article, is developed in terms of the control ideas of state vectors and is connected to the deterministic problem of finding an optimum regulator which minimizes an integral squared error type of loss function.

4. Feedback Filters

In this section we will combine several of the previous results into a linear feedback filtering scheme in the manner of Kalman [12, 13, 15]. First, the discussion will be confined to Gaussian variables, processes, or sequences since we have seen that any non-Gaussian optimal linear filtering problem has the same best filter as that for an associated Gaussian problem. We will show that for the case of Gaussian sequences the best estimate at any time point can be generated by a linear, discrete feedback system. The observation will be the system input, and it will be combined with a feedback function of the previous best estimate.

The following simple example will motivate the subsequent more general results. The best estimate of a zero mean Gaussian random variable z with variance σ_z^2 is to be determined from a sequence of observations x_i defined by

$$x_i = mz + n_i \tag{4.1}$$

where m is a known constant and the n_i are independent, zero mean Gaussian random variables with variances σ_n^2. The m factor is a simple gain constant, and n_i is a Gaussian "white" noise sequence. During one experiment or sequence of observations, the value of z is fixed, although unknown. If we had only one observation then this problem would be much like the earlier one of satellite angle estimation in Section 2.

A feedback approach to this problem is formulated by assuming that we have $\hat{z}_{i-1}$, the best estimate of z based on the past sequence of N observations $x_{i-1}, x_{i-2}, \ldots, x_{i-N}$. We would like to improve this estimate and get $\hat{z}_i$ after the new piece of information x_i arrives. The fact that all the random variables in the problem are Gaussian assures us that the best linear estimate is the conditional expectation, i.e.,

$$\hat{z}_i = E(z \mid \chi_i) = \sum_{j=i}^{i-N} \alpha_j x_j \tag{4.2}$$

where we have let a Greek letter χ_i represent the set $(x_i, x_{i-1}, \ldots, x_{i-N})$.

We will also make use of $\hat{x}_i$, the best estimate of x_i based on the *previous* observations. This best estimate will also be a conditional mean

$$\hat{x}_i = E(x_i \mid \chi_{i-1}) \tag{4.3}$$

or

$$\hat{x}_i = E(mz + n_i \mid \chi_{i-1}) = m\hat{z}_{i-1}$$

where use has been made of Eq. (4.1) and the independence and zero means of the n_i. The error which results from using a best estimate will be designated by $\sim$, namely

$$\tilde{z}_i = (z - \hat{z}_i) \quad \text{and} \quad \tilde{x}_i = (x_i - \hat{x}_i). \tag{4.4}$$

After x_i has been observed, the new best estimate of z is

$$\hat{z}_i = E(\hat{z}_{i-1} + \tilde{z}_{i-1} \mid \chi_i) = \hat{z}_{i-1} + E(\tilde{z}_{i-1} \mid \chi_i). \tag{4.5}$$

The last step follows from the fact that $\hat{z}_{i-1}$ is a deterministic function of the observed quantities $x_{i-1}, x_{i-2}, \ldots, x_{i-N}$. We see from Eq. (4.5) that the problem of finding the best estimate after x_i is observed becomes one of finding the best estimate of the error in the previous estimate, namely†

$$\hat{\tilde{z}}_{i-1} = E(\tilde{z}_{i-1} \mid \chi_i). \tag{4.6}$$

† The reader should be alert to the easily misunderstood notation which uses a caret (^) to signify the conditional mean, because different variables with the subscript i are conditioned on different data: $\hat{z}_i$ is conditioned on $(x_i, x_{i-1}, \ldots, x_{i-N})$; $\hat{x}_i$ is conditioned on $(x_{i-1}, x_{i-2}, \ldots, x_{i-N})$; and $\hat{\tilde{z}}_i$ is conditioned on $(x_{i+1}, x_i, \ldots, x_{i-N})$.

4.1 Preview of Results. We *will show* that $\hat{\tilde{z}}_{i-1}$, the best estimate of the previous error, is a function only of $\tilde{x}_i$, the error in estimating the new observation. Specifically,

$$\hat{\tilde{z}}_{i-1} = a_i \tilde{x}_i$$

so that

$$\hat{z}_i = \hat{z}_{i-1} + a_i \tilde{x}_i \tag{4.7}$$

where

$$a_i = \frac{mP_{i-1}}{m^2 P_{i-1} + \sigma_n^2}.$$

The P_i in Eq. (4.7) is the variance of $\tilde{z}_i$, or equivalently P_i is the mean square error of the ith estimate of the zero mean random variable z. The solution will show that P_i can be generated by a recursion relation

$$P_i = (1 - a_i m) P_{i-1}. \tag{4.8}$$

4.2 Solution. The derivation of the foregoing results will make use of the fact that for any set of α_j there are suitable constants a_j such that

$$\hat{z}_i = \sum_{j=i}^{i-N} \alpha_j x_j = \sum_{j=i}^{i-N} a_j \tilde{x}_j. \tag{4.9}$$

It is easy to outline a procedure for establishing Eq. (4.9) as follows. The linear relation between $\hat{x}_i$ and the previous x_j is

$$\hat{x}_i = \sum_{j=i-1}^{i-N} b_j x_j \tag{4.10}$$

and it leads to

$$\begin{aligned} \sum_{j=i}^{i-N} \alpha_j x_j &= \sum_{j=i-1}^{i-N} \alpha_j x_j + \alpha_i(\hat{x}_i + \tilde{x}_i) \\ &= \sum_{j=i-1}^{i-N} (\alpha_j + \alpha_i b_j) x_j + \alpha_i \tilde{x}_i. \end{aligned} \tag{4.11}$$

This process could be repeated successively to get the coefficients for $\tilde{x}_{i-1}$, $\tilde{x}_{i-2}$, etc., in Eq. (4.9), but we are not interested in deriving the a_j in terms of the α_j and b_j. It is sufficient to show that the two sums in Eq. (4.9) are equivalent so that observation of the set $\tilde{\chi}_i = (\tilde{x}_i, \tilde{x}_{i-1}, \ldots, \tilde{x}_{i-N})$ will lead to the same best estimates as observation of the set $\chi_i = (x_i, x_{i-1}, \ldots, x_{i-N})$. Thus the values of the a_j can be found directly from the Wiener-Hopf equation

$$E(\tilde{z}_{i-1}\tilde{x}_k) = \sum_{j=i}^{i-N} a_j E(\tilde{x}_j \tilde{x}_k); \quad i - N \leqslant k \leqslant i. \tag{4.12}$$

The solution of Eqs. (4.12) is considerably simplified by repeated use of orthogonality relations similar to Eq. (3.20) of the previous section. That equation was developed in connection with optimum linear estimation based on the observation of a segment of a random *process*, and it says that the error resulting from use of the best estimate is orthogonal to any linear functional on the data. It would be straightforward to develop the similar result for random *sequence* data which would state

$$E(h\tilde{z}_i) = 0 \tag{4.13}$$

where h is any linear combination of the data such as

$$h = \sum_{j=i}^{i-N} d_j x_j. \tag{4.14}$$

The estimate $\hat{x}_i$ is an optimum estimate too, so that it is also true that

$$E(h\tilde{x}_i) = 0 \tag{4.15}$$

for any linear combination h.

Application of Eqs. (4.13) and (4.15) to the left and right sides of (4.12) yield, respectively, that

$$E(\tilde{z}_{i-1}\tilde{x}_k) = 0 \quad \text{for } k < i \tag{4.16}$$

since when $k < i$, $\tilde{x}_k$ is trivially a linear combination of the observations $(\tilde{x}_{i-1}, \ldots, \tilde{x}_{i-N})$; and

$$E(\tilde{x}_k\tilde{x}_j) = 0; \quad j \neq k \tag{4.17}$$

because if $j > k$, then $\tilde{x}_k$ is a linear combination of the data upon which $\hat{x}_j$ is based. Thus we have the following simple set of equations for the a_j:

$$0 = a_j E(\tilde{x}_j^2); \quad j \leqslant i - 1 \tag{4.18a}$$

and

$$E(\tilde{z}_{i-1}\tilde{x}_i) = a_i E(\tilde{x}_i^2). \tag{4.18b}$$

It follows that all of the a_j are zero except for a_i, since the variance of $\tilde{x}_j$ will always be positive.

The optimum value for a_i can be expressed in terms of the given information by combining Eqs. (4.3) and (4.4) to get

$$\tilde{x}_i = m\tilde{z}_{i-1} + n_i \tag{4.19}$$

and substituting this form of $\tilde{x}_i$ into Eq. (4.18b). Use of the zero mean and independence properties of the n_i and the definition of P_i as the variance of $\tilde{z}_i$

$$P_i = E(\tilde{z}_i^2) \tag{4.20}$$

reduces the solution to

$$a_i = \frac{mP_{i-1}}{m^2P_{i-1} + \sigma_n^2}. \tag{4.21}$$

In terms of this newly found a_i the best estimate of the previous error is

$$\hat{\tilde{z}}_{i-1} = a_i \tilde{x}_i \tag{4.22}$$

and the best present estimate of z is

$$\hat{z}_i = \hat{z}_{i-1} + a_i \tilde{x}_i. \tag{4.23}$$

Note, however that the expression for a_i, Eq. (4.21), contains the covariance of the previous estimation error, a quantity which is still unknown. A recursion relation can also be developed for P_i as follows. By definition,

$$P_i = E[(z - \hat{z}_i)^2]. \tag{4.24}$$

Substitution of previous expressions for $\hat{z}_i$ and $\tilde{x}_i$ leads to

$$P_i = E[(\tilde{z}_{i-1} - a_i \tilde{x}_i)^2] = E\{[(1 - a_i m)\tilde{z}_{i-1} - a_i n_i]^2\}. \tag{4.25}$$

Finally, after substitution for a_i and some simplification using the properties of n_i, we get

$$P_i = (1 - a_i m) P_{i-1} \tag{4.26}$$

where it should be remembered that the expression for a_i involves P_{i-1}. Equations (4.21), (4.23), and (4.26) represent the recursive solution to the problem stated in connection with Eq. (4.1).

This iterative estimation problem has resulted in a nonstationary solution. Before any observations are made, z is known only to be normal with zero mean and variance σ_z^2. Thus $P_0 = \sigma_z^2$ and $\hat{z}_0 = 0$. Figure 2 shows a data processing system which employs a time-varying gain a_i to generate the sequence of best estimates from the sequence of observations.

Simplification of the variance equation (4.26) shows that

$$P_i = \frac{\sigma_n^2 P_{i-1}}{m^2 P_{i-1} + \sigma_n^2} < P_{i-1} \tag{4.27}$$

so that the mean square error decreases as time goes on. The gain a_i also

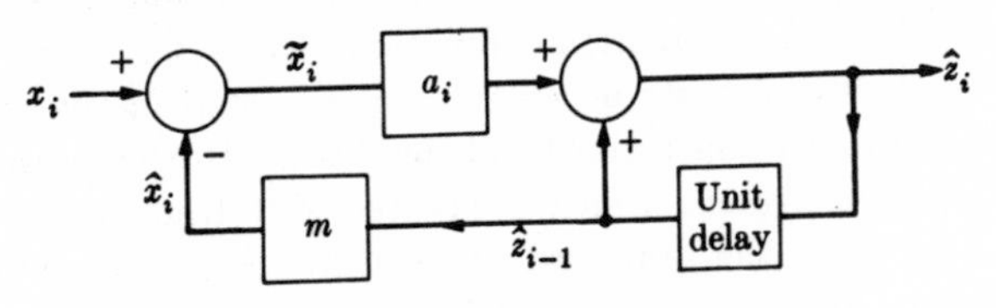

FIGURE 2. Iterative random variable estimator.

decreases, giving less weight to new data, and insuring stability of the feedback filter.

The main value of the foregoing example, in terms of generalizable results, is that an optimum estimate at any time is a sum of the previous optimum estimate and a correction term. The correction is the best estimate of the previous estimation error, in the light of the new observation. The significant result is that the correction is a linear function of only the error in the previous best estimate of the observation. That is, $\hat{\tilde{z}}_i$ depends only on $\tilde{x}_i$, the "part" of x_i not predictable from $(x_{i-1}, x_{i-2}, \ldots, x_{i-N})$.

The reader might get a feel for the properties of this iterative solution by working an example. Values must be chosen for σ_z^2, σ_n^2, and m, and a sequence of random numbers x_i must be listed. If such an example is attempted it will be readily apparent that the a_i coefficients are *independent* of the observation values, and that after N particular x_i have been observed, the best estimate is independent of the order in which they were observed.

4.3 General Discrete Feedback Estimation. The type of problem introduced in Section 3 requires estimation of the value of a random process or sequence $Z(t)$ at time $t = \eta$. In general, the variable $Z(\eta)$ being estimated will change with time rather than having a fixed sample value as in the previous example. The two main parts to the problem statement of that example were the probability density of the desired variable and a description of the relationship of the available observations to the desired variable. A problem of random sequence estimation requires similar descriptive information.

Here we will also assume there is a sequence of observations corrupted with additive, independent white noise. But now the signal part of the observation is a random sequence so that the statistical description may require more than a first-order probability density. In Section 3 we saw that for mean square estimation a sufficient description of $Z(t)$ was given by its auto-covariance function, or its power spectral density. We will now introduce the common trick of assuming that $Z(t)$ is an output of a linear system with a Gaussian white noise input. The system output can be represented as a linear combination of all previous inputs so it will also be Gaussian, as noted in the random process part of Section 1. However, the output spectral density will depend on the system transfer function. Thus specification of the linear system which generates $Z(t)$ from a white noise sequence is comparable to specification of the auto-covariance function of $Z(t)$.

Gaussian statistics constitute no restriction, as noted many times above, when the filter is already constrained to being linear. In this formulation the assumption that the system which generates $Z(t)$ from white noise $u(t)$ is linear, is similar to the standard Wiener filtering assumption that a factorable, rational power spectral density is known for Z. Wiener theory does not impose these stringent restrictions, but in practice such assumptions are often invoked to get more tractable expressions.

State description concepts (see Chapter II) are handy for describing the input-output relationship of the $Z(t)$ generating system in terms of a transition equation. We can write

$$\mathbf{z}_{i+1} = F\mathbf{z}_i + G\mathbf{u}_i \tag{4.28}$$

where $\mathbf{z}_i$ is the state vector; $\mathbf{u}_i$ is the input vector of white Gaussian noise; F is the transition matrix; and G is the input matrix.

We might choose the first component of the vector $\mathbf{z}_i$ as the system output, in which case the system generates a scalar valued random sequence. However, if the complete state *vector* of the system is considered as being observable, then the system output will be a vector-valued random sequence.

The state vectors form a *wide sense Markoff* vector-valued sequence because the zero means and independence of the $\mathbf{u}_i$ imply that

$$E(\mathbf{z}_{i+1} \mid \mathbf{z}_i, \mathbf{z}_{i-1}, \ldots) = E(\mathbf{z}_{i+1} \mid \mathbf{z}_i) = F\mathbf{z}_i. \tag{4.29}$$

It is this Markoff character which is exploited repeatedly below, although we will not stop to identify it at each usage.

A simple first-order Z system example will serve well to introduce the more general discrete prediction problems. A first-order Z system will have the transition equation

$$z_{i+1} = fz_i + gu_i \tag{4.30}$$

where u_i is a white Gaussian noise sequence with zero mean and variance σ_u^2. The observations will be defined by

$$x_i = mz_i + n_i \tag{4.31}$$

where n_i is a zero mean white Gaussian noise sequence with variance σ_n^2. Figure 3 shows a block diagram relating the variables x_i, n_i, z_i, and n_i.

Let us say that we want to predict the next value of Z. Then

$$\hat{z}_{i+1} = E(z_{i+1} \mid x_i, x_{i-1}, \ldots, x_{i-N}) = \hat{z}_{i+1}(\chi_i). \tag{4.32}$$

Equation (4.32) differs from (4.2) in two ways. Here z_{i+1} is the estimate of the *next* value of Z so it is a function of $\chi_i = (x_i, x_{i-1}, \ldots, x_{i-N})$, whereas

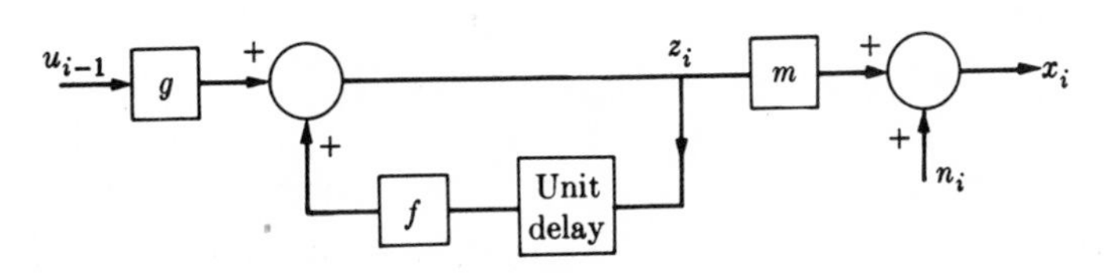

FIGURE 3. Random sequence generator.

we previously estimated the *present* value of Z so that z_{i+1} was a function of χ_{i+1}. A second difference is that in this example we must use the known Z-system dynamics. A combination of the Z transition equation, the properties of u_i, and the definitions

$$\tilde{z}_i = z_i - \hat{z}_i(\chi_{i-1}) \tag{4.33}$$

and

$$\hat{\tilde{z}}_i = E(\tilde{z}_i \mid x_i, x_{i-1}, \ldots, x_{i-N}) = \hat{\tilde{z}}_i(\chi_i)$$

leads to an expression of the best estimate as

$$\hat{z}_{i+1} = f(\hat{z}_i + \hat{\tilde{z}}_i). \tag{4.34}$$

We could use orthogonality relations to show once more that all the useful information contained in x_i is also contained in $\tilde{x}_i$ so that

$$\hat{\tilde{z}}_i = a_i \tilde{x}_i \tag{4.35}$$

where a_i is found from the Wiener-Hopf relation

$$E(\tilde{z}_i \tilde{x}_i) = a_i E(\tilde{x}_i^2). \tag{4.36}$$

Computation of a_i proceeds as it did in the previous feedback filtering example, except that the P_i will be different here. First, the error in estimating the next observation is

$$\begin{aligned} \tilde{x}_i &= mz_i + n_i - m\hat{z}_i \\ &= m\tilde{z}_i + n_i. \end{aligned} \tag{4.37}$$

Substitution of Eq. (4.37) into (4.36), use of the properties of n_i and simplification yields the familiar looking result

$$a_i = \frac{mP_i}{m^2 P_i + \sigma_n^{\,2}}. \tag{4.38}$$

The dynamics of the Z system enter into the recursion relation for P_i which is needed to complete the evaluation of a_i. P_i is defined as

$$P_i = E(\tilde{z}_i^{\,2}) \tag{4.39}$$

and the estimation error is given by

$$\tilde{z}_i = z_i - \hat{z}_i = (fz_{i-1} + gu_{i-1}) - f(\hat{z}_{i-1} + a_{i-1}\tilde{x}_{i-1}). \tag{4.40}$$

If the last three equations are combined and the expectation is evaluated using the properties of u_i and n_i, then P_i is given by the recursion relation

---

$$P_i = \frac{f^2\sigma_n^{\ 2}}{m^2P_{i-1} + \sigma_n^{\ 2}} P_{i-1} + g^2\sigma_u^{\ 2}. \tag{4.41}$$

Equations (4.34)–(4.41) describe the optimum feedback filter which can be displayed in the block diagram form of Fig. 4. Figure 4 reveals a situation which we will prove to hold in general. Namely, the optimum filter is built around a model of the system which generates the Z sequence being estimated. The best estimate is the output of the model. The input to the model is a linear function of the difference between the observation and its best estimate as determined from the best estimate of z_{i-1}. (The actual Z system has the noise input gu_i as in Fig. 3.) Once this form is known, the problem is localized to finding a_i, which in turn requires finding P_i.

It is clear from the variance Eq. (4.41) that the mean square error P_i is always greater than $g^2\sigma_u^{\ 2}$. This result is not surprising since we would not expect to be able to predict the next value of a random sequence without any error. The best possible estimate will occur when an infinite amount of data is available. It can be shown that if f^2 is less than 1 then the sequence of P_i's will converge monotonically to the value found from Eq. (4.41) when P_i is assumed equal to P_{i-1}. An f^2 greater than or equal to 1 would correspond to an unstable Z generating system and a Z-sequence which would not be typical of the kind we are generally interested in.

The two feedback filter problems which we have discussed in detail might be described as zero order and first order, respectively, where the order

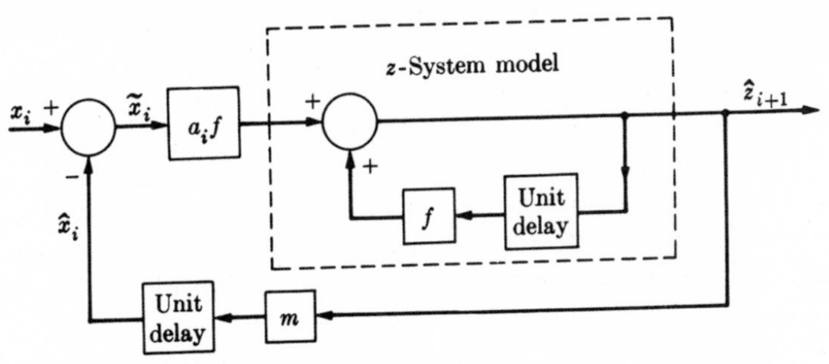

FIGURE 4. Optimum first-order-sequence predictor.

refers to the order of the system which generates the Z-sequence. In the latter case the value of Z at the next sample time was predicted; in the former, Z was the same at all sample times. The natural step now is to consider higher order Z-systems and estimation at times other than the next instant.

4.4 Estimation at $(i + M)$. The best estimate of z_{i+M}, given the observations $(x_i, x_{i-1}, \ldots, x_{i-N})$, is

$$\hat{z}_{i+M} = E(z_{i+M} \mid x_i, x_{i-1}, \ldots, x_{i-N}). \tag{4.42}$$

In our first-order example we can write

$$\begin{aligned} \hat{z}_{i+2} &= E(fz_{i+1} + gu_{i+1} \mid x_i, x_{i-1}, \ldots, x_{i-N}) \\ &= f\hat{z}_{i+1} \end{aligned} \tag{4.43}$$

where use has been made of the zero means and independence of the u_j. All u_j for $j > i$ will be independent of $(x_i, x_{i-1}, \ldots, x_{i-N})$ so that the best estimate at any time greater than $(i + 1)$ will be

$$\hat{z}_{i+M} = f^{M-1}\hat{z}_{i+1}. \tag{4.44}$$

The best estimate at time i (present value) can be found in this first-order case merely by dividing $\hat{z}_{i+1}$ by f. A comment in this regard on the invertability of the transition matrix for higher order systems will appear later.

Interpolation cannot be handled so simply. If z_j is the interpolated value to be estimated after x_i has been observed, we might assume that the best estimate of z_{j-1}, given $(x_{i-1}, x_{i-2}, \ldots, x_{i-N})$, is known ($j = i - K$ where K is positive).

$$\hat{z}_{j-1} = E(z_{j-1} \mid x_{i-1}, x_{i-2}, \ldots, x_{i-N}). \tag{4.45}$$

The desired quantity is

$$\hat{z}_j = E(fz_{j-1} + u_{j-1} \mid x_i, x_{i-1}, \ldots, x_{i-N}). \tag{4.46}$$

However, this problem is different from all previous ones in that

$$E(u_{j-1} \mid x_i, x_{i-1}, \ldots, x_{i-N}) \neq 0 \tag{4.47}$$

in general, since the x_k for $k \geqslant j$ are related to u_{j-1}. Neat feedback solutions for interpolation are not yet known.

4.5 Nonstationary Processes. The block diagrams and the a_i and P_i equations make it quite clear that there is no need for f, m, and g to be constants. We could let them be f_j, m_j, and g_j, respectively, so that x_j and z_j would be nonstationary random sequences. We see that the feedback form of optimum filtering makes the extension to this kind of nonstationary sequences a trivial one as opposed to the ordinary difficult attacks on the nonstationary Wiener-Hopf equation.

4.6 Infinite Data. The typical Wiener problem deals with infinite data, i.e., observations from the present back to the infinite past. The feedback filter operating on a growing amount of data will approach a stationary filter if the sequences are all stationary. In our first-order example, assumption of stationary solutions leads to a quadratic equation for P_∞, the negative solution of which is extraneous since the variance must be positive. The price paid for the conceptual simplicity of this approach is that the resulting expressions for the stationary, infinite data filter is an algebraically complicated combination of the given information: f, g, m, and the variances of the n and u sequences.

The natural form of feedback filtering works on a growing amount of data. We could get a solution for a finite amount of data by fixing the value of i, and by shifting all of the subscript indices on the observed data one unit back at each new time. Thus x_i would become x_{i-1}, etc., and the former x_{i-N} would be discarded.

4.7 Higher Order Z-Systems. When discussing minimum mean square error estimation it is common to assume the availability of power spectral density descriptions of the necessary random processes or sequences. Usually little mention is made of how to measure or determine these power spectral densities. The work which has been done on power spectral density measurement [3, 26] does not always lead to factorable spectral densities or to the specification of a stable linear system which would produce the given sequences from white noise inputs. We will assume here that this latter kind of linear, process generating system description is available. In order to be completely optimistic we should hope for a joint optimization of both aspects of the problem, i.e., going directly from an *observed* sample of the process to the best filter for a *typical* sample of the process. Limiting ourselves to less satisfying but more tractible problems, we press on.

The following transition equation describes an mth-order, discrete, linear system

$$\mathbf{z}_{i+1} = F_i\mathbf{x}_i + G_i\mathbf{u}_i \tag{4.48}$$

where $\mathbf{z}_i$ and $\mathbf{u}_i$ are column vectors with m components (m-vectors) and F_i and G_i are mXm matrices. The vector $\mathbf{u}_i$ is chosen to have components which are white Gaussian random sequences with the result that the vector $\mathbf{z}_i$ has components which are correlated Gaussian random sequences. The observation will be a p-vector ($p \leqslant m$) given by

$$\mathbf{x}_i = M_i\mathbf{z}_i + \mathbf{n}_i \tag{4.49}$$

where M_i is a pXm matrix and $\mathbf{n}_i$ is a p-vector of Gaussian white sequences. By putting subscripts on the matrices F, G, and M we allow them to be functions of time and we include a large class of nonstationary sequence problems along with those involving only stationary sequences.

This matrix formulation includes a common scalar problem as a special case when $z_{i,1}$, the first component of $\mathbf{z}_i$, is the desired sequence; $z_{i,2}$ is the correlated noise; M_i is the row vector $(m_{i,1}, m_{i,2}, 0, 0, \ldots, 0)$; and $\mathbf{n}_i$

is $(n_{i,1}, 0, \ldots, 0)$.† Furthermore, these matrix equations can also describe the multivariable Wiener problem. That is, we can think of one-half of the components of $\mathbf{z}_i$ as correlated signal sequences, and the other one-half as correlated noise sequences. If $z_{i,1}$ is a signal, $z_{i,2}$ a noise, etc., the M_i matrix

$$M_i = \begin{pmatrix} m_{i,11} & m_{i,12} & 0 & 0 & \cdots & & 0 \\ 0 & 0 & m_{i,23} & m_{i,24} & 0 & \cdot\cdot & 0 \\ 0 & 0 & 0 & 0 & 0 & \cdot\cdot & 0 \\ \cdot & & & & & & \\ \cdot & & & & & & \\ 0 & 0 & 0 & 0 & \cdots & & 0 \end{pmatrix} \tag{4.50}$$

will make the components of $\mathbf{x}_i$ into observations of correlated signal variables, each with additive correlated noise and additive uncorrelated noise.

$$x_{i,1} = m_{i,11}z_{i,1} + m_{i,12}z_{i,2} + n_{i,1} \tag{4.51}$$
$$\text{etc.}$$

The uncorrelated noise terms $n_{i,j}$ are not really necessary in this case of a higher order z-system because we can consider some of the $\mathbf{z}_i$ vector components as additive noise. In the zero- and first-order system examples, however, the n_i terms were needed to construct an observation in the form of signal plus noise. The order of the z-system is related to the number of signal variables *and* to the required covariances. A scalar estimation problem might require a high-order system so that the sequences $z_{i,1}$ and $z_{i,2}$ will have the desired auto- and cross-covariances.

We will now solve for the feedback filter which gives the best estimate of a vector from a sequence of x vectors without stating how the components of these vectors might be interpreted in a specific application. The best estimate of a vector consists of the best estimate of each component of the desired vector. Each step of the mth-order system derivation parallels one in the first-order system derivation with matrices replacing some of the scalars. Using $\boldsymbol{\chi}_i$ to denote the set $(\mathbf{x}_i, \mathbf{x}_{i-1}, \ldots, \mathbf{x}_{i-N})$, the best estimate of the Gaussian vector $\mathbf{z}_{i+1}$ at the next sample time is its conditional expectation

$$\hat{\mathbf{z}}_{i+1} = E(\mathbf{z}_{i+1} \mid \boldsymbol{\chi}_i). \tag{4.52}$$

Substituting the transition equation and the definition of $\tilde{\mathbf{z}}_i$

$$\hat{\mathbf{z}}_{i+1} = E[F_i(\hat{\mathbf{z}}_i + \tilde{\mathbf{z}}_i) + G_i\mathbf{u}_i \mid \boldsymbol{\chi}_i]. \tag{4.53}$$

Using the facts that F_i and G_i are deterministic and that successive $\mathbf{u}_i$ are independent and zero mean we have

† $z_{i,j}$ and $m_{i,jk}$ will denote the jth component of vector $\mathbf{z}_i$ and the jkth element of matrix M_i, respectively.

$$\hat{\mathbf{z}}_{i+1} = F_i\hat{\mathbf{z}}_i + F_iE(\tilde{\mathbf{z}}_i \mid \boldsymbol{\chi}_i). \tag{4.54}$$

The expectation in Eq. (4.54) is defined as the best estimate of the error in the previous estimate, and it is a best linear estimate since all variables are Gaussian. Therefore,

$$\hat{\tilde{\mathbf{z}}}_i = E(\tilde{\mathbf{z}}_i \mid \chi_i) = \sum_{j=i}^{i-N} \alpha_j \mathbf{x}_j \tag{4.55}$$

where α_j is an mXp matrix.

The procedure of Eq. (4.11) can be used to show that the optimum linear combination of the $\mathbf{x}_j$ is always representable by an optimum linear combination of the $\tilde{\mathbf{x}}_j$;

$$\hat{\tilde{\mathbf{z}}}_i = \sum_{j=i}^{i-N} \alpha_j \mathbf{x}_j = \sum_{j=i}^{i-N} A_j \tilde{\mathbf{x}}_j \tag{4.56}$$

where the A_j are also mXp matrices. If we concentrate on one component of $\mathbf{z}_i$, Eq. (4.56) states that

$$\hat{\tilde{z}}_{i,r} = \sum_{j=i}^{i-N} \sum_{s=1}^{p} a_{j,rs}\tilde{x}_{j,s} \tag{4.57}$$

so that the best linear estimate of each component of $\hat{\tilde{\mathbf{z}}}_i$ is a linear combination of $p(N+1)$ scalar observations which happen to be observed p at a time.

The fundamental orthogonality relation of Eq. (3.20) can be translated into vector terms by first looking at each component as we did in the previous equation. A scalar estimation error is orthogonal to any linear combination of the data on which the linear estimate was based, so we can say

$$E(\tilde{z}_{i,r}h_q) = 0 \tag{4.58}$$

if h_q can be written as a linear combination

$$h_q = \sum_{j=i-1}^{i-N} \sum_{s=1}^{p} w_{j,qs}\tilde{x}_{j,s}. \tag{4.59}$$

Now the mp scalar equations corresponding to the various combinations of values of r and q in Eq. (4.58) can be written neatly as the matrix equation

$$E(\tilde{\mathbf{z}}_i\mathbf{h}') = 0 \tag{4.60}$$

where the prime denotes the transpose of the column vector $\mathbf{h}$, and $\tilde{\mathbf{z}}_i\mathbf{h}'$ is a matrix with elements

$$(\tilde{\mathbf{z}}_i\mathbf{h}')_{rq} = \tilde{z}_{i,r}h_q. \tag{4.61}$$

It is similarly true that $\tilde{\mathbf{x}}_i$ has the same kind of orthogonality relation with any vector $\mathbf{h}$ of the given form.

Once more we will use orthogonality relations to simplify the calculation of the optimum filter. At this point the problem is isolated to finding the optimum set of $a_{j,rs}$ for generating $\hat{\tilde{z}}_{i,r}$ as in Eq. (4.57). These optimum constants must satisfy the Wiener-Hopf equation

$$E(\tilde{z}_{i,r}\tilde{x}_{k,q}) = \sum_{j=i}^{i-N}\sum_{s=1}^{p} a_{j,rs}E(\tilde{x}_{j,s}\tilde{x}_{k,q}); \quad \begin{array}{l} k = i, i-1, \ldots, i-N \\ q = 1, 2, \ldots, p \end{array} \tag{4.62}$$

which has the matrix form

$$E(\tilde{\mathbf{z}}_i\tilde{\mathbf{x}}_k') = \sum_{j=i}^{i-N} A_j E[\tilde{\mathbf{x}}_j\tilde{\mathbf{x}}_k']. \quad k = i, i-1, \ldots, i-N \tag{4.63}$$

The A_j matrices vanish for $j < i$ by the following argument. For these values of j the left side of Eq. (4.63) vanishes according to Eq. (4.60), and the sum on the right side becomes one term due to the orthogonality of $\tilde{\mathbf{x}}_j$ and $\tilde{\mathbf{x}}_k$ when $j \neq k$. Thus

$$0 = A_j E(\tilde{\mathbf{x}}_j\tilde{\mathbf{x}}_j') = A_j Q_j; \quad j \leqslant i - 1. \tag{4.64}$$

The matrix Q_j defined in Eq. (4.64) will generally be nonsingular, so that the equation requires that all of the A_j matrices for $j \leqslant i - 1$ be zero. A singular Q_j covariance matrix would mean that some of the components of $\tilde{\mathbf{x}}_j$ were linear combinations of the others. Linearly dependent components could be discarded to form a new vector with fewer components and a nonsingular covariance matrix. No information would be lost by this procedure since the results of all possible linear operations on the new vector would coincide with those on the old one.

We see again that the best estimate of the previous estimation error depends only on the unpredicted part of the last observation. The matrix A_i is found from

$$E(\tilde{\mathbf{z}}_i\tilde{\mathbf{x}}_i') = A_i E(\tilde{\mathbf{x}}_i\tilde{\mathbf{x}}_i') \tag{4.65}$$

by substituting the relation

$$\tilde{\mathbf{x}}_i = M_i\tilde{\mathbf{z}}_i + \mathbf{n}_i \tag{4.66}$$

with the result

$$A_i = P_i M_i'(M_i P_i M_i' + N_i)^{-1} \tag{4.67}$$

where we have defined

$$P_i = E(\tilde{\mathbf{z}}_i\tilde{\mathbf{z}}_i') \quad \text{and} \quad N_i = E(\mathbf{n}_i\mathbf{n}_i') \tag{4.68}$$

as the covariance matrices of the estimation error and the additive white noise, respectively. This formal solution for A_i can be used to write an expression for the best estimate as

$$\hat{\mathbf{z}}_{i+1} = F_i(\hat{\mathbf{z}}_i + A_i\tilde{\mathbf{x}}_i) \tag{4.69}$$

but we must still find a recursion relation for the covariance matrix P_i and justify the use of the matrix inverse which appears in Eq. (4.67). We will assume that the matrix inverse exists for the present and comment later on what is done when it does not exist. As for the recursion relation, use of the definition of P_i, the transition equation for $\mathbf{z}_i$ and the formal solutions for A_i and $\hat{\mathbf{z}}_i$, along with algebraic manipulation, yields

$$P_{i+1} = F_i(I - A_iM_i)P_iF_i' + G_iU_iG_i' \tag{4.70}$$

where I is the identity matrix and U_i is the covariance matrix of the vector sequence $\mathbf{u}_i$. Equation (4.70) becomes a nonlinear difference equation for P_i when the expression for A_i is substituted into it.

The iterative relations of Eqs. (4.70) and (4.69) give solutions only after initial values of $\hat{\mathbf{z}}_0$ and P_0 have been specified. The random vector $\mathbf{z}_0$ is zero mean and Gaussian so that before any observations are available its conditional mean, and best estimate, is the zero vector. P_0 is the *a priori* covariance matrix of $\mathbf{z}_0$ since a best estimate of zero means that $\mathbf{z}_0 = \tilde{\mathbf{z}}_0$. The conventional Wiener problem which postulates infinite past data can be handled by finding the stationary value P_∞, if the covariance equation converges. It may seem that the infinite data problem requires less information since a P_0 is not required, but the corresponding initial information in that case is the autocovariance matrix $E(\mathbf{z}_i\mathbf{z}_{i+j}') = R_{\mathbf{zz}}(j)$.

4.8 Summary of Feedback Filtering Results. This feedback filtering section has presented the derivation of the best linear estimator of a vector $\mathbf{z}_{i+1}$ when $\mathbf{z}_j$ is generated by the linear, discrete, white noise excited system described by [from Eq. (4.48)]

$$\mathbf{z}_{j+1} = F_j\mathbf{z}_j + G_j\mathbf{u}_j$$

and when additionally the observation is the sequence of vectors $(\mathbf{x}_i, \mathbf{x}_{i-1}, \ldots, \mathbf{x}_{i-N})$ where $\mathbf{x}_i$ is formed by a linear operation on $\mathbf{z}_i$ plus a white noise vector $\mathbf{n}_i$ [Eq. (4.49)]

$$\mathbf{x}_i = M_i\mathbf{z}_i + \mathbf{n}_i.$$

The optimum filter takes the form shown in Fig. 5 which shows a feedback system built around a model of the transition operator F_i. The double-lined arrows which connect the blocks in the diagram denote vector-valued variables. The filter output is the best estimate $\hat{\mathbf{z}}_{i+1}$ given by Eq. (4.69) when the optimum matrix operator A_i is defined by Eq. (4.67) and the covariance

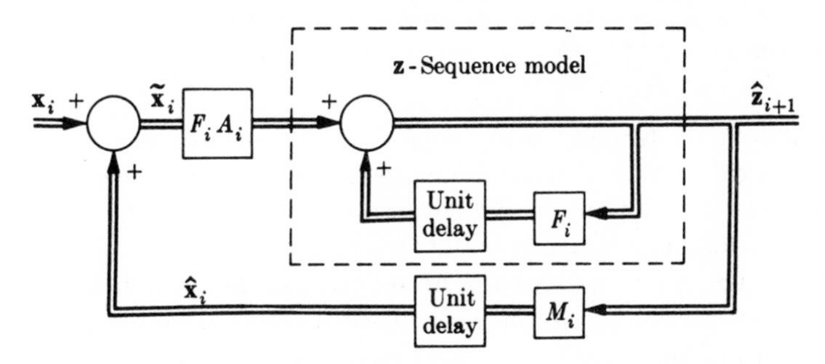

FIGURE 5. Optimum iterative predictor.

matrix of the estimation error P_i is the solution of the recursion relation of Eq. (4.70).

For prediction at any time greater than $i + 1$, the best filter can do no better than extrapolate the best estimate at time $i + 1$.

$$\hat{\mathbf{z}}_{i+M} = \left[\prod_{j=i+1}^{i+M-1} F_j\right]\hat{\mathbf{z}}_{i+1}. \tag{4.71}$$

The justification of this result is a simple extension of the argument used in the case of a first-order Z-system. Interpolation, estimating at a time less than i, is not amenable to the feedback approach, but present value estimation can be expressed by

$$\hat{\mathbf{z}}_i = F_i^{-1}\hat{\mathbf{z}}_{i+1} \tag{4.72}$$

if the transition matrix inverse exists. In the unusual event that F_i^{-1} does not exist we could find $\hat{\mathbf{z}}_i$ directly from the orthogonality relations, but the resulting expressions would not be as neat as those for optimum estimation at the next time instant.

In order to solve a numerical example the following information must be given:

(1) the process model in terms of F_i, G_i, and U_i,
(2) the observation model in terms of M_i and N_i;
(3) the initial values $\mathbf{z}_0$ and P_0.

The solution has the following noteworthy properties.

1. The filter is nonstationary due to the growing amount of data and, if the data are statistically nonstationary, due to the time variation of F_i, G_i, M_i, U_i, and N_i.

2. A_i is a function only of the problem description and not of the observations themselves. This property is related to the fact that the covariance matrix of a multivariate Gaussian conditional distribution is not a function of the values of the conditioning variables.

3. P_i and $\mathbf{z}_i$ contain all of the past information about the Z-process because the linear system description of the random sequence makes it a vector-valued Markoff sequence, and because second-order properties give a complete description of a Gaussian sequence.

The papers of Kalman study many aspects of the feedback filtering problem in great detail. Conditions are given so that the existence uniqueness and stability of solutions of the covariance equation can be insured as i approaches infinity. When the matrix inverse $(M_iP_iM_i' + N_i)^{-1}$ of Eq. (4.67) does not exist, our formal solution can lead to a significant optimum filter if a generalized kind of inverse is used. Lack of existence of an inverse means a lack of uniqueness to the solution of a set of simultaneous equations. The generalized inverse picks out a solution which results in an optimum filter in our mean square sense [10].

The whole feedback filtering approach can be extended to the continuous variable case by letting the time between samples approach zero. A careful evaluation of this limiting case leads to the analogous situation of defining $\mathbf{z}(t)$ and $\mathbf{x}(t)$ in terms of the equations

$$\frac{dz(t)}{dt} = F(t)\mathbf{z}(t) + G(t)\mathbf{u}(t) \tag{4.73}$$

and

$$\mathbf{x}(t) = M(t)\mathbf{z}(t) + \mathbf{n}(t)$$

and getting the optimal filter described by

$$\frac{d\hat{\mathbf{z}}(t)}{dt} = F(t)\hat{\mathbf{z}}(t) + A(t)[\mathbf{x}(t) - M(t)\hat{\mathbf{z}}(t)] \tag{4.74a}$$

where

$$A(t) = [P(t)M'(t) + G(t)C(t)]N^{-1}(t) \tag{4.74b}$$

and

$$\frac{dP}{dt} = F(t)P(t) + P(t)F'(t) + G(t)U(t)G'(t)$$
$$- [P(t)M'(t) + G(t)C(t)]N^{-1}(t)[M(t)P(t) + C'(t)G'(t)]. \tag{4.74c}$$

The time-varying matrices in Eqs. (4.74) are analogous to those in the discrete problem. The matrix $C(t)$ represents the cross-covariance of the $n(t)$ and $u(t)$ processes, a term whose analog in the discrete case was assumed zero for simplicity. For random process filtering the $N(t)$ covariance matrix must be nonsingular, i.e., every component of $\mathbf{x}(t)$ must have an additive white noise component for this solution to lead to a bounded operation which can be represented by a linear system. Justification of these extensions of the discrete data feedback solution to the case of continuous data requires more detailed mathematical considerations.

Kalman has presented derivations of all of these results, many nontrivial examples, computational procedures, conditions for existence and stability of solutions of the nonlinear covariance differential Eq. (4.74c), and a development of the duality between these optimum filtering problems and an optimum deterministic regulator problem.

The flexibility of this state transition approach to optimum estimation suggests that the assumption of knowledge of a linear system which generates the desired sequences from white noise is more useful than the assumption of knowledge of power spectral densities. The two problems of estimating the appropriate linear system characteristics and estimating power spectral densities from observed data are both presently being studied, and they appear to be equally complex.

5. Optimum Stochastic Control

An optimum automatic control system is a device which drives a dynamic plant in a manner which is intended to produce a desired plant output. The plant might be a chemical plant whose yield of various products is to be regulated, or a missile whose impact point must be precisely controlled, etc. The control system is usually designed for assumed plant characteristics which are unalterable, and a class of likely reference signals and plant disturbances. The controller thus designed computes optimum plant driving functions from observations of the plant state and an indication of a particular desired response.

Randomness can enter control problems in many ways. The desired response may be an unpredictable function of time. The measurements of the plant states may be contaminated with noise. The plant may have random disturbances or random parameter variations. A good control system will make use of statistical descriptions of the random phenomena in a control problem so that average performance of the system can be optimized. We have seen in Sections 2–4 how statistical information can be used to design optimum estimating systems, but those estimators were not constrained by unalterable plant dynamics. The optimum filter will generate a voltage which is a prescribed function of time rather than drive a heavy antenna so that its angular position is a prescribed function of time.

Minimum average loss function control system designing is more difficult in many ways than its counterpart in filter designing. Most plants and physically realizable controllers are characterized by nonlinearities which are particularly annoying in their effects on random signal analysis. However, a good first approach to control design is effected by assuming that the plant can be approximately characterized as a linear system. We will extend our minimum mean square error estimation results to the class of control problems in which the plant is linear and in which the controller is supposed to make the plant output follow, as closely as possible, one signal out of a specified class of reference signals.

The study of optimum control problems is best introduced by means of a *deterministic* regulator problem. The state transition approach will be used to find the best control computer when the performance index is quadratic in the errors between a set of reference signals and the plant outputs. The resulting feedback controller will be a linear operator on the data. We will obtain this result with the aid of the dynamic programing point of view, an approach which also will permit us to draw some general conclusions about *optimum stochastic control* problems as well.

5.1 Optimum Deterministic Regulator. In the deterministic regulator problem the reference signals are thought of as being the state variables of an autonomous linear system (one with no inputs). These variables are the

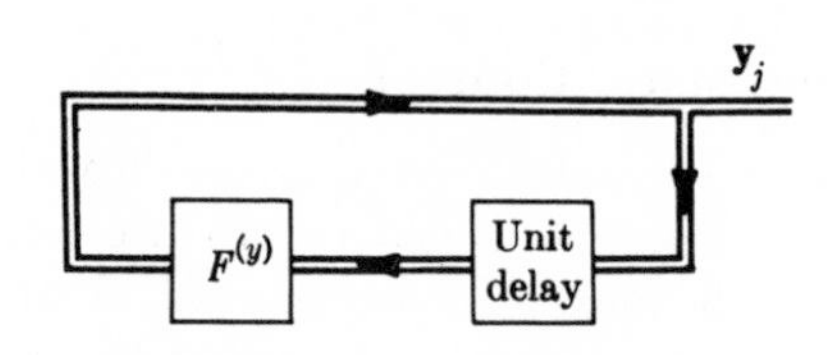

FIGURE 6. Reference sequence generator.

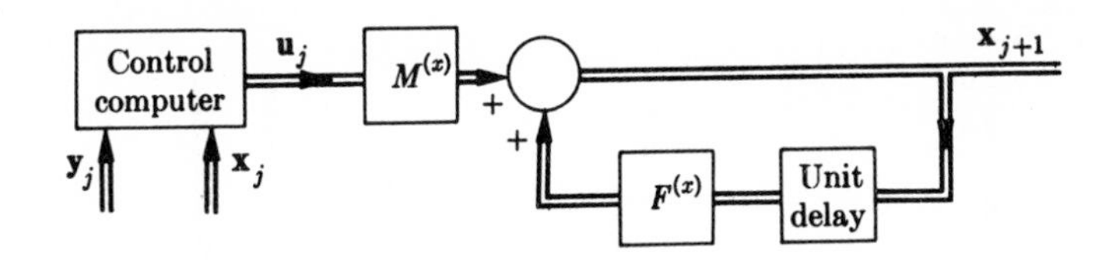

FIGURE 7. Representation of the plant to be controlled.

m-components of the reference signal state vector $\mathbf{y}_j$ where the transition relation for these vectors is given by

$$\mathbf{y}_{j+1} = F^{(y)}\mathbf{y}_j. \tag{5.1}$$

The reference state generating system has the block diagram representation of Fig. 6. The matrix $F^{(y)}$ and all other system matrices to be defined here are to be constants, although it is easy to modify the same derivations so as to extend the results to the case of time-varying systems.

The fixed linear plant is also characterized by a state vector $\mathbf{x}$ which will have n-components for an nth-order system. Control is exerted on the plant through a p-component vector $\mathbf{u}$ ($p \leqslant n$). The plant transition equation is†

$$\mathbf{x}_{j+1} = F^{(x)}\mathbf{x}_j + M^{(x)}\mathbf{u}_j \tag{5.2}$$

where $M^{(x)}$ is an nXp matrix which describes how the inputs can affect the plant state (see Fig. 7). It is the fact that the control vector cannot directly affect every state ($p < n$) that makes the problem nontrivial.

Concise notation is obtained by defining the *total state* of the regulator as an $(m + n)$ component vector $\mathbf{z}$, of which the first m-terms are the components of the vector $\mathbf{y}$ and the remaining n-terms the components of $\mathbf{x}$. In symbols,

$$z = \begin{bmatrix} \mathbf{y} \\ \cdots \\ \mathbf{x} \end{bmatrix}. \tag{5.3}$$

The total state vector has the transition equation

$$\mathbf{z}_{j+1} = F\mathbf{z}_j + M\mathbf{u}_j \tag{5.4}$$

where F and M are the composite matrices

$$F = \begin{pmatrix} F^{(y)} & 0 \\ 0 & F^{(x)} \end{pmatrix} \quad \text{and} \quad M = \begin{bmatrix} 0 \\ \cdots \\ M^{(x)} \end{bmatrix}. \tag{5.5}$$

† The vectors and matrices in this section should not be confused with those in Section 4 designated by the same symbols.

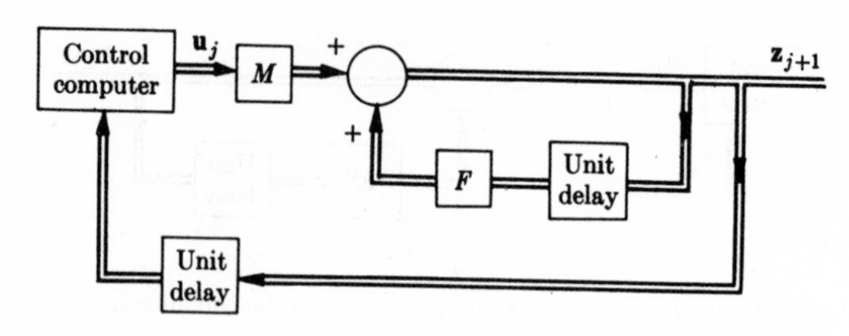

FIGURE 8. Deterministic regulator diagram.

Figure 8 shows a block diagram representation of the regulator problem in terms of the total system described by Eq. (5.4).

Optimum performance is judged in terms of a loss function which measures performance over a period of T time intervals where T can be any integer from 1 to infinity. The performance index is a function of the system state at the beginning of the T interval period and it is defined by

$$V_T(\mathbf{z}_0; \mathbf{u}_0, \ldots, \mathbf{u}_{T-1}) = \sum_{j=1}^{T} [\mathbf{z}_j' Q_j \mathbf{z}_j + \mathbf{u}_{j-1}' \Gamma_j \mathbf{u}_{j-1}]. \tag{5.6}$$

In this definition Q_j is a symmetric *positive* matrix (i.e., a symmetric matrix of a quadratic form for which $\mathbf{r}' Q_j \mathbf{r} \geqslant 0$ for all vectors $\mathbf{r}$) and Γ_j is another positive matrix which associates a cost to the control effort required to produce the control vector $\mathbf{u}_{j-1}$. Suitable choices of Q_j and Γ_j allow this index to include many others as special cases [16]. Inclusion of the control effort cost approximates the common physical restriction of saturation of the control input.

We will want to find the sequence of control vectors $(\mathbf{u}_0, \ldots, \mathbf{u}_{T-1})$ which minimizes V_T. For instance, if the plant has a single output $x_{i,1}$, and this is supposed to follow the single reference $y_{i,1}$, then V_T could be chosen to be a sum of the squares of the errors at the T subsequent sampling instants. This sum squared error criterion would result if

$$\sum_{j,k} q_{i,jk} z_{i,j} z_{i,k} = (z_{i,1})^2 - 2 z_{i,1} z_{i,m+1} + (z_{i,m+1})^2 \tag{5.7}$$

which will be the case if all the $q_{i,jk}$ are zero except for

$$q_{i,11} = q_{i,(m+1)(m+1)} = 1$$

and

$$q_{i,1(m+1)} = q_{i,(m+1)1} = -1.$$

Dynamic programing prescribes the following iterative approach to the minimization of V_T [1, 16]. V_T is a sum of T-terms which measure the effectiveness of the control vector choices at each of the corresponding T

sampling instants. We define I_T as the minimum value of V_T, corresponding to the optimum sequence of $\mathbf{u}_j$ vectors.

$$I_T(\mathbf{z}_0) = \underset{\text{all } \mathbf{u}_j}{\text{Min}} \left[V_T(\mathbf{z}_0; \mathbf{u}_0, \mathbf{u}_1, \ldots, \mathbf{u}_{T-1})\right] \tag{5.8}$$

I_T is temporarily assumed to be known and to be of the form

$$I_T(\mathbf{z}_0) = \mathbf{z}_0' P_T \mathbf{z}_0 \tag{5.9}$$

where P_T is a symmetrical positive matrix. The assumption that I_T can be written in this form will be verified later by induction.

We adopt the dynamic programing point of view here by invoking the *principle of optimality,* a logical truth which is easy to accept but which only recently has been used for solving control problems. When applied to our problem the principle says that the minimum quadratic loss for a $(T + 1)$ stage decision process is the minimum of the sum of two terms: the loss at the next sampling time plus the minimum loss over the T remaining intervals.

$$I_{T+1}(\mathbf{z}_0) = \underset{\mathbf{u}_0}{\text{Min}} \left[V_1(\mathbf{z}_0) + I_T(\mathbf{z}_1)\right]. \tag{5.10}$$

If we assume that we know the solution to any T stage process, then $I_T(\mathbf{z}_1)$ is known for any vector $\mathbf{z}_1$ so that minimization with respect to $\mathbf{u}_0$ in Eq. (5.10) is equivalent to minimization of $V_{T+1}(\mathbf{z}_0)$ with respect to all of the $\mathbf{u}_j$.

Substitution of the assumed form of I_T and the definition of V_T into Eq. (5.10) yields

$$I_{T+1}(\mathbf{z}_0) = \underset{\mathbf{u}_0}{\text{Min}} \left(\mathbf{z}_1' Q_1 \mathbf{z}_1 + \mathbf{u}_0' \Gamma_1 \mathbf{u}_0 + \mathbf{z}_1' P_T \mathbf{z}_1\right). \tag{5.11}$$

Use of the transition equation for $\mathbf{z}$ and some rearrangement brings I_{T+1} into the form

$$I_{T+1}(\mathbf{z}_0) = \underset{\mathbf{u}_0}{\text{Min}} \left[(F\mathbf{z}_0 + M\mathbf{u}_0)'(Q_1 + P_T)(F\mathbf{z}_0 + M\mathbf{u}_0) + \mathbf{u}_0' \Gamma_1 \mathbf{u}_0\right]. \tag{5.12}$$

Minimization with respect to the components of $\mathbf{u}_0$ could be carried out directly by setting partial derivatives equal to zero and checking to see that the result was indeed a minimizing one, but we will avoid this involved constructive procedure by performing a neat factorization (completing a square) which allows minimization by inspection. If $\bar{\mathbf{u}}_0$, B_T, and A'_{T+1} are defined as

$$\begin{aligned} B_T &= M'(Q_1 + P_T)M + \Gamma_1 \\ A'_{T+1} &= B_T^{-1} M'(Q_1 + P_T)F \\ \bar{\mathbf{u}}_0 &= -A'_{T+1}\mathbf{z}_0 \end{aligned} \tag{5.13}$$

then Eq. (5.12) can be written as

$$\begin{aligned} I_{T+1}(\mathbf{z}_0) = \underset{\mathbf{u}_0}{\text{Min}} \{&(\mathbf{u}_0 - \bar{\mathbf{u}}_0)' B_T (\mathbf{u}_0 - \bar{\mathbf{u}}_0) \\ &+ \mathbf{z}_0'[F'(Q_1 + P_T)F - A_{T+1} B_T A'_{T+1}]\mathbf{z}_0\}. \end{aligned} \tag{5.14}$$

A discussion of the existence of the matrix inverse B_T^{-1} will appear below.

The expression to be minimized in Eq. (5.14) is the sum of two terms, the second of which is independent of the choice of control vector. We want to argue that the smallest we can make the first term is zero and that this value will occur only when $\mathbf{u}_0$ is set equal to $\bar{\mathbf{u}}_0$. The conclusion will follow if we can show that the matrix B_T is the matrix of a positive definite quadratic form, i.e.,

$$\mathbf{r}'B_T\mathbf{r} \geqslant 0 \quad \text{for all } \mathbf{r} \tag{5.15}$$

with equality if and only if $\mathbf{r} = 0$.

We have defined P_T and Q_1 to be symmetric and positive, so it is clear that their sum has the properties of a symmetric positive matrix. Since $M\mathbf{r}$ is a vector, and matrix operations are associative, $M'(Q_1 + P_T)M$ is also positive. Γ_1 has been chosen to be positive so that it is easy to see that B_T is positive.

B_T will be positive definite if at least one of the positive matrices which it contains as summands is definite. Choosing Γ_j to be definite would be sufficient. In the event that no control cost was desired in the index ($\Gamma_j = 0$ for all j) we could choose Q_j to be definite and M to have linearly independent columns so that

$$M\mathbf{r} = 0 \quad \text{only if} \quad \mathbf{r} = 0. \tag{5.16}$$

This restriction on M is minor since if it does not hold, at least one of the components of the control vector is redundant and it could be eliminated, resulting in a new M which would satisfy Eq. (5.16). The Q_j were not chosen to be positive definite from the start since such a choice would exclude losses of the form of Eq. (5.7).

If B_T is positive definite then it will possess an inverse and the operations in the definition of A'_{T+1} can be performed. If the given problem has a B_T matrix which is not positive definite then the quadratic form in $(\mathbf{u}_0 - \bar{\mathbf{u}}_0)$ of Eq. (5.14) will be positive but not definite so that $\bar{\mathbf{u}}_0$ will not be a unique minimizing vector. The inverse in A'_{T+1} will not exist either, but our choice of a positive loss function assures that a minimizing sequence of control vectors must exist so that a generalized inverse can be found [9, 10, 12]. We will avoid the details of these more complicated solutions in order to emphasize the main features of this kind of optimum control problem.

The result "$\bar{\mathbf{u}}_0$ is the best value for $\mathbf{u}_0$" was based on the assumed form of I_T and it requires knowledge of P_T in order to evaluate A'_{T+1}. An inductive argument verifies the form of I_T. If the optimum choice of $\mathbf{u}_0$ is used; then Eq. (5.14) becomes

$$I_{T+1}(\mathbf{z}_0) = \mathbf{z}_0'P_{T+1}\mathbf{z}_0 \tag{5.17}$$

when we identify P_{T+1} as

$$\begin{aligned} P_{T+1} &= F'(Q_1 + P_T)F - A_{T+1}B_TA'_{T+1} \\ &= (F - MA'_{T+1})'(Q_1 + P_T)(F - MA'_{T+1}) + A_{T+1}\Gamma_1A'_{T+1}. \end{aligned} \tag{5.18}$$

Verification of the last equality is facilitated by noting that

$$F'(Q_1 + P_T)MA'_{T+1} = A_{T+1}B_TA'_{T+1}. \tag{5.19}$$

Thus P_{T+1} is symmetric and positive, just as P_T was assumed to be. The induction argument is completed by noting that a direct evaluation of I_1 leads to a P_1 which obeys the recursion relation of Eq. (5.18) if $P_0 = 0$.

The solution in terms of Eqs. (5.13), recursion relation (5.18), and initial value $P_0 = 0$ is now complete. It should be emphasized that the control computer is simply the *linear* operator A'_{T+1} acting on the total system state to get the control vector, although at no point did we restrict the controller to be a linear one. The subscript on the control operator indicates the number of steps *remaining* in the performance interval.

The reader has no doubt noticed the suggestive use of the same symbols in this regulator problem and in the matrix form of the feedback filter problem. This notation was motivated by the fact that the equations in the two problems are analogous. The filter equations will become the control equations if every matrix in the filter solution is replaced by the transpose of the analogous one in the regulator problem, and if the ith optimum filter is replaced by the $(T - i)$th optimum controller. In the control problem we need to know how many steps *remain*, and in the filter problem we needed to know how many steps had *elapsed*. Thus the duality relation requires an inversion of the direction of time flow. (See Kalman [13, 14] for a more complete exposition of this duality.)

The optimum regulator is a function of the remaining length of the interval over which performance is being measured. It is of interest to consider the behavior of the solution when we try to let T, the number of steps in the performance interval, approach infinity. Necessary and sufficient conditions for the convergence of the recursion relation for P_T to a value which leads to a stable regulator have been derived [14]. A plant which satisfies the conditions for a stable infinite interval controller is called *completely observable and completely controllable*. The restriction to complete controllability is a restriction on the M- and F-matrices, which corresponds to insuring that there is some sequence of control vectors which could move the plant from any initial state to the zero state in a finite number of steps. Complete observability corresponds to complete controllability of the adjoint of the given plant.

Another point worth emphasizing is the implication of our assumption that the reference signal is the output of an autonomous system whose state is observable. This means that after the first observation we can predict the reference signal perfectly over the entire performance interval. Similarly, one observation of the plant state should be sufficient to predict its future states exactly since we know what driving forces are being applied. It might appear that the optimum controller could be open loop after one observation. However, feedback is used so that we can feel justified in

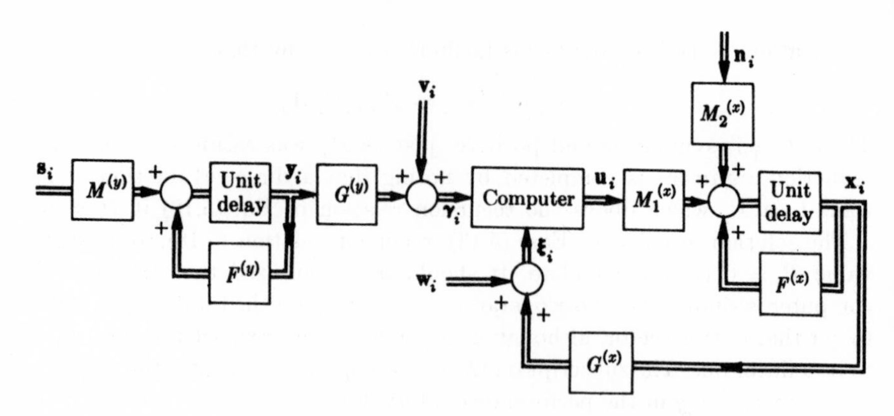

FIGURE 9. Stochastic regulator diagram.

applying this kind of optimum controller to a plant whose characteristics may not be known precisely, and whose output may be subject to unknown disturbances. Feedback makes the performance less sensitive to the precision of our measurements and assumptions.

In the next section, rather than working for insensitivity to unknown variations, we will assume a statistical description for them and try to make good use of this model.

5.2 Stochastic Control. Our purpose here is not to dwell on the details of the deterministic regulator nor to exploit the regulator-filter duality, but rather to find the optimum regulator with stochastic state variables by combining the methods previously used to solve the filtering and regulating problems separately.† Figure 9 shows a regulator with random reference signals $\mathbf{y}_i$, random plants states $\mathbf{x}_i$, and zero mean white random plant disturbances $\mathbf{n}_i$. The reference signals are the states of a linear system excited by a zero mean white sequence $\mathbf{s}_i$. Further randomness appears in the observations of the plant state and reference signals. These observations are chosen to be a sum of white noise plus linear combinations of the actual variables. For example, we can observe $\mathbf{x}_i$ only as

$$\boldsymbol{\xi}_i = G^{(x)}\mathbf{x}_i + \mathbf{w}_i \tag{5.20}$$

and $\mathbf{y}_i$ only as

$$\boldsymbol{\gamma}_i = G^{(y)}\mathbf{y}_i + \mathbf{v}_i \tag{5.21}$$

where $\mathbf{v}_i$ and $\mathbf{w}_i$ are zero mean white sequences. The linear operators $G^{(x)}$ and $G^{(y)}$ might be singular so that all of the states might not be observable even if the additive noise sequences $\mathbf{v}_i$ and $\mathbf{w}_i$ were identically zero.

† Gunckel [9] and Joseph and Tou [11] state the results of this section and motivated the proofs presented here.

A combination of previous techniques will lead us to the major result that the optimum *linear* controller for the stochastic regulator just described, with a quadratic performance criterion, consists of a cascade of two linear operations. First, the observations $\boldsymbol{\gamma}_i$ and $\boldsymbol{\xi}_i$ are used to find $\hat{\mathbf{y}}_i$ and $\hat{\mathbf{x}}_i$ which are the minimum mean square error linear estimates of the states $\mathbf{y}_i$ and $\mathbf{x}_i$. Then the combined state estimate $\hat{\mathbf{z}}_i$ defined by

$$\hat{\mathbf{z}}_i = \begin{bmatrix} \hat{\mathbf{y}}_i \\ \cdots \\ \hat{\mathbf{x}}_i \end{bmatrix} \tag{5.22}$$

is used as if it were the actual observed state vector in a deterministic, quadratic performance criterion regulator problem.

The proof begins by expressing the transition equations

$$\mathbf{x}_{i+1} = F^{(x)}\mathbf{x}_i + M_1^{(x)}\mathbf{u}_i + M_2^{(x)}\mathbf{n}_i \tag{5.23}$$

and

$$\mathbf{y}_{i+1} = F^{(y)}\mathbf{y}_i + M^{(y)}\mathbf{s}_i$$

in the combined form

$$\mathbf{z}_{i+1} = F\mathbf{z}_i + M\mathbf{u}_i + H\boldsymbol{\nu}_i \tag{5.24}$$

where we have defined the composite matrices and vectors as

$$\mathbf{z}_i = \begin{bmatrix} \mathbf{y}_i \\ \cdots \\ \mathbf{x}_i \end{bmatrix}; \quad \boldsymbol{\nu}_i = \begin{bmatrix} \mathbf{s}_i \\ \cdots \\ \mathbf{n}_i \end{bmatrix}; \quad F = \left(\begin{array}{c|c} F^{(y)} & 0 \\ \hline 0 & F^{(x)} \end{array}\right); \quad H = \left(\begin{array}{c|c} M^{(y)} & 0 \\ \hline 0 & M_2^{(x)} \end{array}\right)$$

and

$$M = \left(\begin{array}{c} 0 \\ \hline M_1^{(x)} \end{array}\right). \tag{5.25}$$

The performance criterion is the sum of positive quadratic forms

$$V_T(\mathbf{z}_0; \mathbf{u}_0, \ldots, \mathbf{u}_{T-1}) = \sum_{i=1}^{T} [\mathbf{z}_i' Q_i \mathbf{z}_i + \mathbf{u}_{i-1}' \Gamma_i \mathbf{u}_{i-1}] \tag{5.26}$$

but the $\mathbf{z}_i$ are vector random variables so we want to minimize the *expected value* of V_T.

Minimization in this case means choosing the control vectors $\mathbf{u}_0, \mathbf{u}_1, \ldots, \mathbf{u}_{T-1}$ based on present and past observations of $\boldsymbol{\gamma}_i$ and $\boldsymbol{\xi}_i$ so as to minimize $E(V_T)$. Recall from the section on optimum estimation that the expectation can be thought of in two steps. We can first take the conditional expectation given the observations, and then average over the randomness of the observations. It is clear that the over-all expectation is minimized if the conditional expectation is minimized for each possible set of observations. Thus, optimum performance will be achieved if we choose the $\mathbf{u}_i$ to minimize

$$E(V_T \mid D_0) \tag{5.27}$$

where we use D_0 to symbolize the set of past and present observations.

As in the previous dynamic programing derivation we will assume that the optimum control signals are known for any T stage process, with a resulting minimum conditional loss of $I_T(D_0)$ which can be written as

$$I_T(D_0) = E(\mathbf{z}_0' P_T \mathbf{z}_0 + b_T \mid D_0) \tag{5.28}$$

where P_T is a positive symmetric matrix and b_T is a scalar whose expectation given D_0 is independent of the previous control input. That is,

$$E(b_T \mid D_0) = E(b_T \mid D_{-1}, \boldsymbol{\xi}_0, \boldsymbol{\gamma}_0) \tag{5.29}$$

cannot be a function of the contribution of $\mathbf{u}_{-1}$ to $\boldsymbol{\xi}_0$ and $\boldsymbol{\gamma}_0$. (Recall that D_0 consists of past observations D_{-1} and the present observations $\boldsymbol{\xi}_0$ and $\boldsymbol{\gamma}_0$.)

The principle of optimality implies the relation

$$I_{T+1}(D_0) = \underset{\mathbf{u}_0}{\text{Min}}\, E[\mathbf{z}_1' Q_1 \mathbf{z}_1 + \mathbf{u}_0' \Gamma_1 \mathbf{u}_0 + E(\mathbf{z}_1' P_T \mathbf{z}_1 + b_T \mid D_1) \mid D_0]. \tag{5.30}$$

We must be careful not to confuse the different time sequences in the control and estimation aspects of this problem. The time subscripts in Eq. (5.30) are counted from the beginning of the $T + 1$ stage control performance interval. However, it should be remembered that the statistical observations may extend back N-intervals into the past. For example, the set D_1 will consist of $(\boldsymbol{\gamma}_1, \boldsymbol{\gamma}_0, \ldots, \boldsymbol{\gamma}_{1-N}, \boldsymbol{\xi}_1, \boldsymbol{\xi}_0, \ldots, \boldsymbol{\xi}_{1-N})$.

The compound conditional expectations in Eq. (5.30) simplify readily because the outer expectation merely averages the inner one over the randomness of $\boldsymbol{\gamma}_1$ and $\boldsymbol{\xi}_1$. Thus we can omit the inner expectation and write (5.30) as

$$I_{T+1}(D_0) = \underset{\mathbf{u}_0}{\text{Min}}\, E(\mathbf{z}_1' Q_1 \mathbf{z}_1 + \mathbf{u}_0' \Gamma_1 \mathbf{u}_0 + \mathbf{z}_1' P_T \mathbf{z}_1 + b_T \mid D_0). \tag{5.31}$$

Substitution of the transition equation and rearrangement produces an expression involving the random vectors $\mathbf{z}_0$ and $\boldsymbol{\nu}_0$:

$$I_{T+1}(D_0) = \underset{\mathbf{u}_0}{\text{Min}}\, E[(F\mathbf{z}_0 + M\mathbf{u}_0 + H\boldsymbol{\nu}_0)'(Q_1 + P_T)(F\mathbf{z}_0 + M\mathbf{u}_0 + H\boldsymbol{\nu}_0) + \mathbf{u}_0' \Gamma_1 \mathbf{u}_0 + b_T \mid D_0]. \tag{5.32}$$

The $\boldsymbol{\nu}_i$ vector random sequence has been assumed to be zero mean and white so that $\mathbf{z}_0$ and $\boldsymbol{\nu}_0$ are independent random vectors. Independence of these vectors allows us to take the expectations one at a time with the result

$$I_{T+1}(D_0) = \underset{\mathbf{u}_0}{\text{Min}}\, E_{\mathbf{z}_0}\{(F\mathbf{z}_0 + M\mathbf{u}_0)'(Q_1 + P_T)(F\mathbf{z}_0 + M\mathbf{u}_0) + b_T + \mathbf{u}_0' \Gamma_1 \mathbf{u}_0 + E[\boldsymbol{\nu}_0' H'(Q_1 + P_T) H \boldsymbol{\nu}_0 \mid D_0] \mid D_0\}. \tag{5.33}$$

We will follow the example set in the deterministic regulator problem and find the minimizing conditions by making a special factorization aided by the definitions

$$\begin{aligned} B_T &= M'(Q_1 + P_T)M + \Gamma_1 \\ c_T &= E[\boldsymbol{\nu}_0' H'(Q_1 + P_T)H\boldsymbol{\nu}_0 \mid D_0] \\ A'_{T+1} &= B_T^{-1} M'(Q_1 + P_T)F \\ \bar{\mathbf{u}}_0 &= -A'_{T+1}\mathbf{z}_0. \end{aligned} \tag{5.34}$$

Using these terms, Eq. (5.33) can be written as

$$\begin{aligned} I_{T+1}(D_0) = \min_{\mathbf{u}_0} E_{\mathbf{z}_0}[b_T + c_T + \mathbf{z}_0'(F - MA'_{T+1})'(Q_1 + P_T)(F - MA'_{T+1})\mathbf{z}_0 \\ + (\mathbf{u}_0 - \bar{\mathbf{u}}_0)' B_T(\mathbf{u}_0 - \bar{\mathbf{u}}_0) + \mathbf{z}_0' A_{T+1}\Gamma_1 A'_{T+1}\mathbf{z}_0 \mid D_0]. \end{aligned} \tag{5.35}$$

The only term in Eq. (5.35) which involves the control vector $\mathbf{u}_0$ is the quadratic form in B_T. (Recall the assumed properties of b_T.)

We will now assume that B_T has been made positive definite by one of the procedures mentioned on page 174. It follows that the quadratic form in $(\mathbf{u}_0 - \bar{\mathbf{u}}_0)$ is positive definite and that the matrix inverse in the definition of A'_{T+1} exists. We would like to minimize this quadratic form by setting $\mathbf{u}_0$ equal to $\bar{\mathbf{u}}_0$, but $\bar{\mathbf{u}}_0$ is a random vector so that we do not know its value at the time the choice of the vector $\mathbf{u}_0$ must be made.

At this point in the derivation it is necessary to use the methods of statistical estimation theory to try to choose that control vector $\mathbf{u}_0$ which minimizes the conditional expectation in Eq. (5.35). The only term which is related to $\mathbf{u}_0$ is

$$E_{\mathbf{z}_0}[(\mathbf{u}_0 - \bar{\mathbf{u}}_0)' B_T(\mathbf{u}_0 - \bar{\mathbf{u}}_0) \mid D_0] \tag{5.36}$$

in which the only random term is $\bar{\mathbf{u}}_0$. If we write

$$(\mathbf{u}_0 - \bar{\mathbf{u}}_0) = (\mathbf{u}_0 - \hat{\bar{\mathbf{u}}}_0 + \hat{\bar{\mathbf{u}}}_0 - \bar{\mathbf{u}}_0) \tag{5.37}$$

where

$$\hat{\bar{\mathbf{u}}}_0 = E(\bar{\mathbf{u}}_0 \mid D_0) \tag{5.38}$$

then Eq. (5.36) can be written as

$$(\mathbf{u}_0 - \hat{\bar{\mathbf{u}}}_0)' B_T(\mathbf{u}_0 - \hat{\bar{\mathbf{u}}}_0) + E_{\mathbf{z}_0}[(\hat{\bar{\mathbf{u}}}_0 - \bar{\mathbf{u}}_0)' B_T(\hat{\bar{\mathbf{u}}}_0 - \bar{\mathbf{u}}_0) \mid D_0] \tag{5.39}$$

since $\mathbf{u}_0$ and $\hat{\bar{\mathbf{u}}}_0$ will be deterministic once D_0 is observed, and from Eq. (5.38)

$$E(\bar{\mathbf{u}}_0 - \hat{\bar{\mathbf{u}}}_0 \mid D_0) = 0. \tag{5.40}$$

It is now clear that the choice

$$\mathbf{u}_0 = \hat{\bar{\mathbf{u}}}_0 \tag{5.41}$$

will minimize expression (5.39) and therefore (5.36) and (5.35) also. This minimizing control vector can be rewritten in terms of the best estimate of the state of the system by combining Eqs. (5.41), (5.38), and (5.34) to get

$$\hat{\mathbf{u}}_0 = E(-A'_{T+1}\mathbf{z}_0 \mid D_0)$$

or

$$\hat{\mathbf{u}}_0 = -A'_{T+1}E(\mathbf{z}_0 \mid D_0) \tag{5.42}$$

due to the linearity of the expectation operator.

As a summary of the last few paragraphs we can say that *if* we can verify the assumptions about the form of I_T, then the optimum controller finds the best mean square estimate of the present system state and then treats this estimate as if it were the known, deterministic state in a deterministic regulator problem. The dynamic programing argument is completed by substituting the optimum value of $\mathbf{u}_0$ into Eq. (5.35), so that

$$I_{T+1}(D_0) = E_{\mathbf{z}_0}(b_{T+1} + \mathbf{z}_0'P_{T+1}\mathbf{z}_0 \mid D_0) \tag{5.43}$$

if b_{T+1} and P_{T+1} are defined as

$$P_{T+1} = (F - MA'_{T+1})'(Q_1 + P_T)(F - MA'_{T+1}) + A_{T+1}\Gamma_1 A'_{T+1} \tag{5.44}$$

and

$$b_{T+1} = b_T + c_T + \overset{*}{\mathbf{z}}_0{}'A_{T+1}(Q_1 + P_T)A'_{T+1}\overset{*}{\mathbf{z}}_0 \tag{5.45}$$

where

$$\overset{*}{\mathbf{z}}_0 = \mathbf{z}_0 - E(\mathbf{z}_0 \mid D_0). \tag{5.46}$$

Note that the $E_{\mathbf{z}_0}$ in Eq. (5.42) can be written simply as E since $\mathbf{z}_0$ is the only random quantity within the brackets.

P_{T+1} is a positive matrix and $P_0 = 0$ for the same reasons as in the deterministic dynamic programing example. We must additionally show that $E(b_T \mid D_0)$ is not a function $\mathbf{u}_{-1}$, of the property which b_T was assumed to have. From Eq. (5.34) it is clear that the "whiteness" of the $\mathbf{v}_1$ will make c_T independent of D_0 and $\mathbf{z}_0$. The final step will be a demonstration of the conditions under which

$$\overset{*}{\mathbf{z}}_0{}'A_{T+1}(Q_1 + P_T)A'_{T+1}\overset{*}{\mathbf{z}}_0 \tag{5.47}$$

has the required independence properties.

Expression (5.47) will be a sum of terms which depend on $\mathbf{u}_{-1}$ via factors such as

$$[z_{0,k} - E(z_{0,k} \mid D_0)][z_{0,j} - E(z_{0,j} \mid D_0)] \tag{5.48}$$

Equation (5.24) allows a component $z_{0,k}$ in (5.48) to be expressed in terms of the components of z_{-1}, $\mathbf{u}_{-1}$, and $\mathbf{v}_{-1}$. The $\mathbf{u}_{-1}$ terms inside an expectation of (5.48) cancel with the corresponding ones outside the expectation since $\mathbf{u}_{-1}$ is a known deterministic function of D_{-1} (which is included in D_0). Thus the explicit dependence of (5.48), and therefore of (5.47), on $\mathbf{u}_{-1}$ is removed. Terms such as

$$E(z_{-1,k} \mid D_0) \tag{5.49}$$

in the expanded form of (5.48) might be implicitly related to $\mathbf{u}_{-1}$. However, this dependence also vanishes due to the deterministic nature of $\mathbf{u}_{-1}$ given D_0. That is, the linearity of equations (5.20), (5.21), and (5.24) bring $\mathbf{u}_{-1}$ into D_0 in a deterministic additive way so that the value of (5.49) is independent of the value of $\mathbf{u}_{-1}$.

We can conclude that the optimum control vector for the first step of a $T + 1$ stage control interval of a quadratic loss stochastic regulator problem is the $\hat{\mathbf{u}}_0$ defined by

$$\hat{\mathbf{u}}_0 = -A'_{T+1}\hat{\mathbf{z}}_0 \tag{5.50}$$

where $\hat{\mathbf{z}}_0$ is the minimum mean square error estimate of $\mathbf{z}_0$ given D_0.

If the optimum controller is restricted to be a *linear* one, then the $\hat{\mathbf{u}}_0$ of (5.42) and (5.50) may be ruled out except in special cases; e.g., when all random sequences in the problem are jointly gaussian. That is, the conditional mean of $\mathbf{z}_0$ given D_0 is not generally a linear function of the data in D_0. We will argue that the optimum *linear* controller is given by (5.50) *if* $\hat{\mathbf{z}}_0$ is then interpreted as the best *linear* mean square estimate of $\mathbf{z}_0$ given D_0.

This extension is easy to see after defining a composite data vector $\boldsymbol{\delta}_0$ whose components are all of the components of all of the present and past observations of $\boldsymbol{\gamma}_i$ and $\boldsymbol{\xi}_i$. Then $\hat{\mathbf{u}}_0$, the best linear estimate of $\mathbf{u}_0$, can be written in terms of an optimum linear operator Φ as

$$\hat{\mathbf{u}}_0 = \Phi\boldsymbol{\delta}_0. \tag{5.51}$$

Minimization of Eq. (5.35) with respect to the choice of $\mathbf{u}_0$ would require finding the Φ which minimizes the conditional expectation of a positive definite quadratic form in the vector $(\Phi\boldsymbol{\delta}_0 - A'_{T+1}\mathbf{z}_0)$. The only statistical properties of the components of the random vectors $\boldsymbol{\delta}_0$ and $\mathbf{z}_0$ which will appear in this expectation are auto- and cross-covariances. Therefore we can argue, just as we did in the linear estimation problem, that this non-Gaussian problem will have the same solution as an equivalent Gaussian one in which the random variables all have the same auto- and cross-covariances. This follows because we know the optimum controller for the equivalent Gaussian problem will be linear.

5.3 Summary. An optimum stochastic control problem has been solved by combining the techniques used on deterministic control problems and stochastic estimation problems. The best quadratic loss stochastic controller has the form of a cascade of the best mean square error state estimator and the best controller for use with deterministic state observations. The best *linear* controller for the same system is similar, with the best linear state estimator replacing the best unrestricted state estimator.

It should be recalled that the optimum deterministic regulator for a linear plant and quadratic loss function turned out to be linear without any linearity assumption.

It was noted above that necessary and sufficient conditions have been derived for which the optimum deterministic regulator approaches a stable solution as the number of steps in the control interval approaches infinity. The same conditions apply in the stochastic problem because the P_T and A_{T+1} matrices have identical definitions in the two problems. However, I_T for the stochastic problem will grow without bound since even with an infinite amount of past data, the optimum state estimator will have a nonzero error covariance matrix.

The stochastic control problem which has been presented here is quite general, although many other useful and interesting ones could be formulated. It should be emphasized that the present framework includes a wide variety of situations. The F and G matrices can be chosen so as to correspond to a problem in which the additive noise is not white (see page 164). For example, referring to Fig. 9, $F^{(y)}$ could be arranged so that some of the components of $\mathbf{y}_i$ were the random reference sequences and some were correlated noise sequences. $G^{(y)}$ could then form the sum of reference sequences and correlated nonwhite noise sequences.

6. Summary

This chapter has considered a few applications of statistical methods to the analysis and design of filters and control systems. In each case we tried to determine the optimum filter or controller characteristic for a given problem. The formulation of these problems consisted of three parts:

(1) a class of observations;

(2) a performance criterion;

(3) a class of systems from which to choose that one which demonstrates the best performance for the given class of observations.

Since the descriptions of the observations were in terms of probability distributions, the performance measure had to be an expectation or a probability statement.

In the case of filters we measured performance in terms of the mean square error between a desired variable and its estimate; and in the case of controllers, system performance was based on the mean of a sum or integral of quadratic error functions. Mean square performance indices led to solvable optimization equations, and we saw that the resulting systems would be optimum for a wider class of performance criteria if the observation and desired variable classes were narrowed. The mean square solutions were optimum for random imput sequences which could be generated from white noise by linear systems. (This description restricts only auto- and cross-covariances.) These same solutions were also optimum for the nonsquared error criteria mentioned in Section 2 if the desired variable had a suitable conditional probability density function. For example, the best mean square system would also minimize the expected value of the $F_2(e)$ of Fig. 1, which would lead to a minimum probability of the error exceeding a units in magnitude.

The present discussion suggests many other problems in connection with stochastic systems.

1. In order to use the design results developed here, we must have equations describing the linear system which could generate the inputs and references from a white noise sequence or process. These linear system characteristics must be estimated from a sample of the expected input function. Estimation of linear system characteristics is also necessary in order to get the characteristics of a linear plant for which optimal stochastic control is desired. It is usually possible to apply test signals to an unknown plant, but determination of its characteristics may become a statistical estimation problem if its outputs can be observed only with additive noise. More randomness enters this problem if the determination must be made continuously on a plant which has time varying characteristics and uncontrollable random inputs.

2. There is also much interest in the problems of determining the nth-order joint densities of the output sequence of a linear or nonlinear system with known input-output relations and with an input process or sequence whose joint densities of all orders are known. This problem becomes quite difficult except for the special result that Gaussian process inputs to a linear system will produce system outputs which are also Gaussian. Determination of output statistics is related to optimum stochastic control by way of the loss function generalization theorem whose statement includes restrictions on conditional probability densities.

3. The study of stochastic control presented here has been restricted to discrete-time plants with additive random disturbances. Gunckel [9] solves one class of discrete-time problems with multiplicative noise, i.e. random plant parameters. Optimal control of continuous-time plants is mathematically more difficult than the techniques presented here, but considerable work has been done on such problems. Wonham [27] presents a continuous-time version of our Section 5 result, and has a good bibliography of papers dealing with similar continuous-time control problems.

Finally, we can point out that the major result of Section 5 is a case in which the optimization of a complex system can be achieved by successively optimizing the performance of segments of the over-all system. It is fortuitous that the optimum linear stochastic controller is a cascade of the optimum linear state estimator and the optimum deterministic controller, since it is easy to formulate minimum mean square error problems in which this decomposition is not possible [25].

We will close this discussion of optimum control systems by mentioning that problems can be formulated so that the class of admissible control vector sequences is so small and the performance interval is so short that all possible sequences can be tested out on a high-speed computer simulation of the plant. The existence of the successive optimization of Section 5 is some justification for judging the effectiveness of each control sequence on the basis of an optimum estimate of the present plant state, and optimum predictions of the reference signals and plant disturbances over the duration of the performance interval [6].

BIBLIOGRAPHY

1. Bellman, R., *Dynamic Programming*, Princeton, 1957.
2. Brown, J. L., "Asymmetric Non-mean-square error criteria," IRE Trans. on Automatic Control. **AC-7,** 64 (January, 1962).
3. Blackman, R. B., and Turkey, J. W., *The Measurement of Power Spectra from the Point of View of Communications Engineering*, Dover, 1959.
4. Cramer, H., *The Elements of Probability Theory*, Wiley, 1955.
5. Cramer, H., *Mathematical Methods of Statistics*, Princeton, 1946.
6. Chestnut, H., Sollecito, W. E., and Troutman, P. H., "Predictive-control system application," AIEE Trans. **80,** Part II, 128 (July, 1961).
7. Doob, J. L., *Stochastic Processes*, Wiley, 1953.
8. Feller, W., *An Introduction to Probability Theory and its Applications*, Wiley, 1950, Vol. I.
9. Gunckel, T. L., II, "Optimum Design of Sampled-Data Systems with Random Parameters," Stanford Electronics Laboratories, Tech. Rept. No. 2102-2, 1961; and with Franklin, G. F., "A General Solution for Linear Sampled-Data Control," ASME J. Basic Eng., 1963.
10. Greville, T. N. E., "The pseudo-inverse of a rectangular of singular matrix and its application to the solution of systems of linear equations," SIAM Rev. **1,** No. 1 (January, 1959).
11. Joseph, F. D., and Tou, J. T., "On linear control theory," AIEE Trans. **80,** Part II, 193 (September, 1961).
12. Kalman, R. E., "New Methods and Results in Linear Prediction and Filtering Theory," RIAS, Baltimore, Md., Tech. Rept. 61-1, 1960, and *Proceedings of 1960 Purdue University Random Function Theory Symposium*, Wiley, 1963.
13. Kalman, R. E., "A new approach to linear filtering and prediction problems," J. Basic Eng. (ASME Trans.) **82D,** 35 (March, 1960).
14. Kalman, R. E., "On the General Theory of Control Systems," *Proceedings of the IFAC, Moscow, 1960*, Butterworths, 1961.
15. Kalman, R. E., and Bucy, R. S., "New results in linear filtering and prediction theory," J. Basic Eng. **83D,** 95 (March, 1961).
16. Kalman, R. E., and Koepcke, R. W., "Optimal Synthesis of Linear Sampling Control Systems Using Generalized Performance Indexes," ASME Trans. 1821, Paper No. 58-IRD-6, 1958.
17. Lee, Y. W., *Statistical Theory of Communication*, Wiley, 1960.
18. Loeve, M., *Probability Theory*, 2nd Edition, Van Nostrand, 1960.

19. Lorens, C. S., and Viterbi, A. J., "Optimum Filtering," Jet Propulsion Laboratory External Publication No. 633 (May, 1959).
20. Parzen, E., *Modern Probability and its Applications*, Wiley, 1960.
21. Parzen, E., "Statistical Inference on Time Series by Hilbert Space Methods," Appl. Math. and Stat. Lab. Stanford University, 1959, Tech. Rept. No. 23.
22. Parzen, E., "A New Approach to the Synthesis of Optimal Smoothing and Prediction Systems," Tech. Rept. No. 34, Appl. Math. and Stat. Labs. Stanford University, 1960.
23. Parzen, E., "An approach to time series analysis," Ann. Math. Statistics (December, 1961).
24. Sherman, S., "Non-Mean-Square Error Criteria," IRE Trans. on Information Theory **IT-4,** No. 3, 125 (September, 1958).
25. Shaw, L. G., "Dual Mode Filtering," IRE Trans. on Automatic Control. AC-8, 136 (April, 1963).
26. Technometrics, May, 1961.
27. Wonham, W. M., "Stochastic problems in optimal control," IEEE Convention Record, 1963.
28. Zadeh, L. A., "Prediction and filtering," in "Progress in information theory . . . ," IRE Trans. on Information Theory **IT-7,** No. 3, 139 (July, 1961).

CHAPTER V

Nonlinear Control Systems: Selected Topics

JOHN PESCHON

H. B. SMETS

CONTENTS

1. Introduction and General Theorems

The primary function of a control system is to force the process which we wish to control to behave in some desired manner. We *usually* demand that

$$\lim_{t \to t_0} \mathbf{y}(t) = \tilde{\mathbf{r}}$$

$$\mathbf{r}(t) \begin{cases} = 0 \text{ for } t < 0 \\ = \tilde{\mathbf{r}} = \text{constant for } t > 0 \end{cases} \tag{1.1}$$

where t_0 is usually ∞ and where the y_i, $(i = 1, \ldots, k)$ are the outputs of the process which we frequently call the plant, and the r_i, $(i = 1, \ldots, k)$ are the desired values of these outputs.

Although Eq. (1.1) can be satisfied in a variety of ways, we normally resort to the familiar *feedback* structure of Fig. 1 which is of great practical value because the stated requirement (1.1) can be made to hold approximately even though there are external disturbances u and slow changes $\alpha(t)$ in the plant characteristics.

In this chapter, we consider plants which are (1) stationary—the changes $\alpha(t)$ are assumed to be sufficiently slow—and (2) describable by *ordinary* differential equations.

Furthermore, we assume that the actuator and the controller are (1) time-invariant or stationary, and (2) continuous.

As a consequence of these restrictions, the feedback structure of Fig. 1 is mathematically described by a set of ordinary time-invariant differential equations

$$\begin{aligned} \dot{x}_j &= f_j(x_1 \cdots x_n; r_1 \cdots r_k) \qquad (j = 1 \cdots n) \\ &= f_j(\mathbf{x}, \mathbf{r}) \end{aligned} \tag{1.2}$$

where the x_j are the state variables of the *complete system*. A possible, but not necessary, choice of the x_j is the outputs of all the energy storage elements contained in the plant, the actuator, and the controller.

The plant which we wish to control is in many practical cases *nonlinear*, that is, the mathematical relation between $\mathbf{y}$ and $\mathbf{m}$ constitutes a set of nonlinear differential equations. Plant nonlinearities are termed *unavoidable*.

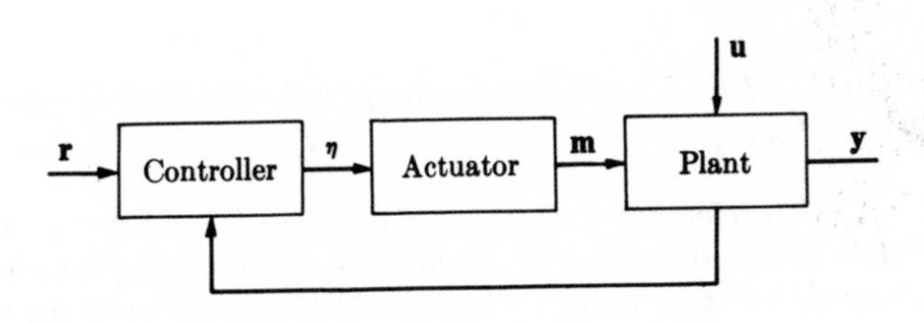

FIGURE 1. Feedback structure comprising plant, actuator, and controller.

They often do not cause extreme concern because one of the fundamental properties of a feedback structure is that nonlinearities contained in the forward loop are, at least to some extent, automatically compensated for and hence may have little effect on closed loop performance. Unless these nonlinearities are pronounced, as in the case of a hard saturation, linear analysis techniques are often sufficiently accurate. This observation usually does not hold in other fields of nonlinear mechanics: the amplitude of a sinusoidal oscillator, for instance, is very sensitive to triode nonlinearities

Many modern feedback control systems contain highly nonlinear actuators, such as relays. These are attractive because of their low cost and because Eq. (1.1) can sometimes be satisfied in *finite time*, ie.,

$$\mathbf{y}(t)\Big|_{t \geqslant t_0} = \tilde{\mathbf{r}} \qquad \begin{array}{l}(\tilde{r}_i = \text{constant})\\ (t_0 = \text{finite positive constant}).\end{array}$$

Such nonlinearities, which as a rule cause vastly nonlinear behavior, are termed *intentional.*

1.1 The Mathematical Tools. Fundamentally, our analysis or design problem consists in detecting certain properties of Eq. (1.2) or of building certain properties into (1.2).

The only *general* procedures to deal with such nonlinear equations are the step-by-step integration techniques, Liapunov's second method, and certain methods based upon integral equations. None of these is easy to apply. All other procedures identify Eq. (1.2) with an *associated linear* system which, we assume, is a sufficiently close approximation in a suitably chosen region of the coordinate space. In this chapter, we will use such *quasi-linear* techniques almost exclusively.

Certain other approximation methods, such as the Ritz-Galerkin method [8],† are very useful in the analysis of sinusoidally excited nonlinear systems, but seem to be of limited applicability in the theory of automatic control.

1.2 Nonlinear Phenomena. Before entering into any further details, the reader should become prepared to expect phenomena which are totally unknown in linear system analysis. Some of these phenomena are listed below.

PHENOMENON 1. *In nonlinear system analysis, the principle of superposition generally does not hold.*

Example. If, with reference to Fig. 2a, r' produces y' and if r'' produces y'', then $r' + r''$ does not produce $y' + y''$. As an illustration of this, we consider the step responses y' and y'' to $\tilde{r}'$ and $\tilde{r}''$, Fig. 2b, which coincide until the first zero-error condition $y' = \tilde{r}'$ is accomplished.

† Numbers in brackets refer to the bibliography at the end of this chapter.

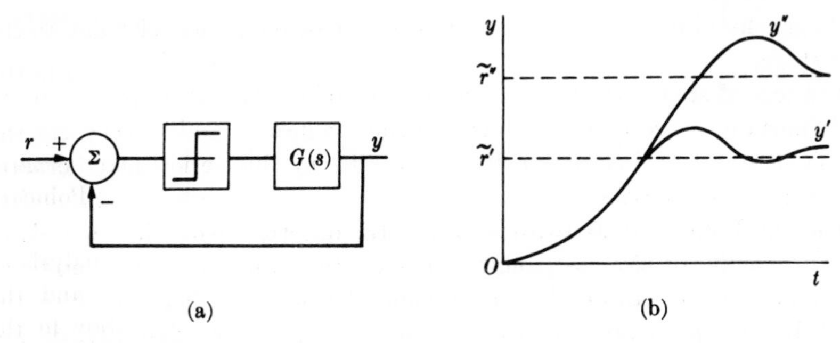

FIGURE 2. (a) Relay-servomechanism; (b) responses y' and y'' to $\tilde{r}'$ and $\tilde{r}''$.

Moreover, if the response of a system initially in the state $\mathbf{x}'(0)$ is $\mathbf{y}'(t)$ and if the response of the same system initially in the state $\mathbf{x}''(0)$ is $\mathbf{y}''(t)$, then, the response associated with $\mathbf{x}'(0) + \mathbf{x}''(0)$ is not $\mathbf{y}'(t) + \mathbf{y}''(t)$ in general.

As a direct consequence of all this, the familiar *convolution integral*

$$y(t) = \int_{\infty}^{t} g(t - \tau) r(\tau)\, d\tau$$

$$g(t) = \text{system impulse response}$$

does not hold as such, though extensions can be made, as discussed in Section 7. The various transform methods (Laplace transform, Mellin transform, etc.) are, as a rule, of little practical interest in the study of nonlinear systems.

PHENOMENON 2. *The stability of a nonlinear system may depend on* $\mathbf{x}(0)$ *and* $\mathbf{r}$.

The statement that the response of a stable linear system is bounded for all t if $\mathbf{r}$ is bounded does not hold here, for certain classes of $\mathbf{r}$ and $\mathbf{x}(0)$ may *shock* a system previously observed to be stable into unbounded motion.

PHENOMENON 3. *A nonlinear system may exhibit one or several periodic steady-state motions in the absence of a periodic forcing vector. Such periodic motions are termed limit cycles, closed solution curves, or stationary oscillations.*

PHENOMENON 4. *A nonlinear system may have several equilibrium states for the same constant forcing vector. The (stable) equilibrium condition ultimately achieved depends on* $\mathbf{x}(0)$.

As an illustration of this we quote the bistable multivibrator.

1.3 A Historical Account. Investigations of nonlinear differential equations were started in the eighteenth and nineteenth century. Solutions to certain nonlinear problems were obtained mostly as a result of appropriate linearizations. A representative example of these efforts is the so-called small oscillation pendulum. Higgins [12], the author of a very comprehensive bibliography of nonlinear systems, classifies these efforts as belonging to the first stage.

The second stage, which comprises the period of 1880–1920, produced the all-important concept of the phase plane (Poincaré) and a very general theory of stability (Liapunov). It was also during this period that Poincaré discovered and analyzed limit cycles.

The third stage (1920–1940) was mostly concerned with the analysis of certain nonlinear electric circuits such as the triode oscillator and the multivibrator. B. van der Pol in Holland, Krylov and Bogoliubov in the U.S.S.R., are probably the best-known investigators of that period. For detailed treatments of these subjects, the reader is referred to Andronow and Chaikin [1], Cunningham [8], and Minorsky [22].

In the fourth stage, which roughly covers the period 1940–1950, considerable attention was devoted to the *analysis* of nonlinear control systems. The Describing Function was developed independently during this period by Kochenburger, Goldfarb, Dutilh, Blaquière, and Loeb. Many books on automatic control, for instance Gille *et al.* [11], Mishkin and Braun [24], Seifert and Steeg [27], Solodownikow [31], Truxal [32] and West [33], have detailed accounts of these investigations.

The fifth and present stage originated about 1950. In addition to successful work toward improving Liapunov's second method as a powerful and generally applicable analysis tool, much research has been devoted to the optimization—according to specific criteria—of control systems by deliberate inclusion of nonlinear elements. Measures of performance of nonlinear systems under transient conditions and the relations with variational methods of system optimization have recently been found and are described in Chapter VI and in Kalman and Bertram [16]. Liapunov's second method, which, as Kalman pointed out, should be considered as a point of view or a philosophy rather than a method, has permitted the solution of many problems.

Much of the work accomplished in the Soviet Union during the past twenty years is now available in translations. The most relevant of these are listed in the Bibliography at the end of this chapter.

2. The Phase Plane and the State Space: the Topological Methods

The concept of the *phase plane* is fundamental in nonlinear mechanics in spite of the fact that all too often its application to specific problems is *in practice* restricted to systems described by ordinary, second-order, autonomous differential equations of the form

$$\dot{x}_1 = f_1(x_1, x_2)$$
$$\dot{x}_2 = f_2(x_1, x_2) \tag{2.1}$$

where f_1 and f_2 have continuous partial derivatives for all x_1 and x_2.

The fundamental idea is to associate the motion of a *representative point* of coordinates x_1, x_2 in the x_1, x_2 plane with the solution of Eq. (2.1), time t being reduced to the role of a parameter. Many of the *notions* and definitions arrived at can be and have been extended to more complex and hence more realistic situations, such as forced systems and higher order systems; in the latter case we speak of the phase space or the state space. The manipulation of specific problems, however, becomes very laborious.

Unlike the describing function method, "the phase plane and the state space are not just clever methods directed toward solving particular problems, but are the most fundamental concept of the entire theory of ordinary differential equations (linear or nonlinear, time-dependent or time-invariant) at the present time. This is because the state space is a way of representing, sometimes only in an abstract sense, all possible solutions of a differential equation.†

2.1 The Phase Trajectory. Let $\mathbf{x}^* = \{x_1^*, x_2^*\}$ be the state observed at t^*. The state $\mathbf{x}^* + \boldsymbol{\delta}\mathbf{x}$ corresponding to $t^* + \delta t$, δt being a small positive time increment, is obtained from Eq. (2.1) by

$$\begin{aligned} \delta x_1 &= f_1(x_1^*, x_2^*)\,\delta t \\ \delta x_2 &= f_2(x_1^*, x_2^*)\,\delta t. \end{aligned} \tag{2.2}$$

By repeatedly applying Eq. (2.2), the coordinates of $\{x_1, x_2\}$ can be computed and plotted with the result that a continuous curve is obtained in the x_1, x_2 plane. Exactly the same computations can be carried out for n-order autonomous systems of the form

$$\dot{x}_k = f_k(x_1, \ldots, x_n) \qquad (k = 1, \ldots, n) \tag{2.3}$$

although the curve or trajectory of the state vector $\{x_1 \cdots x_n\}$ can no longer be visualized for $n > 3$.

When Eq. (2.2) is applied for the first time, generally at time $t = 0$, we need to know n real numbers $x_1^* \cdots x_n^*$ describing the state at $t = 0$. These numbers are the coordinates of the *initial state* $\mathbf{x}(0)$ and are labeled $x_1(0), \ldots, x_n(0)$. As a result of this, we conclude that Eqs. (2.1) and (2.3) do not lead to one trajectory but to a family of trajectories, each of which is associated with one *particular initial state* $\mathbf{x}(0)$.

2.2 The Velocity Vector. At each point along a given trajectory, we define a vector $\mathbf{v}$, called the *velocity vector*, of components $f_1 \cdots f_n$. The vector $\mathbf{v}$ describes the activity, or rate of change, of the system at the point whose coordinates are $\mathbf{x}$; hence the name velocity vector. Since $\mathbf{v}$ is related to $\mathbf{x}$ through the vector equation,

† Statement due to R. E. Kalman in the discussion of "Quasi-linearization techniques for transient study of nonlinear feedback control systems," K. Chen, AIEE Trans. **74,** part II, 354 (1955).

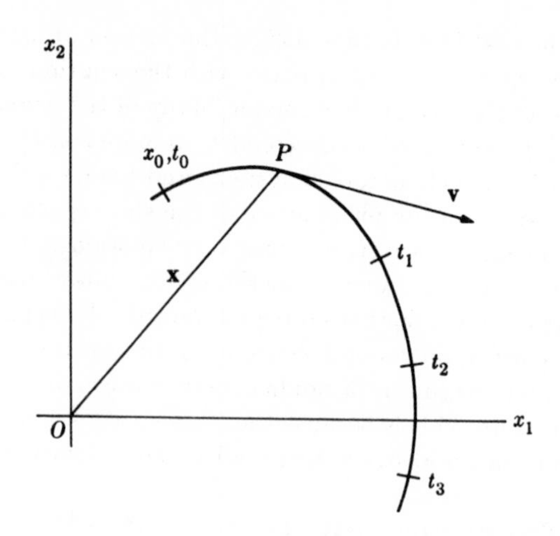

FIGURE 3. State vector $\mathbf{x}$ and velocity $\mathbf{v}$ at some representative point P. Time t is considered as a parameter.

$$\mathbf{v} = \frac{d}{dt}\mathbf{x} \tag{2.4}$$

it is clear that $\mathbf{v}$ is *tangent* to the trajectory described by $\mathbf{x}$, as shown in Fig. 3.

2.3 The Singular Points.

DEFINITION. *Any point* $\hat{\mathbf{x}}$ *at which* $\mathbf{v} = 0$, *implying that* $f_k = 0$, $(k = 1, 2, \ldots, n)$, *is a singular point, equilibrium point, or critical point.*†

It is apparent from Eq. (2.1), (2.2), or (2.3) that there is no motion at a singular point. Hence it is easy to determine such points, since it suffices to solve the n algebraic equations

$$f_k(x_1 \cdots x_n) = 0. \qquad (k = 1, \ldots, n) \tag{2.5}$$

The number of singular points $\hat{\mathbf{x}}$ is independent of n and depends only on the nonlinearities contained in Eqs. (2.1) and (2.3). If the system under consideration is linear, that is, if all the f_k are linear functions of the x_i, $(i = 1, \ldots, n)$, there is generally only one singular point. For an exception, see Kaplan [17], page 423.

A further property is that trajectories corresponding to different initial states $\mathbf{x}(0)$ may cross at singular points and nowhere else, since the tangent $\mathbf{v}$ to a trajectory is uniquely defined at all other points $\mathbf{x}$. Trajectories

† These terms are used indifferently by most authors, although certain mathematical texts make a distinction between singular points on the one hand, and equilibrium or critical points on the other hand. See, for example, Kaplan [17].

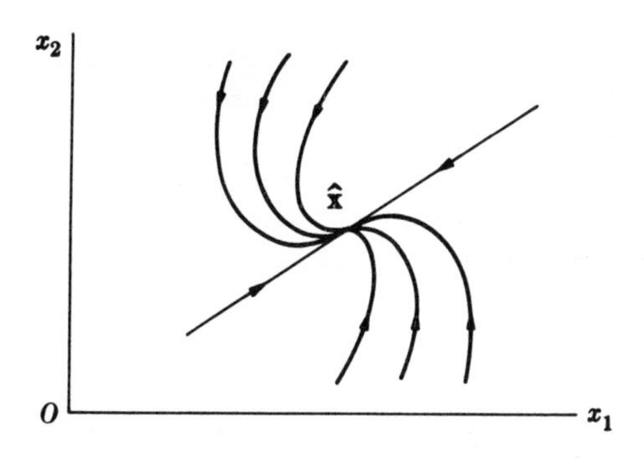

FIGURE 4. Phase trajectories in the vicinity of the singular point $\hat{x}$.

corresponding to different initial conditions, therefore, bunch together in the vicinity of a singular point $\hat{\mathbf{x}}$, as shown in Fig. 4.

If one wishes to analyze a solution in the vicinity of a singular point $\hat{\mathbf{x}}$, one generally selects a new set of state variables ξ_k, $k = 1, \ldots, n$, whose origin 0 coincides with $\hat{\mathbf{x}}$. The simplest way to arrive at this is to perform the shift

$$\xi_k = x_k - \hat{x}_k. \tag{2.6}$$

Hence the corresponding set of differential equations,

$$\dot{\xi}_k = \bar{f}_k(\xi_1, \ldots, \xi_n) \qquad (k = 1, \ldots, n) \tag{2.7}$$

where the $\bar{f}_k$ are obtained from the f_k of Eqs. (2.3)–(2.6), has a singular point at the origin.

2.4 The Stability of Singular Points. For the purposes of this section, it suffices to define stability as follows.†

DEFINITION. *Consider an arbitrary initial state* $\boldsymbol{\xi}(0)$ *contained in a domain D surrounding* 0. *A necessary and sufficient condition for Eq.* (2.7) *to be stable in D is that* $\boldsymbol{\xi}(t) \equiv 0$ *for all* $t \geqslant t_0$, $t_0 > 0$. *If this condition holds, we say that* 0 *is a stable singular point. Moreover, if* $t_0 \to \infty$, 0 *is asymptotically stable.*

In practice this means that the so-called *obvious* or *trivial solution* of Eq. (2.7), $\boldsymbol{\xi} = 0$, is *physically realizable.*

The classical approach to the analysis of motion in the immediate vicinity of 0 is to perform a MacLaurin expansion of Eq. (2.7)

$$\dot{\xi}_k = \sum_{l=1}^{n} a_{kl}\xi_l + O_k(\xi_1, \ldots, \xi_n)$$
$$a_{kl} = \frac{\partial \bar{f}_k(0 \cdots 0)}{\partial \xi_l} \qquad (k, l = 1, \ldots, n) \tag{2.8}$$

† For a less superficial definition of stability of nonlinear systems, see Chapter VI.

where the functions $O_k(\xi_1, \ldots, \xi_n)$ comprise terms of not less than the second order of smallness and where the a_{kl} are the elements of the Jacobian matrix evaluated at 0.

If all the a_{kl} are zero, system (2.7) maintains its nonlinear characteristics in the vicinity of 0, in which case we say that 0 is not a simple singular point.

If at least some of the $a_{kl} \neq 0$, we define the *associated linear system*

$$\dot{\xi}_k = \sum_{l=1}^{n} a_{kl}\xi_l \qquad (k, l = 1, \ldots, n) \qquad (2.9)$$

and assume that in the immediate vicinity of 0, Eq. (2.9) exhibits all the essential features of (2.7). It was shown by A. M. Liapunov (see, for example, Kaplan [17] or Letov [20]) that this assumption is legitimate if and only if none of the n eigenvalues λ_i of (2.9) has zero real part. Linearization (2.9) is frequently referred to as Liapunov's first method.

If the associated linear system does not exist or is not legitimate according to Liapunov, the nonlinear terms $O_k(\xi_1, \ldots, \xi_n)$ must be considered. In this chapter, we shall generally assume that a legitimate associated linear system exists.

System (2.9) is stable if *all* the eigenvalues λ_i have negative real part and is unstable if one or more of the λ_i have positive real part. If it is stable, any state $\boldsymbol{\xi}(0)$ sufficiently close to 0 is brought into 0 after an infinitely long time according to the familiar exponential law

$$\xi_k(t) = C_1 e^{\lambda_1 t} + \cdots C_n e^{\lambda_n t} \qquad (2.10)$$

where the n integration constants C_i are uniquely determined by the known initial state $\boldsymbol{\xi}(0)$.

The shape of the resulting trajectory depends on the location of the eigenvalues in the complex λ-plane. In the case of a two-state system, we may have *nodes*, *foci*, *saddles*, and *vortices* (or centers) depending on the values of the four parameters a_{11}, a_{12}, a_{21}, a_{22}. In the n-dimensional space, $n > 2$, these simple notions continue to have significance but do not describe *all* the motions observed in the vicinity of the origin. We will show the general shape of these four types of singular points in Fig. 5 in terms of the location of the eigenvalues λ_1 and λ_2 in the complex λ-plane. The reader who wishes actually to sketch a phase plane diagram corresponding to a specific problem is advised to consult a more detailed treatment of the subject, in particular Cunningham [8] and Kalman [14], where many patterns of trajectories close to a singular point are shown.

2.5 The Second-order Differential Equation. We consider the autonomous second-order differential equation

$$\ddot{x} + F(\dot{x}, x) = 0 \qquad (2.11)$$

which we can write in the form of (2.1) by letting

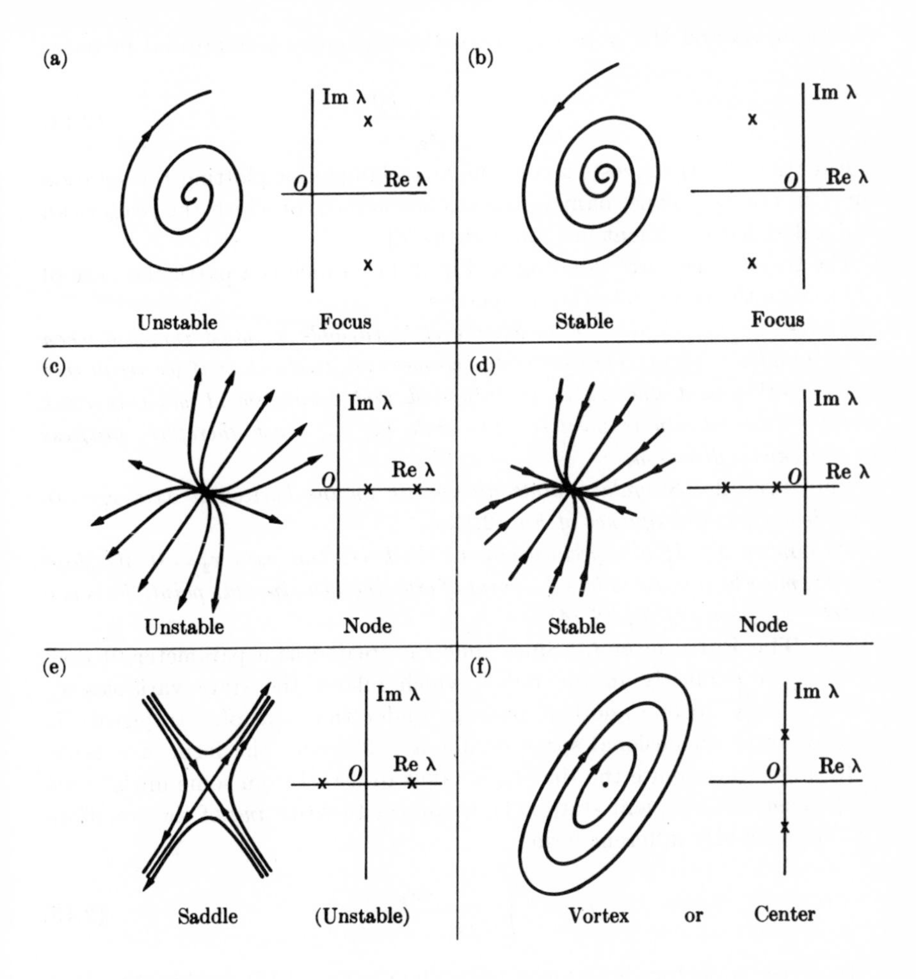

FIGURE 5. Types of singular points in terms of the location of the eigenvalues λ_1 and λ_2 in the complex λ-plane.

$$x = x_1$$

$$\dot{x}_1 = x_2 \tag{2.12}$$

in which case (2.11) becomes

$$\dot{x}_1 = x_2 \tag{2.13a}$$

$$\dot{x}_2 = -F(x_1, x_2), \tag{2.13b}$$

The state variables x_1 and x_2 are frequently called *displacement* and *velocity* because many mechanical problems described by Eq. (2.11) precisely involve these two quantities. If one divides Eq. (2.13b) by (2.13a), the time increment

dt disappears and the *slope* dx_2/dx_1 of the trajectory is expressed in terms of x_1, x_2

$$\frac{dx_2}{dx_1} = \frac{-F(x_1, x_2)}{x_2}. \tag{2.14}$$

Equation (2.14) suggests a convenient technique for plotting the solution curve in the x_1x_2 plane, namely the *isocline method*, of which the reader can find a detailed treatment in Cunningham [8].

The trajectories corresponding to Eq. (2.11), which is a particular case of (2.1), have the three following properties.

PROPERTY 1. *Because* $\dot{x}_1 = x_2$, *the state variable* x_1 *must increase when* $x_2 > 0$ *and vice versa. This property becomes intuitively clear if we recall that* x_1 *is displacement and* x_2 *is velocity and that displacement must increase whenever the velocity is positive. The state* $\{x_1, x_2\}$ *must, therefore, progress in a clockwise direction.*

PROPERTY 2. *Singular points always lie on the horizontal axis* $x_2 = 0$. *This is a direct consequence of Eq.* (2.13*a*).

PROPERTY 3. *If a trajectory crosses the horizontal axis* $x_2 = 0$, *its slope* dx_2/dx_1 *must be infinite unless the point of crossing is a singular point. This is a direct consequence of Eq.* (2.14).

2.6 The Parameter *t*. Since time t is treated as a parameter, it does not appear explicitly in the result which relates the state variables x_k, $k = 1, \ldots, n$, to one another, perhaps under the form of a trajectory in two- or three-dimensional space or, for $n > 3$, under the form of a table.

In order to compute the time t_{01} it takes to travel from some initial state $\mathbf{x}(0)$ to some subsequent state $\mathbf{x}(1)$, it suffices to write *any* of the equations (2.3) in a slightly different form

$$t_{01} = \int_{x_k(0)}^{x_k(1)} \frac{dx_k}{f_k(x_1, \ldots, x_n)}. \tag{2.15}$$

Since the trajectory is assumed to be known, Eq. (2.15) can be integrated.

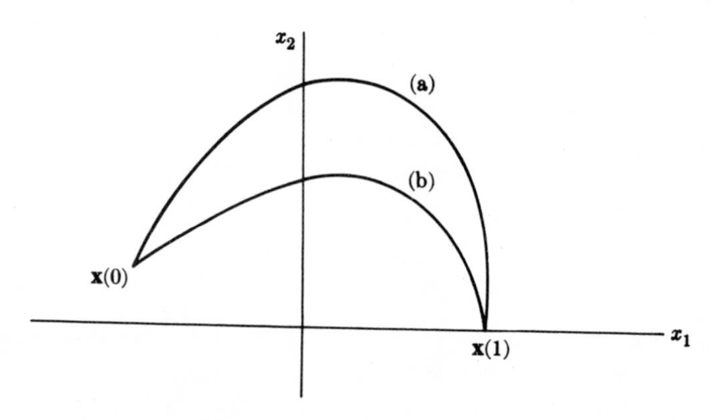

FIGURE 6. Fast trajectory (a), and slow trajectory (b).

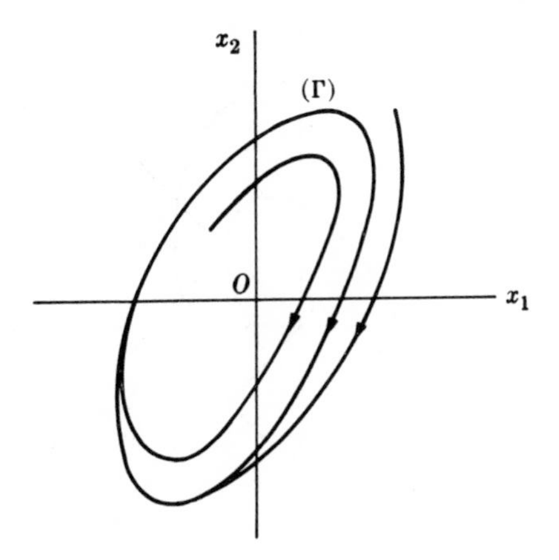

FIGURE 7. Stable limit cycle (Γ) of a second-order system.

In the special case of the second-order differential equation, we rewrite (2.15) and obtain the particularly simple expression

$$t_{01} = \int_{x_1(0)}^{x_1(1)} \frac{dx_1}{x_2}. \tag{2.16}$$

It is evident from Eq. (2.16) that t_{01} would decrease if x_2 were made larger, perhaps by an appropriate choice of the free parameters entering into (2.1). Given $\mathbf{x}(0)$ and $\mathbf{x}(1)$, it is apparent from Fig. 6 that one would normally prefer the system producing the upper trajectory (a) to that producing (b).

2.7 Limit Cycles.

DEFINITION. *A limit cycle is a nonself-intersecting closed solution curve*† *such that*

$$\mathbf{x}(t + lT) = \mathbf{x}(t) \qquad (l = 1, 2, \ldots,) \tag{2.17}$$

where T is a positive and real constant called the period of the limit cycle, and such that the magnitude of $\mathbf{x}(t)$ for sufficiently large values of t is the same for two initial states $\mathbf{x}(0)$ and $\mathbf{x}(0) + \delta\mathbf{x}(0)$ separated by the arbitrarily small increment $\delta\mathbf{x}(0)$.

This last restriction distinguishes limit cycles from vortices which are characteristic of conservative systems. In the time domain, both limit cycles and vortices correspond to periodic motion. Figure 7 shows a limit cycle of a second-order system.

† The terms limit cycle, closed solution curve, periodic solution, and stationary oscillation are used indifferently in the literature.

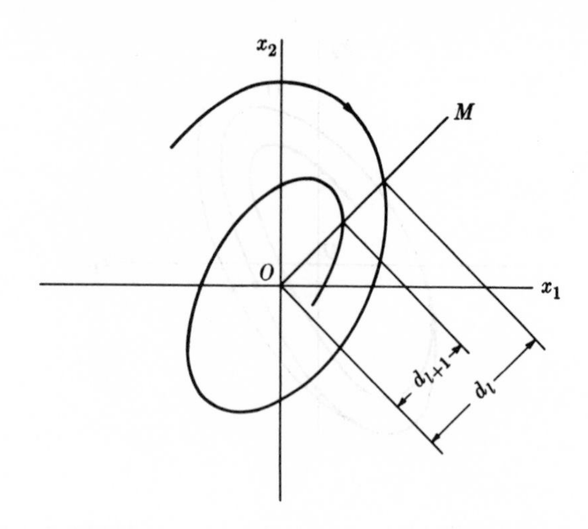

FIGURE 8. Distances d_l and d_{l+1} measured at successive crossings of OM.

Nearby trajectories may converge toward the solution curve, in which case we speak of a stable limit cycle; or they may diverge from it (unstable limit cycle).

Limit cycles are comparable to singular points in that we have a steady-state solution which may be stable or unstable. This comparison is further developed in Section 2.8. Limit cycles do not exist in the theory of linear systems; they are entirely different from vortices or centers, in that a stable limit cycle is structurally stable† whereas a vortex is not.

The study of limit cycles is extremely important because their presence is generally undesirable (except of course in oscillators) and their existence is difficult to predict with mathematical rigor.

2.8 Stability of Limit Cycles. Let us assume that there exists a closed solution curve (Γ) satisfying Eq. (2.17). For the purpose of this section, it suffices to define the stability of (Γ) as follows:

DEFINITION. *If, after the motion* $\mathbf{x}$ *has been slightly displaced from* (Γ), *it returns to* (Γ) *as* $t \to \infty$, *then* (Γ) *is a stable limit cycle. If* $\mathbf{x}$ *does not return to* (Γ) *for* $t \to \infty$, *then* (Γ) *is an unstable limit cycle.*

The seldom encountered case of a semistable limit cycle is subsequently discussed.

† We quite generally define a system to be structurally stable if a small parameter change does not cause radically different system behavior. A vortex is not structurally stable since an arbitrarily small amount of friction would ultimately bring the motion to rest.

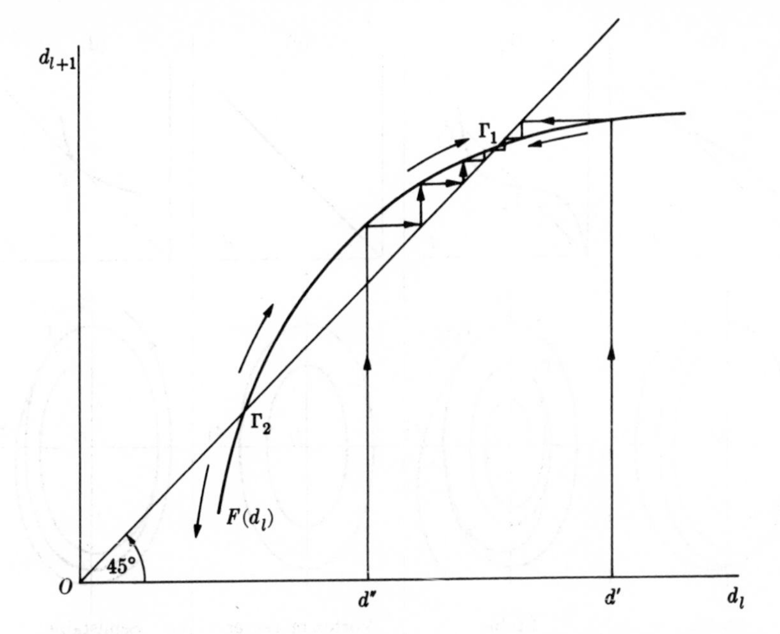

FIGURE 9. Plot of d_{l+1} as a function of d_l. Two arbitrarily chosen initial distances d' and d'' are seen to converge at the stable limit cycle (Γ_1). (Γ_2) is unstable.

2.9 Classification of Limit Cycles.† Let us consider a two-state system and let us plot the distance $d_{l+1} = \sqrt{\sum_1^n x_k^2}$ measured on a line OM of arbitrary slope in terms of d_l. The index l indicates how often OM has been intersected by some trajectory $\mathbf{x}(t)$, as shown in Fig. 8.

If we now plot d_{l+1} as a function of d_l for several values of l, we obtain a set of points, which we join by a smooth curve $F(d_l)$, as shown in Fig. 9. Having obtained this curve, we study the variation of d_l as time progresses, by means of the geometrical construction shown. It is observed that (Γ_1) corresponds to a stable limit cycle whereas (Γ_2) corresponds to an unstable limit cycle.

On the basis of the geometrical construction of Fig. 9, we can imagine different situations corresponding to different curves $F(d_l)$ as shown in Fig. 10. It is seen that the stability of a limit cycle depends on the magnitude of the derivative $dF/d(d_l)$ at some point of intersection such as Γ_1. More specifically, if

$$\left[\frac{dF}{d(d_l)}\right]_\Gamma < 1 \tag{2.18}$$

† A more detailed treatment of this section can be found in Solodownikow [31].

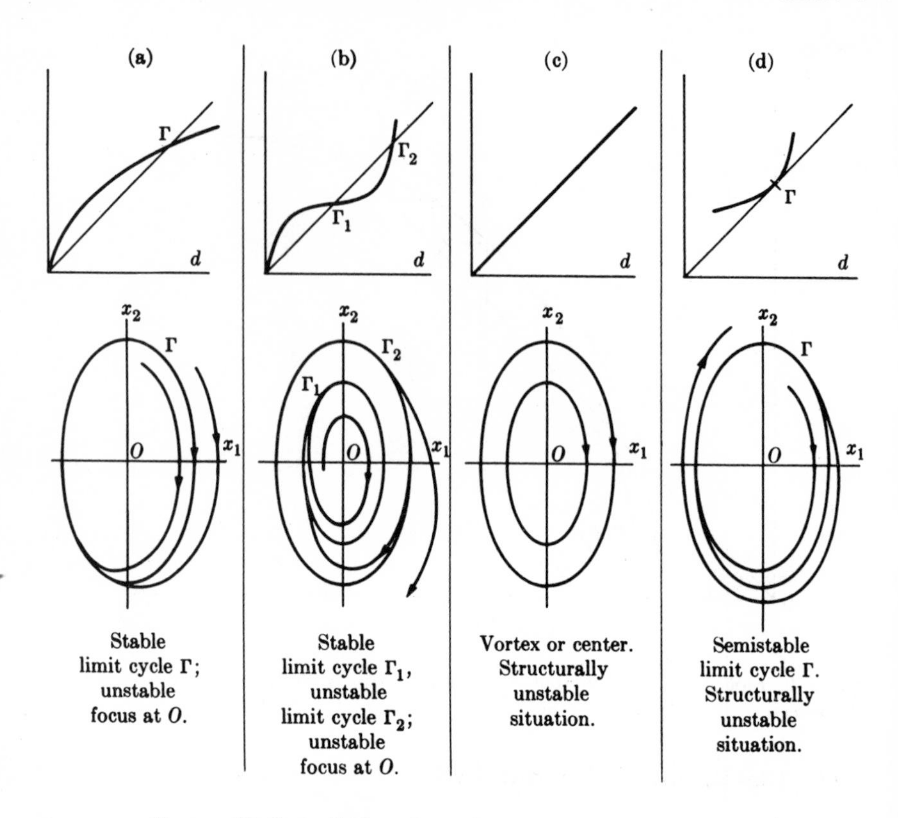

FIGURE 10. Some limit cycle configurations in terms of $F(d_l)$.

then (Γ) is stable, and if

$$\left[\frac{dF}{d(d_l)}\right]_{\Gamma} > 1$$

then (Γ) is unstable.

It is further concluded that stable and unstable limit cycles must alternate, a focus being considered as a special case of a limit cycle.

N. Minorsky has investigated the properties of limit cycles by a similar method [23], which he refers to as the *stroboscopic method*. The reason for this terminology is that, in fact, we look at the trajectory only at the discrete instants of time T when it crosses the line OM. For the purpose of this investigation, the original differential equation has, therefore, been replaced by a difference equation, in which the radius vector d observed at T_{l+1} is related to d_l observed at T_l. If, as $l \to \infty$, $d_l \to$ constant, we know that there exists a stable limit cycle. In other words, the stable limit cycle of the original differential equation corresponds to a stable equilibrium point of the stroboscopic difference equation. This is a most important result, since

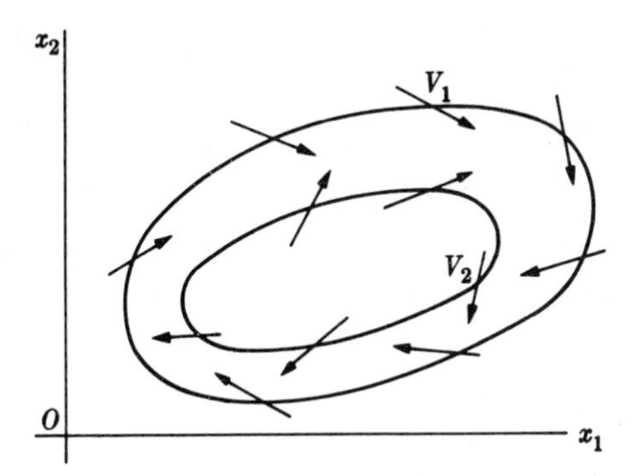

FIGURE 11. The contours V_1 and V_2.

it is often not too difficult to study the properties of stability of such singular points.

It is shown in Minorsky [23] that this difference equation can be obtained in certain cases in a straightforward fashion from the given differential equation.

2.10 A Geometric Argument. Let us first consider the case of an autonomous two-state system and let us assume that we have found two simple closed contours V_1 and V_2 such that V_2 is entirely contained in V_1. Now suppose that we have ascertained that all the trajectories on V_1 point inside V_1 and that all the trajectories on V_2 point outside V_2. This situation is shown in Fig. 11.

Under these conditions, we are certain that there exists at least one stable limit cycle inside the annular defined by V_1 and V_2, provided it does not contain any singular point. There could be k stable limit cycles and $k - 1$ unstable limit cycles, where k is odd.

If all the trajectories on V_1 pointed outside V_1, and all the trajectories on V_2 pointed inside V_2, we could draw the same conclusions except that "stable" would be replaced by "unstable" and vice versa.

If the system were of an order higher than second, we would no longer be in a position to conclude that there was an odd number of limit cycles since *almost* periodic solutions could exist within the annular defined by V_1 and V_2. An example of this situation is the spherical pendulum which yields a pattern of Lissajou figures; these obviously do not satisfy Eq. (2.17).

The major difficulty of this procedure is to find suitable contours V_1 and V_2, and to make certain that *all* the trajectories point in the right directions. The second method of Liapunov turns out to be most helpful in those instances where it is possible to find a positive definite function $V(\mathbf{x})$ such that the total derivative dV/dt is negative definite on all of V_1 and positive definite on all of V_2. V_1 and V_2 are the closed surfaces obtained by letting $V(\mathbf{x}) = C_1$, $V(\mathbf{x}) = C_2$, where C_1 and C_2 are two positive constants such that $C_1 > C_2$.

2.11 Van der Pol's Equation. We consider the now classical second-order system first investigated by B. van der Pol.

$$\dot{x}_1 = x_2$$
$$\dot{x}_2 = -x_1 + \mu(1 - x_1^2)x_2 \quad (\mu > 0). \tag{2.19}$$

The obvious solution is $x_1 = 0$, $x_2 = 0$, but this obvious solution is unstable since the eigenvalues of the linearized system are

$$\lambda_1, \lambda_2 = \frac{\mu \pm \sqrt{\mu^2 - 4}}{2}.$$

For $\mu < 2$, the origin is an unstable focus.

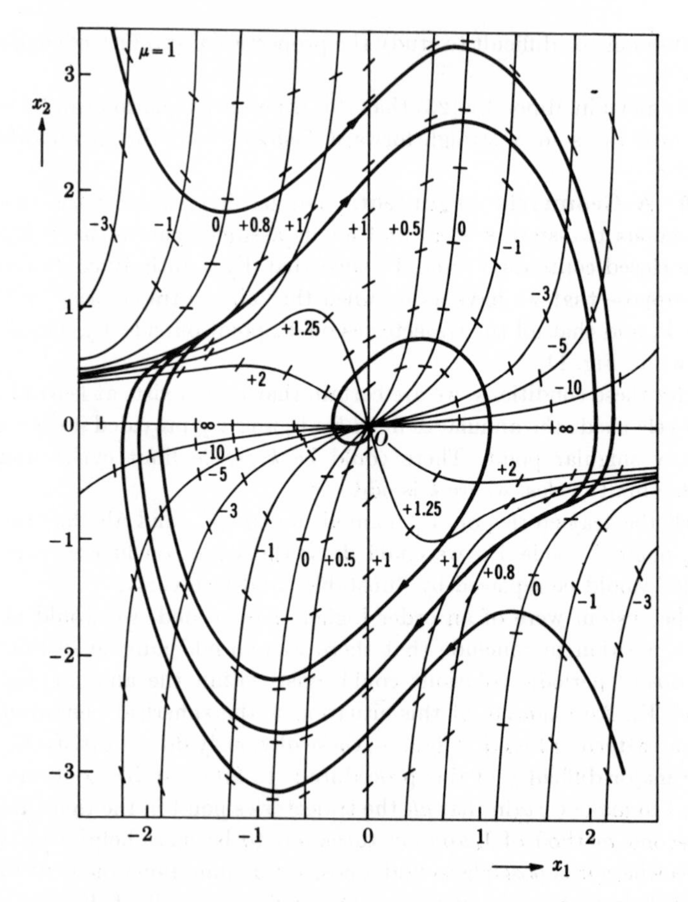

FIGURE 12. Isoclynes in a z, v diagram. The heavy lines follow the slopes indicated on the isoclynes; they form a solution of the differential equation.

The various classical analysis methods thus far presented do not tell us very much more about the behavior of Eq. (2.19). Our next step would be to construct the phase plane, using the isocline method and assuming several sets of initial conditions. This, of course, is involved and time-consuming.

Our engineering familiarity with the properties of linear second-order systems might suggest that Eq. (2.19) is stable for sufficiently large values of x_1, since the damping term $-\mu(1 - x_1^2)$ would ultimately become positive. This then suggests the existence of at least one stable limit cycle surrounding the origin.

The phase plane corresponding to $\mu = 1$ is obtained graphically by the isocline method and is shown in Fig. 12. There is indeed one stable limit cycle.

The heuristic methods, to be presented in Section 3, yield this same result with practically no labor. Liapunov's second method also may be used to advantage as it specifies *that* region of the phase plane where all transients diminish.

2.12 Control of a Representative Nonlinear Process. As a further illustration of the topological techniques, we consider a pendulum type of plant. Such plants are frequently encountered in nonlinear mechanics and are not easily tractable by the methods presented in the subsequent sections.

We investigate the classical problem of the synchronization (or pull-in) of a synchronous motor and we describe a scheme whereby the critical

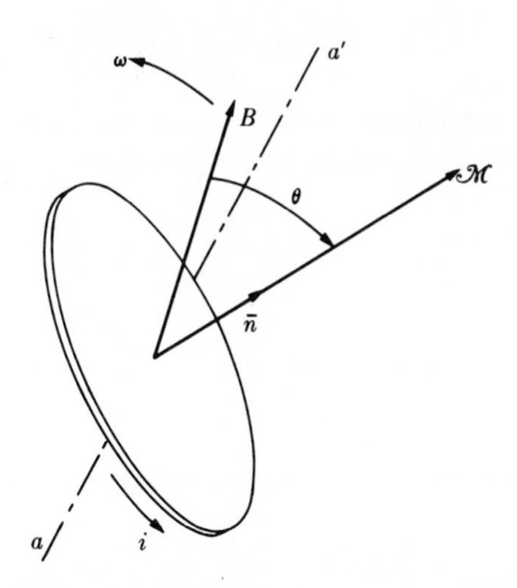

FIGURE 13. Model of polyphase synchronous motor. B = rotating field set up by the stator. The velocity of B is ω radians per second. $\mathfrak{M}$ = magnetic moment of the rotor. i = *total* current in the rotor coil. $\mathfrak{M}$ is proportional to i. θ = angle between B and $\bar{n}$, which is a normal direction to the coil.

process of pull-in is facilitated. The conclusions we arrive at hold for a large class of electro-mechanical structures, ranging from pendula to satellite attitude controls.

A simplified model of the polyphase synchronous motor under discussion is shown in Fig. 13. The vectors B, (magnetic field), and $\mathscr{M}$, (magnetic moment), rotate in the same plane, which is perpendicular to the axis aa' of the rotor coil.

Below synchronism, $\bar{n}$ rotates in the same counter clockwise direction as B, but at a lower angular velocity. Therefore, θ constantly increases.

We assume that in this hypothetical machine, the coil is connected to a constant current source. The torque due to the interaction of B on $\mathscr{M}$ is, therefore,

$$\begin{aligned} T_{B\mathscr{M}} &= -B\mathscr{M} \sin \theta \\ B, \mathscr{M} &= \text{constants.} \end{aligned} \tag{2.20}$$

It is apparent from Eq. (2.20) that the average motive torque is zero unless the average rotor speed is ω.

Furthermore, we assume that there is a constant resistive torque C due to an external load and a small frictional torque, $f\dot{\theta}, f =$ constant, due to the presence of damper windings.

Denoting by J the total inertia of the rotating parts, we write the system equations in terms of the state variables $\theta_1 = \theta$, $\theta_2 = \dot{\theta}$

$$\begin{aligned} \dot{\theta}_1 &= \theta_2 \\ \dot{\theta}_2 &= -\frac{B\mathscr{M}}{J} \sin \theta_1 - \frac{f}{J}\theta_2 + \frac{C}{J}. \end{aligned} \tag{2.21}$$

The problem is to determine those regions in the phase plane from where the motor pulls into synchronism, that is, for which Eq. (2.21) has a stable solution

$$\begin{aligned} \theta_{1e} &= \sin^{-1} \frac{C}{B\mathscr{M}} \\ \theta_{2e} &= 0. \end{aligned} \tag{2.22}$$

Obviously, Eq. (2.22) is possible only if

$$C < B\mathscr{M}. \tag{2.23}$$

To proceed, we assume that for some stated value of C, Eq. (2.21) has been normalized to

$$\begin{aligned} \dot{\theta}_1 &= \theta_2 \\ \dot{\theta}_2 &= -\sin \theta_1 - f\theta_2 + \tfrac{1}{2} \end{aligned} \tag{2.24}$$

and that the motion is very lightly damped, i.e.,

$$0 < f \ll \sqrt{2}. \tag{2.25}$$

System (2.24) has equilibrium points at

$$\theta_{1e} = \frac{\pi}{6} + k\pi \qquad (k = \text{integer})$$

$$\theta_{2e} = 0, \tag{2.26}$$

Linearization of Eq. (2.24) about the equilibrium points (2.26) indicates that the stable and unstable solutions denoted by the indices *es* and *eu* alternate;

$$\theta_{1es} = \frac{\pi}{6} + 2l\pi \qquad (l = \text{integer})$$

is stable and

$$\theta_{1e\mu} = \frac{\pi}{6} + (2l + 1)\pi$$

is unstable.

As a result of assumption (2.25), the θ_{1es} are foci and the θ_{1eu} are saddle points.

In order to determine those regions in the phase plane from which all the trajectories converge toward any of the foci, we consider the frictionless (or conservative) system

$$\begin{aligned} \dot{\theta}_1 &= \theta_2 \\ \dot{\theta}_2 &= -\sin\theta_1 + \tfrac{1}{2}. \end{aligned} \tag{2.27}$$

The second equation of (2.27) can be integrated once as a consequence of the relation

$$\int \dot{\theta}_2 \, d\theta_1 = \tfrac{1}{2}\theta_2^{\,2}.$$

Therefore

$$\tfrac{1}{2}\theta_2^{\,2} = \cos\theta_1 + \frac{\theta_1}{2} + a \tag{2.28}$$

where a is an integration constant which is determined by the initial conditions $\{\theta_1(0), \theta_2(0)\}$. Equation (2.28) is the explicit solution of the conservative system (2.27). We note that for sufficiently large values of θ_1, Eq. (2.28) reduces to a family of parabolas

$$\tfrac{1}{2}\theta_2^{\,2} = \frac{\theta_1}{2} + a. \tag{2.29}$$

The resulting phase-plane diagram is shown in Fig. 14.

A trajectory of particular interest is the solution curve passing through the saddles $\theta_{1e\mu}$. These curves divide the plane into stable (shaded) and unstable regions and are therefore termed *separatrices*. The trajectories inside a separatrix are *vortices*.

Returning now to the lightly damped system (2.24), it may be expected that the global aspect of its phase plane does not differ very much from that

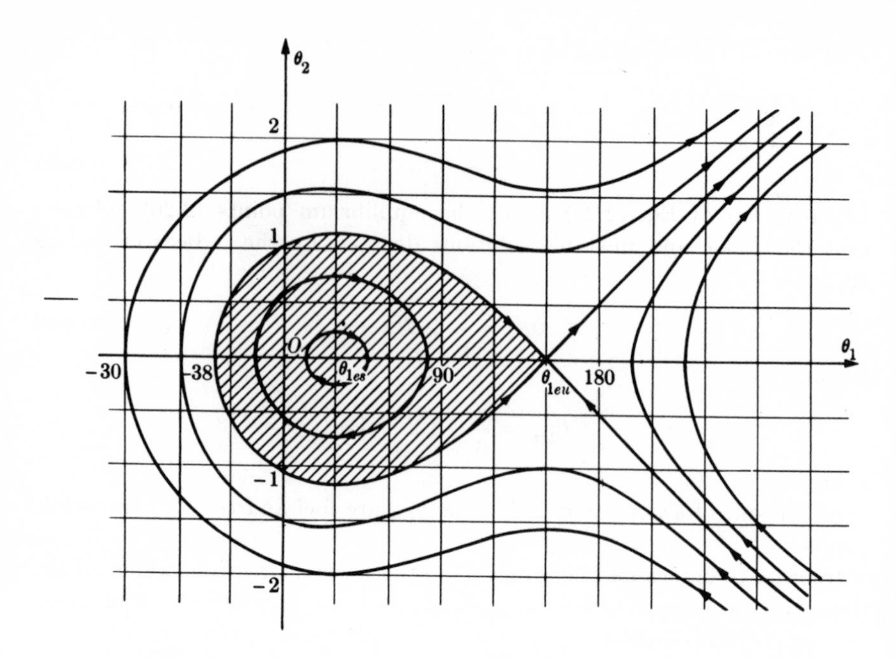

FIGURE 14. Phase-plane diagram of Eq. (2.27). The shaded region is stable.

shown in Fig. 14. The vortices, in particular, become stable spirals terminating at $\{\theta_{1es}, \theta_{2es}\}$. We continue to assume that the separatrix of Fig. 14 approximately defines the region from which pull-in occurs.

Since a synchronous motor is usually brought near synchronism as an induction motor,† $\theta_2(0)$ is always positive, but $\theta_1(0)$ can assume any value when the current i is switched on. Therefore, it happens frequently that the hypothetical synchronous motor under discussion does not pull in, especially when $\theta_2(0)$ is not sufficiently small. Moreover, if C is made larger, it can be shown that the area inside the separatrix further decreases.

These difficulties are partly due to the fact that the net torque

$$T = -B\mathscr{M} \sin \theta_1 + C \qquad (C > 0) \quad (2.30)$$

is not *sign definite*. By virtue of the fact that $\theta_2(0)$ is positive, we wish to render T as negative as possible. The constant excitation model thus far discussed is clearly not very efficient in this respect. Therefore we propose to reverse the polarity of the excitation for

$$(2l - 1)\pi < \theta < 2l\pi \quad (l = \text{integer})$$

† In this mode of operation, the rotor coil is short-circuited and no current is supplied by the external exciter.

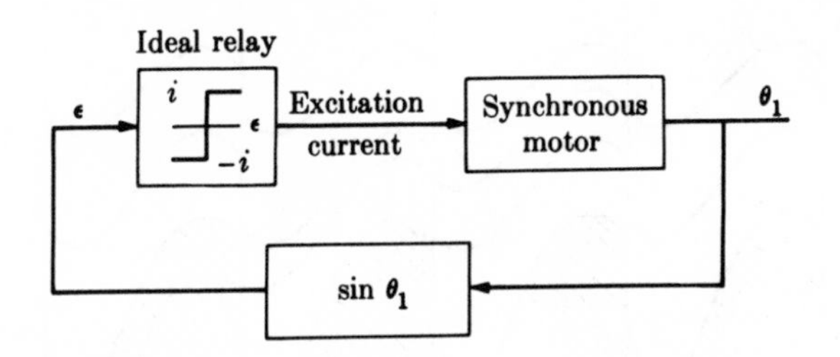

FIGURE 15. Control system corresponding to an excitation switched machine. The nonlinear network $\epsilon = \sin \theta_1$ supplies the proper coil voltage to the ideal relay, which provides the plant with the piecewise constant current $\pm i$.

in order to render the net torque as negative as possible and thus facilitate pull-in.

It can be shown by elementary algebra that under these conditions the net torque, averaged over θ_1, is

$$\bar{T} = C - \frac{2B\mathcal{M}}{\pi} = C - 0.636B\mathcal{M} \tag{2.31}$$

and that no other switching strategy renders $\bar{T}$ more negative. Since $\bar{T}$ is negative for

$$C < \frac{2B\mathcal{M}}{\pi} \tag{2.32}$$

we expect the motor ultimately to pull into synchronism, whatever the values of $\{\theta_1(0),\ \theta_2(0)\}$. This, we recall, was not the case for the constant excitation model.

A control system corresponding to the switched excitation machine is shown in Fig. 15.

When the excitation current is $-i$, Eqs. (2.24) and (2.27) become, respectively,

$$\begin{aligned} \dot{\theta}_1 &= \theta_2 \\ \dot{\theta}_2 &= +\sin \theta_1 - f\theta_2 + \tfrac{1}{2} \end{aligned} \tag{2.33}$$

and

$$\begin{aligned} \dot{\theta}_1 &= \theta_2 \\ \dot{\theta}_2 &= +\sin \theta_1 + \tfrac{1}{2}. \end{aligned} \tag{2.34}$$

The shift $\bar{\theta} = \theta \pm \pi$ clearly transforms Eqs. (2.33) and (2.34) into (2.24) and (2.27), respectively. This means that the phase diagram of (2.34) is precisely that of Fig. 14, except for a shift of π to the right or to the left.

In order to see how equilibrium is reached in the case of the nonlinear control system of Fig. 15, we consider the *combined* diagram of Fig. 16.

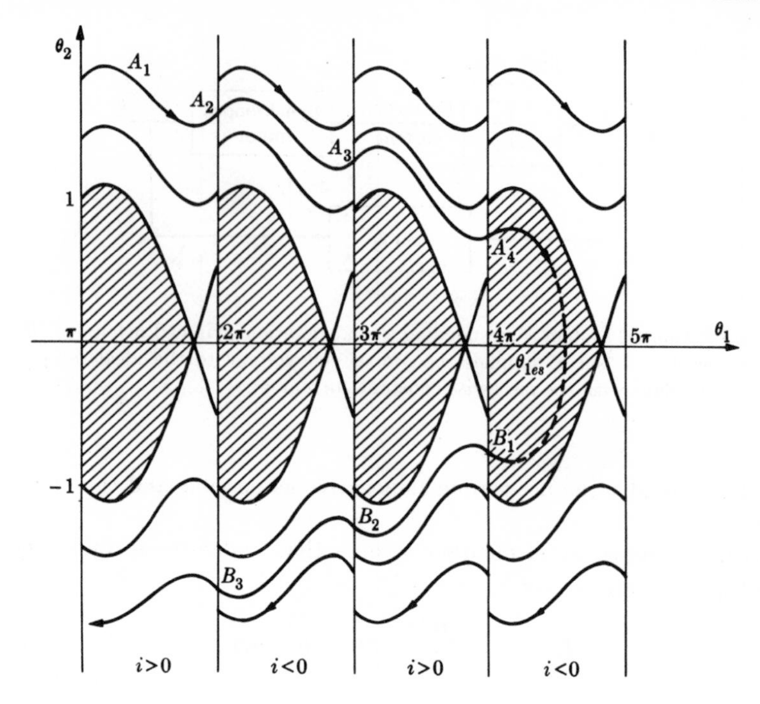

FIGURE 16. Combined phase diagram. The trajectories corresponding to the stable condition A_1 and the unstable condition B_1 are shown.

It is seen that any initial disturbance such as A_1, $\theta_2(0) > 0$, is brought inside one of the stable shaded areas. This is not so for initial conditions such as B_1, $\theta_2(0) < 0$. The reason for this is that the switching strategy adopted here supplies a net torque which, on the average, diminishes θ_2. If initial conditions such as B_1 were expected to occur, a different strategy would have to be adopted.

Following A_1 as it passes the various *switching boundaries* at A_2, A_3, and finally arrives inside a stable area at A_4, we observe that it would not remain inside this area, but would leave it at B_1—see the dashed curve of Fig. 16—unless a slightly more complex switching strategy were adopted. We might, for instance, prohibit all further switchings after the condition $\theta_2 = 0$ has been accomplished once.

We now recapitulate.

The excitation switched motor moves to a stable equilibrium point regardless of the initial state, provided $C < 0.636B\mathscr{M}$ and $\theta_2(0) > 0$.

The switching strategy is optimal, in that equilibrium is reached with a minimum number of switchings.

3. The Heuristic† Methods

The approximation techniques to be discussed in this section comprise the harmonic methods and the nonlinear root locus.

The harmonic methods, first discussed by Poincaré and extensively applied under the name of Describing Function during the last two decades, are generally preferred to other methods when a harmonic forcing function is present or when a limit cycle is anticipated. The fundamental idea is to replace the nonlinear portion(*s*) by a gain which is dependent on the amplitude and sometimes the frequency of the steady-state periodic motion *whose existence one assumes*. It is important to understand that the nonlinear system is replaced by an *associated linear system* and that linearization is performed in such a way that the approximation is valid for periodic motion. Previously, Eq. (2.9), higher order terms have been neglected and the analysis of small motions became possible. Here, higher order terms are considered in a *plausible* way, and the analysis is no longer restricted to small motions.

A further advantage of the harmonic approach is that it generally accommodates nonlinear systems which cannot be represented by the first approximation (2.9), because $\bar{f}_k$ is not regular.

We will assume here that there is only *one* singular point and that the nonlinearities are *odd*. The linear portions of the system must be low-pass in order that the higher harmonics generated in the nonlinearity will be suppressed when reentering the nonlinear two-port. In other words, the system output $y(t)$ is assumed to be nearly sinusoidal.

3.1 The Harmonic Balance [8]. The oldest method, which is known under the name of *harmonic balance*, indicates whether periodic motion is possible, that is, whether limit cycles can exist, but does not yield any information on their stability. Because of the extreme simplicity of the concept, we confine ourselves to one example.

Example. We consider van der Pol's equation

$$\ddot{x} - \mu(1 - x^2)\dot{x} + x = 0. \qquad (\mu > 0) \qquad (3.1)$$

Neglecting higher order terms, as in Eq. (2.9), we obtain the unstable small motion

$$\ddot{x} - \mu\dot{x} + x = 0 \qquad (3.2)$$

but we learn nothing about system behavior after $\mathbf{x}$ leaves the immediate vicinity of 0.

According to the harmonic balance method, motion is approximately described in terms of the unknowns (A, ω)

$$x = A \sin \omega t \qquad (3.3)$$

if in fact motion is periodic. The method then is:

† From the Greek "heurisko": to aid or to guide in discovery, to find out.

(1) To express any nonlinear portions of the system differential equation, here $\mu(1 - x^2)\dot{x}$ in terms of Eq. (3.3).

(2) To obtain the *fundamental* Fourier component of the nonlinear term

$$\mu(1 - A^2\omega^2 \sin^2 \omega t)A\omega \cos \omega t$$

namely

$$\mu\left(1 - \frac{A^2}{4}\right)(A\omega \cos \omega t).$$

The linear equation associated with (3.1) is thus

$$\ddot{x} - \mu\left(1 - \frac{A^2}{4}\right)\dot{x} + x = 0. \tag{3.4}$$

(3) To determine the unknowns (A, ω) by matching the sine and cosine terms of

$$-A\omega^2 \sin \omega t - \mu\left(1 - \frac{A^2}{4}\right)\omega A \cos \omega t + A \sin \omega t \tag{3.5}$$

with the result that

$$A = 2, \omega = 1.$$

3.2 The Describing Function [32, 27, 18]. This method, developed almost two decades ago, is an adaptation of Nyquist's stability criterion. It may indicate whether a nonlinear system is stable for small and for large motion, but it is generally used to investigate the existence and stability properties of limit cycles. The basic principle again is to linearize all nonlinear components by assuming that harmonic motion (A, ω) exists and by assigning a complex nonlinear gain $J(A, j\omega)$ to each nonlinearity. This gain J is called the describing function; hence the name of the method.

We consider the stable single-input nonlinear component N, Fig. 17, excited by

$$\eta = A \sin \omega t$$

and perform a Fourier expansion of

$$\sigma = B_0 + B_1 \sin(\omega t + \varphi_1) + \cdots + B_l \sin(l\omega t + \varphi_l) + \cdots$$

$$(l = 0, 1, \ldots, \infty) \tag{3.6}$$

where the B_l and φ_l are functions of A and of ω.

We assume for simplicity that $B_0 = 0$—the nonlinearity is supposed to be odd—and we consider only the fundamental component of σ, namely

$$B_1 \sin(\omega t + \varphi_1) = (B_1 \cos \varphi_1) \sin \omega t + (B_1 \sin \varphi_1) \cos \omega t. \tag{3.7}$$

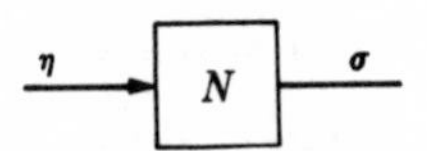

FIGURE 17. Stable single input nonlinear component $\sigma = N(\eta)$.

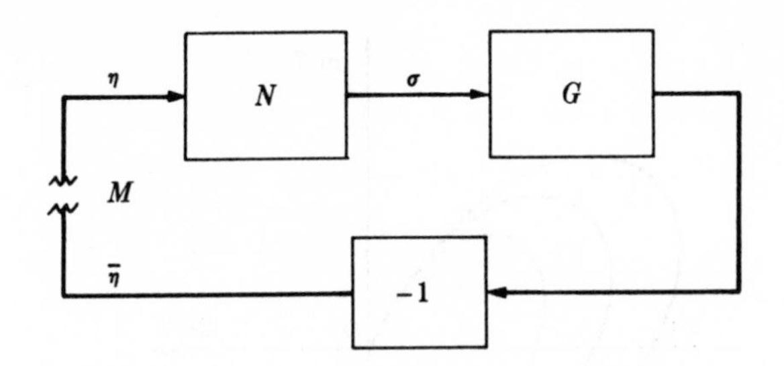

FIGURE 18. Nonlinear system under consideration.

We define

$$P = \frac{\omega}{\pi A}\int_0^{2\pi/\omega} N(A \sin \omega t) \sin \omega t \, dt = B_1 \cos \varphi_1$$

$$Q = \frac{\omega}{\pi A}\int_0^{2\pi/\omega} N(A \sin \omega t) \cos \omega t \, dt = B_1 \sin \varphi_1 \tag{3.8}$$

which is related to the *complex nonlinear gain*, or describing function

$$J(A, j\omega) \triangleq P + jQ \tag{3.9}$$

and connect the (presumably) sinusoidal quantities η and σ by

$$\sigma(j\omega) \cong J(A, j\omega)\eta(j\omega). \tag{3.10}$$

The complex quantity J frequently does not depend on ω; those situations where the describing function is ω-dependent are discussed in the subsequent section.

Having thus defined J, we adapt Nyquist's stability criterion [6] of linear system analysis to the nonlinear system under consideration. We restrict ourselves to unforced structures comprising one nonlinear block N and one linear block G, as shown in Fig. 18.

The fundamental idea now is to replace N by $J(A, j\omega)$ and thus arrive at an associated linear system, whose properties we analyze by opening the loop at M, by letting

$$\eta(t) = A \sin \omega t$$

and by sketching the familiar Nyquist diagram of the *normalized* return ratio

$$T(A, j\omega) = J(A, j\omega)G(j\omega) = \frac{\bar{\eta}(A, j\omega)}{A} \quad (0 \leqslant A \leqslant \infty). \tag{3.11}$$

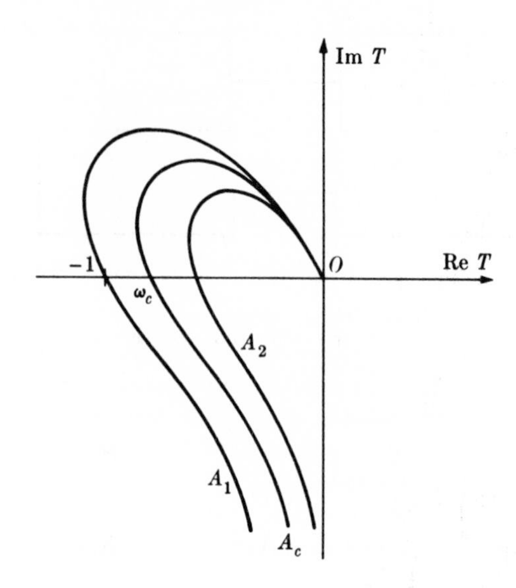

FIGURE 19. Family of Nyquist curves. The values A_c, ω_c are assigned to the curve passing through the critical point $-1 + j0$.

Since the system under consideration is nonlinear, we obtain a family of curves, each curve corresponding to one particular value of the real and positive parameter A, as shown in Fig. 19.

We deduce from this family of Nyquist curves

(1) the characteristics (A, ω) of existing stationary oscillations;
(2) the stability of these oscillations;
(3) stability in the large and small motion stability, in accordance with the three rules listed below.

RULE 1. *If*

$$T(A_c, j\omega_c) = -1 \tag{3.12}$$

for one or several parameter pairs A_c, ω_c, *then there exist one, or several, stationary oscillations* (A_c, ω_c) *which may be stable or unstable.*

RULE 2. *Let* (A_c, ω_c) *be a parameter pair such that Eq.* (3.12) *is satisfied. Let* $T(A_c + \delta A, j\omega)$ *be the adjacent Nyquist plot corresponding to the small positive increment* δA. *If* $T(A_c + \delta A, j\omega)$ *is stable,*† *then the stationary oscillation* (A_c, ω_c) *is stable. Conversely, if* $T(A_c + \delta A, j\omega)$ *is unstable, then the stationary oscillation* (A_c, ω_c) *is unstable.*

† If T is minimum phase, stability simply requires that $T(A_c + \delta A, j\omega)$ should not enclose the critical point $-1 + j0$ as ω varies from $-\infty$ to $+\infty$.

RULE 3. *If $T(A, j\omega)$ is stable for all $A > A_l$, then the motion may be expected to be bounded regardless of initial conditions. Also, if $T(A, j\omega)$ is stable for all $A < A_s$, the system has stable small motion near $A = 0$. This does not necessarily mean that there is a stable equilibrium point, since the system may chatter at infinite frequency and zero amplitude.*

For computational reasons, many authors prefer to make separate plots of $G(j\omega)$, and of $-\dfrac{1}{J(A, j\omega)}$ as shown in Fig. 20. Stationary oscillations generally exist at those intersection points M where the angular frequencies ω are identical. Although this procedure requires less effort to determine the characteristics (A_c, ω_c) of stationary oscillations, it may be more difficult to analyze stability. For further information and example-problems, the reader is referred to (Kochenburger [18, 19] and Seifert and Steeg [27]).

3.3 Types of Nonlinearities. In the previous section, we have concerned ourselves with single-variable nonlinearities $\sigma = N(\eta)$ which were subject to the additional constraint that

$$N(-\eta) = -N(\eta) \tag{3.13}$$

as a consequence of which the dc Fourier component B_0 vanishes.

Within the stated class of nonlinearities, we distinguish between

(1) frequency-independent single-valued nonlinearities;
(2) frequency-independent double-valued nonlinearities;
(3) frequency-dependent nonlinearities.

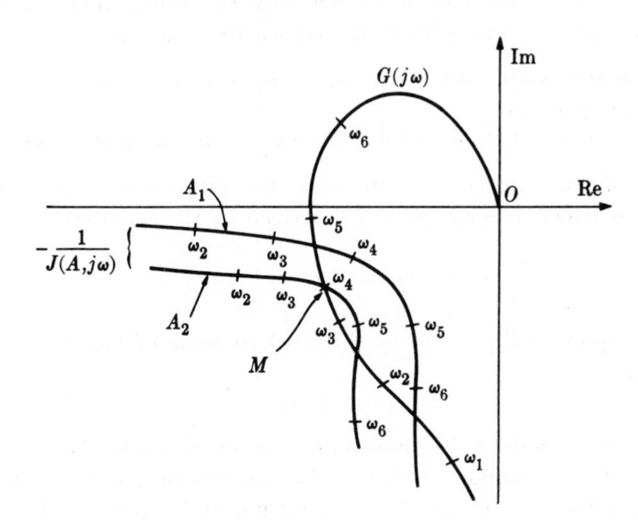

FIGURE 20. Plot of $G(j\omega)$ and $-\dfrac{1}{J(A, j\omega)}$. A limit cycle exists at N where the two curves intersect at the same angular frequency ω_4.

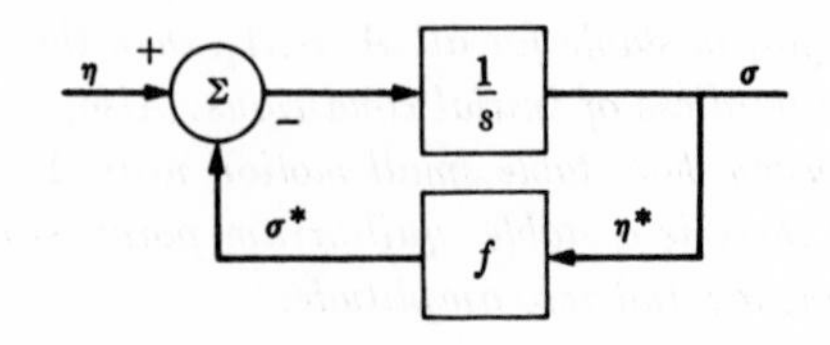

FIGURE 21. Transformation of frequency-dependent nonlinearity into frequency-independent nonlinearity and energy storage elements.

With reference to Fig. 17 we say that a nonlinearity is frequency-independent if the characteristic $\sigma = N(\eta)$ depends only on η and not on $\dot{\eta}$, $\ddot{\eta}$, etc. If, in a specific experiment, we selected a forcing function,

$$\eta = A \sin \omega t \tag{3.14}$$

then $\sigma(t)$ would be a function of A, but not of ω.

Because of this restriction, nonlinearities of type (1) are represented by a describing function which is not dependent on ω and which is real if the function $\sigma = N(\eta)$ is single-valued; see the second equation (3.8).

The describing function corresponding to a nonlinearity of type (2) is complex, but not dependent on ω either.

Nonlinearities of type (3) are frequently encountered in practice. Most texts concerned with the describing function do not discuss such nonlinearities, whose describing functions cannot be computed by the straightforward approach of the previous section; see Eqs. (3.8) and (3.9).

We now present two techniques whereby the conventional describing function concept is extended to such nonlinearities, namely:

(1) the transformation into a frequency-independent nonlinearity and linear energy-storage elements;

(2) the calculation of the describing function via the harmonic balance.

By way of example, we assume that the given frequency-dependent nonlinear phenomenon is adequately described by the equation

$$\frac{d\sigma}{dt} + f(\sigma) = \eta \qquad f(-\sigma) = -f(\sigma). \tag{3.15}$$

We may represent Eq. (3.15) by the block diagram of Fig. 21, where the nonlinearity

$$\sigma^* = f(\eta^*) \tag{3.16}$$

is frequency-independent. We next lump the linear portion together with all the other linear components included in the system and thus obtain the required structure of Fig. 18. This constitutes technique (1). A complete example is given in Section 3.8.

We alternatively assume that the steady-state response of σ to (2) is approximately

$$\sigma = S \sin (\omega t - \varphi). \tag{3.17}$$

Substituting Eq. (3.17) into (3.15) and taking the fundamental Fourier component $\mathscr{F}_1$ of $f(\sigma)$, we obtain in the case of a single-valued nonlinearity f

$$S\omega \cos (\omega t - \varphi) + \mathscr{F}_1(S) \sin (\omega t - \varphi) = A \sin \omega t. \tag{3.18}$$

Thereafter we determine, by matching the sine and cosine terms of Eq. (3.18), the *frequency-dependent ratio* $\sigma(j\omega)/\eta(j\omega)$ which is precisely the describing function J of the nonlinear phenomenon (3.15).

This constitutes the second technique.

It is generally less laborious to break a frequency-dependent nonlinearity down into its constituents by block-diagram transformation than to calculate a frequency-dependent describing function.

A straightforward extension of technique (2) may be used to accommodate double-valued nonlinearities or nonlinearities that depend on several inputs $\eta_1, \eta_2, \ldots$; the latter situation is characteristic of multivariable processes.

The *general method* to be discussed in the subsequent section bypasses in a very elegant way some of the untidy algebra associated with this second technique.

3.4 The General Method [24]. We consider the nth-order system

$$\frac{dx_i}{dt} = \sum_{l=1}^{n} a_{il}x_l + \rho_i(x_1 \cdots x_n). \quad (a_{il} = \text{constant}) \quad (i, = 1 \cdots n) \tag{3.19}$$

The various nonlinearities are accounted for by the n functions $\rho_i(x_1 \cdots x_n)$ upon which we place two restrictions, namely

$$\rho_i(0, \ldots, 0) = 0 \tag{3.20}$$

and

$$\rho_i(-x_1, \ldots, -x_n) = -\rho_i(x_1, \ldots, x_n). \tag{3.21}$$

We seek an associated linear system of the form

$$\frac{dx_i}{dt} = \sum_{l=1}^{n} \bar{a}_{il}x_l + \bar{a}_{il}{}^* \frac{dx_l}{dt} \quad (i, l = 1, \ldots, n) \tag{3.22}$$

where the parameters $\bar{a}_{il}$, $\bar{a}^*_{il}$ are functions of the characteristics (A, ω) of the assumed harmonic motion

$$x_1 = A \sin \omega t. \tag{3.23}$$

If x_1 varies according to Eq. (3.23), then the motion of the remaining state variables $x_2, \ldots, x_n$ is computed in terms of the unknowns $\bar{a}_{il}$, $\bar{a}^*_{il}$ from the linear set (3.22). Thus

$$x_i = A_i \sin(\omega t + \varphi_i) = A\xi_i \sin(\omega t + \varphi_i) \tag{3.24}$$

where for convenience we define the $n - 1$ dimensionless real constants

$$\xi_i = \frac{A_i}{A}. \tag{3.25}$$

If Eqs. (3.23) and (3.24) hold, we perform a Fourier expansion of each nonlinear term

$$\rho_i(x_1, \ldots, x_n) = \rho_i[A \sin \omega t, \ldots, A\xi_n \sin(\omega t + \varphi_n) \qquad (i = 1, \ldots, n) \tag{3.26}$$

and obtain

$$\rho_i[A \sin \omega t, \ldots, A\xi_n \sin(\omega t + \varphi_n) = B_{i1} \sin(\omega t + \Psi_{i1}) + \cdots + B_{iq} \sin(q\omega t + \Psi_{iq}). \tag{3.27}$$

We assume that the harmonics $B_{iq} \sin(q\omega t + \Psi_{iq})$, $(q = 2, \ldots)$, can be neglected and we refer the fundamental component $B_{i1} \sin(\omega t + \Psi_{i1})$ to the phase $\varphi_1 = 0$ of x_1. Therefore

$$B_{i1} \sin(\omega t + \Psi_{i1}) = C_{i1} \sin \omega t + C^*_{il} \cos \omega t \tag{3.28}$$

where

$$\begin{aligned} C_{i1} &= \frac{1}{\pi} \int_0^{2\pi} \rho_i[A \sin \omega t, \ldots, A_n\xi_n \sin(\omega t + \varphi_n)] \sin \omega t \, d(\omega t) \\ C^*_{il} &= \frac{1}{\pi} \int_0^{2\pi} \rho_i[A \sin \omega t, \ldots, A_n\xi_n \sin(\omega t + \varphi_n)] \cos \omega t \, d(\omega t) \end{aligned} \tag{3.29}$$

and where

$$C_{il} = C^*_{li} = 0. \qquad (l = 2, \ldots, n)$$

The $n^2 + 2n$ parameters $\bar{a}_{il}$, $\bar{a}^*_{il}$ are then related to the fundamental Fourier components by

$$\begin{aligned} \bar{a}_{i1} &= a_{i1} + \frac{C_{i1}}{A} \\ \bar{a}^*_{il} &= \frac{C^*_{i1}}{\omega A} \end{aligned} \tag{3.30}$$

$$\left.\begin{aligned} \bar{a}_{il} &= a_{il} \\ \bar{a}^*_{il} &= 0 \end{aligned}\right\}. \qquad (l = 2, \ldots, n) \tag{3.31}$$

The nonlinear terms $f_i(x_1, \ldots, x_n)$ are frequently such that

$$\rho_i(x_1, \ldots, x_n) = \sum_{l=1}^{n} \rho_{il}(x_l) \tag{3.32}$$

in which case we prefer to compute or look up in existing tables [21] the $2n^2$

parameters $\bar{a}_{il}$, $\bar{a}^*_{il}$ from

$$\begin{aligned} \bar{a}_{il} &= a_{il} + \frac{1}{\pi A \xi_l} \int_0^{2\pi} \rho_{il}[A\xi_l \sin(\omega t + \varphi_l)] \sin(\omega t + \varphi_l)\, d(\omega t) \\ \bar{a}^*_{il} &= \frac{1}{\pi \omega A \xi_l} \int_0^{2\pi} \rho_{il}[A\xi_l \sin(\omega t + \varphi_l)] \cos(\omega t + \varphi_l)\, d(\omega t). \end{aligned} \tag{3.33}$$

Example. We consider van der Pol's equation

$$\begin{aligned} \dot{x}_1 &= x_2 \\ \dot{x}_2 &= -x_1 + \mu x_2 - \mu {x_1}^2 x_2 \end{aligned} \tag{3.34}$$

and apply (3.32)

$$\begin{aligned} &\bar{a}_{11} = 0 \qquad \bar{a}_{22} = \mu \qquad \bar{a}_{12} = 0 \\ &\bar{a}^*_{11} = 0 \qquad \bar{a}^*_{22} = 0 \qquad \bar{a}^*_{12} = 0 \end{aligned}$$

$$\begin{aligned} \bar{a}_{21} &= -1 - \frac{\mu}{\pi A} \int_0^{2\pi} [A^2 \sin^2 \omega t A\xi_2 \sin(\omega t + \varphi_2)] \sin \omega t\, d(\omega t) \\ &= -1 - \frac{3\mu A^2 \xi_2}{4} \cos \varphi_2. \end{aligned}$$

Similarly

$$\bar{a}^*_{21} = -\frac{\mu A^2 \xi_2}{4\omega} \sin \varphi_2. \tag{3.35}$$

Now, since by definition, $x_2 = \dot{x}_1$, it follows that

$$\begin{aligned} \xi_2 &= \omega \\ \varphi_2 &= \frac{\pi}{2}. \end{aligned} \tag{3.36}$$

Therefore

$$\begin{aligned} \bar{a}_{21} &= -1 \\ \bar{a}^*_{21} &= \frac{\mu A^2}{4}. \end{aligned} \tag{3.37}$$

The associated linear system of Eq. (3.34) is thus

$$\begin{aligned} \dot{x}_1 &= x_2 \\ \dot{x}_2 &= -x_1 + \mu\left(1 - \frac{A^2}{4}\right) x_2. \end{aligned} \tag{3.38}$$

Result (3.38) is of course identical with that of (3.4).

We procede to determine the *stability* properties of the associated linear system (3.22) by considering the n eigenvalues λ, which are the roots of

$$\det(\bar{A} + \lambda \bar{A}^* - \lambda I) = 0. \tag{3.39}$$

Here, the $n \times n$ matrices $\bar{A}$ and $\bar{A}^*$ have elements $\bar{a}_{il}$ and $\bar{a}^*_{il}$, respectively. As a result of this step, an nth-order polynomial

$$b_0\lambda^n + \cdots b_n = 0 \qquad (b_0 > 0) \quad (3.40)$$

is obtained.

We next seek conditions under which stable harmonic motion can exist by considering the Hurwitz determinants H_k, $(k = 1, \ldots, n)$, which, we recall, are minor determinants of the array

$$\begin{vmatrix} b_1 & b_0 & 0 & 0 & 0 & 0 & \cdots & \cdots \\ b_3 & b_2 & b_1 & b_0 & 0 & 0 & \cdots & \cdots \\ b_5 & b_4 & b_3 & b_2 & b_1 & b_0 & 0 & \cdots \\ b_7 & b_6 & b_5 & b_4 & b_3 & b_2 & b_1 & b_0 \\ \cdot & & & & & & & \\ \cdot & & & & & & & \\ \cdot & & & & & & & \end{vmatrix} \quad (3.41)$$

For example

$$H_1 = b_1$$
$$H_2 = b_1 b_2 - b_0 b_3.$$

A *linear* system having a characteristic equation of the form (3.40) is stable if and only if *all* the H_k are positive. Moreover, if $H_{n-1} = 0$ and all the remaining H_k are positive, then the linear system under consideration can be shown

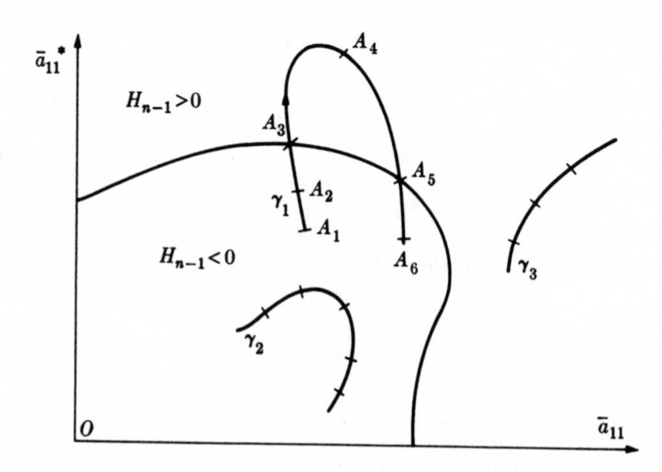

FIGURE 22. Plot of $H_{n-1} = 0$ in terms of $\bar{a}_{11}$, $\bar{a}_{11}^*$ and plots of γ upon which A is marked as a parameter.

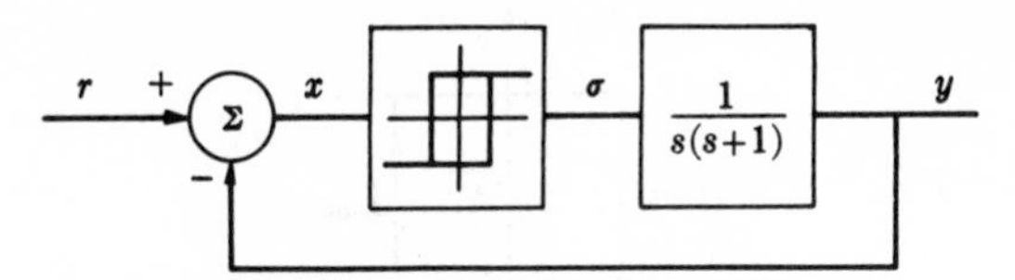

FIGURE 23. Relay servomechanism.

to have a pair of complex eigenvalues $\lambda = j\omega$ such that

$$\omega^2 = \frac{b_n H_{n-3}}{H_{n-2}}. \tag{3.42}$$

If, possibly as a consequence of a slight parameter variation, H_{n-1} becomes positive (negative), all transients decay to zero (increase without bound).

In order to extend these two properties to the nonlinear system under consideration, we first plot the surface $H_{n-1} = 0$ in the parameter space $\bar{a}_{il}$, $\bar{a}^*_{il}$ and mark the regions $H_{n-1} > 0$ and $H_{n-1} < 0$. We next make use of Eq. (3.29), (3.30), or (3.33) to compute $\bar{a}_{il}$ and $\bar{a}^*_{il}$, respectively, in terms of A, $0 \leqslant A < \infty$. As a result of this second step, we obtain in the $\bar{a}_{il}$, $\bar{a}^*_{il}$ parameter space a curve γ upon which the appropriate values of A are marked. This is shown in Fig. 22.

We interpret this plot as follows.

Stationary oscillations exist at the intersections of γ with $H_{n-1} = 0$. A is read directly from γ, and ω is computed from Eq. (3.42). The oscillations are stable (unstable) if γ moves from the region $H_{n-1} < 0$, $(H_{n-1} > 0)$ into the region $H_{n-1} > 0$, $(H_{n-1} < 0)$ as A increases. If γ remains in the region $H_{n-1} > 0$ for all *possible* values of A, system (3.22) is likely to be stable in the large, i.e., stable for all initial conditions.†

With reference to Fig. 22, we conclude that γ_1 has a stable limit cycle at A_3 and an unstable limit cycle at A_5. γ_2 is unstable and γ_3 is likely to be stable in the large.

3.5 Application of the Three Harmonic Methods. We consider the relay servomechanism of Fig. 23. The relay has hysteresis as shown in Fig. 24.

Example. If the forcing function r is a constant, this system is described by

$$\ddot{x} + \dot{x} + N(x) = 0 \tag{3.43}$$

or alternatively, by letting $x_1 = x$, $x_2 = \dot{x}$

$$\begin{aligned} \dot{x}_1 &= x_2 \\ \dot{x}_2 &= -N(x_1) - x_2. \end{aligned} \tag{3.44}$$

† We usually focus our attention upon the condition $H_{n-1} > 0$ which is generally the most stringent of the n Hurwitz conditions. Before definitely concluding that some intersection of γ and $H_{n-1} = 0$ corresponds to a stable limit cycle, we must ascertain that the remaining $n - 1$ Hurwitz determinants are indeed positive.

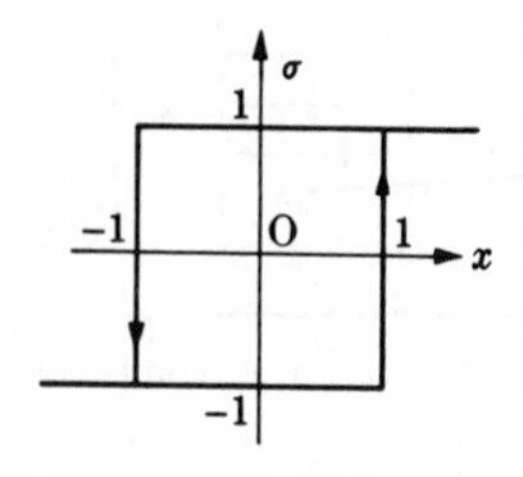

FIGURE 24. Nonlinear relay characteristic $\sigma = N(x)$.

The complex nonlinear gain is

$$J(A, j\omega) = 0 \qquad A \leqslant 1$$
$$J(A, j\omega) = \frac{4}{\pi A}\left[\sqrt{1 - \left(\frac{1}{A}\right)^2} - \frac{j}{A}\right], \qquad A > 1. \tag{3.45}$$

The Harmonic Balance Method. If x varies as $A \sin \omega t$, Eq. (3.43) is replaced by

$$\ddot{x} + \left(1 - \frac{4}{\pi A^2 \omega}\right)\dot{x} + \frac{4}{\pi A}\left(\sqrt{1 - \frac{1}{A^2}}\right)x = 0. \tag{3.46}$$

We match the real and imaginary parts

$$-\omega^2 + \frac{4}{\pi A}\sqrt{1 - \frac{1}{A^2}} = 0$$
$$1 - \frac{4}{\pi A^2 \omega} = 0 \tag{3.47}$$

and, solving for A and ω, we conclude that there exists a limit cycle ($A = 1.27$, $\omega = 0.79$) which may or may not be stable.

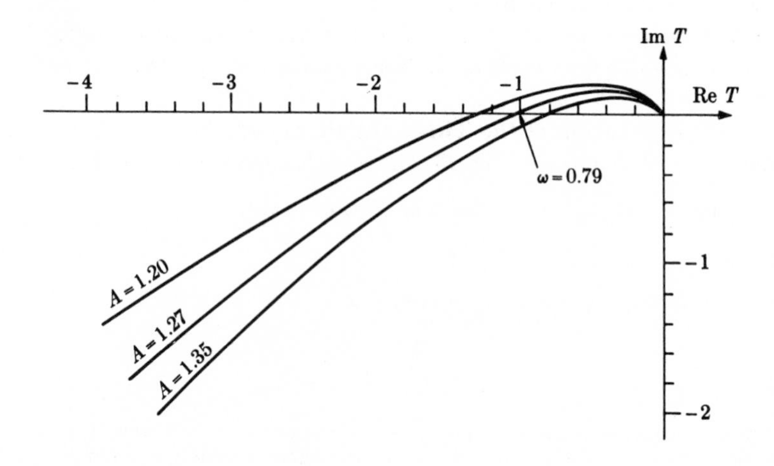

FIGURE 25. Plot of $T(A, j\omega)$. There is a stable limit cycle $\omega = 0.79$, $A = 1.27$.

The Describing Function. The plot

$$T(A, j\omega) = \frac{4}{\pi A}\left(\sqrt{1 - \frac{1}{A^2}} - \frac{j}{A}\right)\frac{1}{j\omega(1 + j\omega)} \tag{3.48}$$

shown in Fig. 25 reveals a limit cycle ($A = 1.27$, $\omega = 0.79$) which is stable according to Rule 2 of Section 3.2.

The General Method. We obtain the associated linear system

$$\begin{aligned} \dot{x}_1 &= x_2 \\ \dot{x}_2 &= \bar{a}x_1 + \bar{a}^*\dot{x}_1 - x_2 \end{aligned} \tag{3.49}$$

where

$$\begin{aligned} \bar{a} &= 0 & A &\leqslant 1 \\ \bar{a} &= \frac{-4}{\pi A}\sqrt{1 - \frac{1}{A^2}} & A &> 1 \\ \bar{a}^* &= 0 & A &\leqslant 1 \\ \bar{a}^* &= \frac{4}{\pi A^2 \omega} & A &> 1. \end{aligned} \tag{3.50}$$

The characteristic equation

$$\lambda^2 + \lambda(1 - \bar{a}^*) - \bar{a} = 0 \tag{3.51}$$

yields

$$H_{n-1} = 1 - \bar{a}^*. \tag{3.52}$$

It follows from Eq. (3.42) that

$$\omega^2 = 1 - \bar{a}^*. \tag{3.53}$$

Figure 26 shows the plot $H_{n-1} = 0$ and the curve obtained from Eqs. (3.50) and (3.53). Accordingly, there is a stable limit cycle ($\omega = 0.79$, $A = 1.27$).

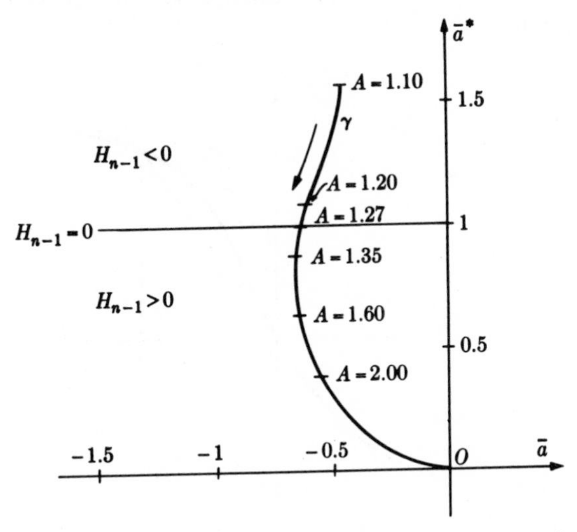

FIGURE 26. The general method. There is a stable limit cycle at $A = 1.27$, $\omega = 0.79$.

3.6 The Concept of the Nonlinear Root Locus. The harmonic techniques presented in the previous sections are seen to be natural extensions of certain well-known theorems concerned with the properties of linear systems subjected to harmonic signals. The nonlinear root locus, to be discussed now, is similarly related to Evans' root locus technique, which consists of observing the motion of the closed-loop poles λ_i in the complex λ-plane as one or more of the free system parameters are altered.

Forgetting for the time being all about nonlinear *differential equations*, we represent a nonlinear time-invariant system by means of the familiar *block diagram*, in which one or more of the free parameters are not constants, but depend on the present (and sometimes on the past) state. There is a great temptation to design the desired nonlinear system by means of available linear techniques and to take into account, in some plausible way, the fact that the gains are not constant.

The nonlinear root locus technique then consists in plotting the poles of an *associated linear* system. These poles describe trajectories in the λ-plane; their actual position depends—and this is where the nonlinear root locus differs from the linear root locus—on the amplitudes of the inputs to the nonlinearities.

The control engineer versed in interpreting conventional root loci can frequently derive a surprising number of clues about the performance of the nonlinear system to be analyzed. If, regardless of signal amplitude, these poles remain in the left half of the λ-plane, he will conclude that there are no limit cycles.

Some of the rules discussed below do not actually require that a root locus be drawn. We shall, however, include these in the present section because of their obvious affinity.

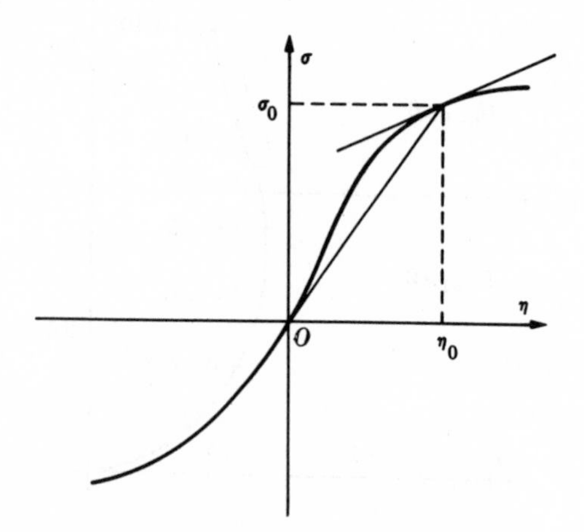

FIGURE 27. Single-valued nonlinear characteristic $\sigma = N(\eta)$.

The nonlinear root locus was first discussed by J. G. Truxal [32], and was systematically used as a heuristic design tool by S. F. Schmidt [26].

3.7 The Choice of the Equivalent Gain. With reference to the single-valued frequency-independent nonlinear characteristic $\sigma = N(\eta)$ shown in Fig. 27, we need to know which value of the gain ought to be used to describe the associated linear system under a stated set of circumstances.

At least three definitions of the *equivalent nonlinear* gain have been proposed to account for an excitation whose instantaneous value is σ_0. These are

(1) the *static* gain (chord approximation)

$$g_s = \frac{\sigma_0}{\eta_0} \tag{3.54}$$

(2) the *dynamic* gain (tangent approximation)

$$g_d = \left.\frac{d\sigma}{d\eta}\right|_{\eta=\eta_0} \tag{3.55}$$

(3) the *describing function* gain

$$J = \frac{\omega}{\pi\eta_0} \int_0^{2\pi/\omega} \sigma(\eta_0 \sin \omega t) \sin \omega t \, dt. \tag{3.56}$$

Since N is assumed to be single-valued and frequency-independent, J is real and not a function of ω.

We now enunciate three rules and we substantiate these by presenting an example which is frequently quoted in the literature [16]. *None* of these rules has been mathematically proven to be correct in all cases, but experience tells that they generally provide results of surprising accuracy at the cost of comparatively little labor.

RULE 1. *A sufficient condition for a nonlinear system to be globally stable or stable in the large is that for each possible value of the equivalent nonlinear gains* g_s, *Eq.* (3.54), *the associated linear system is stable.*

This rule was proposed by J. C. Gille and S. Wegrzyn [10].

RULE 2. *An nth-order ordinary nonlinear differential equation containing an arbitrary number of single-valued frequency-independent continuous nonlinearities is stable if the incremental linear differential equation obtained by use of Eq.* (3.55) *at each point in the phase space is stable.*

RULE 3. *A necessary and sufficient condition for a globally stable nonlinear system to have one* (*or several*) *limit cycles is that one or several pairs of the eigenvalues of the associated linear system enter into the right half of the complex* λ-*plane for one* (*or several*) *finite ranges of the equivalent nonlinear gain defined as in Eqs.* (3.54), (3.55), *or* (3.56). *The period* T *of the limit cycle*(*s*) *is such that*

$T = (2\pi/\omega_c)$ where ω_c is the imaginary value of the pair(s) of eigenvalues λ on the imaginary axis. The amplitude of the limit cycle is determined by the gain which must be such that the real part of one pair of eigenvalues vanishes. This limit cycle is stable (unstable) if an increased amplitude forces the pair of eigenvalues into the left half-plane (right half-plane).

Rule 2, which was suggested among others by R. E. Kalman [15], is based on a very simple and straightforward argument. We make several observations.

(a) The rule requires that the nonlinearities be *continuous*. Since this does not hold in a large number of instances of practical importance, we may circumvent this formal difficulty by replacing the corners of the discontinuity with arcs of infinitesimal radius.

(b) Application of the rule requires that we determine the ranges over which the tangent to each nonlinearity can vary and ascertain that the incremental linear differential equation is stable at each point in the region of the g_d-space thus defined.

(c) The rule states a sufficient, but not necessary, condition of stability, and consequently leads to designs which may be overly conservative. To conclude that the system is globally unstable or has a stable limit cycle if the conditions of the rule do not hold everywhere in the above-defined region of the tangent space, would not be correct.

R. E. Kalman and J. E. Bertram discuss such "linearized" systems in some detail [16] for both the g_s and g_d definitions of the gains which are formally treated as constants. They consider two examples, of which we reproduce the first. Let

$$\begin{aligned} \dot{x}_1 &= x_2 \\ \dot{x}_2 &= x_3 \\ \dot{x}_3 &= -f_1(x_1) - f_2(x_2) - a_3 x_3 \quad (a_3 = \text{constant}) \end{aligned} \tag{3.57}$$

where $f_1(0) = f_2(0) = 0$ and where f_1 and f_2 are differentiable functions. Now let $(f_1/x_1) = a_1$ and $(f_2/x_2) = a_2$ and consider the linearized system

$$\begin{aligned} \dot{x}_1 &= x_2 \\ \dot{x}_2 &= x_3 \\ \dot{x}_3 &= -a_1 x_1 - a_2 x_2 - a_3 x_3. \end{aligned} \tag{3.58}$$

This linearized system is stable, according to Hurwitz, if

$$a_3 > 0 \quad a_1 > 0 \quad a_3 a_2 - a_1 > 0. \tag{3.59}$$

Using Liapunov's second method, Barbashin demonstrated that the original nonlinear system (3.57) is asymptotically stable in the large only if

$$a_3 > 0 \quad \frac{f_1}{x_1} > 0 \quad a_3 \frac{f_2}{x_2} - \frac{\partial f_1}{\partial x_1} > 0. \tag{3.60}$$

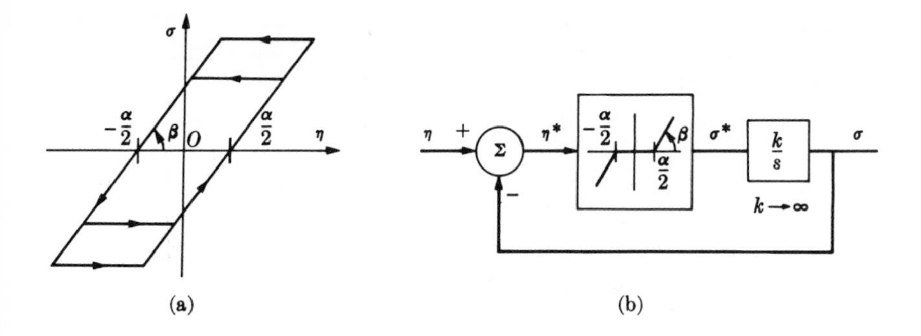

FIGURE 28. Transformation of backlash characteristic into dead zone characteristic and integrator, $k \to \infty$.

Comparison of these two sets of stability conditions indicates that the linearization is justified here if a_1 and a_2 are defined in accordance with *both* Eqs. (3.54) and (3.55).

3.8 Reduction of Frequency-dependent and Double-valued Nonlinearities. Unlike the harmonic methods previously discussed, the nonlinear root locus technique does not accommodate frequency-dependent and double-valued nonlinearities.

In Section 3.3, we presented a fairly general method whereby frequency-dependent nonlinearities are transformed into frequency-independent nonlinearities and linear energy storage elements.

A similar reduction technique can often be used to transform double-valued nonlinearities into single-valued nonlinearities.

By way of example, we consider the backlash characteristic shown in Fig. 28a. This double-valued nonlinearity is broken down into a dead-zone characteristic and an energy-storage element, as indicated in Fig. 28b.

Suggestions on how to reduce other double-valued nonlinearities are found in any good text on analog computers.

We now make use of this reduction to investigate the existence and the properties of the limit cycles occurring in a servomechanism whose actuator has backlash.

We consider the control system of Fig. 29a, which we transform into that of Fig. 29b using the transformation suggested in Fig. 28b.

We next plot the root locus corresponding to Fig. 29b in terms of the combined equivalent nonlinear gain kg_s or kg_d, either of which is such that

$$\begin{aligned} kg &= 0 \qquad |\eta^*| < \frac{\alpha}{2} \\ kg &\to \infty \qquad |\eta^*| > \frac{\alpha}{2}. \end{aligned} \tag{3.61}$$

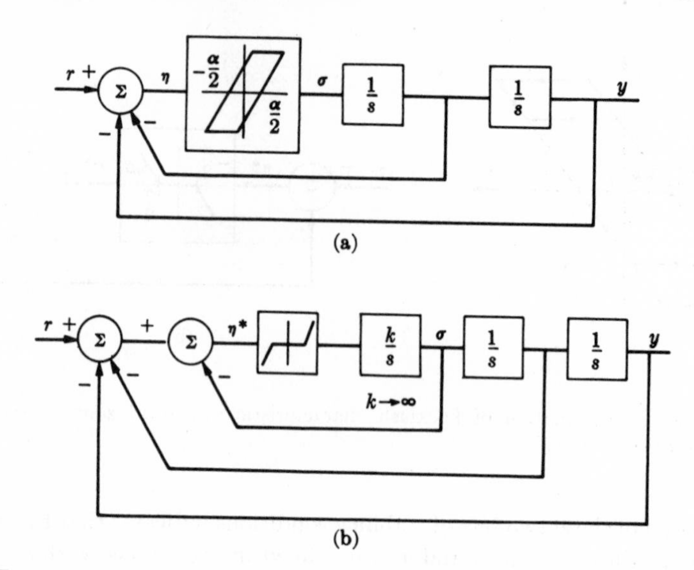

FIGURE 29. Second-order servomechanism whose actuator has backlash α.

This root locus is shown in Fig. 30.

Using Rule 3 of Section 3.6, we conclude with very little computational effort that the servomechanism under discussion has a stable limit cycle of angular frequency $\omega = 1$ and of amplitude such that $|\eta^*| \approx \frac{\alpha}{2}$.

The nonlinear root locus plot of Fig. 30, moreover, suggests that this undesirable limit cycle could be eliminated by injecting a periodic forcing function of

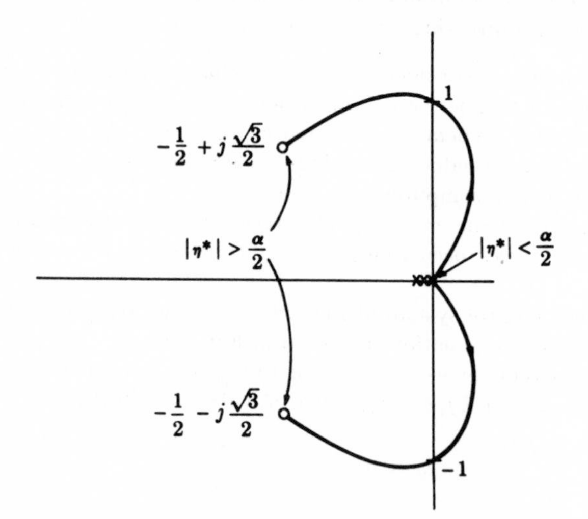

FIGURE 30. Nonlinear root locus corresponding to the system of Fig. 29.

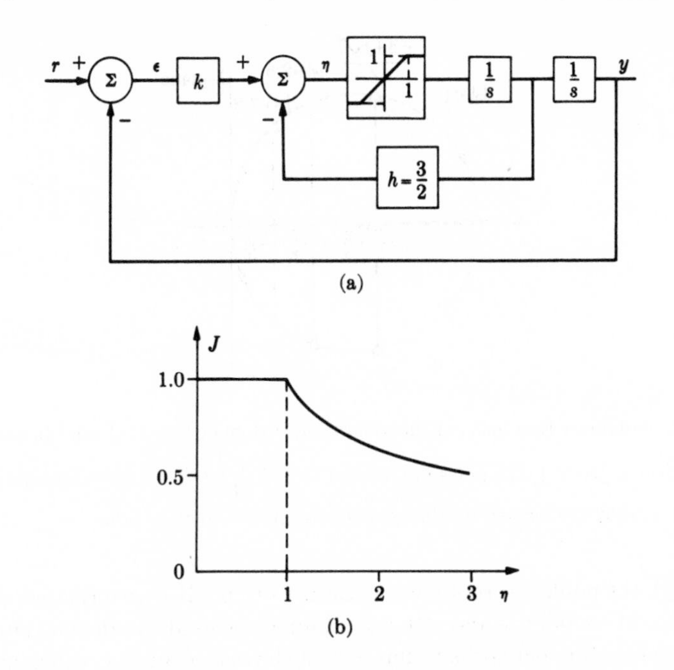

FIGURE 31. (a) Saturating servomechanism; (b) equivalent nonlinear gain J as a function of η.

sufficient amplitude and frequency at either of the two summing nodes of Fig. 29b. This forcing function, generally termed *dither*, moves the poles into the left half-plane and does not appreciably affect the system output y if its frequency is chosen to be sufficiently large.

3.9 An Important Example. As a further application of these techniques, we consider a servomechanism which is linear for small motion and which saturates for large motion. This is shown in Fig. 31a; the equivalent nonlinear gain J of the saturating actuator is represented in Fig. 31b.

The characteristic equation of this system is written by inspection for constant J

$$\lambda^2 + J(\tfrac{3}{2}\lambda + 1) = 0. \tag{3.62}$$

The resulting nonlinear root locus, together with the pertinent values of η, is shown in Fig. 32.

As a consequence of the fact that the damping steadily decreases as $|\eta|$ becomes larger, $|\eta| \geqslant 1$, we surmise that the response to large disturbances will consist of lightly damped oscillations whose approximate frequency can be estimated under stated operating conditions from the root locus of Fig. 32. Such temporal behavior is shown in Fig. 34 in connection with another discussion of this very important topic.

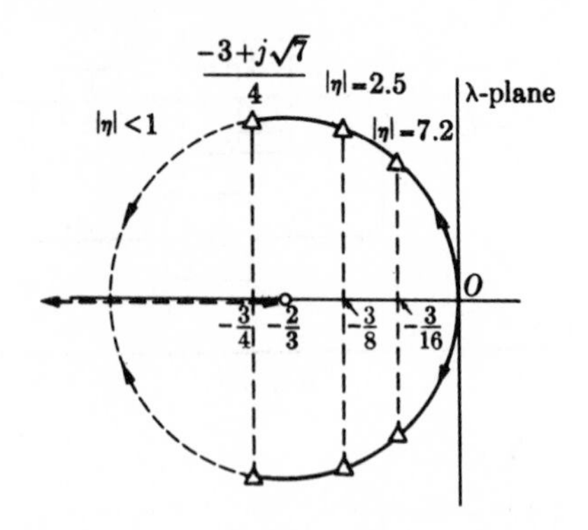

FIGURE 32. Nonlinear root locus of the saturating system of Fig. 31. Under linear operating conditions, $|\eta| \leqslant 1$, the poles are located at $\dfrac{-3 + j\sqrt{7}}{4}$. Under nonlinear conditions $|\eta| \geqslant 1$, they are located on that part of the circle shown in full.

Although the nonlinear root locus permits us to predict performance with a good degree of confidence and although it might be used to calculate suitable *linear* compensating networks to improve such performance, it will generally do no more than suggest proper nonlinear compensation networks, to be subsequently verified and accurately determined by computer simulation.

In order to fulfil the performance criteria which we qualify as optimum at this time, we generally require nonlinear compensation schemes. In the case of the saturating servomechanism under discussion, we specify that any initial disturbance be eliminated in the shortest possible time. It will be seen in Section 4 that this specification is met precisely by the so-called optimum relay design. Structurally, this leads to nonlinear gains $h(\dot{y})$ *or* $k(\epsilon)$, Fig. 31a, inserted into the inner feedback loop or into the forward path, respectively.

It is not possible to design any of these nonlinearities, at least not as long as no comprehensive methodology has been worked out, by conventional pole zero considerations. In response to a large-amplitude step, the poles of the optimum system, assumed to be initially at rest, would leave the origin, enter the complex portion of the left half λ-plane, and finally move toward $-\infty$ on the real axis. Such complicated pole trajectories could obviously not be known beforehand, as we ignore the relation between pole location and the performance criterion under discussion.

3.10 Concluding Comments. The heuristic techniques which consist of the harmonic methods and of the nonlinear root locus are probably the most general and widely used design tools for nonlinear control systems of any order, in spite of their obvious lack of mathematical justification.

In both cases, we define an *associated linear* system, which, unlike the associated linear system of Section 2, constitutes a plausible description for nearly periodic motions of finite amplitude. Certain nonlinearities of the multivalued type can be accomodated directly by the harmonic methods and are accessible to the nonlinear root locus after a suitable transformation has been carried out.

There exists at the present time no exact procedure to predict the errors caused by these approximations. Several authors, in particular Magnus [21] and Johnson [13], quote examples where the harmonic methods yield surprising accuracy. Applying the exact method described in Section 5 to the system of Fig. 23, one obtains a half-period of 3.92, $\omega = 0.80$, and a maximum deviation $y = 1.29$. These results are indeed of surprising accuracy if one considers the fact that the nonlinearity under discussion is rather substantial.

The literature contains hardly any information on the accuracy to be expected from the nonlinear root locus technique, except of course in those cases where the equivalent nonlinear gain is defined as J and where consequently the results are identical with those of the describing function.

It is known that the harmonic methods and the nonlinear root locus sometimes completely fail. R. W. Bass [3] has formulated a rigorous criterion which indicates when failure must be expected. This criterion, however, is not easy to apply, and it seems that the most convenient way to verify applicability at the present time is to run a computer check.

In this short discussion on heuristic techniques, we have omitted to mention certain refinements, such as the *dual input describing* function which does not neglect some of the higher harmonics. As a consequence of this more accurate description, such nonlinear phenomena as subharmonic oscillations can be predicted. A detailed coverage of the dual input describing function will be found in West [33].

4. On Optimum Relay Controls

It is likely that those nonlinear control systems which contain a relay-type nonlinearity have attracted more research effort over the past twenty years than any other class of nonlinear systems.

Most of the literature is concerned with systems where the actuator consists of an inexpensive relay, solenoid valve, or clutch, i.e., where the nonlinearity is *intentional*, since conventional linear power amplifiers could have been used.

It was pointed out by S. F. Schmidt [26] that plant saturation, which is an *unavoidable* nonlinearity, has the same effect on system behavior, for sufficiently large disturbances, as a relay. Assuming that the plant saturates as shown in Fig. 33, and that a purely linear design corresponding to the portion aa' of the saturation characteristic has been carried out, we might observe the totally unacceptable response to a large-amplitude step shown in Fig. 34.

Although poorly designed relay systems will perform less well than their linear counterparts, it is known that such systems, if correctly designed, have the property that any initial error condition is eliminated in *finite time*. Linear

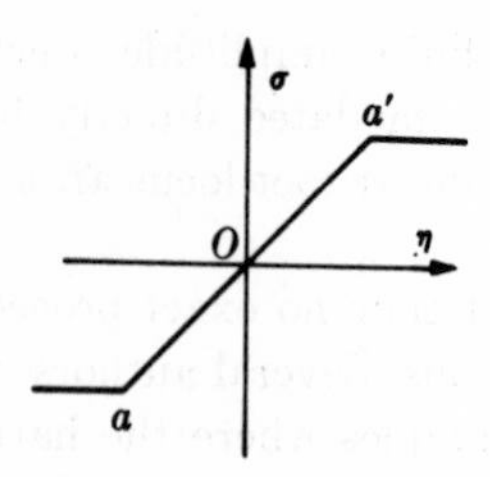

FIGURE 33. Saturation characteristic $\sigma = N(\eta)$.

systems with constant coefficients and most other nonlinear systems never have this property. The price that we must pay for this desirable feature is a nonlinear controller whose synthesis is difficult in all but the simplest cases.

Until a very few years ago, we did not know how to design such controllers, except in the case of certain second- and third-order plants. The design of optimum second-order relay servomechanisms is discussed in detail in most modern texts on automatic control. We refer the reader to Truxal [32].

Third-order linear plants having zeros and complex poles were studied by I. Flugge-Lotz in a series of papers [9].

A formal solution in the case of certain nth-order linear plants, $n > 3$, was recently published by M. Athanassiades and O. J. M. Smith in the United States [2], and by Pontriagin, Boltianskii, and Gamkrelidze in the Soviet Union [7].

An effective, nearly optimum design procedure applicable to nth-order linear plants having zeros and, in certain cases, complex poles is due to Schmidt [26].

In this section we shall synthesize the exact optimum controller for a linear plant of arbitrary order n. We assume that there are no zeros and no complex poles. The procedure which is to be presented differs from that outlined in Athanassiades and Smith [2] and Boltianskii *et al.* [7] and constitutes a straightforward extension of Schmidt's work.

A largely unsolved problem which is attracting considerable research effort at this time is that of *multivariable* relay systems. Although it is always

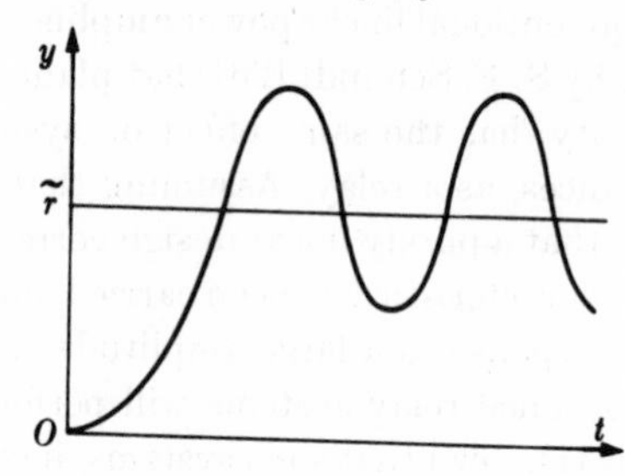

FIGURE 34. Response $y(t)$ of the linear design to a large-amplitude step $\tilde{r}$.

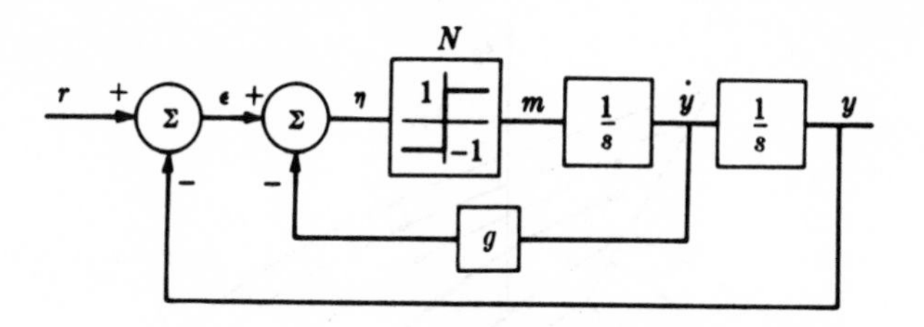

FIGURE 35. Second-order relay servomechanism.

possible to diagonalize the multivariable plant and to design optimum controllers for each of the now independent channels, it is known that this procedure does not generally lead to an optimum over-all design. The multivariable relay problem is briefly outlined in Chapter III.

Other aspects of relay systems are investigated in Chapters VI and VII.

For obvious reasons, relay systems are also referred to in the literature as bang-bang systems, on-off systems and contactor controls.

4.1 The Second-order Relay Servomechanism. We wish to recall some of the properties of relay systems by considering the classical second-order structure shown in Fig. 35.

For constant command input, $r(t) = \tilde{r}$, the equations are written by inspection in terms of the state variables

$$\epsilon_1 = \tilde{r} - y$$

$$\epsilon_2 = \dot{\epsilon}_1$$

as

$$\dot{\epsilon}_1 = \epsilon_2$$

$$\dot{\epsilon}_2 = -N(\eta) = -N(\epsilon_1 + g\epsilon_2)$$

$$N(\epsilon_1 + g\epsilon_2) = \pm 1. \tag{4.1}$$

Since Eq. (4.1) is piecewise linear, integration is straightforward. The reader may verify that the phase trajectories of (4.1) are parabolas shifted to the right and to the left of

$$\epsilon_2 = \pm\sqrt{2\epsilon_1} \qquad \epsilon_1 > 0$$
$$N = \mp 1 \tag{4.2}$$

and

$$\epsilon_2 = \pm\sqrt{-2\epsilon_1} \qquad \epsilon_1 < 0$$
$$N = +1 \tag{4.3}$$

We would like to combine the trajectories corresponding to Eqs. (4.2) and (4.3) in a *single* phase-plane diagram. As this would violate the continuity requirements set forth in Eq. (2.1), we may assume that the corners of the discontinuous function N have been replaced by arcs of infinitesimal radius

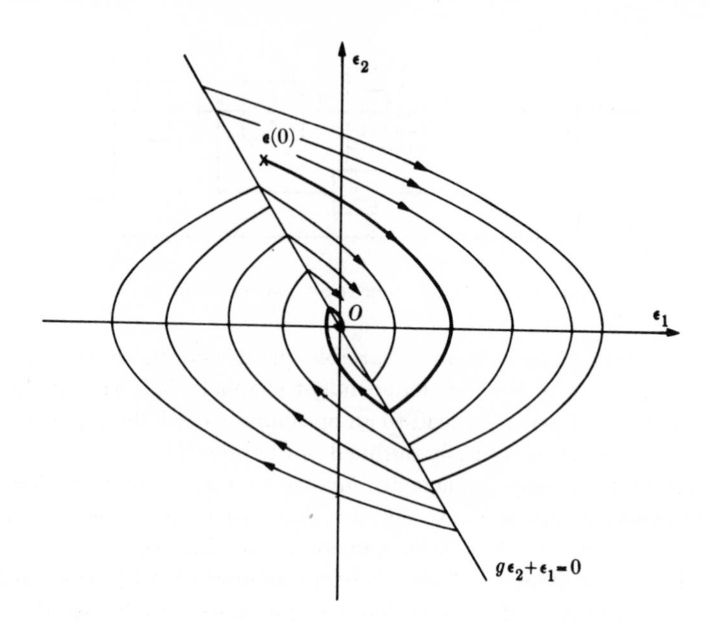

FIGURE 36. Phase plane plot of Eq. (4.1). The trajectory corresponding to the initial $\epsilon(0) = [\epsilon_1(0), \epsilon_2(0)]$ is shown.

and that the central portion of the relay characteristic is almost, but not quite, vertical.

Having thus eliminated the formal difficulty of lack of continuity, we may sketch the customary phase-plane plot of Fig. 36.

The locus of the points where the relay reverses polarity is a straight line

$$g\epsilon_2 + \epsilon_1 = 0 \qquad (g = \text{constant}) \qquad (4.4)$$

which is termed the switching line.

We recall some of the widely publicized conclusions derived from the phase-plane diagram of Fig. 36.

1. If no "velocity signal" is returned to the relay-input ($g = 0$), the oscillations will not vanish. The steady-state trajectory is a *vortex*.

2. For $g > 0$, any arbitrary initial state $\boldsymbol{\epsilon}(0)$ is brought to the origin after an infinite number of switchings. For $g < 0$, the system is unstable.

3. If the relay is not perfect, i.e., has hysteresis or dead time, the steady-state motion is a stable limit cycle around the origin for $g > 0$.

4. If the perfect relay were made to switch on precisely those trajectories passing through the origin, the steady-state condition $\epsilon_1 = 0$, $\epsilon_2 = 0$ would result after at most one reversal. Such a switching strategy is optimum in the sense that the equilibrium point is reached in the shortest possible time and with the minimum number of switchings.

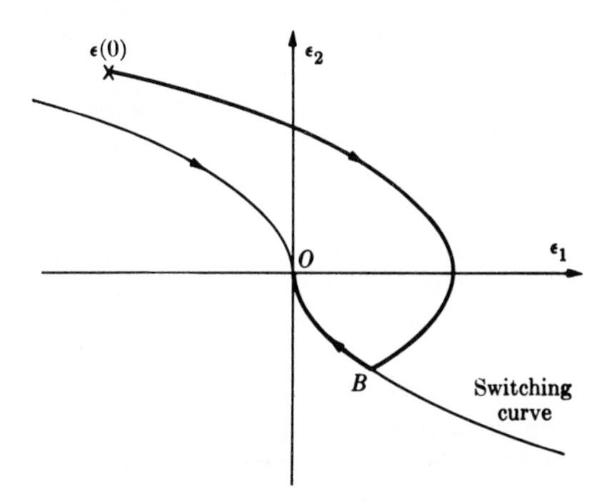

FIGURE 37. Optimum switching curve in the case of a perfect relay. Switching occurs at B.

This strategy, shown in Fig. 37, could be implemented by making the gain g a function of either of the two state variables.

All of these results can be extended to the case of a plant containing one time constant. If the plant had two time constants, i.e., no integration, the problem would become somewhat more involved as a consequence of the fact that the command input $\tilde{r}$ does not disappear from Eq. (4.1). In the subsequent discussion, we always assume that the plant has at least one integration. Relay systems excited by nonconstant command signals $r(t)$ are considered in Chapter VII.

The important general conclusion is that the two-state system of Fig. 35 can be brought to rest in finite time after at most one reversal and that this particular strategy minimizes the duration of the transient. Switching should occur when the state vector $\boldsymbol{\epsilon}$ crosses a known curve termed the switching curve. Since this curve is expressible as a nonlinear relation between ϵ_1 and ϵ_2, the relay must be controlled by a nonlinear controller.

4.2 The Switching Surfaces. A very considerable effort has been made to extend the theory of the second-order optimum contactor control to plants of arbitrary order n, and to include zeros and complex poles. The configuration considered is generally that of Fig. 38 where one and only one relay N is

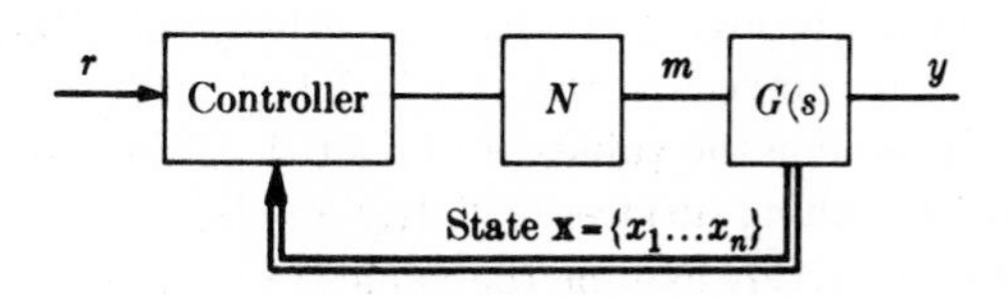

FIGURE 38. nth-Order relay system.

included in the *forward* loop, and where $G(s)$ has no zeros and no complex poles and contains at least one integration.

The optimum control problem is stated as follows. Given a linear plant of known parameters and a *constant* input, find *the* sequence of actuating signals $m(t) = \pm 1$ such that an arbitrary initial error state $\boldsymbol{\epsilon}(0)$ is brought to zero in minimum time.

We observe that imperfections of the relay have been eliminated by the above phrasing of the problem. Clearly, if we know *when* the relay ought to produce $m(t) = \pm 1$, it is possible to control it to do so if its imperfections are known.

An important step toward the solution of the stated problem is to determine the maximum number of reversals required. We shall state the following theorem which is a direct consequence of two theorems proved by R. Bellman [4].

THEOREM. *Given an nth-order linear time-invariant system, with poles real and nonpositive, the error state* $\boldsymbol{\epsilon}$ *may be reduced to zero simultaneously, in the minimum possible time, with at most n-trajectories, that is* $(n - 1)$ *reversals, provided* $r(t)$ *is a constant. If, in addition, the plant has no zeros, the actuating signal* $m(t)$ *should assume the values of* $+1$ *and* -1 *only.*

It was shown by Schmidt [26] that plants containing zeros can be brought to rest in $(n - 1)$ reversals and that the optimum forcing function $m(t)$ is not necessarily a sequence of steps.

In the subsequent discussion, we shall determine the loci in n-dimensional space on which reversal must occur if control is to be optimum.

We assume that the $(n - 1)$th reversal (which brings $\boldsymbol{\epsilon}$ to 0) is such that $m = +1$. Then, all the error states $\boldsymbol{\epsilon}_{n-1}$ located on *the* trajectory corresponding to $m = +1$ are brought to rest without further reversal. We label the locus of these points $[\epsilon_{n-1}]$.

This particular trajectory is called the *final trajectory*. If a state not located on the final trajectory is to be brought to rest in minimum time, then it must first be brought to $[\epsilon_{n-1}]$.

All those trajectories corresponding to $m = -1$ and terminating at $[\epsilon_{n-1}]$ form a surface $[\epsilon_{n-2}]$ which is precisely the locus of the points that can be brought to rest in exactly one reversal. Proceeding similarly, one establishes that there exists a hypersurface $[\epsilon_1]$ of order $n - 1$ which is the locus of all those points which are brought to 0 after $n - 2$ reversals. Hence, an arbitrary initial state must be moved to the loci $[\epsilon_1], [\epsilon_2] \cdots [\epsilon_{n-2}], [\epsilon_{n-1}]$ and $m(t)$ must successively assume the values $\cdots 1, -1, 1$. If the last actuating signal were -1, a set of switching surfaces $[\epsilon_1]', [\epsilon_2]' \cdots [\epsilon_{n-2}]', [\epsilon_{n-1}]'$ would result, and $m(t)$ would successively assume the values $\cdots -1, 1, -1$. The computer or controller required to achieve optimal control must, therefore, first determine the proper polarity of the first actuating signal and then force a reversal each time the state vector crosses a switching surface.

4.3 The Switch-time Method. We shall determine the switching surfaces by means of the switch-time method, which is based on a theorem of Laplace transform theory:

THEOREM. *If a Laplace transformable bounded function of time, $f(t)$, is truncated, that is, if*

$$f_T(t) \neq 0 \qquad a < t < b, \qquad b > a$$
$$f_T(t) = 0 \qquad \text{otherwise}$$

where $f_T(t)$ is the truncated signal, then the Laplace transform $F_T(s) = \mathscr{L}\{f_T(t)\}$ is an entire function, that is, a function which is bounded in the finite s-plane.

Proof. We consider

$$F_T(s) = \int_0^\infty f_T(t)e^{-st}\,dt = \int_a^b f_T(t)e^{-st}\,dt. \tag{4.5}$$

Expanding the exponential in an infinite series, it follows that

$$F_T(s) = \sum_{N=0}^\infty \frac{(-s)^N}{N!}\int_a^b f_T(t)t^N\,dt. \tag{4.6}$$

Now since $f_T(t)$ is bounded, i.e.,

$$|f_T(t)| \leqslant M \tag{4.7}$$

where M is a finite positive real constant,

$$|F_T(s)| \leqslant M\sum_{N=0}^\infty \frac{(-s)^N}{n!}\int_a^b t^N\,dt = M\sum_{N=0}^\infty \frac{(-s)^N}{n!}\,\frac{b^{N+1}-a^{N+1}}{N+1}. \tag{4.8}$$

The reader may verify that Eq. (4.8) reduces to

$$|F_T(s)| \leqslant -M\,\frac{e^{-bs}-e^{-as}}{s}. \tag{4.9}$$

Since

$$\frac{e^{-bs}-e^{-as}}{s}$$

is bounded in the finite portion of the s-plane, $F_T(s)$ must also be bounded, or *entire*. This proves the theorem.

If the error state $\boldsymbol{\epsilon}(t) = \{\epsilon_1(t), \epsilon_2(t)\cdots\epsilon_n(t)\}$ is to be brought to 0 in finite time, the Laplace transform $\epsilon_i(s)$ of *any* of the n-components of $\epsilon_i(t)$ must be entire. Assuming that for a given initial error, the required forcing function is

$$M(s) = \frac{(-1)^{n-1}}{s}[1 - 2e^{-sT_1} + 2e^{-sT_2}\cdots + 2(-1)^{n-1}e^{-sT_{n-1}} + (-1)^n e^{-sT_n}] \tag{4.10}$$

where the T_i denote the as yet unknown times at which switching occurs, we can determine any of the $\epsilon_i(s)$, for instance, $\epsilon_1(s) = -Y(s)$

$$\epsilon_1(s) = \sum_{j=1}^{n} a_{1j}(s)\epsilon_j(0) - M(s)G(s) \tag{4.11}$$

where the $a_{1j}(s)$ and $G(s)$ are known.

Since $G(s)$ has "n" poles, we must impose "n" conditions on the unknowns $T_1, T_2 \cdots T_n$ in order to cause Eq. (4.11) to be entire. Hence

$$\varphi_l[T_1, T_2 \cdots T_n; \epsilon_1(0), \epsilon_2(0) \cdots \epsilon_n(0)] = 0. \qquad (l = 1, 2, \ldots, n) \tag{4.12}$$

A computer included in the system could solve for the various T_j in terms of the known initial state $\boldsymbol{\epsilon}(0)$ and cause polarity reversals at the appropriate times.

The switching surface $[\epsilon_j]$ is obtained by letting

$$T_1 = T_2 = \cdots T_j = 0 \tag{4.13}$$

in Eq. (4.11). The first hypersurface $[\epsilon_1]$, for instance, is the locus of all initial states $\boldsymbol{\epsilon}(0)$ where T_1 becomes vanishingly small. Therefore

$$\varphi_k[0, T_2, \ldots, T_n; \epsilon_1, \epsilon_2, \ldots, \epsilon_n] = 0 \qquad (k = 1, 2, \ldots, n) \tag{4.14}$$

is the equation of $[\epsilon_1]$.

This equation could be obtained explicitly by eliminating the $n - 1$ remaining times $T_2, \ldots, T_n$ between the "n" equation (4.14), if this proved to be desirable. The next switching surface $[\epsilon_2]$ is obtained by letting $T_2 = T_1 = 0$. It is evident from Eq. (4.11) that $[\epsilon_2]$ is contained in $[\epsilon_1]$ and, generally speaking, that $[\epsilon_j]$ is contained in $[\epsilon_1], [\epsilon_2] \cdots [\epsilon_{j-1}]$.

So far we have assumed that the $M(s)$ of Eq. (4.10) had the initial polarity $(-1)^{n-1}$. If $\boldsymbol{\epsilon}(0)$ were located in a portion of the state space requiring the initial polarity to be $-(-1)^{n-1}$, then $\boldsymbol{\epsilon}(0)$ could not be brought to 0 in $(m - 1)$ reversals if the $M(s)$ of Eq. (4.10) were used. This impossibility appears as soon as one attempts to solve for the various T_j of Eq. (4.12), which must clearly be real and positive numbers. If this is not the case, then the initial polarity $-(-1)^{n-1}$ is required and the switching surfaces become $[\epsilon_1]', [\epsilon_2]' \cdots [\epsilon_{n-1}]'$ where the $[\epsilon_j]'$ are symmetric to the $[\epsilon_j]$ with respect to 0.

Example 1. We consider the second-order plant

$$G(s) = \frac{1}{s(s+1)}. \tag{4.15}$$

We select the state variables

$$\begin{aligned} \epsilon_1 &= -y \\ \epsilon_2 &= -\dot{y}. \end{aligned} \tag{4.16}$$

It is seen that

$$\epsilon_1(s) = \frac{\epsilon_1(0)}{s} + \frac{\epsilon_2(0)}{s(s+1)} - \frac{M(s)}{s(s+1)}. \tag{4.17}$$

We assume that the initial state $\boldsymbol{\epsilon}(0)$ is such that the actuating signal m is first equal to $+1$ and then becomes -1 at time $t = T_1$. Hence

$$M(s) = \frac{1 - 2e^{-T_1 s} + e^{-T_2 s}}{s}. \tag{4.18}$$

Substituting Eq. (4.18) into (4.17), it follows that

$$\epsilon_1(s) = \frac{s(s+1)\epsilon_1(0) + s\epsilon_2(0) - (1 - 2e^{-T_1 s} + e^{-T_2 s})}{s^2(s+1)}. \tag{4.19}$$

Equation (4.19) has poles at $s = 0$ and at $s = -1$. In order to force $\epsilon_1(s)$ to be an entire function, the numerator must vanish at $s = 0$ and $s = -1$. Hence

$$\begin{aligned} s = 0: &\quad \epsilon_1(0) + \epsilon_2(0) - 2T_1 + T_2 = 0 \\ s = -1: &\quad -\epsilon_2(0) - 1 + 2e^{T_1} - e^{T_2} = 0. \end{aligned} \tag{4.20}$$

Elimination of T_2 from Eq. (4.20) yields

$$-\epsilon_2(0) - 1 + 2e^{T_1} - e^{2T_1 - [\epsilon_1(0) + \epsilon_2(0)]} = 0. \tag{4.21}$$

If $\boldsymbol{\epsilon}(0)$ were chosen such that T_1 could be zero, then $\boldsymbol{\epsilon}(0)$ would be located on the switching curve $[\epsilon_1]'$ of equation

$$\epsilon_2 + e^{-(\epsilon_1 + \epsilon_2)} - 1 = 0. \tag{4.22}$$

The switching curve $[\epsilon_1]$ corresponding to an actuating signal which is first negative is symmetric to $[\epsilon_1]'$ about 0, i.e.,

$$\epsilon_2 - e^{(\epsilon_1 + \epsilon_2)} + 1 = 0.$$

Example 2. We consider the third-order plant $G(s) = (1/s^3)$ and assume

$$M(s) = \frac{1 - 2e^{-T_1 s} + 2e^{-T_2 s} - e^{-T_3 s}}{s}. \tag{4.23}$$

The function $\epsilon_1(s)$ to be rendered entire is

$$\epsilon_1(s) = \frac{\epsilon_1(0)s^3 + \epsilon_2(0)s^2 + \epsilon_3(0)s - (1 - 2e^{-T_1 s} + 2e^{-T_2 s} - e^{-T_3 s})}{s^4}. \tag{4.24}$$

The reader may verify that the following three conditions must hold if Eq. (4.24) is to be entire

$$\begin{aligned} \epsilon_3(0) &= 2T_1 - 2T_2 + T_3 \\ \epsilon_2(0) &= \frac{-2T_1^2 + 2T_2^2 - T_3^2}{2} \\ \epsilon_1(0) &= \frac{2T_1^3 - 2T_2^3 + T_3^3}{6}. \end{aligned} \tag{4.25}$$

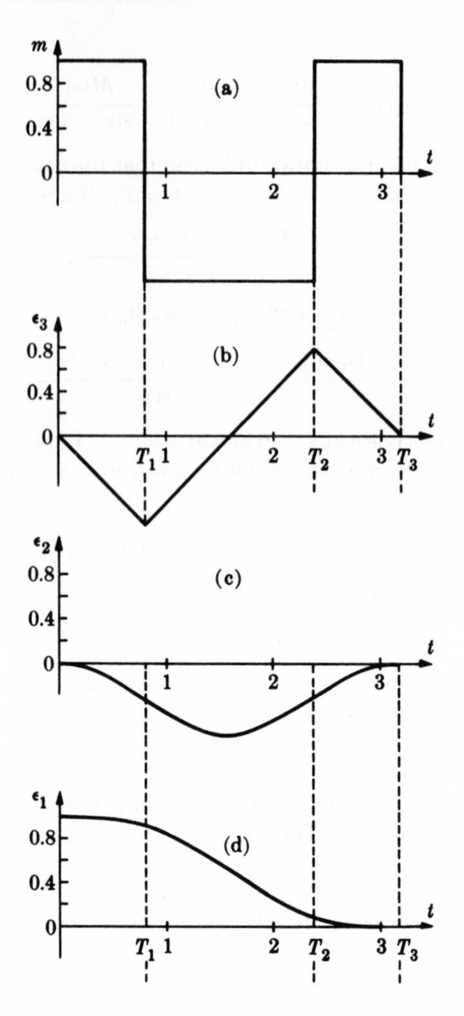

FIGURE 39. Plot of (a) $m(t)$; (b) $\epsilon_3(t)$; (c) $\epsilon_2(t)$; (d) $\epsilon_1(t)$ in the case of optimal control. The initial state is $\epsilon(0) = \{1,0,0\}$.

The switching surface $[\epsilon_1]$ can be expressed in terms of the two positive parameters T_2 and T_3 by

$$\begin{aligned} \epsilon_3 &= -2T_2 + T_3 \\ \epsilon_2 &= \frac{2T_2^2 - T_3^2}{2} \\ \epsilon_1 &= \frac{-2T_2^3 + T_3^3}{6}. \end{aligned} \tag{4.26}$$

The switching *curve* $[\epsilon_2]$ is expressed in terms of the sole positive parameter T_3

$$\epsilon_3 = T_3$$
$$\epsilon_2 = -\frac{T_3^2}{2}$$
$$\epsilon_1 = \frac{T_3^3}{6}. \tag{4.27}$$

It is clear that the curve $[\epsilon_2]$ is contained in the surface $[\epsilon_1]$.

The optimal trajectory corresponding to an initial disturbance $\boldsymbol{\epsilon}(0) = \{1, 0, 0\}$ is shown in Figs. 39 and 40.

The switching times T_1, T_2, and T_3 are easily obtained in this particular example by solving (4.25). In the general case where $G(s)$ is allowed to have real poles not located at the origin, the solution of Eq. (4.25) may involve tedious algebra, but the important point is that a complex optimization problem has been reduced to a straightforward algebraic problem.

4.4 Concluding Comments. We have shown in this section that on-off systems, if properly adjusted, are optimal in the sense that any initial disturbance is eliminated in the shortest possible time.

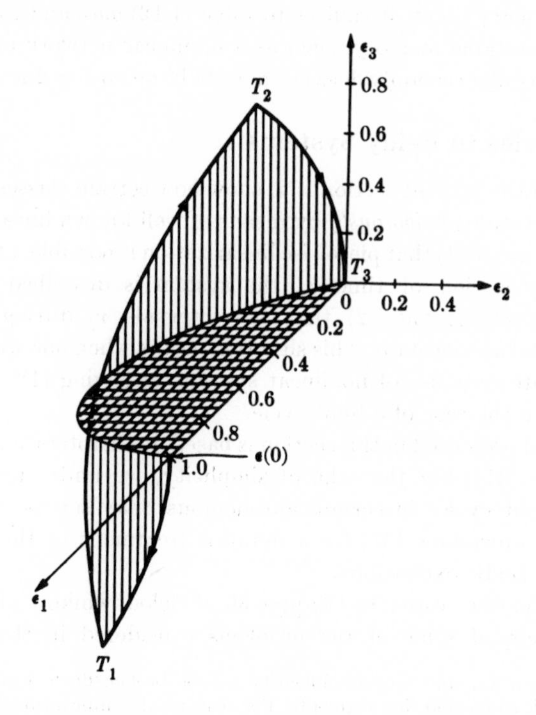

FIGURE 40. Optimal trajectory for $\epsilon(0) = \{1,0,0\}$. The switching times are $T_1 = 2^{-1/3}$; $T_2 = 3\ 2^{-1/3}$; $T_3 = 4\ 2^{-1/3}$.

It would be a mistake to conclude from this statement that a properly adjusted relay system always has a better response than a linear system. For, if an actuator of sufficient linear range, i.e., great power, were used, its response might be preferable. The important point is that a comparison makes sense only if actuators of comparable power levels, which often implies comparable cost, are used.

The next important point is that, although the linear design might perform perfectly well in its linear range, its response might become totally unacceptable if the actuator became saturated as a consequence of excessive disturbances. In a high-performance application, therefore, we have the choice between a relay design of relatively low-power components and a linear design of relatively high-power components, assuming that the plant itself does not saturate. If the plant itself were subject to saturation, the design principles of this section could also be used to eliminate undesirable transient response.

Having thus demonstrated that relay systems are not only of academic interest, our next problem is to synthesize a suitable controller. It is clear that the solution of the controller equation (4.12) is not straightforward, but requires a fairly powerful computer. It should be noted, however, that in the case of a stationary plant, it suffices to solve (4.12) *once* and to inscribe the results into a suitable memory, such as a nonlinear network or a magnetic drum. The controller certainly does not have to be an on-line digital computer.

5. Limit Cycles in Relay Systems

The scope of the present section is to show how certain classes of nonlinear systems can be studied *rigorously* by means of well-known linear techniques. The assumptions are (1) that piecewise linearization is possible, in other words, that for some period of time τ_j, the system is described by a linear differential equation; and (2) that the intervals τ_j during which this equation is valid are constant. This situation occurs when one wishes to study the steady-state response of nonlinear systems satisfying (1)† to a periodic excitation or in the case of a limit cycle.

The material presented in this section is based on Chapters 35, 36, and 37 of Solodownikow [31]. For the sake of simplicity, we limit ourselves to the analysis of limit cycles in certain autonomous relay servos, and refer the reader to Solodownikow [31] for a detailed treatment of the steady-state response to periodic excitations.

We also refer the reader to Chapter 36 of Solodownikow [31] for a very elegant solution of some of the problems considered in this section via

† Most of them do, since any nonlinearity can be broken down into a sequence of arbitrarily small connected line segments. For reasons of computational simplicity, we here focus our attention upon nonlinearities which consist of a *small* number of connected line segments.

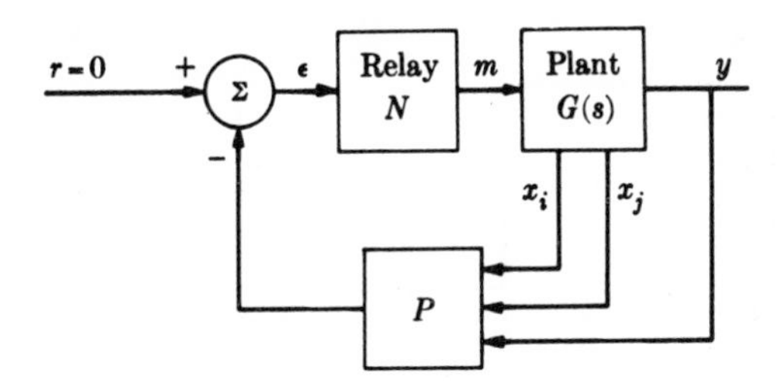

FIGURE 41. Relay system. The relay output $m(t)$ is normalized to $\pm$ 1.

A. I. Lur'e's transformation to canonical variables. This transformation, which is extensively used in the Soviet literature, will be discussed in the subsequent chapter by A. M. Letov in connection with Liapunov's second method.

5.1 Problem Description. If a relay system contains no nonlinearity other than the relay and its associated control equipment, then the over-all system is described by a set of linear differential equations valid as long as the relay maintains the same polarity. Such systems are often termed "piecewise linear."

Relay systems exhibit most of the phenomena encountered in nonlinear systems, namely limit cycles, the jump phenomenon, frequency entrainment, etc. In this section, we will determine rigorously the characteristics of limit cycles and indicate a method of investigating their stability. The system under consideration is shown in Fig. 41.

The relay N may be perfect or else may have dead zone, dead time, and hysteresis. For the sake of simplicity we shall not specifically include the dead zone defect, although this could be done. As a consequence of this restriction, the signal $m(t)$ which forces the states $\mathbf{x}(t)$ of the plant $G(s)$ can only assume two values, which we normalize to ± 1.

We further restrict ourselves to systems which do not receive any external inputs, that is $r(t) = 0$. If, as is usually the case, the linear plant contains at least one integration, this restriction can be broadened to include the case $r =$ constant.

5.2 The Calculation of Limit Cycles. Let us assume for the time being that a limit cycle of *half-period* T exists and that the relay under consideration is perfect. The resulting functions $m(t)$, $\epsilon(t)$, $x_i(t)$ are plotted in Figs. 42a, 42b, and 42c.

We first note that the relay input ϵ as well as the arbitrary state variable x_i must be periodic with half-period T. Hence

$$\begin{aligned} \mathbf{x}(t) &= -\mathbf{x}(t + T) \\ \epsilon(t) &= -\epsilon(t + T). \end{aligned} \tag{5.1}$$

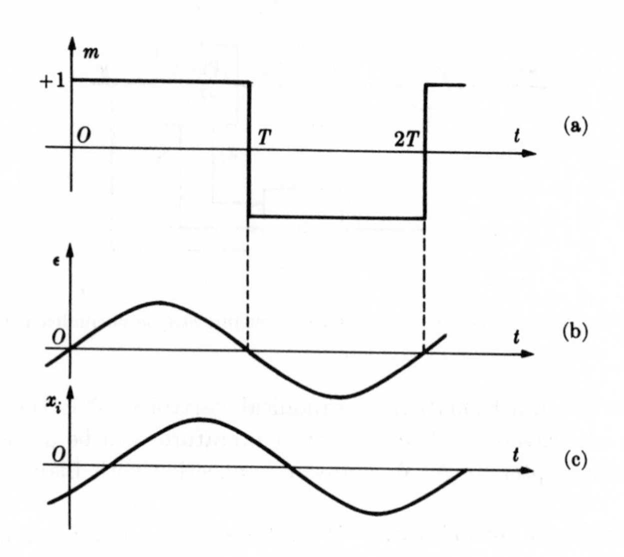

FIGURE 42. Variations of m, ϵ, and of some state variable x_i with time in the case of a perfect relay.

Also, since a perfect relay is used

$$\epsilon(t)\,\Big|_{t=kT} = 0 \quad k = 0, 1, 2, \ldots \tag{5.2}$$

and

$$\frac{d\epsilon}{dt}\bigg|_{t=kT} \begin{matrix} > 0 & \text{for } k \text{ even} \\ < 0 & \text{for } k \text{ odd.} \end{matrix} \tag{5.3}$$

Furthermore, it is evident from Fig. 42 that ϵ must not become zero at times other than $t = kT$; otherwise the function $m(t)$ could not be of the form shown.

Nonperfect Relays. If the relay has dead time or hysteresis, the function ϵ goes through zero at times $t^* + kT$, where the value of t^* is determined by dead time and/or hysteresis. The ensuing events are shown in Fig. 43.

Equation (5.1) holds regardless of relay imperfections as long as the relay characteristic $m = N(\epsilon)$ remains symmetric with respect to the origin. Equations (5.2) and (5.3) become

$$\epsilon(t)\bigg|_{t=t^*+kT} = 0 \quad k = \text{integer} \tag{5.2a}$$

$$\frac{d\epsilon}{dt}\bigg|_{t=t^*+kT} \begin{matrix} < 0 & \text{for } k \text{ even} \\ > 0 & \text{for } k \text{ odd.} \end{matrix} \tag{5.3a}$$

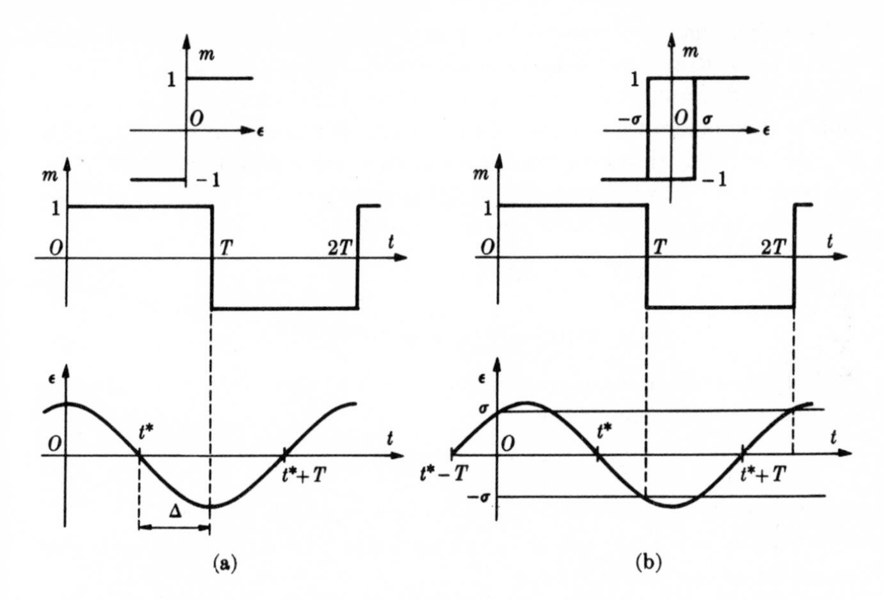

FIGURE 43. Variations of m and ϵ with time in the case of a relay having (a) dead time Δ; and (b) hysteresis σ.

In the case of dead time, $t^* = T - \Delta$, where Δ is the time which elapses between relay excitation and actual polarity reversal.

Similarly, if there is hysteresis σ, we have

$$\epsilon(t)\Big|_{t=kT} \begin{matrix} = \sigma & \text{for } k \text{ even} \\ = -\sigma & \text{for } k \text{ odd.} \end{matrix} \tag{5.2b}$$

$$\frac{d\epsilon}{dt}\Big|_{t=kT} \begin{matrix} > 0 & \text{for } k \text{ even} \\ < 0 & \text{for } k \text{ odd.} \end{matrix} \tag{5.3b}$$

5.3 The System Equations. Since the system is linear within any half-period T, the changes in the state vector $\mathbf{x}(t)$ can be computed by the well-known techniques of linear system analysis, *viz.*, Laplace-transform, Fourier-transform, and time-domain integration. We choose the latter method.†

We may write for the first half-period, $(m = +1)$,

$$\mathbf{x}(t) = g(t)\mathbf{x}(0) + \mathbf{h}(t) \tag{5.4}$$

where $g(t)$ is the transition matrix and $\mathbf{h}(t)$ is the distribution matrix.

In particular, at the first reversal time T, Eq. (5.4) becomes

$$\mathbf{x}(T) = g(T)\mathbf{x}(0) + \mathbf{h}(T). \tag{5.4a}$$

† An original solution via the Fourier-Transform is given in Solodownikow [31], Chapter 37.

Assuming that the system describes a limit cycle, the initial state $\mathbf{x}(0)$ cannot be arbitrary, but must be equal to the system state at $t = kT$, k even, which would result from the application of a square wave of half-period T an infinite time before we observe events. Hence, the proper initial state, which we label $\mathbf{x}^*(0)$, is the permanent solution of a linear difference equation and can be calculated by known sampled data techniques. An easier way of finding $\mathbf{x}^*(0)$ is to revert to Eq. (5.1) and to demand that

$$\mathbf{x}(T) = -\mathbf{x}^*(0) = g(T)\mathbf{x}^*(0) + \mathbf{h}(T) \tag{5.5}$$

or

$$\mathbf{x}^*(0) = -[I + g(T)]^{-1}\mathbf{h}(T). \tag{5.6}$$

The system under consideration, Fig. 41, is so designed that the relay input is a linear combination of the x_i

$$\epsilon(t) = P\mathbf{x}(t) = p_1x_1(t) + \cdots p_nx_n(t) \tag{5.7}$$

where P is an "n" row consisting of the real constants p_i, $(1 \cdots n)$.

Combining Eqs. (5.4) and (5.7) and assuming that a perfect relay is used, we obtain an expression for $\epsilon(t)$

$$\epsilon(t) = P[g(t)\mathbf{x}^*(0) + \mathbf{h}(t)], \quad 0 \leqslant t \leqslant T. \tag{5.8}$$

In the case of a perfect relay, ϵ becomes zero at $t = T$. The positive and real roots T_l of Eq. (5.9) thus define the limit cycles which can exist in the system under consideration:

$$P[g(T)\mathbf{x}^*(0) + \mathbf{h}(T)] = 0 \tag{5.9}$$

that is

$$p_1x_1(T) + p_2x_2(T) + \cdots + p_nx_n(T) = 0.$$

Here the $x_i(T)$ are functions of the initial state $\mathbf{x}^*(0)$ and of T. For greater clarity, the $x_i(T)$ should be written $x_i[\mathbf{x}^*(0), T]$.

Equation (5.9) is changed to (5.9a) or (5.9b) if the relay has dead time or hysteresis. Thus

$$P[g(t^*)\mathbf{x}^*(0) + \mathbf{h}(t^*)] = 0 \tag{5.9a}$$

and

$$P[g(T)\mathbf{x}^*(0) + \mathbf{h}(T)] = -\sigma, \tag{5.9b}$$

Example. We consider the relay system shown in Fig. 44 and assume that there is no input. The selected states are the output x_1 and the output velocity x_2.

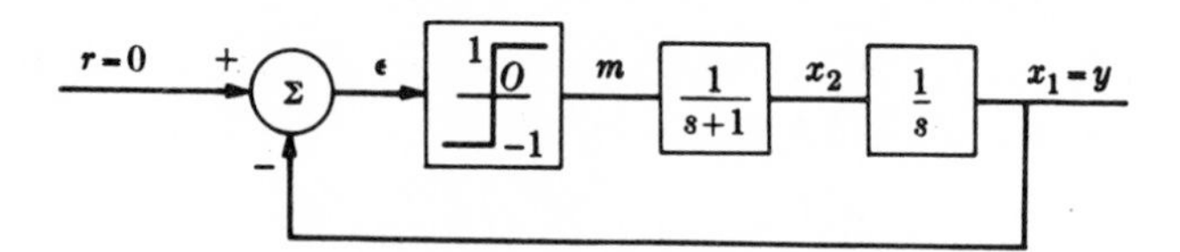

FIGURE 44. Relay system of example.

The parallel network P reduces to

$$P = \{-1, 0\}. \tag{5.10}$$

The reader may verify that the $g(t)$ and $h(t)$ matrices of Eq. (5.4) are

$$g(t) = \begin{bmatrix} 1 & 1 - e^{-t} \\ 0 & e^{-t} \end{bmatrix} \quad \mathbf{h}(t) = \begin{bmatrix} t - 1 + e^{-t} \\ 1 - e^{-t} \end{bmatrix}. \tag{5.11}$$

The proper initial state $\mathbf{x}^*(0)$ is obtained from Eq. (5.5) and expressed in terms of the unknown half-period T by

$$\begin{aligned} x_1^*(0) &= \frac{1 - T - e^{-T} + (1 - e^{-T}) \tanh (T/2)}{2} \\ x_2^*(0) &= -\tanh \frac{T}{2} \,. \end{aligned} \tag{5.12}$$

During the first half-period, $0 \leqslant t \leqslant T$, the relay input becomes

$$\epsilon(t) = -t + 1 + \frac{T}{2} - e^{-t}\left(1 + \tanh \frac{T}{2}\right). \tag{5.13}$$

At time $t = T$, ϵ must reduce to zero in the case of a perfect relay. Hence

$$\epsilon(T) = -\frac{T}{2} + \tanh \frac{T}{2} = 0. \tag{5.14}$$

Condition (5.14) has only one root, namely $T = 0$. This confirms the familiar result that the relay system of Fig. 44 chatters at infinitely high frequency with zero amplitude.

If the relay were to have dead time Δ, condition (5.14) would change to

$$\epsilon(t^*) = \frac{-T}{2} + \Delta + 1 - \left(1 - \tanh \frac{T}{2}\right)e^{\Delta} = 0. \tag{5.15}$$

Equation 5.15 has two roots, T_1 and T_2. For $\Delta = 0.5$, the quantities shown in Table I are obtained.

TABLE I

	$T_1 = 0.48$	$T_2 = 2.55$
$t^* = T - \Delta$	-0.02	2.05
$x_1(T)$	-0.398	0.421
$x_2(T)$	0.235	0.854
$\epsilon(T)$	0.398	-0.421

5.4 Stability of Limit Cycles. Equations (5.9) indicate possible limit cycles, but we do not know if these limit cycles are stable. In order to investigate limit cycle stability, we assume that at time $t = 0$, the actual system state differs slightly from the proper state $x^*(0)$. We then observe the *perturbed* system as it evolves during a complete half-period and calculate the state at the first relay reversal time. We shall show that the ensuing perturbed state is related to the initial perturbed state by a linear difference equation, and we shall conclude that the limit cycle is stable if this difference equation is stable.

Notation. If the initial state $\mathbf{x}^*(0)$ is perturbed by a small quantity $\boldsymbol{\delta}_0\mathbf{x}$ then the time t^* at which the perturbed error becomes zero, the time at which the relay reverses polarity, and the state corresponding to this time will change. Perturbed and unperturbed motion is compared in Table II.

TABLE II

	Unperturbed motion	Perturbed motion
State at $t = 0$	$\mathbf{x}^*(0)$	$\mathbf{x}^*(0) + \boldsymbol{\delta}_0\mathbf{x}$
Time when ϵ becomes zero	t^*	$t^* + \delta_0 t$
First reversal time	T	$T + \delta_0 T$
State at first reversal time	$\mathbf{x}[\mathbf{x}^*(0), T] = -\mathbf{x}^*(0)$	$\mathbf{x}[\mathbf{x}^*(0) + \boldsymbol{\delta}_0\mathbf{x}, T + \delta_0 T]$ $= -\mathbf{x}^*(0) + \boldsymbol{\delta}_1\mathbf{x}$

Since we assume arbitrarily small perturbations, we may perform a Taylor series expansion about Eqs. (5.9) and (5.4a), reproduced below for the case of a perfect relay

$$\epsilon(T) = P[g(T)\mathbf{x}^*(0) + \mathbf{h}(T)] = 0 \tag{5.9}$$

$$\mathbf{x}(T) = g(T)\mathbf{x}(0) + \mathbf{h}(T). \tag{5.4a}$$

In the case of the example of Fig. 44, these equations are, respectively, in the case of a perfect relay

$$\epsilon(T) = -x_1^*(0) - (1 - e^{-T})x_2^*(0) - (T - 1 + e^{-T}) = 0 \tag{5.16}$$

$$\begin{aligned} x_1(T) &= x_1^*(0) + (1 - e^{-T})x_2^*(0) + (T - 1 + e^{-T}) \\ x_2(T) &= e^{-T}x_2^*(0) + 1 - e^{-T}. \end{aligned} \tag{5.17}$$

If the relay has dead time Δ, Eq. (5.16) changes to

$$-x_1^*(0) - (1 - e^{-t^*})x_2^*(0) - (t^* - 1 + e^{-t^*}) = 0 \tag{5.18}$$

where

$$t^* = T - \Delta.$$

A Taylor series expansion of Eq. (5.9) about $\mathbf{x}^*(0)$, T relates $\delta_0 T$ to the chosen initial perturbation $\boldsymbol{\delta}_0\mathbf{x}$. In the case of Eq. (5.18) this becomes

$$\delta_0 t^* = \frac{-\delta_0 x_1 - (1 - e^{-t^*})\,\delta_0 x_2}{1 - e^{-t^*}[1 - x_2^*(0)]}. \tag{5.19}$$

A similar Taylor series expansion of Eq. (5.17) yields

$$\begin{aligned} \delta_1 x_1 &= \delta_0 x_1 + (1 - e^{-T})\,\delta_0 x_2 + \{1 - e^{-T}[1 - x_2^*(0)]\}\,\delta_0 T \\ \delta_1 x_2 &= e^{-T}\,\delta_0 x_2 + e^{-T}[1 - x_2^*(0)]\,\delta_0 T. \end{aligned} \tag{5.20}$$

By eliminating $\delta_0 T$ between Eqs. (5.19) and (5.20), we relate the new perturbed state to the initial perturbed state through a set of linear equations of the form

$$\boldsymbol{\delta}_1\mathbf{x} = A\boldsymbol{\delta}_0\mathbf{x} \tag{5.21}$$

where A is an $n \times n$ matrix whose elements are real constants.

It is clear that Eq. (5.21) holds as well for the first as for the lth reversal time. Therefore, we write the recurrence relation

$$\boldsymbol{\delta}_l\mathbf{x} = A\boldsymbol{\delta}_{l-1}\mathbf{x}. \qquad (l = 1, 2, \ldots) \tag{5.22}$$

The important conclusion is that Eq. (5.22) constitutes a set of linear difference equations which are stable if and only if the "n" eigenvalues of A, λ_i, are all located inside the unit circle. These eigenvalues are, we recall, the roots of

$$\det [A - \lambda I] = 0. \tag{5.23}$$

The reader may verify that in the case of the example-problem, the numerical results given in Table III are obtained for the two limit cycles previously found. The limit cycle of half-period T_1 is unstable; the other one is stable.

TABLE III

	$T_1 = 0.48$	$T_2 = 2.55$
$\delta_0 T$	$3.85\,\delta_0 x_1 - 0.077\,\delta_0 x_2$	$-1.31\,\delta_0 x_1$ $-1.14\,\delta_0 x_2$
Matrix A	$\begin{bmatrix} 1.905 & 0.363 \\ 0.294 & 0.560 \end{bmatrix}$	$\begin{bmatrix} -0.120 & -0.053 \\ -0.190 & -0.087 \end{bmatrix}$
Eigenvalues	$\lambda_1 = 1.97$ $\lambda_2 = 0.49$	$\lambda_1 = 0.0$ $\lambda_2 = -0.207$

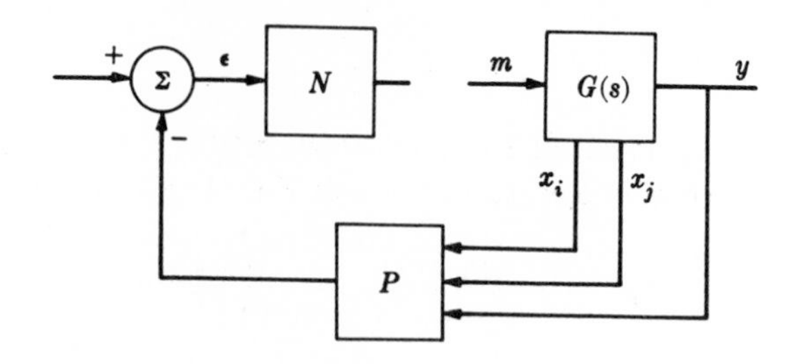

FIGURE 45. Simplified analysis of limit cycle stability.

5.5 Stability of Limit Cycles. A Simplified Criterion. The rigorous stability analysis of the previous section requires fairly lengthy computations. A simpler, though less rigorous method, is described in the literature [34], Chapter 35.

We consider Fig. 45, which is identical to Fig. 41 except for the broken connection between the relay and the plant. A square-wave signal $m(t)$ of amplitude 1 and half-period T is externally impressed upon $G(s)$. If the steady-state signal $\epsilon(t)$ returned by $G(s)$ is such that the relay can exactly reproduce $m(t)$ for some value T_i, then the closed-loop system has a limit cycle at T_i. This statement is rigorous.

The following method of investigating orbital stability gives correct results in a large percentage of trials and has the advantage of requiring little additional work.

We assume that Eq. (5.9), which does no more than mathematically summarize the results of the previous experiment, yields a limit cycle of half-period T_i. We then let the *half-period* of $m(t)$ increase by δT and we observe the polarity of the resulting error, $\epsilon_\delta(t)$, at $t = T_i + \delta T$, $\delta t > 0$.

In Fig. 46, $\epsilon_\delta(T_i + \delta T)$ is positive; this suggests a further increase in T_i if the loop were closed now. The corresponding limit cycle would, therefore, be

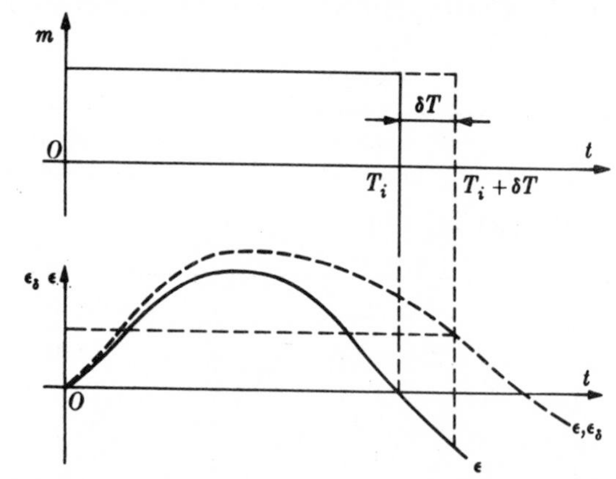

FIGURE 46. Error signals $\epsilon(t)$ (————), and $\epsilon_\delta(t)$ (– – – –).

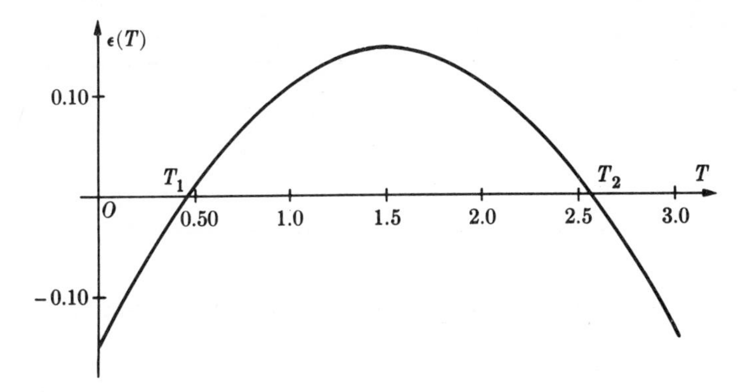

FIGURE 47. Variation of $\epsilon(T)$ with T according to Eq. (5.9). The limit cycle of half-period T_1 is unstable, the one of half-period T_2 is stable.

unstable. A plot of the transcendental equation (5.9), which one would normally sketch anyway to find the roots T_i graphically, supplies the required information on the polarity of $\epsilon_\delta(T_i + \delta T)$. This plot is shown in Fig. 47 for the two limit cycles found in the example of Section 5.3.

These arguments are summarized in the stability criterion below.

If

$$\left.\frac{d\epsilon}{dT}\right|_{T=T_i} > 0, \text{ the limit cycle is unstable}$$

$$\left.\frac{d\epsilon}{dT}\right|_{T=T_i} < 0, \text{ the limit cycle is stable.}$$

The reader may verify that these stability conditions also apply to systems containing nonperfect relays with hysteresis.

6. The Effect of Multiple Nonlinearities on Large Systems

Most of the mathematical techniques now available in nonlinear mechanics accommodate fairly simple systems only. It should be realized, however, that high-order multivariable nonlinear systems are becoming quite common, in spite of the fact that no satisfactory analysis procedures exist. The design of such systems is ultimately achieved as a consequence of computer simulations, daring approximations, and ingenuity.

In many practical problems, it is relatively easy to ascertain *global* stability and to achieve acceptable transient behavior for large deviations from equilibrium. Then the next problem is to determine motion in the vicinity of the singular point at which the system, we hope, will settle. This is not difficult if linearization is permissible, that is, if the nonlinearities are regular in the vicinity of the singular point. In many practical situations, however,

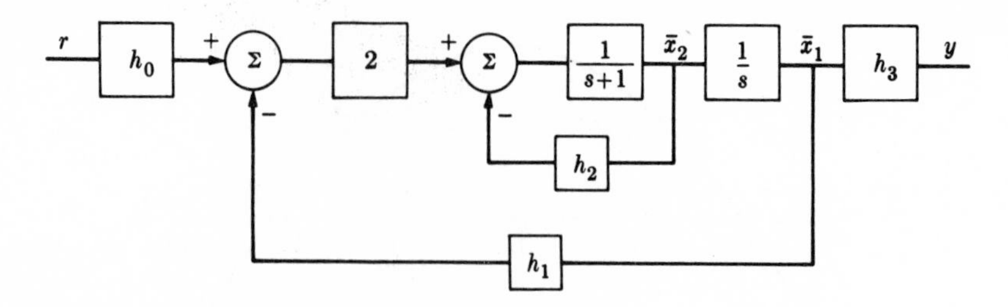

FIGURE 48. Example-problem of control system containing four nonlinearities N_0, N_1, N_2, and N_3.

discontinuous nonlinearities such as Coulomb friction or quantization are present with the result that a *small-motion* linear system cannot be defined.

It is the scope of this section to determine an *upper bound* of the effects of such discontinuous nonlinearities. The problem of estimating steady-state inaccuracies in large systems was first formulated in this fashion by J. E. Bertram [5], who confines himself to sampled data systems which are linear except for an arbitrary number of quantizers. He moreover assumes that there are stable equilibrium points and does not consider the possibility of stable limit cycles.

In the present section, we concern ourselves with continuous, rather than sampled data systems and we envisage the possibility of limit cycles. The digital servomechanisms, which are now frequently used in high-accuracy applications, may be continuous or sampled. The determination of the upper bound of the error, to be presented here, is identical with that worked out by Bertram [5]. Nonlinearities other than those due to quantization will also be envisaged.

Consideration of this upper bound always leads to a pessimistic evaluation of system performance, in that the actual error may be much smaller than the upper bound. Scheidenhelm [25] and Senouillet [28] have determined the exact and the nearly exact errors, respectively, as well as the characteristics of limit cycles in low-order quantized and sampled systems using describing function and phase-plane techniques.

6.1 Some Discontinuous Nonlinearities. We will consider nonlinearities of the form $\sigma = N(\eta)$ such that

$$\sigma = N(\eta) = h\eta + \varphi(\eta) \qquad (h = \text{constant}) \tag{6.1}$$

and

$$|\varphi(\eta)| \leqslant M \tag{6.2}$$

where M is a finite positive number.

Some common nonlinearities of the type considered are shown in Table IV.

6.2 System Equations. Consider a system which is linear except for p nonlinearities of the type (6.2). A second-order example problem is shown in

Fig. 48. We may write by inspection that

$$\begin{aligned} \dot{x}_1 &= x_2 \\ \dot{x}_2 &= -2N_1(x_1) - x_2 - N_2(x_2) + 2N_0(r). \end{aligned} \tag{6.3}$$

We wish to find an upper bound E of the steady-state error

$$\lim_{t\to\infty} (r - y) = \lim_{t\to\infty} [r - N_3(x_1)] = E \quad (r = \text{constant}). \tag{6.4}$$

We now define an *associated linear system* by replacing each of the $N_i(\eta)$ by $h_i\eta$ and by neglecting the effects of $\varphi_i(\eta)$. The corresponding state variables are marked $\bar{x}_l$, $(l = 1, \ldots, n)$. For the example problem, we obtain

$$\begin{aligned} \dot{\bar{x}}_1 &= \bar{x}_2 \\ \dot{\bar{x}}_2 &= -2h_1\bar{x}_1 - (1 + h_2)\bar{x}_2 + 2h_0 r. \end{aligned} \tag{6.5}$$

This associated linear system is shown in Fig. 49. We assume that the h_i, $(i = 1, \ldots, p)$, have been chosen in such a way that the associated linear system is stable and has satisfactory transient behavior. For the example-problem, we select

$$\begin{aligned} h_0 &= 1 \quad h_2 = 2 \\ h_1 &= 1 \quad h_3 = 1 \end{aligned} \tag{6.6}$$

TABLE IV

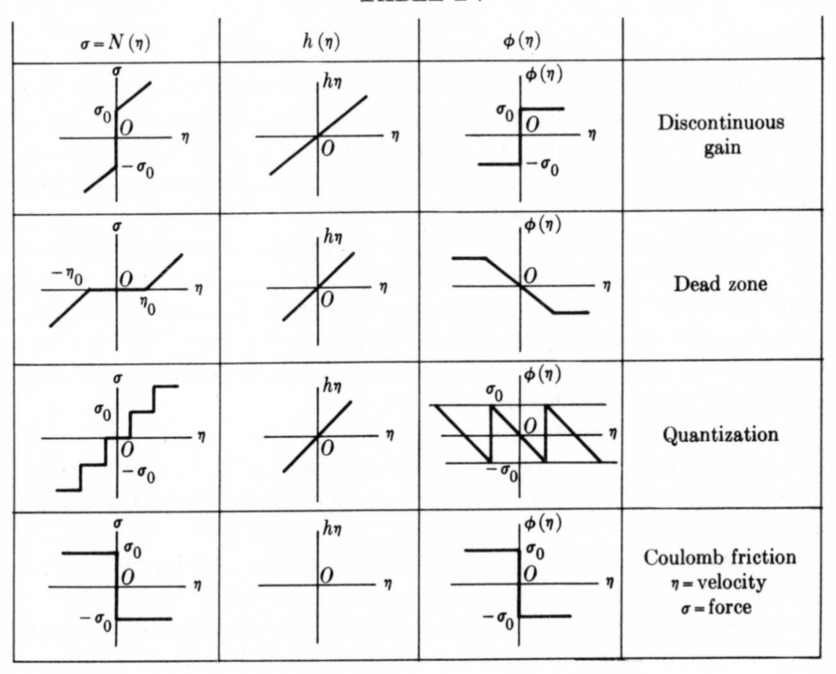

$\sigma = N(\eta)$	$h(\eta)$	$\phi(\eta)$	
σ, σ_0, O, η, $-\sigma_0$	$h\eta$, O, η	$\phi(\eta)$, σ_0, O, η, $-\sigma_0$	Discontinuous gain
σ, $-\eta_0$, O, η_0, η	$h\eta$, O, η	$\phi(\eta)$, O, η	Dead zone
σ, σ_0, O, η, $-\sigma_0$	$h\eta$, O, η	$\phi(\eta)$, σ_0, O, η, $-\sigma_0$	Quantization
σ, σ_0, O, η, $-\sigma_0$	$h\eta$, O, η	$\phi(\eta)$, σ_0, O, η, $-\sigma_0$	Coulomb friction η = velocity σ = force

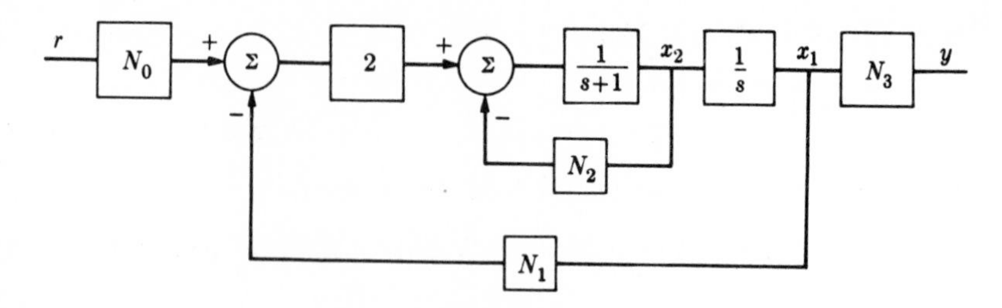

FIGURE 49. Associated linear system.

in which case the characteristic roots are

$$\lambda_1 = -1, \quad \lambda_2 = -2.$$

We next rewrite the nonlinear system Eq. (6.3), using (6.1) and (6.6)

$$\begin{aligned}
\dot{x}_1 &= x_2 \\
\dot{x}_2 &= -2x_1 - 3x_2 + 2r - 2\varphi_1(x_1) - \varphi_2(x_2) + 2\varphi_0(r) \\
\epsilon &= r - y = r - x_1 - \varphi_3(x_1).
\end{aligned} \tag{6.7}$$

We will now treat the *bounded* functions $\varphi_i(\eta)$, $(i = 1, \ldots, p)$ as *inputs* in Eq. (6.7) and conclude that:

If the associated linear system (6.5) is stable, i.e., has bounded output in response to bounded input, then the nonlinear system (6.7) is stable in the same sense.

It is necessary here to specify what is meant by stability. Clearly, $\mathbf{x} = 0$ is not, in general, a stable singular point, since we cannot be certain that all the functions $\varphi_i(\eta)$, considered to be forcing functions, tend to zero as $t \to \infty$. Therefore we agree that the system is stable, although there may be limit cycles, as long as there is no unbounded motion.

We qualify the nonlinear system (6.7) as stable if the trajectory starting at *any* initial $\mathbf{x}(0)$ will enter a closed surface S (Fig. 50) containing the origin, and remain there after a sufficiently long time has elapsed. S is bounded but not infinitesimal. As $t \to \infty$, the motion may terminate at a singular point which is not necessarily 0 and which is not necessarily the same for different experiments, or else may become a limit cycle.

The kind of stability defined here is different from the various other types of stability usually discussed in nonlinear mechanics. It is, in particular, different from "stability in the large," which rules out the possibility of limit cycles.

Our problem in this section consists, roughly speaking, of determining the closed and bounded surface S.

The difference between the associated linear system (6.5) and the nonlinear system (6.7) is further clarified if we compare Figs. 49 and 51.

As a next step, we define a forcing vector **R** consisting of external inputs **r** and of the nonlinearities $\varphi(\eta)$. In the case of the example-problem,

$$\begin{aligned} R_1 &= 0 \\ R_2 &= 2r - 2\varphi_1(x_1) - \varphi_2(x_2) + 2\varphi_0(r). \end{aligned} \tag{6.8}$$

Assuming for the time being that **R** is explicitly known, we may write

$$\mathbf{x}(s) = A(s)\mathbf{x}(0) + B(s)\mathbf{R}(s). \tag{6.9}$$

Thus, for the example-problem

$$A(s) = \begin{bmatrix} \dfrac{s+3}{(s+1)(s+2)} & \dfrac{1}{(s+1)(s+2)} \\ \dfrac{-2}{(s+1)(s+2)} & \dfrac{s}{(s+1)(s+2)} \end{bmatrix} \tag{6.10}$$

$$B(s) = A(s).$$

Since Eq. (6.9) is stable, the effect of initial conditions will ultimately vanish. Hence, in the steady state

$$\mathbf{x}(s) = B(s)\mathbf{R}(s). \tag{6.11}$$

Moreover, the upper bound E of the error ϵ can be obtained by assuming that all the inputs φ_i, $(i = 1, \ldots, p)$, are least favorable. It follows from Eqs. (6.7) and (6.10) that

$$\epsilon(s) = r(s) - \frac{2r(s) - 2\varphi_1(s) - \varphi_2(s) + 2\varphi_0(s)}{(s+1)(s+2)} - \varphi_3(s) \tag{6.12}$$

where the $\varphi_i(s)$ are the Laplace transforms of the inputs $\varphi_i(t)$ which take into

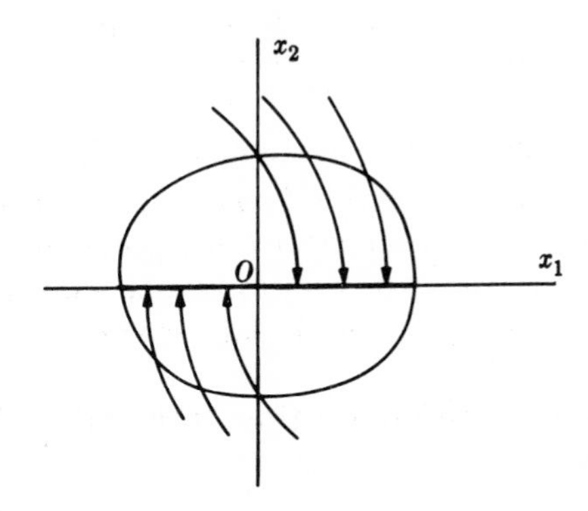

FIGURE 50. Definition of stability. In the situation shown, the initial state $\mathbf{x}(0)$ terminates inside S on a curve.

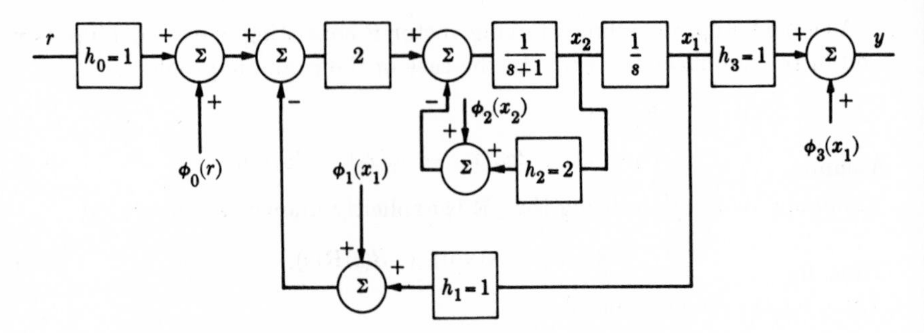

FIGURE 51. Original nonlinear system in which the bounded nonlinearities are viewed as inputs.

account the nonlinearities $\varphi_i(\eta)$. It is clear that

$$\varphi_i(s) \neq \varphi_i(\eta) \big|_{\eta=s}$$

To estimate E, we assume that there is either

(1) a constant steady state condition such that each

$$\varphi_i(t) = \pm M_i. \tag{6.13}$$

or,

(2) a stationary oscillation such that each

$$\varphi_i(t) \cong M_i \sin(\omega t + \theta_i). \quad (i = 1, \ldots, p) \tag{6.14}$$

In the first case, we select the signs so as to maximize E; in the second case, we select the least favorable ω and θ_i. For example

(1)
$$E = \frac{2M_1 + M_2 + 2M_0}{2} + M_3 \tag{6.15}$$

(2)
$$E = \sup_{\omega,\theta_i} \left\{ \left| \frac{2M_1 \underline{|\theta_1} + M_2 \underline{|\theta_2} + 2M_0 \underline{|\theta_0}}{(j+1)(j+2)} + M_3 \underline{|\theta_3} \right| \right\} \tag{6.16}$$

where $M_i \underline{|\theta_i}$ signifies that φ_i has amplitude M_i and phase angle θ_i. When $\omega = 0$, assumption (1) is more conservative than assumption (2), and the maximum steady-state error that we can expect is given by Eq. (6.15). If the associated linear system (6.5) were to have a *resonance* at some frequency, then assumption (2) might yield the largest error.

7. Extension of the Convolution Integral to Nonlinear Structures

In a linear system, the response to an excitation is given by a convolution integral. This description can be generalized to a large class of nonlinear systems by making use of multiple convolution integrals and by writing the response of a nonlinear system to an excitation as a finite or an infinite series

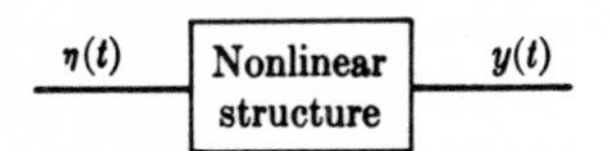

FIGURE 52. Black-box representation of a nonlinear structure.

of such integrals. These integrals give a complete description of the nonlinear system just as the convolution integral does for a linear system.

The mathematical techniques used in such descriptions were first developed by V. Volterra and M. Fréchet at the beginning of this century. In view of the complexity of the topic, it will not be possible here to give more than a short survey of the main results and to point out only a few applications. The interested readers will find a more detailed treatment elsewhere [29, 30].

The main results are that a nonlinear system can be completely analyzed by measuring the response to a series of pulses and that it can be synthesized by means of linear structures, multipliers, and nonlinear amplifiers with lth-power characteristics. This method can be used practically only when the number of multiple convolution integrals is not too large and is of little use for closed loop nonlinear structures because their response is an infinite series of such integrals.

As will be shown in the following, the method of description developed applies very well to structures consisting of a cascade of linear systems and nonlinear amplifiers.

The response $y(t)$ to an excitation $\eta(t)$ which is given by

$$y(t) = \int_0^t W(t - u)\eta(u)\, du \tag{7.1}$$

in a linear system, can be written for a wide class of nonlinear systems (Fig. 52) as

$$y(t) = \sum_{p=1}^{N} \sum_{\alpha=1}^{M} \underbrace{\int_0^t \cdots \int_0^t}_{p} g_{p\alpha}(t - u_1, \ldots, t - u_p)\eta^\alpha(u_1) \cdots \eta^\alpha(u_p)\, du_1 \cdots du_p \tag{7.2}$$

where p and α are positive integers and where N and M may have to be infinite. Examples of nonlinear systems of this class are given below.

It is assumed that the kernels $g_{p\alpha}$ are sufficiently regular and that the sum (7.2) exists for the class of all real, bounded, piecewise continuous functions $\eta(t)$. M. Fréchet proved that any continuous functional corresponding to a nonlinear physical system can be developed in a series of elementary functionals (called normal homogeneous functionals)

$$G_{p\alpha}(t) = \underbrace{\int_0^t \cdots \int_0^t}_{p} g_{p\alpha}(t - u_1, \ldots, t - u_p)\eta^\alpha(u_1) \cdots \eta^\alpha(u_p) \cdot du_1 \cdots du_p \tag{7.3}$$

and that the approximation becomes closer as the number of elementary functions $G_{p\alpha}$ increases.

The analysis of a physical system represented by Eq. (7.2) consists in the determination of the kernels $g_{p\alpha}$ which characterize the system under study. If the excitation $\eta(t)$ is $af(t)$, the response is a polynomial in a

$$y(t) = \sum_{j=1}^{q} B_j(t)a^j \tag{7.4}$$

where q is the maximum value of the product $p\alpha$.

The functions $B_j(t)$ can be found by measuring the response of the system to excitations $af(t)$ with varying amplitudes a. If $f(t)$ is a rectangular pulse

$$\Delta(t) = U(t) - U(t - h)$$

where h is a small delay compared to the time constants of the system, and where $U(t)$ is a unit step, the functions $B_j(t)$ are polynomials in h

$$B_j(t) = \sum_{\substack{\alpha \\ \alpha p = j}} \sum_{p} g_{p\alpha}(t, t, \ldots, t)h^p. \tag{7.5}$$

Each kernel $g_{p\alpha}$ can be found by measuring the response of the system to rectangular pulses with varying delays h. This is also true if $f(t)$ is a sum of rectangular pulses.

As $g_{p\alpha}(t, t, \ldots, t)$ does not usually enable the determination of the function of p variables

$$g_{p\alpha}(u_1, u_2, \ldots, u_p)$$

it is necessary to use more than one type of excitation function. The kernel $g_{p\alpha}$ can be determined by measuring the response to p-types of excitation which are, for instance, $\Delta(t)$ and the $p - 1$ series of $2, 3, \ldots, p$ pulses

$$\begin{aligned}
&\Delta(t) + \Delta(t - T_2) \\
&\Delta(t) + \Delta(t - T_2) + \Delta(t - T_3) \\
&\cdot \\
&\cdot \\
&\cdot \\
&\Delta(t) + \Delta(t - T_2) + \Delta(t - T_3) + \cdots + \Delta(t - T_p).
\end{aligned}$$

In general, $p - 1$ infinity of such excitations are required where p is the largest number of variables found in all the kernels $g_{p\alpha}$. In view of the generality of the description, the number of measures required is indeed very large. In special cases, this number can be reduced.

Example. If the responses to $\Delta(t)$ and $\Delta(t) + \Delta(t - T_2)$ of a system represented by

$$y(t) = \int_0^t \int_0^t g_{21}(t - u_1, t - u_2)\eta(u_1)\eta(u_2)\, du_1\, du_2 \tag{7.6}$$

are

$$\bar{y}_1(t) = g_{21}(t, t)h^2 \tag{7.7}$$

and

$$\bar{y}_2(t) = [g_{21}(t, t) + 2g_{21}(t, t - T_2) + g_{21}(t - T_2, t - T_2)]h^2 \tag{7.8}$$

the kernel g_{21} is given by

$$g_{21}(t, t - T_2) = \frac{1}{2h^2}[\bar{y}_2(t) - \bar{y}_1(t) - \bar{y}_1(t - T_2)]. \tag{7.9}$$

The kernel g_{21} is obtained by measuring the response to a single infinity of excitations differing by the delay T_2.

Once a kernel $g_{p\alpha}$ has been determined, it must be shown that it can be synthesized. If $g_{p\alpha}(u_1, \ldots, u_p)$ is written as a sum or a series

$$g_{p\alpha}(u_1, \ldots, u_p) = \sum_{m_1} \cdots \sum_{m_i} \cdots \sum_{m_p} W_{m_1}(u_1) W_{m_2}(u_2) \cdots W_{m_i}(u_i) \cdots W_{m_p}(u_p) \qquad (m_i = 1, 2, \ldots) \tag{7.10}$$

where the functions $W_{m_i}(u_i)$ are impulse responses of physically realizable linear systems, each term of the sum can be synthesized by nonlinear amplifiers, linear circuits, and a multiplier with p-inputs as shown in Fig. 53. Typical complete sets of functions are the power functions

$$W_m(t) = t^m; \; m = 0, 1, \ldots, \infty$$

and the Laguerre functions

$$W_v(t) = \sum_{v=0}^{\infty} \binom{n}{v} \frac{(-t)^v}{v!} e^{-t/2}.$$

If one of the terms is a product of p identical functions, i.e., $W(u_1)W(u_2) \cdots W(u_p)$, it can be synthesized with two nonlinear amplifiers and a linear circuit, Fig. 54.

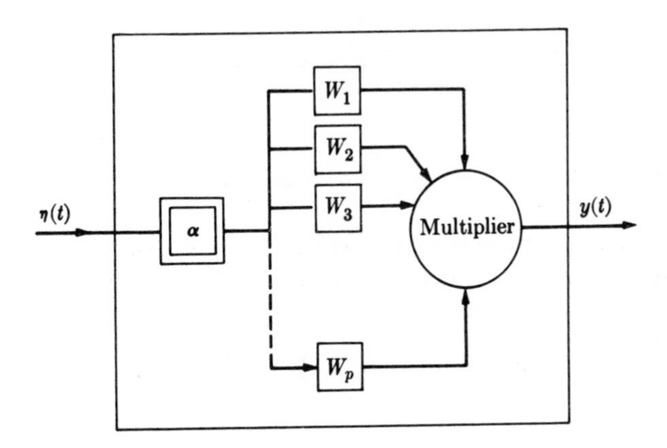

FIGURE 53. Synthesis of a factorized kernel $g_{p\alpha} = W_1 W_2 W_3 \ldots W_p$. The double-lined square box means that the input is elevated to the αth power.

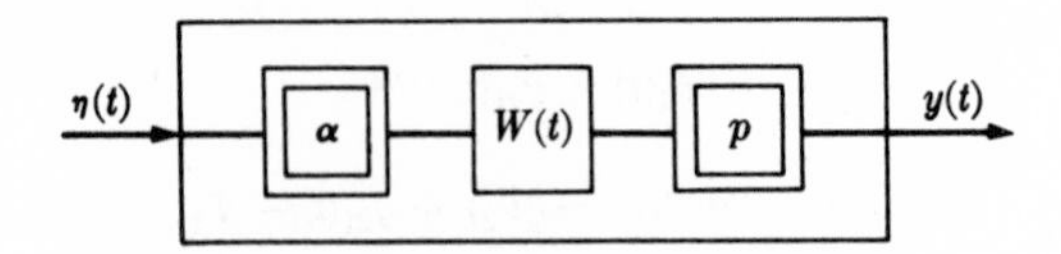

FIGURE 54. Synthesis of a symmetrically factorized kernel $g_{p\alpha} = WWW \ldots W$.

Example.
If

$$g_{21}(t, t - T) = e^{-bt}(e^{dT} + e^{mT})$$

then

$$g_{21}(u_1, u_2) = e^{-(b-d)u_1}e^{-du_2} + e^{-(b-m)u_1}e^{-mu_2}.$$

Here the functions $W(t)$ are exponential functions.

Special Cases. (a) The response of a system consisting of a nonlinear amplifier followed by a linear structure, Fig. 55a, is

$$y(t) = \int_0^t W(t - u)F_1[\eta(u)]\, du = \sum a_i \int_0^t W(t - u)\eta^i(u)\, du \qquad (7.11)$$

where $W(t)$ is the impulse response of the linear structure and $F_1(\eta) = \Sigma\, a_i\eta^i$ is the characteristic of the amplifier. In this case the index p is unity and all the kernels are identical.

(b) If the linear structure is followed by the nonlinear amplifier, Fig. 55b,

$$y(t) = F_1\left[\int_0^t W(t - u)\eta(u)\, du\right] = \sum a_i \left[\int_0^t W(t - u)\eta(u)\, du\right]^i$$

$$= \sum a_i \underbrace{\int_0^t \cdots \int_0^t}_{i} W(t - u_1) \cdots W(t - u_i)\eta(u_1) \cdots \eta(u_i)\, du_1 \cdots du_i \qquad (7.12)$$

In this case the index α is unity and each kernel is the product of i identical functions $W(t)$.

(c) The response of a system consisting of a nonlinear amplifier followed by a linear structure and a nonlinear amplifier, Fig. 55c, is

$$y(t) = F_2\left\{\int_0^t W(t - u)F_1[\eta(u)]\, du\right\} = F_2\left\{\sum a_i \int_0^t W(t - u) \cdot \eta^i(u)\, du\right\}$$

$$= \sum \sum b_j a_i^j \underbrace{\int_0^t \cdots \int_0^t}_{j} W(t - u_1) \cdots W(t - u_j)\eta^i(u_1) \cdots \eta^i(u_j) \cdot du_1 \cdots du_j \qquad (7.13)$$

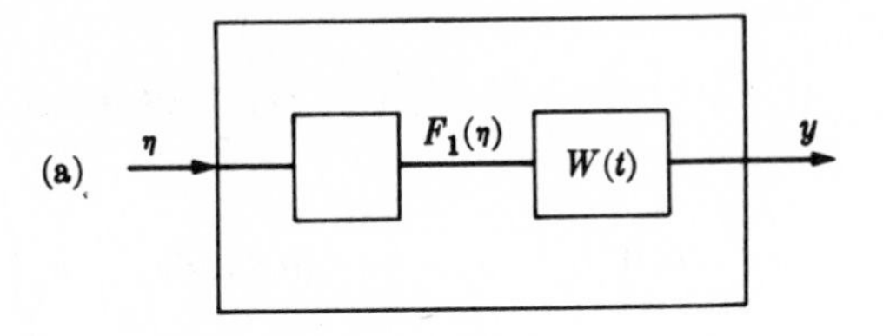

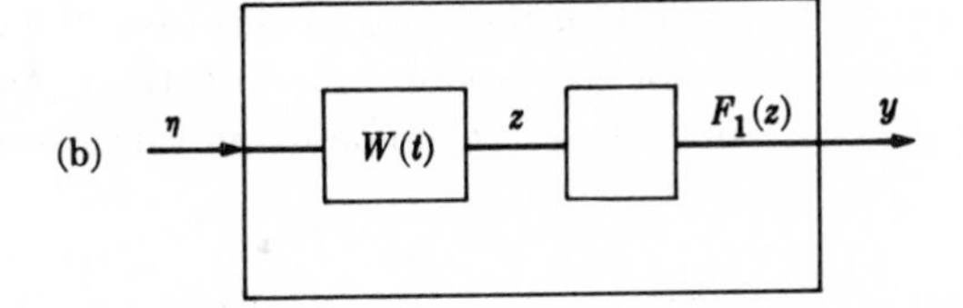

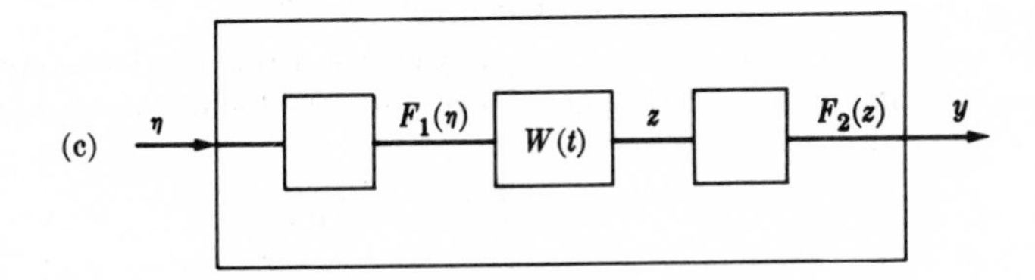

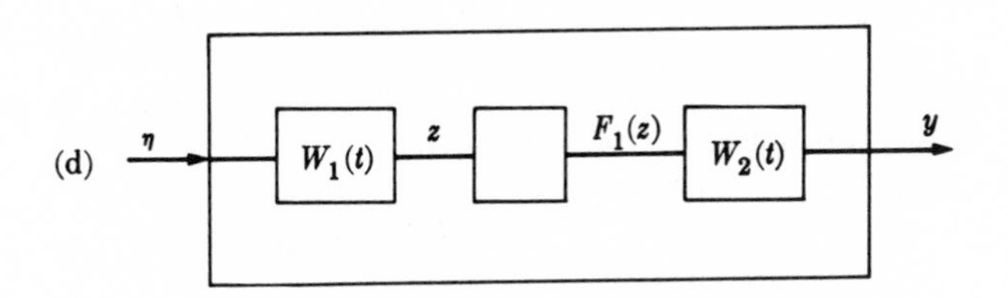

FIGURE 55. Elementary nonlinear systems.

where $F_2(z) = \Sigma\, b_j z^j$ is the characteristic of the second nonlinear amplifier.

In this case the index α is equal to i and all the kernels are the products of j identical functions $W(t)$.

(d) The response of a linear structure followed by a nonlinear amplifier and another linear structure, Fig. 55d, is

$$y(t) = \int_0^t W_2(t-u) F_1\left[\int_0^u W_1(u-\theta)\eta(\theta)\, d\theta\right] du$$

$$= \sum a_i \int_0^t W_2(t-u)\left[\int_0^u W_1(u-\theta)\eta(\theta)\, d\theta\right]^i du$$

$$= a_1 \int_0^t \eta(u) \int_0^{t-u} W_2(\theta) W_1(t-u-\theta)\, d\theta\, du + a_2 \int_0^t \int_0^t \eta(u_1)\eta(u_2)$$

$$\times \int_0^{\min t-u_1, t-u_2} W_2(\theta) W_1(t-u_1-\theta) W_1(t-u_2-\theta) \cdot d\theta\, du_1\, du_2 + a_3 \int_0^t \int_0^t \int_0^t \cdots \tag{7.14}$$

according to the generalized convolution theorem. In this case, the index α is equal to 1 but the kernels are not the products of i-functions. As shown in the following example, the analysis can be simplified in this special case.

Example.

If

$$y(t) = aA(e^{-t/T_2} - e^{-t/T_1}) + a^3 B(e^{-t/T_2} - e^{-3t/T_1}) \tag{7.15}$$

for

$$\eta(t) = a\delta(t) \qquad \delta(t) = \text{unit impulse}$$

and if the system can be represented by a cascade consisting of a linear structure, a nonlinear amplifier, and another linear structure, the following should be true

$$e^{-t/T_2} - e^{-t/T_1} = k_1 \int_0^t W_2(t-u) W_1(u)\, du \tag{7.16}$$

$$e^{-t/T_2} - e^{-3t/T_1} = k_2 \int_0^t W_2(t-u) W_1^3(u)\, du \tag{7.17}$$

$(k_1, k_2 = \text{constants})$

or when Laplace transforms are taken

$$\frac{T_2 - T_1}{(T_2 s + 1)(T_1 s + 1)} = k_1 W_2(s) W_1(s) \tag{7.18}$$

$$\frac{3T_2 - T_1}{(T_2 s + 1)(T_1 s + 3)} = k_2 W_2(s) [W_1(s)]_3 \tag{7.19}$$

where

$$[W_1(s)]_3 = \mathscr{L}\{W_1^3(t)\}. \tag{7.20}$$

As $(T_2 s + 1)$ is a common factor in Eqs. (7.18) and (7.19), we will assume that $W_2(s) = \dfrac{1}{T_2 s + 1}$ and hence $W_1(s) = \dfrac{1}{T_1 s + 1}$; if so, both Eqs. (7.18) and (7.19) are solved.

If the characteristic of the amplifier is $c_1 z + c_3 z^3$, the coefficients c_1 and c_3 are given by

$$c_1 = A(T_2 - T_1)$$
$$c_2 = B(3T_2 - T_1).$$

(e) If a nonlinear system represented by Eq. (7.1) is in a closed-loop configuration (Fig. 56) and is excited by the signal $r(t)$, the response $\eta(t)$ is the solution of

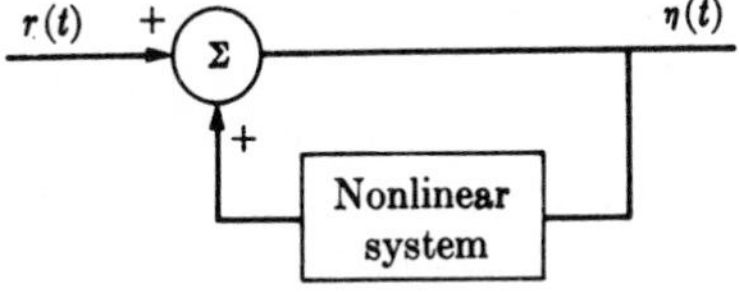

FIGURE 56. Closed-loop nonlinear structure.

the integral equation

$$\eta(t) = r(t) + \sum_{p=1}^{N} \sum_{\alpha=1}^{M} \underbrace{\int_0^t \cdots \int_0^t}_{p} g_{p\alpha}(t - u_1, \ldots, t - u_p) \cdot \eta^\alpha(u_1) \cdots \eta^\alpha(u_p)\, du_1 \cdots du_p \tag{7.21}$$

and is an infinite series of the type (7.2)

$$\eta(t) = \sum_{\alpha}^{\infty} \sum_{p}^{\infty} \underbrace{\int_0^t \cdots \int_0^t}_{p} k_{p\alpha}(t - u_1, \ldots, t - u_p) r^\alpha(u_1) \cdots r^\alpha(u_p)\, du_1 \cdots du_p \tag{7.22}$$

even when the nonlinear system is represented by a very simple functional. The series (7.22) diverges when the system is unstable.

8. Conclusion

In view of the fact that almost any nonlinear differential equation which has a solution can in fact be solved by available computing machines, the reader might mistakenly believe that the approximate and oftentimes unjustified procedures described in the present chapter have become superfluous. One reason for their great value is that our problem is not to find the solution of a differential equation under a given set of circumstances, i.e., initial conditions, but to design a system. While it is possible to judge the performance of a linear system from a small number of particular solutions of its differential equation, this is certainly not true for nonlinear systems. Another reason for using these heuristic techniques is that they may suggest clever design approaches more readily than the maze of numbers or curves turned out by the computer.

The most important recent development of nonlinear system analysis, namely, Liapunov's second method which has been revived and extended during the last two decades, is largely ignored in this present chapter because it is dealt with in Chapter VI. It should be clear, however, that modern research on nonlinear systems is unthinkable without detailed knowledge of this subject. It is erroneous to believe that Liapunov's second method constitutes no more than a method for determining the stability of certain classes of nonlinear differential equations. The concept has, in fact, been extended to the solution of other problems of great importance. It may be used to yield a measure of nonlinear system performance, which is roughly equivalent to the time constant of linear systems. A. M. Letov discusses this topic under the heading "The Problem of Quality" in Chapter VI. Furthermore, the concept has been used to synthesize controllers such that the derivative of the so-called Liapunov function behaves in a specified manner.

The relation which exists between Bellman's principle of optimality applied to the optimization of a class of nonlinear systems and the Liapunov functions is explored in Chapter VI. In particular, it is proved as a consequence of this relation, that optimization of this class of systems must result in a stable design.

It can be quite generally stated that Liapunov's second method requires a considerable amount of ingenuity, except in certain frequently encountered situations where the theorems of M. A. Aizerman, N. N. Krasovskii, E. A. Barbashin, A. M. Letov, A. I. Lur'e, and others apply.

There is little hope at present that rigorous and general mathematical analysis procedures applicable to all nonlinear systems of realistic complexity can ever be worked out. Judging from attempts made in this direction, it appears that engineers would probably be reluctant to handle these discouragingly complicated techniques. It is fortunate, as observed by R. Bellman,† that the synthesis of nonlinear systems may turn out to be simpler than their analysis in that the requirement that we exert control in the most efficient fashion often yields considerable simplification. If such a simplification does not materialize, and if no suitable Liapunov function can be found, the most fruitful approach seems to consist of an intelligent combination of analytical and experimental techniques. Understanding some of the basic phenomena, such as limit cycles, and the ability to use the procedures described in the present chapter should allow the designer to make an educated guess on the performance of simple models. As a next step, he should check his conjecture by performing a computer simulation. Having thus acquired confidence, he could slowly work up to models of realistic complexity and still maintain the feel of his system. This iteration procedure, similar to that for obtaining the proof of a theorem by working out numerical examples, certainly lacks elegance, and probably leaves the analytical mind unsatisfied. But requirements today are such that complex nonlinear systems have to be designed in spite of the absence of a general, accurate, and rigorous analytical background.

† See "Directions of mathematical research in nonlinear circuit theory," IRE Trans. on Circuit Theory, 542–553 (December, 1960).

BIBLIOGRAPHY

1. Andronow, A. A., and Chaikin, C. E., *Theory of Oscillations*, Princeton, 1949.
2. Athanassiades, M., and Smith, O. J. M., "Theory and design of high-order bang-bang control systems," IRE Trans. on Automatic Control 125–134 (May, 1961).
3. Bass, R. W., "Mathematical Legitimacy of Equivalent Linearization by Describing Functions," *Proceedings of the IFAC, Moscow, 1960*, Butterworths, 1961.
4. Bellman, R., Glicksberg, I., and Gross, O., "On the bang-bang control problem," Quart. Appl. Math. **14**, 11–18 (1956).
5. Bertram, J. E., "The effect of quantization in sampled feedback systems," AIEE Trans. (1958).
6. Bode, H. W., *Network Analysis and Feedback Amplifier Design*, Van Nostrand, 1945.
7. Boltianskii, V. G., Gamkrelidze, R. V., and Pontriagin, L. S., "On the theory of optimal processes," C.R. Acad. Sci. U.S.S.R. **110** (1956).
8. Cunningham, W. H., *Introduction to Nonlinear Analysis*, McGraw-Hill, 1958.
9. Flugge-Lotz, I., "Synthesis of Third-Order Contactor Control Systems," *Proceedings of the IFAC, Moscow, 1960*, Butterworths, 1961.
10. Gille, J., and Wegrzyn, S., "Une condition suffisante de Stabilité pour asservissements nonlinéaires," Automation 89–93 (March, 1961).
11. Gille, J. C., Decaulne, P., and Pelegrin, M., *Méthodes modernes d'étude des systèmes asservis*, Dunod, 1960, 460 pp. *Feedback Control Systems*, McGraw-Hill, 1959, 793 pp.
12. Higgins, T. J., "A Resumé of the Development and Literature of Nonlinear Control System Theory," ASME Paper No. 56, IRD **4**, 5 pp. (1957).
13. Johnson, E. C., "Sinusoidal Techniques Applied to Nonlinear Feedback Systems," Symposium on Nonlinear Circuit Analysis, Polytechnic Institute of Brooklyn, 1953.
14. Kalman, R. E., "Analysis and design principles of second and higher order saturating servomechanisms," Trans, AIEE **74**, 294–310 (1955).
15. Kalman, R. E., "Physical and Mathematical Mechanisms of Instability in Nonlinear Automatic Control Systems," ASME Paper No. 56, IRD **16** (1956).
16. Kalman, R. E., and Bertram, J. E., "Control system analysis and design via the second method of Liapunov," J. Basic Eng. (June, 1960).
17. Kaplan, W., *Ordinary Differential Equations*, Addison-Wesley, 1958.
18. Kochenburger, R. J., "A frequency response method for analyzing contactor servomechanisms," Trans. AIEE **69**, Part 2 (1947).
19. Kochenburger, R. J., "Analyzing contactor servomechanisms by frequency response methods," Trans. AIEE **69**, (1950).
20. Letov, A. M., *Stability in Nonlinear Control Systems*, Princeton, 1961.
21. Magnus, K., *Ueber ein Verfahren zur Untersuchung nicht-linearer Schwingungs- und Regelungs-Systeme*, VDI-Verlag, VDI-Forschungsheft 451, 1955.
22. Minorsky, N., *Introduction to Nonlinear Mechanics*, J. W. Edwards, 1947.
23. Minorsky, N., "Theoretical aspects of nonlinear oscillations," IRE Trans. on Circuit Theory, 368–381 (December. 1960).

24. Mishkin, E., and Braun, L., Editors, *Adaptive Control Systems*, McGraw-Hill, 1961.
25. Scheidenhelm, R. E., "The Analysis and Design of Digitally Controlled Instrument Servos," U.S. Department of Commerce, Office of Technical Services, Tech. Report No. 7890-TR-1.
26. Schmidt, S. F., "The analysis and design of continuous and sampled-data feedback control systems with saturating type nonlinearity," NASA TN D-20, Washington, 1959.
27. Seifert, W. W., and Steeg, C. W., Editors, *Control Systems Engineering*, McGraw-Hill, 1960.
28. Senouillet, G., and Guichet, P., "Etude de la stabilité d'un asservissement échantillonné et quantifié," L'Onde Elect. 611–627 (July-August, 1961).
29. Smets, H. B., "Analysis and synthesis of nonlinear systems," IRE Trans. On Circuit Theory **7**, 459–469 (December, 1960).
30. Smets, H. B., "Représentation des systèmes physiques nonlinéaires sur les calculateurs analogiques," *Actes des Secondes Journées internationales de calcul analogique*, Presses Académiques de Bruxelles, 1959, pp. 486–493.
31. Solodownikow, W. W., Editor, *Grundlagen der Selbsttätigen Regelung*, Oldenbourg, 1959, Vol. II.
32. Truxal, J. G., *Automatic Feedback Control System Synthesis*, McGraw-Hill, 1955.
33. West, J. C., *Analytical Techniques for Nonlinear Control Systems*, Van Nostrand, 1960.

Selected Soviet Texts Available in Translation.

Letov, A. M., *The Problem of Stability of Nonlinear Systems*, Princeton, 350 pp. 1960.

Lur'e, A. I., *Einige Nichtlineare Probleme aus der Theorie der selbsttätigen Regelung*, Akademie Verlag, 167 pp. 1957.

Some Nonlinear Problems in the Theory of Control, Her Majesty's Stationery Office, 1957, 165 pp.

Malkin, I. G., "Theory of Stability of Motion," AEC-tr-3352, U.S. Atomic Energy Commission, 1958.

Nemitskii, V. V., and Stepanov, V. V., *Qualitative Theory of Differential Equations*, Princeton, 1960.

Solodovnikov, V. V., Editor, *Grundlagen der Selbsttätigen Regelung*, Oldenbourg, 1959, 2 Vols.

Tsypkin, Ia, Z., *Nonlinear Automatic Control Systems*, Cleaver-Hume.

Tsypkin, Ia, Z., *Theorie der Relaissysteme der Automatischen Regelung*, R. Oldenbourg und VEB Verlag Technik, 472 pp. 1958.

CHAPTER VI

Liapunov's Theory of Stability of Motion

ALEXANDER M. LETOV

CONTENTS

1. Liapunov's Direct Method for the Solution of the Problem of Stability

1.1 Statement of the Problem of Stability. The modern theory of automatic control, in whatever form it may be presented, rests on a single and solid foundation—A. M. Liapunov's theory of stability of motion. This theory has been developed, for the most part, by Soviet scientists. During the last years, valuable contributions to the theory of stability have been made by the scientists of the United States, Argentina, Italy, Germany, and other countries. A considerable proportion of the achievements already attained in this field is to be found in the bibliography [3, 5, 7, 9, 12, 14, 22, 24, 26, 28].†

We shall assume that to every automatic control system there corresponds a completely defined set of original differential equations of the form

$$\dot{x}_k = X_k\,(x_1, \ldots, x_n) \qquad (k = 1, \ldots, n) \quad (1.1)$$

where x_k are variables, X_k are known functions of these variables defined in a given region G of the space of the x_k, and $t \geqslant 0$. In many-dimensional Euclidean geometry, this space is called a Euclidean space E_n.

In this space, Eqs. (1.1) express the physical laws obeyed by the control system, and geometrically define the components of the velocity v of the motion of a certain point M, which is called the representative point.

The properties and singularities of these laws are completely or sufficiently closely determined by the character of the functions X_k, and the region G is that part of the space E_n over which these laws have effect.

It is assumed that Eqs. (1.1) contain the parameters $p_1, \ldots, p_m$, which we can choose within certain limits, denoted by the symbol P.

In the more general case, the functions X_k may include time, and

$$\dot{x}_k = X_k\,(x_1, \ldots, x_n; t). \qquad (k = 1, \ldots, n) \quad (1.2)$$

Although the formal substitutions $t = x_{n+1}$, $X_{n+1} = 1$, and extension of the region G by including the half-interval $x_{n+1} \epsilon [0, \infty)$, allow Eq. (1.2) to be brought to the form of (1.1), still, in view of the special significance of the variable $t = x_{n+1}$, the treatment of problems of stability cannot be the same for all cases. We shall base our general presentation of the problem, therefore, on Eqs. (1.1) and, where necessary, making individula observations in those cases when Eq. (1.2) applies.

Suppose that we want to realize a certain motion of a controlled system (1.1), which is described by

$$x_k = x_k^*(t). \qquad (k = 1, \ldots, n) \quad (1.3)$$

† Numbers in brackets refer to the bibliography at the end of this chapter,

The functions $x_k^*(t)$ cannot be chosen at will. They must be solutions of Eq. (1.1); that is, the following identities must hold:

$$\dot{x}_k^* = X_k (x_1^*, \ldots, x_n^*). \qquad (k = 1, \ldots, n) \qquad (1.4)$$

In the special case when

$$x_k^* = \text{constant} \qquad (k = 1, \ldots, n) \qquad (1.5)$$

the identity must be

$$X_k (x_1^*, \ldots, x_n^*) = 0. \qquad (k = 1, \ldots, n) \qquad (1.6)$$

In Liapunov's terminology, the motion described by Eq. (1.3) is called *undisturbed motion.*

The first and fundamental question that arises in the theory of automatic control is this: does the solution (1.3) correspond to a physically possible and observed motion or equilibrium? This question, which is of great practical importance, can be answered by an investigation of the solution (1.3) for stability.

The solutions we call stable correspond to physically realizable processes, and unstable solutions to physically impossible processes. Consequently, the question whether the solution (1.3) corresponds to a physically realizable motion of the controlled system is, mathematically, the question of the stability or instability of the solution (1.3).

It will be convenient in future to consider equations derived from (1.1) by a transformation of the variables according to

$$x_k = x_k^* + y_k. \qquad (1.7)$$

Here the x_k^* are the functions of Eq. (1.3) or the constants of (1.5).

The equations in the new variables are called equations of disturbed motion. They have the form

$$\begin{aligned} \dot{y}_k &= Y_k (y_1, \ldots, y_n; t) \\ Y_k &= X_k (x_1^* + y_1, \ldots, x_n^* + y_n). \end{aligned} \qquad (1.8)$$

Equation (1.7) indicates a translation of the origin of the coordinate system to a point with coordinates x_k^*. As a result of this, there corresponds an undisturbed motion to the undisturbed motion of Eq. (1.3)

$$y_1^* = 0, \ldots, y_n^* = 0 \qquad (1.9)$$

in the new variables; and, conversely, to the undisturbed motion (1.9) there corresponds the undisturbed motion (1.3).

This one-to-one correspondence permits us to study the stability of solution (1.9), instead of studying the same property of solution (1.3).

Although Eq. (1.1) does not include time, the equations of disturbed motion (1.8) will, generally speaking, depend explicitly on time if the solution (1.3) is not constant.

When $t = t_0$, let the variables $y_1, \ldots, y_n$ take any initial values $y_{10}, \ldots, y_{n0}$, of which at least one is nonzero; these will be called disturbances. The functions Y_k are assumed to be such that to every given set of such disturbances there corresponds a unique and continuous solution

$$y_k = y_k(t, y_{10}, \ldots, y_{n0}) \qquad (k = 1, \ldots, n) \quad (1.10)$$

of Eq. (1.8); this solution is called the disturbed motion of the system. In some textbooks on automatic control, (1.10) are called the equations of the transient process.

If we could know all the solutions (1.10), we would know all the disturbed motions of the system. But to find the solutions of (1.10) would be a problem of insuperable difficulty; this means that we are deprived of the possibility of obtaining a guiding principle for a rational selection of the parameters of the regulator. This being so, a general approach to a purely qualitative, simultaneous survey of the whole family of disturbed motions (1.10) is of interest; this should enable us, without integrating, to estimate their individual tendencies to converge towards the undisturbed motion (1.9) as $t \to \infty$, independently of the particular values of the disturbances $y_{10}, \ldots, y_{n0}$ which determine the motion (1.10).

In future we shall only consider cases in which the choice of the initial instant of time t_0 does not affect this property of convergence of the disturbed motions, and we shall suppose that $t_0 = 0$.

Liapunov's theory of stability of motion enables us to arrive at an estimate of those properties of disturbed motion which concern us, without having recourse, in the end, to integration of Eq. (1.8), and it points the way to a rational design methodology of automatic control systems.

If it happens that for a given adjustment of the controller, solution (1.9) is stable, this means that the controlled system itself, without outside intervention, chooses the mode of undisturbed motion corresponding to this solution. If the solution (1.9) is unstable, it will not be possible to realize physically a steady state of this kind, since the very smallest disturbances will cause the system to diverge from it.

Thus we see that Liapunov's definition of stability of motion, Eq. (1.9), is of great practical value in the study of some important problems of modern engineering. This definition, in the sense in which it is applicable to problems in the theory of automatic control based on Eq. (1.1), is as follows.†

DEFINITION. *The undisturbed motion, Eq.* (1.9), *is said to be stable with respect to the quantities* y_k *if for any given positive number* A, *however small, there is another positive number* $\lambda(A)$ *such that for all disturbances satisfying the condition*

† The definition of stability given by Liapunov is considerably wider than that given here.

$$\sum y_{k0}^2 \leqslant \lambda \tag{1.11}$$

the disturbed motion (1.10) *will, in consequence, satisfy the inequality*

$$\sum y_k^2(t) < A \tag{1.12}$$

for all $t > 0$.

If, however, it is impossible to find for any given number A, however small, a number $\lambda(A)$ such that for any disturbances y_{k0} satisfying conditions (1.11), inequality (1.12) shall also be satisfied, then the undisturbed motion (1.9) is said to be unstable.

Inequality (1.11) restricts the set of initial disturbances of the system; inequality (1.12) restricts the character of the progression of its disturbed motion. In all cases in which these inequalities are satisfied, it is said that the disturbed motion of the system converges toward the undisturbed motion, which is the physical expression of stability of undisturbed motion according to Liapunov.

As it is defined here, however, the character of the convergence of the disturbed motion upon the undisturbed motion (or the character of the stability of undisturbed motion, which comes to the same thing), may be ambiguous.

Thus, if A is any chosen and fixed number, then, after examining the stability of the solutions which concern us, we can generally assert that the disturbed motion may very well continue in the A-vicinity of the undisturbed motion.

Secondly, a more detailed investigation of the disturbed motion, carried out in connection with the possibility of varying A, and, in particular, of choosing it as small as is desired, enables us to reveal either the asymptotic character of the disturbed motion, in which case $\Sigma\, y_k^2(t) \to 0$, or its tendency to remain in A—a narrower neighborhood than that which was defined in the first place.

N. G. Chetaev [5] has investigated a problem which is of fundamental importance for stability, namely, that the number λ, figuring in Liapunov's formulation of stability, can always be determined. Liapunov has given a method for calculating λ in the proof of one of his theorems on stability. The value of this quantity is substantially dependent on the form of the so-called Liapunov V-functions and on the parameters of the equations of disturbed motion. Chetaev gives an example of calculation of λ. It turns out that we are always able, in every particular problem, to establish the dimensions of the region of admissible disturbances by calculating λ. This region is termed the λ-vicinity

$$\sum y_{k0}^2 \leqslant \lambda$$

where λ is not necessarily infinitesimal, but may be finite.

It may turn out that whatever the fixed number A may be, it is possible to choose $\lambda(A)$ so that inequalities (1.11) and (1.12) are satisfied for any y_k

belonging to G; then we speak of stability of undisturbed motion in the large. However, if satisfaction of Eqs. (1.11) and (1.12) places an upper bound on y_{k0}, we speak of stability in the small.

In certain very important cases of the operation of an automatic control system, it is required that the parameters of the regulator be selected in such a way that the steady-state regime which is being investigated should be absolutely unstable, that is, that it should be impossible to realize physically. The flight of an aircraft in a spin is a case of this kind. The theory of stability of motion enables us to solve even this very complex and important problem by the aid of the well-known theories of stability due to Liapunov and Chetaev.

1.2 Liapunov's Direct Method. In essence, Liapunov's direct method of stability consists of the construction of certain functions V of the variables $y_1, \ldots, y_n$. The total derivative of V with respect to time, expressed in terms of Eq. (1.8), possesses certain properties which characterize stability.

Every V-function is defined in a region G', given by

$$\sum y_k^2 < L \tag{1.13}$$

where L is some constant, which can take any positive values. Then G' will be contained in the region G, if L is sufficiently small, or will contain in itself, or coincide with, G if L is sufficiently large.

We shall call a V-function "sign-invariant" if everywhere in G' it takes values of one sign only, or of zero values. A sign-invariant function which takes zero value only at the origin of the coordinate system will be called "sign-definite," or, if we wish to call attention to the sign, "positive definite" or "negative definite."

For instance, of the two functions

$$V_1 = y_1^2 + y_2^2 + y_3^2; \quad V_2 = (y_1 + y_2)^2 + y_3^2$$

V_1 is sign-definite, whereas V_2 is only sign-invariant.

For any sign-definite function, the equation $V = C$, $C =$ constant, represents, generally speaking, a one-parameter family of closed surfaces. As C diminishes, the surfaces contract toward the origin of the coordinate system, and in the limit, when $C \to 0$, they become a point—the origin itself. These surfaces intersect with all paths from the origin to infinity.

A V-function may include time in explicit form,

$$V = V(y_1, \ldots, y_n, t). \tag{1.14}$$

Then we can say that this function is positive definite if there exists another positive definite function $W(y_1, \ldots, y_n)$ not dependent on t, such that

$$V > W. \tag{1.15}$$

Together with the V-functions, we shall consider their total derivative with respect to time

$$\frac{dV}{dt} = \sum \frac{\partial V}{\partial y_k} \frac{dy_k}{dt} + \frac{\partial V}{\partial t}. \tag{1.16}$$

LIAPUNOV'S FIRST THEOREM. *If the differential equations of disturbed motion are such that it is possible to find a sign-definite function V, of which the derivative is, by virtue of these equations, a sign-constant function of opposite sign to V, or is identically zero, then the undisturbed motion is stable.*

V-functions satisfying the conditions of this theorem are called Liapunov functions.

For the proof, we shall assume that, for the present problem, some positive definite Liapunov function is known for the region G'. Let us calculate its total derivative, using Eq. (1.8). We get

$$\frac{dV}{dt} = \sum \frac{\partial V}{\partial y_k} Y_k + \frac{\partial V}{dt}. \tag{1.17}$$

Let us examine the surfaces $V = C$, and some point on one of them. In many-dimensional Euclidean geometry, the quantities $\partial V/\partial y_k$ are proportional to the direction cosines of the normal $\bar{n}$ to the surface $V = C$. Thus:

$$\frac{\partial V}{\partial y_k} = +\sqrt{\sum\left(\frac{\partial V}{\partial y_k}\right)^2} \cos(\bar{n}y_k). \tag{1.18}$$

The positive direction of the normal is assumed to be from within outward. According to Eq. (1.18), the expression (1.17) takes the form

$$\frac{dV}{dt} = \sqrt{\sum\left(\frac{\partial V}{\partial y_k}\right)^2} V_{\bar{n}} + \frac{\partial V}{\partial t}$$

where $V_{\bar{n}}$ is the projection of the velocity of the representative point M upon the normal to the surface

$$V_{\bar{n}} = \sum Y_k \cos(\bar{n}y_k) + \frac{\partial V}{\partial t}.$$

By the conditions of the theorem, this projection is negative everywhere in the region G', since $dV/dt < 0$, or else is identically equal to zero. Consequently, within the phase space E_n the point M moves along trajectories which intersect with the family of surfaces $V = C$ from the outside inward; that is, it passes from surfaces with higher values of C to surfaces with lower values of C when $\dot{V} < 0$, or else remains all the time on one surface when $\dot{V} \equiv 0$. Let A be some given positive number. We shall select a number $\lambda(A)$ such that the λ-vicinity of the obvious solution (1.9) shall be contained entirely in the A-vicinity, and we shall place there the representative point M at time $t = 0$. From what has been said above, ($\dot{V} < 0$), it is obvious that the point M does not leave the λ-vicinity when $t > 0$; consequently, neither does it leave the A-vicinity of the obvious solution. But this means that solution (1.9) is stable.

LIAPUNOV'S SECOND THEOREM. *If the differential equations of disturbed motion are such that it is possible to find a sign-definite function V, of which the derivative is, by virtue of these equations, a sign-definite function of sign opposite to V, then the disturbed motion is asymptotically stable.*

The proof of the second theorem is the same as for the first. This time, however, the function $\dot{V}$ is sign-definite; so now the representative point M cannot remain all the time on some one surface $V = C$, $(C \neq 0)$, since $\dot{V}$ can become zero only at the origin of the phase space. Consequently, as $t \to \infty$, the disturbed motion will converge upon the undisturbed motion,

$$\lim_{t \to \infty} y_k(t) = y_k^*. \qquad (k = 1, \ldots, n)$$

In this case, the undisturbed motion is said to be asymptotically stable.

There is an important observation to be made here.

Recently [12], attention has been drawn to the fact that the surfaces $V = C$ will be closed, provided that C be sufficiently small. For instance, the function

$$V = y_1^2 + \frac{y_2^2}{1 + y_2^2}$$

defines a family of closed curves $V = C$ only when $C \leqslant 1$; for any $C > 1$, the curve $V = C$ consists of two branches having no points in common (Fig. 1). Consequently a given V-function can serve as a Liapunov function

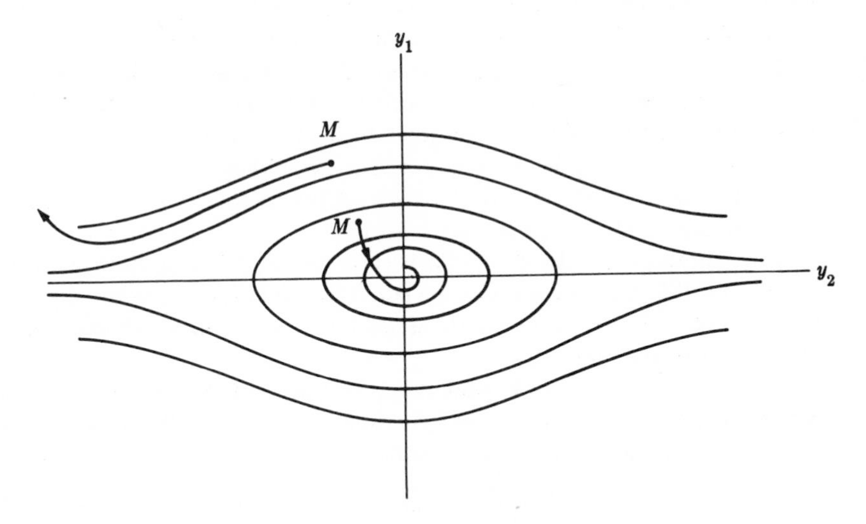

FIGURE 1. Illustration of the theorem of E. A. Barbashin and N. N. Krasovskii.

only for investigations of stability in which the disturbances are restricted by the condition

$$y_{10}^2 + \frac{y_2^2}{1 + y_2^2} \leqslant 1.$$

When this condition is not observed, the representative point can go outside the limits of the curve $V = C$ through the zone of discontinuity of its component branches.

For another example [8], take the function

$$V(y_1, y_2) = \int_0^{y_1} \varphi(y_1)\, dy_1 + y_2^2$$

where $\varphi(y_1)$ is such that $\varphi(0) = 0$, $y_1\varphi(y_1) > 0$ when $y_1 \neq 0$. Let us construct the curve

$$\int_0^{y_1} \varphi(y_1)\, dy_1 + y_2^2 = C.$$

It will certainly be closed if C is sufficiently small. But the function $\varphi(y_1)$ may be such that

$$\lim_{y_1 \to \infty} \int_0^{y_1} \varphi(y_1)\, dy_1 \to a > 0.$$

In this case, closure of the curves $V = C$ can be guaranteed only for values of $C < a$. Consequently, in all cases where the constant C is not sufficiently small, we should check whether the surfaces $V = C$ are closed.

Closure of these surfaces is guaranteed if, in addition to what has been said already, the Liapunov function becomes unbounded when $\Sigma\, y_k^2 \to \infty$. This means that whatever the value of a positive number N may be, it is always possible to choose a value for L so large that when $\Sigma\, y_k^2 > L$ the function V takes values such that $V > N$. A function of this kind is said to be unbounded.

As has been proved by E. A. Barbashin and N. N. Krasovskii, both of Liapunov's theorems on stability remain valid, however large the positive number L may be for any region G' if the function V which figures in these theorems is unbounded [12].

1.3 Statement of the Problem of Stability of Nonlinear Control Systems. In this section we shall consider plants whose disturbed motion is described by linear differential equations of the form

$$\dot{\eta}_k = \sum b_{k\alpha}\eta_\alpha + m_k\xi \qquad (k = 1, \ldots, n) \quad (1.19)$$

where the b_k are parameters and the η_k the generalized coordinates of the

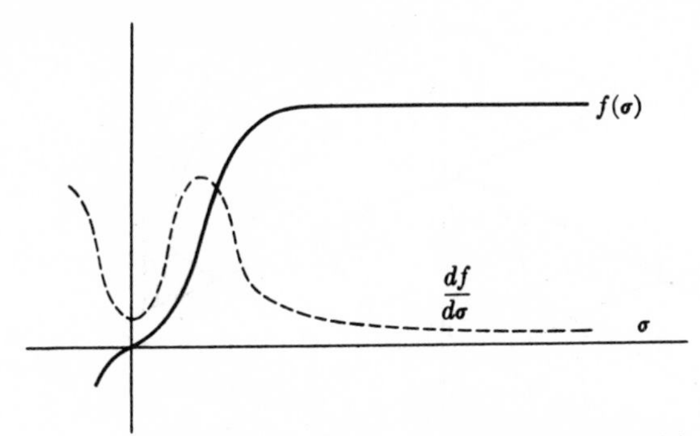

FIGURE 2. To determine the function $f(\sigma)$.

plant; m_k are the parameters and ξ is the coordinate of the actuator. All the $b_{k\alpha}$ and m_k may be either constants or continuous functions of time t defined in the interval $[0, \infty)$.

In order that the system may be closed, we shall write the equation of the actuator

$$V^2\ddot{\xi} + W\dot{\xi} + S\xi = f^*(\sigma)\psi(\omega) \tag{1.20}$$

$$\sigma = \sum p_\alpha \eta_\alpha - r\xi - N\dot{\xi} \tag{1.21}$$

$$\omega = 1 - (\sum q_\alpha \eta_\alpha + q\xi) \operatorname{sgn} \sigma. \tag{1.22}$$

Here:

V^2 is the constant of inertia of the servomotor and connected blocks;
W characterizes viscous damping;
S is a constant characterizing the compressibility of the working fluid of the servomotor;
$f^*(\sigma)$ is a function of the argument σ, shown in Fig. 2; hereafter this will be called a function in the class A;
r, p_α, N are adjustable parameters of the regulator;
ψ is a bounded function, defined for nonconservative servomotors by the following relation:

$$\psi(\omega) = \begin{matrix} 1 & \text{if} & \omega > 1 \\ \sqrt{\omega} & \text{if} & 0 \leqslant \omega \leqslant 1 \\ 0 & \text{if} & \omega < 0. \end{matrix} \tag{1.23}$$

The numbers q, q_α are constants.

The function $\psi(\omega)$ characterizes the effect of the load on the servomotor. For instance, in the case when the load depends only on the single coordinate ξ, then $q_\alpha = 0$. The form of this function is shown in Fig. 3.

If, however, q is so small as to make $q\xi$ negligible by comparison with unity, then $\psi(\omega) \equiv 1$, and we have the equation of a servomotor, whose speed does not depend on the load of the control element.

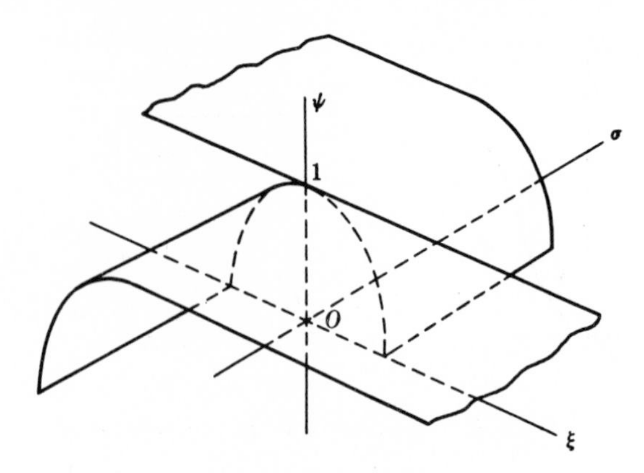

FIGURE 3. To determine the function $\psi(\omega)$.

Equations (1.19) and (1.20) are given for any values of the variables for which they retain physical meaning.

The system of Eqs. (1.19) and (1.20) has a state of equilibrium at the point

$$\eta_k = \eta_k{}^* = 0, \quad \xi = \xi^* = 0. \qquad (k = 1, \ldots, n) \quad (1.24)$$

The first and fundamental problem of the theory of automatic control is to determine the parameters r, N, p_α of the regulator such that the state of the system characterized by Eq. (1.24) is stable, regardless of the disturbances η_{k0}, ξ_0, and the function $f(\sigma)$ belonging to class A.

The following considerations speak in favor of this formulation of the problem.

It is assumed that for a known class of actuators the quantities S, V^2 may be regarded as negligibly small, and the speed of the servomotor as not dependent on the load. In this case the equation of the servomotor has the form

$$\dot{\xi} = \frac{1}{W} f^*(\sigma) = f(\sigma) \quad (1.25)$$

which relates the velocity of the actuator output to the actuator input σ. The function $f^*(\sigma)$ represents the acting generalized force developed by the actuator, in response to σ. In all control systems σ represents the total controller output which is a signal obtained according to the law of control assumed for the problem.

In the general form, σ is defined as

$$\sigma = \sum p_\alpha \eta_\alpha - r\xi - N\dot{\xi} \quad (1.26)$$

where p_α, r, N are constant parameters of the controller.

We shall use this equation in what follows.

We will examine in parallel two kinds of bounded functions $f(\sigma)$, belonging to the same class of A-functions. This class is characterized by the properties:

$$\begin{aligned} &(1)\ \ f(\sigma) = 0 \quad \text{when} \quad |\sigma| \leqslant \sigma_* \\ &(2)\ \ \sigma f(\sigma) > 0 \quad \text{when} \quad |\sigma| > \sigma_* \end{aligned} \tag{1.27}$$

where σ_* is some fixed nonnegative number characterizing the dead zone of the regulator to deviations of $|\sigma| \leqslant \sigma_*$. For all values of $|\sigma| > \sigma_*$, $f(\sigma)$ is continuous; at points where $\sigma = \pm\sigma_*$, a discontinuity of $f(\sigma)$ is admissible.

In investigations of systems which are unstable when the controller is cut out in some cases (which will be discussed later), we meet with functions $f(\sigma)$ which have the additional properties

$$(1) \qquad \sigma_* = 0$$

$$(2) \qquad \left[\frac{df}{d\sigma}\right]_{\sigma=0} \geqslant h > 0 \tag{1.28}$$

$$(3) \qquad \sigma\varphi(\sigma) > 0, \quad \sigma \neq 0; \quad \varphi(\sigma) = f(\sigma) - h\sigma$$

where h is a given constant.

We shall say of such functions that they form a subclass A' of the functions $f(\sigma)$ in class A. The purpose of singling out a subclass A' is to select, out of all possible actuators characterized by functions $f(\sigma)$ belonging to class A, those with significant speed of response to incoming signals σ. Thus if h is a fixed number, the third condition of Eq. (1.28) means that the absolute value of the speed $f(\sigma)$ is always greater than $h\,|\sigma|$. If the actuator is characterized by a function belonging to subclass A', then the regulator has no dead zone.

For functions in the subclass A' we shall envisage another straight line $H\sigma$ which bounds the curve $f(\sigma)$ from above when $\sigma > 0$. Thus all functions in subclass A' are represented by curves which lie in their entirety between $y = h$ and $y = H$ (Fig. 4).

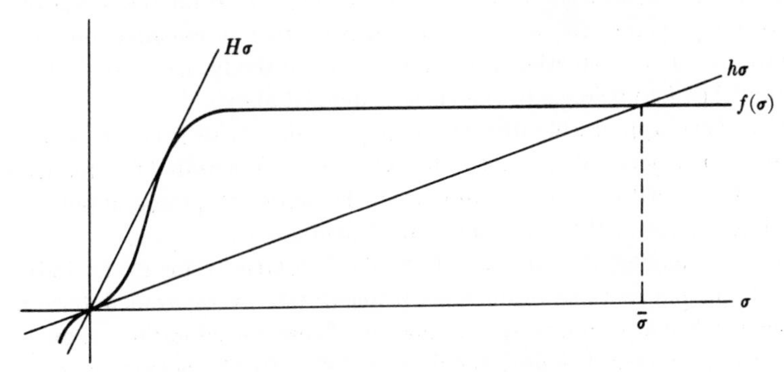

FIGURE 4. To determine the function $f(\sigma) \in A'$.

Nevertheless, if a function $f(\sigma)$ has an intersection with $h\sigma$ at a point with abscissa $\bar{\sigma}$, we shall say that the control range of the system with respect to σ is $2\,|\bar{\sigma}|$.

We should also include in subclass A' the "Γ-form function" $f(\sigma) = Q \operatorname{sgn} \sigma$, belonging to class A of functions:

$$f(\sigma) = \begin{matrix} +Q & \text{when} & \sigma \geqslant \sigma_* \\ 0 & \text{when} & |\sigma| < \sigma_* \\ -Q & \text{when} & \sigma \leqslant -\sigma_*. \end{matrix} \tag{1.29}$$

It is assumed that for Γ-form functions in subclass A' $h = 0$ and $H = \tan \dfrac{\pi}{2}$. In special limiting cases, it may happen that for some Γ-form functions in subclass A', $Q = \infty$, and that the band $2\,|\bar{\sigma}|$ of control with respect to σ is zero. We shall call an actuator characterized by this function perfect; that is, it switches infinitely fast.

In accordance with this definition, the equation of such a perfect actuator is written thus:

$$\sum p_\alpha \eta_\alpha - r\xi = N\dot{\xi}. \tag{1.30}$$

The class of functions $f(\sigma)$ we have in mind includes the characteristics of the vast majority of the actuators in use in modern engineering practice. There is a very important consideration of a mechanical nature which justifies our taking this rather wide view, and describing them by a class of functions.

It is usual for the functions $f(\sigma)$ to be found experimentally for every individual case, by measuring the speed of the actuator under so-called static conditions, i.e., the argument σ changes stepwise, taking distinct discrete values $\sigma_1, \ldots, \sigma_k$, which remain constant for the time of one experiment. Generally speaking, the result of this is a family of curves $f(\sigma)$, depending on the load, which is fixed during the experiment.

The actual operating conditions of the actuator, however, include continuous variation of the load. The effect of the load on the actuator is to appreciably distort the form of the function $f(\sigma)$ as recorded under static conditions. This distortion cannot be quantitatively assessed, but we are certain that $f(\sigma)$ belongs to the class A defined above.

Also, very appreciable distortions of $f(\sigma)$ may arise from other material causes, which generally cannot be foreseen and compensated for; for example, fluctuations, within known limits, of the external power supply to the regulator is one of the most common of such causes.

In consequence, it is impossible to fix $f(\sigma)$ strictly for every individual case, and even more so to linearize it accurately by rigorous determination of the coefficient of linear approximation. These considerations show that in all these problems it is only possible to define $f(\sigma)$ as belonging to class A or to subclass A'. However, this is perfectly sufficient for the solution of the problem of stability of a given automatic control system, provided that we use Liapunov's direct method.

Of course, Eq. (1.25) is the most primitive of the equations of actuators. Nevertheless, in a great many cases of considerable practical importance, it accurately represents their physical peculiarities, and so may properly be used in theoretical investigations. Indeed, a still more primitive equation than Eq. (1.25), in which $f(\sigma)$ is either a linear or a step function of σ, and $\psi(\omega) \equiv 1$, lies at the foundation of the classic theory of automatic control.

In the theory of stability of control systems which follows, we shall assume that $\psi(\omega) \equiv 1$; we shall indicate those cases in which the criteria of stability obtained by us are also valid when $\psi(\omega) \neq 1$.

We shall examine controlled processes for which all the $b_{k\alpha}$, m_k are constants. These processes are classified on the basis of the roots of the equation

$$D(\rho) = |b_{k\alpha} + \rho\delta_{k\alpha}| = 0 \tag{1.31}$$

where $\delta_{k\alpha}$ is the Kronecker delta.

We shall say that:

(1) a plant is inherently stable if

$$\operatorname{Re} \rho_k > 0; \qquad (k = 1, \ldots, n)$$

(2) a plant is neutral with respect to the coordinates $\eta_1, \ldots, \eta_s$, if

$$\rho_1 = \cdots = \rho_s = 0, \operatorname{Re} \rho_{s+\alpha} > 0; \qquad (\alpha = 1, \ldots, n - s)$$

(3) a plant is inherently unstable if $\operatorname{Re} \rho_k < 0$ for even one value of k.

The methods for constructing Liapunov functions given below solve the problem of the stability of control systems in a number of different cases.

2. Methods for Constructing Liapunov Functions

2.1 Method of Canonical Variables. The method is due to A. I. Lur'e [18, 23].

In order to solve the problem stated in the previous section, we shall bring the original equations to the canonical form. This is not obligatory; it is indicated solely because of the difficulty of constructing Liapunov functions for the original equations.

Let us first consider A. I. Lur'e's form, which is convenient for investigations of inherently stable controlled systems, or of systems which are neutral with respect to one coordinate.

We shall define the canonical variables by

$$x_s = \sum C_\alpha^{(s)} \eta_\alpha + \xi. \qquad (s = 1, \ldots, n) \tag{2.1}$$

Differentiating Eq. (2.1), and using (1.19) in order to eliminate the derivatives, we find

$$\dot{x}_s = \sum_\alpha C_\alpha^{(s)} \left[\sum_\beta b_{k\beta}\eta_\beta + m_\alpha \xi \right] + f(\sigma).$$

If it is required that the equations in the new variables have the canonical form

$$\dot{x}_s = -\rho_s x_s + f(\sigma) \tag{2.2}$$

the choice of the constants defining the transformation must be subject to the relations

$$-\rho_s C_\beta^{(s)} = \sum_\alpha b_{\alpha\beta} C_\alpha^{(s)} \tag{2.3}$$

$$-\rho_s = \sum_\alpha m_\alpha C_\alpha^{(s)}. \qquad (s, \beta = 1, \ldots, n) \tag{2.4}$$

The ρ_s are the parameters of the transformation. They are the roots of the equation

$$D(\rho) = \begin{vmatrix} b_{11} + \rho, & \ldots, & b_{1n} \\ \ldots & \ldots & \ldots \\ b_{n1}, & \ldots, & b_{nn} + \rho \end{vmatrix} = 0. \tag{2.5}$$

We assume that all the roots ρ_s of this equation are simple, and possess the property

$$\operatorname{Re} \rho_k \geqslant 0. \qquad (k = 1, \ldots, n) \tag{2.6}$$

It is assumed that the equal sign, if applicable, refers to ρ_1. This restriction implies the necessity of observing the inequalities

$$\Delta_1 > 0, \ldots, \Delta_{n-1} > 0, \quad \Delta_n \geqslant 0 \tag{2.7}$$

where the Δ_k are the Hurwitz determinants corresponding to Eq. (2.5). In (2.7), Δ_n is zero only when $\rho_1 = 0$.

It is characteristic of the first canonical form of the equations of the control system that the parameters of the controller are not among the coefficients of Eq. (2.5), and that inequalities (2.7) are always satisfied if the system is inherently stable or neutral with respect to one coordinate.

If all the roots of Eq. (2.5) are simple, then, as is proved in algebra, Eq. (2.3) can always be solved, and the transformation (2.1) exists and is nonsingular. This makes it possible to solve (2.1) for η_k. Assume that this operation has been carried out and that we have found

$$\eta_\alpha = \sum D_k^{(\alpha)} x_k + G_\alpha \xi \qquad (\alpha = 1, \ldots, n) \tag{2.8}$$

where the $D_k^{(\alpha)}$, G_α are known constants.

To complete the reduction of the original equations to the canonical form, it remains to express σ and $\dot{\sigma}$ in terms of the new variables. From Eq. (2.8) we find

$$\sigma = \gamma_k x_k + \gamma_{n+1} \xi. \tag{2.9}$$

If we now introduce the notation

$$\begin{aligned} \sum G_\alpha p_\alpha &= \gamma_{n+1} + r; \\ \sum p_\alpha D_k^{(\alpha)} &= \gamma_k; \qquad (k = 1, \ldots, n) \\ -\gamma_k \rho_k &= \beta_k \end{aligned} \tag{2.10}$$

the complete set of canonical equations takes the final form

$$\begin{aligned} \dot{x}_k &= -\rho_k x_k + f(\sigma) \qquad (k = 1, \ldots, n) \\ \dot{\sigma} &= \sum \beta_k x_k - rf(\sigma). \end{aligned} \tag{2.11}$$

In order to complete the canonical equations, let us bring in the equations for the coefficients of direct and inverse transformations obtained by Lur'e.

$$H_i(\rho_s) = \sum m_k D_{ik}(\rho_s) \neq 0 \quad (s = 1, \ldots, n) \tag{2.12}$$

represent the determinant of Eq. (2.5), in which the elements of the rows are replaced by m_k, $(k = 1, \ldots, n)$. Then we have

$$C_k^{(s)} = -\frac{\rho_s}{H_i(\rho_s)} D_{ik}(\rho_s) \tag{2.13}$$

$$D_s^{(k)} = \frac{H_k(\rho_s)}{-\rho_s D'(\rho_s)}; \quad G_k = -\sum D_s^{(k)}. \quad (k, s = 1, \ldots, n) \tag{2.14}$$

Like the original equations, (2.11) have either only one obvious solution, or an uninterrupted continuum of solutions, forming the dead zone of the controlled system. This solution shall be denoted by

$$x_k = x^*, \quad \sigma = \sigma^*. \qquad (k = 1, \ldots, n) \tag{2.15}$$

There is a one-to-one correspondence between the solutions (1.24) and (2.15), which can always be established with the aid of the canonical transformation formulas. Therefore, if the steady state of the control system, described by solution (2.15), can be realized physically, it will be stable.

Let us suppose that among the n-roots of Eq. (2.5) there are s real roots $\rho_1, \ldots, \rho_s$ and $(n - s)/2$ pairs of complex conjugate roots $\rho_{s+1}, \ldots, \rho_n$. The corresponding constants $\gamma_1, \ldots, \gamma_s$, $\beta_1, \ldots, \beta_s$ and variables $x_1, \ldots, \ldots, x_s$ will be real, while the constants $\gamma_{s+1}, \ldots, \gamma_n$, $\beta_{s+1}, \ldots, \beta_n$ and variables $x_{s+1}, \ldots, x_n$ will be complex and form conjugate pairs. All the roots ρ_k are distinct, possess the property

$$\operatorname{Re} \rho_k \geqslant 0 \qquad (k = 1, \ldots, n) \tag{2.16}$$

and only one of the real roots can become zero, thus characterizing the neutrality of the system with respect to one of its coordinates.

The problem is to find those values for the parameters of the controller, which guarantee absolute stability of solution (2.15). Consider the quadratic form

$$F(a_1x_1, \dots, a_nx_n) = \sum_i \sum_k \frac{a_i a_k}{\rho_i + \rho_k} x_i x_k \qquad (2.17)$$

where $a_1, \dots, a_s$ are arbitrary real numbers and $a_{s+1}, \dots, a_n$ are arbitrary complex numbers forming conjugate pairs.

The form (2.17) is a positive definite function of the variables x_k. We have the obvious equality

$$\frac{1}{\rho_k + \rho_i} = \int_0^\infty \exp -(\rho_i + \rho_k)\tau \, d\tau$$

by means of which the form (2.17) can be rewritten

$$F = \sum_i \sum_k \left[a_k a_i \int_0^\infty \exp -(\rho_i + \rho_k)\tau \, d\tau \right] x_k x_i = \int_0^\infty \left[\sum_k a_k x_k \exp -\rho_k \tau \right]^2 d\tau \qquad (2.18)$$

The integrand in Eq. (2.18) is the square of a real number, since the complex terms are conjugate in pairs; this integrand can only vanish for $x_k = 0$, $(k = 1, \dots, n)$, regardless of τ. Consequently, the function F takes only real and positive values, and becomes zero only at the origin of the coordinate system; that is, it is a positive-definite function of the variables x_k.

Consider the quadratic form

$$\Phi(x_1, \dots, x_n) = \frac{1}{2}\left(\sum_1^s A_k x_k \right) + C_1 x_{s+1} x_{s+2} + C_3 x_{s+3} x_{s+4} + \cdots$$

in which $A_1, \dots, A_s, C_1, C_3, C_5, \dots$ are positive real numbers. It is obvious that Φ takes only real and positive values, since the product of any pair of complex conjugate numbers of the form $x_{s+1}x_{s+2}$ always yields the magnitude of this product. The function Φ takes zero value only at the origin, and is sign-definite.

Finally, we observe that whatever the function $f(\sigma)$ belonging to class A may be, the integral

$$\int_0^\sigma f(\sigma)\, d\sigma$$

is positive for any value of $|\sigma| > \sigma_*$; for $|\sigma| \leqslant \sigma_*$ the integral equals zero.

Similarly, the integral

$$\int_0^\sigma \varphi(\sigma)\, d\sigma$$

possesses this same property.

There is an important and noteworthy difference between these integrals. With the characteristics assumed for actuators, the integral of $f(\sigma)$ is unbounded; that is,

$$\lim_{\sigma\to\infty} \int_0^\sigma f(\sigma)\, d\sigma \to \infty$$

whereas the integral of $\varphi(\sigma)$ can be bounded. We must bear this difference in mind when we construct Liapunov functions and draw conclusions as to the stability of a system in the whole of the phase space according to the theorem of Barbashin and Krasovskii.

We now begin our examination of the stability of solution (2.15); we assume $\psi(\omega) \equiv 1$, and we shall consider the positive definite function

$$V = \Phi + F + \int_0^\sigma f(\sigma)\, d\sigma. \tag{2.19}$$

The construction of all possible sufficiency criteria of stability of a solution involves calculating its total derivative with respect to t. According to Eq. (2.11) we find

$$\begin{aligned}\dot V = &\sum A_k x_k[-\rho_k x_k + f(\sigma)] + C_1 x_{s+2}[-\rho_{s+1} x_{s+1} + f(\sigma)] \\ &+ C_1 x_{s+1}[-\rho_{s+2} x_{s+2} + f(\sigma)] + \cdots \\ &+ \sum_i \sum_k \frac{a_i a_k}{\rho_i + \rho_k}\{x_k[-\rho_i x_i + f(\sigma)] + x_i[-\rho_k x_k + f(\sigma)]\} \\ &+ f(\sigma)[\sum \beta_k x_k - r f(\sigma)].\end{aligned} \tag{2.20}$$

If we take it into account that

$$\sum_i \sum_k a_k a_i x_k x_i = (\sum a_k x_k)^2$$

$$\sum_i \sum_k \frac{a_k a_i}{\rho_k + \rho_i}(x_k + x_i) = 2 \sum_k \frac{a_k a_i}{\rho_k + \rho_i} x_k$$

and add and subtract to the right of Eq. (2.20) the expression

$$\pm 2\sqrt{r} f(\sigma) \sum a_k x_k$$

the total derivative of the function V, (2.19), can be reduced to

$$\begin{aligned}\dot V = &-\sum \rho_k A_k x_k^2 - C_1(\rho_{s+1} + \rho_{s+2}) x_{s+1} x_{s+2} - \cdots \\ &- (\sum a_k x_k)^2 - [\sqrt{r} f(\sigma)]^2 - 2\sqrt{r} f(\sigma) \sum a_k x_k \\ &+ f(\sigma)\left[\sum_{k=1}^{s}\left(A_k + \beta_k + 2\sqrt{r} a_k + 2a_k \sum_{i=1}^{n} \frac{a_i}{\rho_k + \rho_i}\right)\right.\end{aligned}$$

$$+\sum_{\alpha=1}^{n-s}\left(C_\alpha+\beta_{s+\alpha}+2\sqrt{r}a_{s+\alpha}+2a_{s+\alpha}\sum_{i=1}^{n}\frac{a_i}{\rho_{s+\alpha}+\rho_i}\right)\Bigg].$$

For convenience of writing the sum of the last brackets of this expression, we use the notation $C_1 = C_2$; $C_3 = C_4, \ldots$.

We shall always obtain a derivative of $\dot{V}$ which is sign definite and of opposite sign to V, if we require fulfillment of the relations

$$A_k+\beta_k+2\sqrt{r}a_k+2a_k\sum_{i=1}^{n}\frac{a_i}{\rho_k+\rho_i}=0$$

$$C_\alpha+\beta_{s+\alpha}+2\sqrt{r}a_{s+\alpha}+2a_{s+\alpha}\sum_{i=1}^{n}\frac{a_i}{\rho_{s+\alpha}+\rho_i}=0. \tag{2.21}$$

$$(k = 1, \ldots, s; \quad \alpha = 1, \ldots, n-s)$$

This derivative has the form

$$\frac{dV}{dt}=-\sum_{k=1}^{s}\rho_k A_k x_k^{\,2}-C_1(\rho_{s+1}+\rho_{s+2})x_{s+1}x_{s+2}-\cdots$$
$$-\left[\sum a_k x_k+\sqrt{r}f(\sigma)\right]^2. \tag{2.22}$$

Provided that relations (2.21) do, in fact, hold, then for a given problem it is possible to construct a Liapunov function (2.19) having a sign-definite derivative (2.22) of opposite sign to V; this guarantees absolute stability of solution (2.15). This stability is asymptotic.

Relations (2.21) include arbitrary positive constants $A_1, \ldots, A_s$, C_1, $C_3, \ldots$, and also the real numbers $a_1, \ldots, a_s$ and the complex conjugate pairs $a_{s+1}, \ldots, a_n$. If it is possible to specify the first group of numbers in some way, relations (2.21) may be regarded as equations defining the constants a_k.

In future we shall concern ourselves only with the criterion of solvability of these equations, which give a corresponding set of values for the numbers $a_1, \ldots, a_n$, and shall disregard the numbers themselves.

Assume that this criterion can be expressed as a form consisting of a certain number of inequalities

$$F_m(\beta_1, \ldots, \beta_n, A_1, \ldots, A_s, C_1, C_3, \ldots) > 0. \tag{2.23}$$

$$(m = 1, 2, 3, \ldots)$$

If the controller constants are chosen to satisfy inequalities (2.23), this will guarantee the asymptotic stability of solution (2.15).

Let us consider the special case of Eq. (2.23) when $A_1 = \cdots = A_s = C_1 = \cdots = 0$, and when Φ does not enter into the Liapunov function. Equations (2.21) have the form

$$\beta_k+2\sqrt{r}a_k+2a_k\sum_{i=1}^{n}\frac{a_i}{\rho_i+\rho_k}=0. \tag{2.24}$$

$$(k = 1, \ldots, n)$$

The criterion of solvability of these equations can be written, as in the previous case, as a form consisting of the same number of inequalities

$$F_m(\beta_1, \ldots, \beta_n) > 0. \quad (m = 1, 2, 3, \ldots) \quad (2.25)$$

If the controller constants satisfy inequalities (2.25), there exists a positive definite function

$$V = F + \int_0^\sigma f(\sigma)\, d\sigma \qquad (2.26)$$

the total derivative of which, calculated according to Eqs. (2.11)

$$\dot{V} = -\left[\sum_{k=1}^{n} a_k x_k + \sqrt{r} f(\sigma)\right]^2$$

is a sign-constant function of opposite sign to V. Therefore, if inequality (2.25) is satisfied, stability of (2.15) is guaranteed.

If the constants $A_1, \ldots, A_s, C_1, \ldots$ are positive and arbitrarily small numbers, we can assert that the criterion of stability given by inequalities (2.25) is as close as is desired to the criterion of asymptotic stability given by inequalities (2.23).

With this in mind, we shall consider in the following the Liapunov functions (2.26), and we shall speak of the asymptotic absolute stability of solution (2.15) as guaranteed by the satisfaction of inequalities (2.25).

And so we have obtained the theorem first proved by Lur'e:

The set S of parameters of the regulator for which the set of quadratic equations (2.24) *has at least one set of solutions containing the real numbers $a_1, \ldots, a_s$ and the complex conjugate pairs $a_{s+1}, \ldots, a_n$ guarantees asymptotic absolute stability of* (2.11).

We note that the theorem is also valid in the case when the speed of the servomotor depends on the load, and is described by the function (1.23).

Now assume that the control system is neutral with respect to one coordinate, and that $\rho_1 = 0$. Then, in accordance with Eqs. (2.10) and (2.14), we find

$$\beta_1 = -\rho_1 \sum p_\alpha D_1^{(\alpha)} = -\sum p_\alpha \frac{N_\alpha(\rho_1)\rho_1}{(-\rho_1)D'(\rho_1)} = \sum p_\alpha \frac{N_\alpha(0)}{D'(0)}$$

and the canonical equations of the problem have the form

$$\begin{aligned} \dot{x}_1 &= f(\sigma) \\ \dot{x}_k &= -\rho_k x_k + f(\sigma) \qquad (k = 2, \ldots, n) \\ \dot{\sigma} &= \beta_1 x_1 + \sum_{k=2}^{n} \beta_k x_k - r f(\sigma). \end{aligned}$$

The Liapunov function may be chosen as follows:

$$V = \tfrac{1}{2}Ax_1^2 + \sum_{i=2}^{n}\sum_{k=2}^{n} \frac{a_k a_i}{\rho_k + \rho_i} x_k x_i + \int_0^\sigma f(\sigma)\, d\sigma$$

where A is a positive number.

If we perform all the operations for calculating the total derivative of V, we obtain the following conditions

$$A + \beta_1 = 0$$

$$\beta_k + 2\sqrt{r}a_k + 2a_k \sum_{i=2}^{n} \frac{a_i}{\rho_k + \rho_i} = 0. \qquad (k = 2, \ldots, n)$$

Obviously, for stability, it is required that $\beta_1 < 0$; the remaining equations should be examined from the same standpoint as Eqs. (2.24).

It can be shown that the criteria of stability obtained here are also valid when $\psi(\omega) \not\equiv 1$.

2.2 Second Method of Canonical Variables. The method is due to A. M. Letov [15].

If a process is inherently unstable, or is neutral with respect to more than one coordinate, then Eq. (2.5) has roots such that Re $\rho_k < 0$, $k = 1, 2, \ldots$. For these cases, which are very difficult to investigate, it is desirable to use another form of canonical transformation that enables us to construct Liapunov functions

First of all, we shall adopt as a new variable the function

$$\sigma = \sum p_\alpha \eta_\alpha - r\xi. \qquad (2.27)$$

We shall assume that $r \neq 0$. If we denote

$$\bar{b}_{k\alpha} = b_{k\alpha} + \frac{n_k p_\alpha}{r} \qquad (\alpha, k = 1, \ldots, n) \qquad (2.28)$$

Eqs. (1.19), after elimination of the old variable, can be rewritten as

$$\dot{\eta}_k = \sum b_{k\alpha}\eta_\alpha - \frac{n_k}{r}\sigma. \qquad (k = 1, \ldots, n) \qquad (2.29)$$

Furthermore, differentiating σ and denoting

$$\sum p_\alpha \bar{b}_{\alpha\beta} = \bar{p}_\beta; \quad \frac{1}{r}\sum p_\alpha n_\alpha = \rho \qquad (2.30)$$

we obtain in conjunction with Eqs. (2.28)

$$\begin{aligned} \dot{\eta}_k &= \sum b_{k\alpha}\eta_\alpha - \frac{n_k}{r}\sigma \qquad (k = 1, \ldots, n) \\ \dot{\sigma} &= \sum \bar{p}_\alpha \eta_\alpha - \rho\sigma - rf(\sigma). \end{aligned} \qquad (2.31)$$

Consider the linear transformation

$$x_s = \sum \bar{C}_\alpha^{(s)} \eta_\alpha. \qquad (s = 1, \ldots, n) \quad (2.32)$$

Differentiating Eq. (2.32) and using (2.31), we obtain

$$\dot{x}_s = \sum_\alpha \bar{C}_\alpha^{(s)} \left(\sum_\beta \bar{b}_{\alpha\beta} \eta_\beta - \frac{n_\alpha}{r} \sigma \right).$$

Since we want to give the equations in the new variables the canonical form

$$\dot{x}_s = -r_s x_s + \sigma \qquad (s = 1, \ldots, n)$$

we shall choose the constants of transformation in accordance with the relations

$$-r_s \bar{C}_\beta^{(s)} = \sum_\alpha \bar{b}_{\alpha\beta} C_\alpha^{(s)} \quad (s, \beta = 1, \ldots, n) \quad (2.33)$$

$$-r = \sum_\alpha C_\alpha^{(s)} n_\alpha. \qquad (2.34)$$

As before, this transformation is only possible when the parameters r_s are chosen as the roots of the equation

$$\bar{D}(r) = \begin{vmatrix} \bar{b}_{11} + r \cdots \bar{b}_{n1} \\ \cdots\cdots\cdots\cdots \\ \bar{b}_{1n} \cdots \bar{b}_{nn} + r \end{vmatrix} = 0. \qquad (2.35)$$

We assume the roots of this equation to be distinct and such that Re $r_s > 0$, $(s = 1, \ldots, n)$. The physical meaning of this condition is, essentially, that with a perfect regulator the system possesses stability. Since the coefficients of Eq. (2.35) include the constants of the controller, they can always be so selected that the condition indicated is satisfied. Consequently, in this case the controller constants must be such as to satisfy the inequalities

$$\Delta_1 > 0, \ldots, \Delta_n > 0$$

where the Δ_k are the Hurwitz determinants of the equation derived from (2.35) by substituting $-r$ for r.

In the case when the roots of Eq. (2.35) are simple, the transformation (2.32) is nonsingular, and can be solved for the old variables. Assume that we find

$$\eta_k = \sum_\alpha \bar{D}_\alpha^{(k)} x_\alpha. \qquad (k = 1, \ldots, n) \quad (2.36)$$

Relations (2.36) allow us to eliminate all the old variables in the last equation of set (2.31). Therefore, if we introduce the notation

$$\bar{\beta}_k = \sum_\alpha \bar{D}_k^{(\alpha)} \bar{p}_\alpha \qquad (k = 1, \ldots, n) \quad (2.37)$$

the canonical equations take the following final form:

$$\dot{x}_k = -r_k x_k + \sigma \qquad (k = 1, \ldots, n) \quad (2.38)$$
$$\dot{\sigma} = \sum \bar{\beta}_k x_k - \rho\sigma - rf(\sigma).$$

Let the numbers $\bar{D}_{ik}(r_s)$ be the cofactors of the elements of the ith row and kth column of the determinant (2.35), while the numbers $\bar{N}_i(r_s)$ are

$$\bar{N}_i(r_s) = \sum m_k \bar{D}_{ik}(r_s) \neq 0. \quad (s = 1, \ldots, n) \quad (2.39)$$

It is useful to observe that $\bar{N}_i(r_s)$ is the determinant (2.35), in which the elements of the ith row have been replaced by the numbers m_k. So we find

$$\bar{C}_k^{(s)} = -\frac{r}{\bar{N}_i(s)} \bar{D}_{ik}(r_s); \quad \bar{D}_\alpha^{(k)} = \frac{\bar{N}_k(r_\alpha)}{r\bar{D}'(r_\alpha)}$$
$$(\alpha, k, s = 1, \ldots, n) \quad (2.40)$$

where $\bar{D}'(r_\alpha)$ is the derivative of the determinant (2.35) with respect to r_α.

Assume that Eq. (2.35) has the real roots $r_1, \ldots, r_s$ and the complex conjugate roots $r_{s+1}, \ldots, \ldots, r_n$. Now let us consider the positive definite function

$$V = \sum_k \sum_i \frac{a_k a_i}{r_k + r_i} x_k x_i + \frac{\mathscr{H}^2}{2} \sigma^2 \quad (2.41)$$

where $\mathscr{H}^2 > 0$, $a_1, \ldots, a_s$ are real numbers, and $a_{s+1}, \ldots, \ldots, a_n$ are complex conjugate numbers. Its total derivative, obtained by using Eq. (2.38), is

$$\dot{V} = -\sum_k \sum_i a_k a_i x_k x_i + 2\sigma \sum_k \sum_i \frac{a_k a_i}{r_k + r_i} x_k$$
$$+ \mathscr{H}^2 \sigma \sum \bar{\beta}_k x_k - \rho \mathscr{H}^2 \sigma^2 - \mathscr{H}^2 \sigma f(\sigma).$$

But since

$$\sum_k \sum_i a_k a_i x_k x_i = \left(\sum_k a_k x_k\right)^2$$

then, adding and subtracting $(\sigma^2 + 2\sigma \Sigma a_k x_k)$ on the right side of $\dot{V}$, we obtain

$$\dot{V} = -[\Sigma a_k x_k + \sigma]^2 - (\mathscr{H}^2 \rho - 1)\sigma^2 - \mathscr{H}^2 \sigma f(\sigma)$$
$$+ \sigma \sum_k \left(\mathscr{H}^2 \bar{\beta}_k + 2a_k + 2a_k \sum_i \frac{a_i}{r_k + r_i} \right) x_k. \quad (2.42)$$

Assume that $0 < h < (df/d\sigma)_{\sigma=0}$ is a fixed number, and that the function $\varphi(\sigma) = f(\sigma) - h\sigma$ is defined as in Eq. (1.28). Then for any function $f(\sigma)$ belonging to A', which requires satisfaction of the conditions

$$\mathscr{H}^2 \bar{\beta}_k + 2a_k + 2a_k \sum_i \frac{a_i}{r_k + r_i} \quad (k = 1, \ldots, n) \quad (2.43)$$

$$\mathscr{H}^2(\rho + h) - 1 > 0 \quad (2.44)$$

we reduce the expression for $\dot{V}$ to the form

$$\dot{V} = -[\sum a_k x_k + \sigma]^2 - [\mathscr{H}^2(\rho + h) - 1]\sigma^2 - \mathscr{H}^2 \sigma\varphi(\sigma). \quad (2.45)$$

The function $\dot{V}$ can take only negative or, failing this, zero values, and satisfaction of conditions (2.43) and (2.44) guarantees stability of the system.

This proves the theorem [15].

That set S of the parameters of the regulator with which inequalities (2.36) and (2.44) are satisfied and with which the system of quadratic equations (2.43) has at least one set of solutions containing the real numbers $a_1, \ldots, a_s$ and the complex pairs $a_{s+1}, \ldots, a_n$, guarantees asymptotic stability with any $f(\sigma)$ belonging to subclass A' and any $|\sigma| \leqslant \bar{\sigma}$.

2.3 Method of Separation of the Variables. The method is due to E. A. Barbashin [1].

Assume that the system of equations of disturbed motion of a control system can be presented in the form

$$\dot{x}_i = \sum_k p_{ik} f_k(\sigma_k). \qquad (i = 1, \ldots, n) \quad (2.46)$$

Here the p_{ik} are known functions of the coordinates, of time, and of the regulator parameters, while the $f_k(\sigma_k)$ are functions belonging to class A', such that

$$\sigma_k = \sum a_{km} x_m \quad (2.47)$$

where the a_{km} are constants.

In particular, any linear system can be reduced to form (2.46). For this form, E. A. Barbashin has proposed to use the following Liapunov function:

$$V = \alpha \sum C_{ii} \int_0^{\sigma_i} f_i(\sigma)\, d\sigma + \beta \sum_{i \neq k} \sum C_{ik} f_i(\sigma_i) f_k(\sigma_k). \quad (2.48)$$

Here α, β_1, C_{ii}, C_{ik} are arbitrary positive constants, and the C_{ik} satisfy Sylvester's criterion.†

The total derivative of the function (2.48), calculated according to Eqs. (2.46), gives a quadratic form with respect to the functions $f_i(\sigma_i)$, $f_k(\sigma_k)$; the conditions for which this form is negative definite constitute the criterion of stability of (2.46).

† Sylvester's criterion permits us to recognize whether the quadratic form $W = \sum_i \sum_j C_{ij} f_i f_j$ be positive definite or not. Namely, in order that the quadratic form W be positive definite, it is necessary and sufficient that the coefficients should satisfy the inequalities:

$$\begin{vmatrix} C_{11}, \ldots, C_{1k} \\ \cdots\cdots\cdots \\ C_{k1}, \ldots, C_{kk} \end{vmatrix} > 0. \qquad (k = 1, 2, \ldots, n)$$

Let us see how this method applies to our systems. As we do so, the order in which the calculation of $\dot{V}$ is carried out will be clearly seen. We shall return to Eqs. (2.38) and shall postulate

$$x_k = f_k(\sigma_k), \ \sigma_k = x_k, \ \sigma = \psi(\sigma), \ \alpha = 1, \ \beta = 0. \tag{2.49}$$

We shall then obtain in E. A. Barbashin's notation

$$\begin{aligned} \dot{\sigma} &= -r_k f_k(\sigma_k) + \psi(\sigma) \\ \dot{\sigma} &= \sum \beta_k f_k(\sigma_k) - (\rho + rh)\psi(\sigma) - r\varphi(\sigma). \end{aligned}$$

We shall choose the function (2.48) so that $\alpha C_{ii} = 1$, $\beta = 0$, and we shall add to it $\int_0^\sigma \psi(\sigma)\, d\sigma$. After calculating the derivative we obtain

$$\begin{aligned} \dot{V} &= \sum_i f_i(\sigma_i)[-r_i f_i(\sigma_i) + \psi(\sigma)] \\ &\quad + \psi(\sigma)[\sum \beta_i f_i(\sigma_i) - (\rho + rh)\psi(\sigma) - r\varphi(\sigma)] \\ &= -\sum_i r_i f_i^2(\sigma_i) + \sum_i (1 + \beta_i)\psi(\sigma) f_i(\sigma_i) \\ &\quad - (\rho + rh)\psi^2(\sigma) - r\varphi(\sigma)\psi(\sigma). \end{aligned}$$

Obviously, the criterion of stability of the system reduces to the satisfaction of inequalities (2.36) and the inequality

$$\begin{vmatrix} r_1, & 0, & \cdots & 0, & \dfrac{1+\beta_1}{2} \\ \cdots & \cdots & \cdots & \cdots & \cdots \\ 0, & 0, & \cdots & r_n, & \dfrac{1+\beta_n}{2} \\ \dfrac{1+\beta_1}{2}, & \dfrac{1+\beta_2}{2}, & \cdots, & \dfrac{1+\beta_n}{2}, & \rho + rh \end{vmatrix} > 0. \tag{2.50}$$

2.4 Method of Squaring. The method is due to N. N. Krasovskii [10].

This is a very general method for constructing Liapunov functions, applicable to cases of both steady-state and transient motion; it is essentially as follows. Given the equations of disturbed motion, (1.8), it is further assumed that the functions Y_1 are differentiable once with respect to $y_1, \ldots, y_n$, and that these derivatives are continuous functions of their variables. It is obvious that the V-function

$$V = \tfrac{1}{2} \sum [Y_k(y_1, \ldots, y_n, t)]^2 \tag{2.51}$$

may be regarded as a Liapunov function under certain conditions. These conditions are easily found. We have

$$\dot{V} = \sum_k \sum_j \frac{1}{2}\left(\frac{\partial Y_k}{\partial y_j} + \frac{\partial Y_j}{\partial y_k}\right) Y_k Y_j + \frac{\partial V}{\partial t}. \tag{2.52}$$

In the case when $\partial Y_k/\partial t = 0$, the total derivative is a quadratic form with respect to Y_k and Y_j; therefore in order that V should be a Liapunov function for a system of the form (1.8), it is necessary and sufficient that the coefficients entering into form (2.52) should satisfy Sylvester's inequalities. These inequalities also form a sufficient criterion of optimality.

We shall illustrate the effectiveness of this method by applying it to the solution of the following problem.

Let $f(\sigma)$ belong to the class A'. A linear nonsingular transformation reduces the original system to the form

$$\begin{aligned} \dot{y}_k &= -u_k y_k - \varphi(\sigma) \quad (k = 1, \ldots, n+1) \\ \sigma &= \sum \gamma_k y_k \end{aligned} \tag{2.53}$$

where $u_1, \ldots, u_{n+1}$ are the roots of the equation

$$\begin{vmatrix} b_{11} + u, & \cdots\cdots & b_{1n}, & m_1 \\ \cdots & \cdots & \cdots & \cdots \\ b_{n1}, & \cdots\cdots & b_{nn} + u, & m_n \\ hp_1 & \cdots\cdots & hp_n, & -rh + u \end{vmatrix} = 0. \tag{2.54}$$

For simplicity, we shall assume the u_k to be real. Then, denoting

$$Y_k = -u_k y_k + \varphi(\sigma)$$

we find the form of $\dot{V}$

$$\dot{V} = -\sum u_k Y_k^2 + \sum_i \sum_k \gamma_i \frac{\partial \varphi}{\partial \sigma} Y_k Y_i.$$

Sylvester's determinant has the form

$$\begin{vmatrix} u_1 - \gamma_1 \dfrac{\partial \varphi}{\partial \sigma} & \cdots\cdots & \dfrac{\gamma_n}{2} \dfrac{\partial \varphi}{\partial \sigma} \\ \cdots & \cdots & \cdots \\ \dfrac{\gamma_n}{2} \dfrac{\partial \varphi}{\partial \sigma} & \cdots\cdots & \mu_{n+1} - \gamma_{n+1} \dfrac{\partial \varphi}{\partial \sigma} \end{vmatrix} > 0. \tag{2.55}$$

The effectiveness of Krasovskii's method can be seen at once from the determinant (2.55). In the case of a strictly linear system, $\partial\varphi/\partial\sigma = 0$ and Sylvester's inequalities, formed from the determinant (2.55), are equivalent to the Hurwitz inequalities for the given system.

2.5 The Method of Apparent Linearization.

The method is due to V. I. Zubov [27].

The differential equations of the system are written in the form

$$\dot{x}_k = \sum f_{ki} x_i \qquad (k = 1, \ldots, n) \tag{2.56}$$

where the f_{ki} are, generally speaking, functions of time and of the coordinates. In the case when f_{ki} = constant, we have linear equations with constant coefficients; in the general case, the functions f_{ki} allow the presence of any nonlinear characteristics in the system to be taken into account.

We assume that Eq. (2.56) is defined in a region $N(x, t)$ containing the origin of the coordinate system, that $t > 0$, and that there is a unique solution for any point belonging to N and chosen as an origin.

In the simplest case, the V-function is defined by

$$V = \tfrac{1}{2} \sum_k x_k^2 \tag{2.57}$$

Its total derivative, according to Eqs. (2.56), is

$$\dot{V} = \sum_k \sum_i B_{ki} x_k x_i \tag{2.58}$$

where

$$B_{ki} = \tfrac{1}{2}(f_{ki} + f_{ik}). \tag{2.59}$$

The method is based on the idea that Eq. (2.58) may be regarded as a quadratic form, whose coefficients (2.59) are known functions of time and of the coordinates. If, therefore, the f_{ki} are such that in a certain region $D(x_1, \ldots, x_n)$ including the origin of the coordinate system, the form $\dot{V}$ is negative for any $t > 0$ and any $x_1, \ldots, x_n$ belonging to D, the system is stable. The stability will be asymptotic if $\dot{V}$ is negative definite. The criterion of stability of the system can be obtained from Sylvester's inequalities for $\dot{V}$ or from Hurwitz's inequalities for the equation

$$|B_{ki} - \lambda \delta_{ki}| = 0 \tag{2.60}$$

defining the characteristic roots of $\dot{V}$ in D for $t > 0$. Obviously, when this criterion is satisfied, all $\lambda_k = \lambda_k\ (t, x_1, \ldots, x_n)$ must be nonpositive in the region D.

Moreover, we observe that if $x_i = f_i(\sigma_i)$, $\sigma_i = x_i$, the solutions obtained by this method coincide with those obtained by Barbashin. The method has been used by Chzhan Zhen'-Wei [6], to obtain an elegant solution to a problem of some practical importance, which was formulated in a joint report by A. I. Lur'e and the author [21].

2.6 Systems with Tachometer Feedback [16]. These methods for constructing Liapunov functions are applicable to the case when the law of control σ includes a tachometer feedback component $N\dot{\xi}$.

The process of transforming the original equations into canonical form is the same, in the case of tachometer feedback, as that considered above, except for the transformation of the last equation in σ. If the plant is inherently stable, differentiation of Eq. (1.21) and use of (1.25) gives

$$\dot{\sigma} = \sum p_\alpha \dot{\eta}_\alpha - rf(\sigma) - N \frac{df}{d\sigma} \dot{\sigma}. \tag{2.61}$$

Consequently, if we introduce the notation

$$\mathscr{H} = 1 + N \frac{df}{d\sigma} \tag{2.62}$$

we obtain the equation for control systems with tachometer feedback in canonical form

$$\begin{aligned} \dot{x}_s &= -\rho_s x_s + f(\sigma) \\ \mathscr{H}\dot{\sigma} &= \sum \beta_s x_s - rf(\sigma). \end{aligned} \tag{2.63}$$

Here β_s, ρ_s, r have their former significance, as in Eq. (2.10).

Unlike the equations considered so far, we now have a nonlinear factor $\mathscr{H}$, which is always positive when $N > 0$, and is greater than unity since $df/d\sigma > 0$ (Fig. 2).

If the plant is inherently unstable, we introduce a new σ, defined as

$$\sigma = \sum p_\alpha \eta_\alpha - r\xi - Nf(\sigma). \tag{2.64}$$

Elimination of the old ξ gives

$$\dot{\eta}_k = \sum \bar{b}_{k\alpha}\eta_\alpha - \frac{n_k}{r}(\sigma + Nf(\sigma)) \qquad (k = 1, \ldots, n)$$

$$\mathscr{H}\dot{\sigma} = \sum \bar{p}_\alpha \eta_\alpha - \rho\sigma - (r + \rho N)f(\sigma) \tag{2.65}$$

where all the symbols have their former meaning, defined by Eqs. (2.28), (2.30), and (2.62). In the function $f(\sigma)$, eliminate the linear part $h\sigma$. The nonsingular linear transformation (2.32) converts Eqs. (2.65) to the canonical form

$$\begin{aligned} \dot{x}_s &= -r_s x_s + M\sigma + N\varphi(\sigma) \quad (s = 1, \ldots, n) \\ \mathscr{H}\dot{\sigma} &= \sum \bar{\beta}_s x_s - S\sigma - R\varphi(\sigma). \end{aligned} \tag{2.66}$$

Here the r_s are simple roots of Eq. (2.35), and the $\bar{\beta}_s$ are defined by (2.37), while the remaining constants are

$$M = 1 + hN; \; S = \rho + (r + \rho N)h; \; R = r + \rho N. \tag{2.67}$$

It is easy to show that if the constant $N > 0$, Lur'e's theorem can be extended to systems with tachometer feedback if we use a V-function of the form

$$V = F + \int_0^\sigma \mathscr{H} f(\sigma)\, d\sigma + \Phi.$$

However, if the plant is inherently unstable, the V-function must have the form

$$V = \sum_k \sum_i \frac{a_k a_i}{r_k + r_i} x_k x_i + \int_0^\sigma \mathscr{H}[M\sigma + N\varphi(\sigma)]\, d\sigma + \Phi.$$

It is easily shown that in this case the conditions of stability obtained in Section 2.2 are supplemented by the condition of constant tachometer feedback

$$S > M. \tag{2.68}$$

3. The Problem of Quality

3.1 Statement of the Problem. Consider an automatic control system where the disturbed motion is described by equations of the form

$$\dot{x}_k = \sum_\alpha b_{k\alpha} x_\alpha + f_k(x_1, \ldots, x_n, t) \tag{3.1}$$

which are defined in a certain region N of the Euclidean space E_n with a quadratic metric R^2 and with t in the closed interval $[0, T]$ or in the half-closed interval $[0, \infty)$. Here x_k are the generalized coordinates of the system, $b_{k\alpha}$ are parameters, and f_k are nonlinear functions satisfying the following condition.

(1) The f_k are defined in the region N, containing the origin of the coordinate system, and are bounded.

(2)
$$f_k(0, \ldots, 0, t) = 0. \qquad (k = 1, \ldots, n) \tag{3.2}$$

(3) There exist positive numbers L_k such that everywhere in N

$$|f_k(x_1, \ldots, x_n, t)| < L_k^{(N)} R, \quad t \in [0, T].$$

We assume that the $b_{k\alpha}$ are, generally speaking, certain functions of time t defined in the interval $[0, T]$ in which T is any positive number or infinity; in the latter case t is in the half-closed interval $[0, \infty)$.

Furthermore, we assume that for any point $M(x_{10}, \ldots, x_{n0})$ belonging to N, $t = 0$, Eq. (3.1) has a unique solution.

It is also assumed that Eq. (3.2) contains free parameters $P(p_1, \ldots, p_m)$, which can be selected. These parameters not only are among $b_{k\alpha}$, but also may enter into the composition of the function f_k. The number m of these parameters gives the dimensions of the space $P(p_1, \ldots, p_m)$ in which the problem of quality is to be investigated.

The quantity R^2 defines the square of the distance between the representative point M of Eq. (3.3) and the origin of the coordinate system.

The problem of quality may be formulated in various ways.† Here, two of its more important aspects are examined.

Let us denote by B that region in the parameter space P in which the system is stable. Then it is necessary:

(1) for every point in B to determine the instant of time t^* at which the distance R of the representative point satisfies the condition

† See Letov [18]. This book contains a bibliography on the problem of quality.

$$\frac{R(t)}{R(0)} < e^{-a}, \quad t \geqslant t^* \tag{3.3}$$

where a is a given positive number;

(2) to determine the subset B' in the region B for which the time t^* does not exceed a given number t^{**}.

The time t^* is called the *time of conditional attenuation.*

Secondly, we are interested in forming estimates of overshoot for the regulated coordinates.

Investigation of t^* and estimation of the overshoot form the time and space aspects, respectively, of the problem of quality.

Let us introduce a new set of variables, defined by

$$\sum_k a_{ki} x_k = \sqrt{a_{ii}}\, R y_i; \qquad (i = 1, \ldots, n) \tag{3.4}$$

$$R^2 = \sum_k \sum_i a_{ki} x_k x_i. \tag{3.5}$$

Obviously, the y_i are the direction cosines of the radius-vector $\bar{R}$ of the representative point.

The square of the length of this vector, Eq. (3.5), is given by a quadratic form, the coefficients a_{ki} of which are subject to the condition that this form represent a metric for the space of system (3.1).

It is obvious that the a_{ki} must satisfy Sylvester's inequalities

$$\Delta_k = \begin{vmatrix} a_{11}, \ldots, a_{1k} \\ \cdots\cdots\cdots \\ a_{k1}, \ldots, a_{kk} \end{vmatrix} > 0. \qquad (k = 1, \ldots, n) \tag{3.6}$$

Let $\Delta = \Delta_n$ be the last determinant of Eq. (3.6), and let Δ_{rs} be its minors with respect to the element a_{rs}, r being the row number and s the column number. Since $\Delta \neq 0$, Eq. (3.4) gives

$$x_r = \frac{R}{\Delta} \sum_s \sqrt{a_{ss}}\, \Delta_{sr} y_s \qquad (r = 1, \ldots, n) \tag{3.7}$$

so that (3.4) and (3.5) establish a one-to-one correspondence between the old and the new variables.

For the present, we need not be concerned about the increase of the number of the new variables by one, or about the evident complexity of the conversion. For our problem, all this is outweighed by the geometric significance of the new variables. Let us construct the differential equations which they satisfy.

To this end, we shall differentiate Eqs. (3.4) and (3.5). Eliminating the old variables and their derivatives, in accordance with Eqs. (3.7) and (3.1), we obtain

$$\dot{R} = -WR + \Phi/R \tag{3.8}$$

$$\dot{y}_i = Wy_i + \frac{1}{\Delta\sqrt{a_{ii}}} \sum_s \left[\sum_\alpha \left(\sum_k a_{ik} b_{k\alpha}\right)\Delta_{s\alpha}\right]\sqrt{a_{ss}}\, y_s. \tag{3.9}$$

Here W is the quadratic form

$$W = \sum_s \sum_r B_{sr} y_s y_r \tag{3.10}$$

where the coefficients are given by

$$B_{sr} = -\frac{\sqrt{a_{ss}a_{rr}}}{\Delta^2} \sum_k \sum_i \left[\sum_\alpha a_{k\alpha} b_{\alpha i}\right]\Delta_{sk}\Delta_{ri} \tag{3.11}$$

and the function Φ is defined by

$$\Phi = \frac{R}{\Delta} \sum_s \sum_i \left[\sum_k a_{ki}\Delta_{sk}\sqrt{a_{ss}}\right] y_s f_i(R, y_1, \ldots, y_n, t) \tag{3.12}$$

3.2 First Integral. It is material to note that Eqs. (3.8) and (3.9) have a first integral defined by the equality

$$F = \sum_s \sum_r A_{sr} y_s y_r = 1 \tag{3.13}$$

where

$$A_{sr} = \frac{\sqrt{a_{ss}a_{rr}}}{\Delta^2}\Delta_{sr}. \tag{3.14}$$

We omit the proof of this assertion, which can be easily obtained by calculating the total derivative of the function F in accordance with Eqs. (3.4) and (3.5).

For the rest, it is necessary to show that the quadratic form F is positive definite and equals zero only at the origin of the coordinate system. In fact,

$$\Delta_k^* = \begin{vmatrix} A_{11}, \ldots, A_{1k} \\ \cdots\cdots\cdots \\ A_{k1}, \ldots, A_{kk} \end{vmatrix} = \frac{a_{11}, \ldots, a_{kk}}{\Delta^2} \begin{vmatrix} \Delta_{11}, \ldots, \Delta_{1k} \\ \cdots\cdots\cdots \\ \Delta_{k1}, \ldots, \Delta_{kk} \end{vmatrix}. \tag{3.15}$$

But in accordance with the well-known formula for calculating determinants whose elements are given by the minors of certain other determinants, we obtain

$$\Delta_k^* = \frac{a_{11}, \ldots, a_{kk}}{\Delta^2}\Delta_k^{k-1}. \tag{3.16}$$

Consequently, by force of Eq. (3.6) we have $\Delta_k^* > 0$ for all k, which is what we wanted to show.

3.3 The Case of the Strictly Linear System. In accordance with the view of the problem of quality adopted here, it is sufficient for us to analyze Eq. (3.8), in which the form W is defined on the surface of (3.13).

In the case of a strictly linear system, (3.8) yields

$$R(t) = R(0)e^{-\int_0^t W\,dt} \tag{3.17}$$

Thus the problem of quality reduces to a study of the quadratic form W, defined on the surface of Eq. (3.13). Obviously, to every stable system there corresponds a form W taking positive values on the surface of (3.13). Such a form satisfies the inequalities of Sylvester

$$\begin{vmatrix} B_{11}, \ldots, B_{1k} \\ \cdots\cdots\cdots \\ B_{k1}, \ldots, B_{kk} \end{vmatrix} > 0 \qquad t \text{ in the interval } [0, T]. \tag{3.18}$$

The region B of stability in the space of the parameters $p_1, \ldots, p_m$ of the system is defined by the intersections of inequalities (3.18).

Now let us examine a family of quadratic forms $W - uF$. In the case when F is a positive definite form, there exists a nonsingular linear transformation to the new variables $z_1, \ldots, z_n$, which makes the forms W, F canonical

$$W = \sum u_k z_k^2; \ F = \sum z_k^2.$$

Here the numbers u_k are roots of

$$\begin{vmatrix} B_{11} - uA_{11}, \ldots, B_{1n} - uA_{1n} \\ \cdots\cdots\cdots\cdots\cdots\cdots \\ B_{n1} - uA_{n1}, \ldots, B_{nn} - uA_{nn} \end{vmatrix} = 0. \tag{3.19}$$

In the region B these roots will be real and positive functions of time defined for any t in the interval $[0, T]$. We shall arrange them in order of increasing index

$$u_1 \leqslant u_2 \leqslant \cdots \leqslant u_n. \tag{3.20}$$

These functions have different values for every point P included in B. Consequently, Eq. (3.14) defines a set of functions (3.20) for the given region B.

Moreover, it is known that the numbers $u_k(t)$ are extreme values of the form W which it takes on the surface of Eq. (3.13). From this it is clear that the distance diminishes no slower than $\exp\left(-\int_0^t u_1(t)\,dt\right)$, and no faster than $\exp\left(-\int_0^t u_n(t)\,dt\right)$.

Let a be a given number. Since $u_1(t)$ is nonnegative, the integral $\int_0^t u_1(t)\,dt$ is a function of the upper limit taking only positive values, and the time of conditional attenuation of the system is given by

$$\int_0^t u_1(t)\,dt = a. \tag{3.21}$$

Equation (3.21) clarifies the time aspect of the problem of quality. For, having constructed the set of functions $u_1(t)$, we can define by (3.21) the value of t^* for every point of B. Conversely, assigning an upper limit t^{**}, we obtain a condition defining the function $u_1(t)$ which ensures the prescribed quality of the regulated system.

In the case when all $b_{k\alpha}$ = constants and E_n is a space with orthogonal coordinates, $a_{ki} = \delta_{ki}$, where δ_{ki} is the Kronecker delta. Then, too, $\Delta_{ki} = \delta_{ki}$, and

$$\begin{aligned} A_{sr} &= \delta_{sr} \\ B_{sr} &= -\frac{b_{rs} + b_{sr}}{2}. \end{aligned} \tag{3.22}$$

Equations (3.22) are particularly simple when the original equations are in canonical form. Use of these is especially convenient in many problems. For instance, if a system is described by

$$\ddot{x} + 2n\dot{x} + k^2 x = 0$$
$$n > 0, \quad k^2 > 0$$

we have

$$\dot{x}_1 = x_2$$
$$\dot{x}_2 = b_{21}x_1 + b_{22}x_2.$$

Here

$$x = x_1,\ \dot{x}_1 = x_2,\ b_{21} = -2n,\ b_{22} = -k^2.$$

Then we obtain

$$B_{11} = 0; \quad B_{22} = k^2; \quad B_{12} = -\frac{1 - 2n}{2}$$

and it is impossible to satisfy conditions (3.18) with any values of $n > 0$, $k^2 > 0$.

If, on the other hand, we apply a nonsingular linear transformation, we can always bring the original equations to the canonical form

$$\dot{\zeta}_s = \lambda_s \zeta_s \qquad (s = 1, \ldots, n) \tag{3.23}$$

where the λ_s are the roots of

$$|b_{k\alpha} + \delta_{k\alpha}\lambda| = 0 \tag{3.24}$$

assumed, for simplicity, to be distinct.

Let us also assume that the roots λ_k are real. Let them be so arranged that

$$\lambda_n < \lambda_{n-1} < \cdots < \lambda_1. \tag{3.25}$$

In this case we find

$$B_{ss} = -\lambda_s, \ B_{sr} = 0 \tag{3.26}$$

and the conditions of stability (3.18) finally reduce to the inequalities of Hurwitz written for (3.24).

To evaluate the measure of attenuation of the transient process, we shall form Eq. (3.19). It is

$$|\lambda_k + u| = 0.$$

Hence

$$u_k = -\lambda_k. \qquad (k = 1, \ldots, n) \tag{3.27}$$

Consequently, the least value of the quadratic form W is $u_1 = -\lambda_1$, that is, the root of the characteristic equation having the smallest absolute value.

In the case when $\lambda_1 = -\alpha + i\beta$, the smallest value of the form W will be $u_1 = \alpha$. The proof of this assertion is easily obtained, and we shall omit it.

Thus in the case of strictly linear systems with constant coefficients, an estimation of the time of conditional attenuation of the transient process by the minimum of the quadratic form W coincides exactly with the estimation we obtain on the basis of the concept of the degree of stability [25]. Under these circumstances, the quality of the control system will be best at that point P belonging to B for which $|\lambda_1|$ has the greatest value.

The results of this section solve the problem of quality of linear systems as far as estimation of the time of attenuation is concerned.

3.4 Estimation of the Time of Conditional Attenuation for Nonlinear Systems. As is well-known, we are able to write an integral equation equivalent to a given differential equation

$$R(t) = \left[R(0) + \int_0^t \frac{\Phi(s)}{R(s)} e^{\int W\,ds}\, ds\right] e^{-\int W\,ds}. \tag{3.28}$$

This equation enables us to obtain the required estimate for $R(t)$. Thus we have

$$\left| R(t) e^{\int W\,ds} \right| \leqslant R(0) + \int_0^t \frac{|\Phi|}{R^2} \left| R e^{\int W\,ds} \right| ds.$$

In accordance with a lemma in [3] we find

$$R(t) \leqslant R(0) \exp\left[-\int_0^t \left(W - \frac{|\Phi|}{R^2}\right) ds\right]. \tag{3.29}$$

Now let us turn to the expression Φ/R^2. It is required that its upper bound be estimated. Since

$$\sum_k a_{ik}\sqrt{a_{ss}}\Delta_{sk} = \sqrt{a_{ss}}\sum_k a_{ik}\Delta_{sk} = \sqrt{a_{ss}}\Delta$$

then

$$\frac{\Phi}{R^2} = \frac{1}{R}\sum_s \sqrt{a_{ss}}y_s f_s(y_1, \ldots, y_n, t, R) \tag{3.30}$$

and we find, according to conditions (3.2)

$$\frac{|\Phi|}{R^2} \leqslant \frac{1}{R}\sum_s \sqrt{a_{ss}}\,|y_s|\,L_s^{(N)}R. \tag{3.31}$$

But the region N is bounded, and the $|y_s|$ have upper limits $l_s = 1$; therefore there exists a number E

$$E = \sum \sqrt{a_{ss}}\,L_s^{(N)} \tag{3.32}$$

such that

$$\frac{|\Phi|}{R^2} \leqslant E. \tag{3.33}$$

In the case of an orthogonal space, a_{ss} is set equal to 1 in Eq. (3.32). Thus, we can formulate the theorem:

The control system (3.1) *will be stable if the quadratic form W satisfies the conditions of Sylvester* (3.18), *and if it satisfies the inequality*

$$W > E \tag{3.34}$$

everywhere on the surface of (3.13).

Since $\lambda_1(t) = \min W$, $\lambda_n(t) = \max W$, the function $R(t)$ diminishes, with condition (3.34) no slower than $R(0) \exp{(E - \lambda_1)t}$, and no faster than $R(0) \exp{(E - \lambda_n)t}$. From this there follows the theorem:

The control system (3.1) *will have the best quality for that point P belonging to B for which the minimal $\lambda_1(t) > E$ of the form W on surface* (3.13) *has the largest value.*

Thus the problem of quality of nonlinear control systems in its time aspect reduces to the construction of the quadratic form W in the space B and the investigation of its extreme properties.

In the case of the nonlinear system (2.53), with $a_{kj} = \delta_{kj}$, and taking Eq. (3.12) into account, we find

$$\Phi = R\sum \zeta_k \varphi(\sigma). \tag{3.35}$$

If $f(\sigma)$ is a function belonging to subclass A', there exist two numbers h, $H > 0$ such that $H\,|\sigma| \geqslant |f(\sigma)| \geqslant h\,|\sigma|$ when $|\sigma| \leqslant \sigma_*$, where σ_* is a positive root of the equation $\varphi(\sigma) = 0$. The region N is defined by the choice either of h or of σ_*. Then

$$|\varphi(\sigma)| = |H - h|\,|\sigma| = (H - h)\,|\sum \gamma_k x_k|.$$

But, according to the Cauchy-Buniakovskii inequality

$$|\varphi(\sigma)| = (H - h)\sqrt{\sum \gamma_k^2}R. \tag{3.36}$$

Hence we find

$$E = (H - h)\sqrt{\sum \gamma_k^2}. \tag{3.37}$$

4. The Connection between Liapunov Functions and the Problem of Optimality

4.1 The Method of Dynamic Programming. In a series of works on optimal control [11, 13], N. N. Krasovskii has studied the connection between Liapunov functions and the problem of optimal control. More recently, this problem has also been studied by R. E. Kalman and J. E. Bertram [9].

The fact that this connection exists is a substantially new discovery; it is significant both for the theory of stability and the theory of optimal control.

We shall try to show this connection, basing our demonstration on the method of Dynamic Programming [19]. First, however, we should mention the considerable number of works which have been published recently by Pontriagin, Gamkrelidze, Boltyanskii, Krasovskii, Roitenberg, Kulikowski, Bellman, Glicksberg, Gross, LaSalle, Bass, Kalman, and Bertram, of which an incomplete list is given in Letov [19].

The solutions obtained there give the law of control as a function of time and of the initial and final states of the system. These solutions can be realized by the aid of a digital computer operating according to the resulting algorithm and will consist of the discrete instants of time at which the plant excitation should be altered.

In the works of Pontriagin, Gamkrelidze, Boltyanskii, and Krasovskii, the so-called "problem of synthesis," that is, the problem of expressing the law of control as a known function of the coordinates of the system, is formulated.

In our own papers, we have analyzed the simplest cases of the solution of this problem, known by the special term of "analytical design"[17]. We formulate the problem of the analytical design of control systems as a problem of the classical Calculus of Variations, in which the law of control is determined in accordance with a certain previously chosen optimizing functional. Moreover, the law of control is obtained analytically and is written in that form in which it is usually realized by means of an appropriate selection of the transducers and the servomotor.

It is an inconvenience of the methods using the Calculus of Variations that they involve writing the equations of the variational problem which then have to be solved.

Here, however, we observe that R. Bellman's method of Dynamic Programing [4] allows the same results to be obtained, but by another process, which may sometimes be more acceptable for computational reasons.

For the convenience of our readers, we shall explain the method of Dynamic Programming by means of a simple example.

Given the differential equation

$$\dot{x} = G(x, y), \quad x(t_0) = u \tag{4.1}$$

with an initial condition for the variable x. We assume the function G to be bounded and continuous with respect to x, y in the open region $N(x, y)$. Here y is a control function, minimizing the functional

$$J(y) = \int_0^\infty F(x, y)\, dt \tag{4.2}$$

in the class of functions x, y belonging to C_1.

Let y be the function causing Eq. (4.2) to be minimum. It is assumed that the integral (4.2) has meaning. This minimum is a function $\psi(u)$ of the initial state u, and is defined as

$$\psi(u) = \min_y J(y). \tag{4.3}$$

Let S be a positive number. We have

$$\Psi(u) = \min_y \left[\int_0^S F(x, y)\, dt + \int_S^\infty F(x, y)\, dt \right]. \tag{4.4}$$

R. Bellman's principle of optimality is, essentially, as follows: if $y = y(t)$ ensures that the functional $J(y)$ has a minimum, then it will also ensure that the functional $\int_S^\infty F(x, y)\, dt$ has a minimum, independently of the first integral. In the case in question, this principle is expressed quite naturally by the Calculus of Variations, according to which any part of an extremum of $y(t)$ is also an extremum. It enabled R. Bellman to develop the original iterative process described below. According to this principle of optimality, Eq. (4.4) may be written

$$\Psi(u) = \min_y \left\{ \int_0^S F(x, y)\, dt + \Psi[x(S)] \right\}. \tag{4.5}$$

The symbol $\min_y$ denotes that Eq. (4.5) has a minimum for some function y belonging to class C_1.

We assume that S is sufficiently small, and that $y(t_0) = v$. Then, if ψ has a derivative when x lies in the interval $[x(0), x(S)]$, we obtain by expanding

$$\Psi[u + G(u, v)S] = \Psi(u) + G(u, v)S \frac{\partial \Psi}{\partial u}$$

$$\Psi(u) = \min_{y} \left[F(u, v)S + \Psi(u) + G(u, v)S \frac{\partial \Psi}{\partial u} + 0(s) \right].$$

Here $0(S)$ is the remainder, which is such that $\lim 0/S \to 0$ when $S \to 0$. In the limit when $S \to 0$ we find

$$\min_{y} \left[F(u, v) + G(u, v) \frac{\partial \Psi}{\partial u} \right] = 0. \tag{4.6}$$

In order that the expression in brackets should, in fact, give a minimum for y, its derivative with respect to v must be zero. So we have

$$\begin{aligned} F(u, v) + G(u, v) \frac{\partial \Psi}{\partial u} &= 0 \\ \frac{\partial F}{\partial v} + \frac{\partial G}{\partial v} \frac{\partial \Psi}{\partial u} &= 0. \end{aligned} \tag{4.7}$$

After eliminating $\psi'(u)$, we find the equation

$$F(u, v) \frac{\partial G}{\partial v} = \frac{\partial F}{\partial v} G(u, v) \tag{4.8}$$

which relates u and v for every instant of time t_0.

It is the chief aim of the method of Dynamic Programming to derive the functionals of Eq. (4.7). We shall apply the method to the solution of the problem of analytic design. Before we do this, we shall make two observations.

NOTE 1. Since Eq. (4.8) establishes the dependence $v = v(u)$ for every instant of time t_0, and since by force of the principle of optimality this equation does not depend on the choice of t_0, the dependence $v = v(u)$ is equivalent to the dependence $y = y(x)$; knowing thus $y(x)$, the system (4.1) is completely defined.

Therefore for simplicity we shall in future write the functional equations in the original coordinates straight away, since this will not lead to confusion.

NOTE 2. In the case when the function G is defined in the closed region $\bar{N}(x, y)$ and the optimal solution may pass along the boundary of the region, the requirement that the functions x, y should be continuous and differentiable may generally be omitted.

The difficulty in solving the problem of Dynamic Programming lies in the fact that the second equation of (4.7) cannot, generally speaking, be written, because the expression $\partial G/\partial v$ ceases to be defined along the boundary of $\bar{N}$.

The author of Dynamic Programming himself proposes here a very complicated process for finding the optimal solution when x and y belong to the class C; we shall not use this process.

In the course of solving the problem of analytic design, we shall show how an optimal solution can be simply obtained, in the case of a closed region $\bar{N}$ delimiting the problem, both for continuous x, y, and for continuous $x(t)$ and discontinuous $y(t)$.

The value of the method lies in the fact that we can obtain a closed solution of the problem of analytic design in the cases we are considering.

First let us examine the simplest problem of optimization of the functional (4.2) for the class of functions C_1.

We have the equation of the plant

$$\dot{\eta} = b\eta + m\xi \tag{4.9}$$

and the optimizing functional

$$J(\xi) = \int_0^\infty (a\eta^2 + c\xi^2)\, dt \qquad \eta(0) = \eta_0. \tag{4.10}$$

The equations of Dynamic Programming (4.7) are

$$\begin{aligned} a\eta^2 + c\xi^2 + (b\eta + m\xi)\frac{\partial \Psi}{\partial \eta} &= 0 \\ 2c\xi + m\frac{\partial \Psi}{\partial \eta} &= 0. \end{aligned} \tag{4.11}$$

Hence we find

$$mc\xi^2 + 2bc\eta\xi - am\eta^2 = 0 \tag{4.12}$$

and the solution is

$$\xi = -\frac{b+k}{m}\eta, \quad k = \sqrt{b^2 + \frac{a}{c}m^2}. \tag{4.13}$$

In solving Eq. (4.12) for ξ, we have rejected the solution $\xi = \dfrac{k-b}{m}\eta$ which does not meet the requirements of system stability.

Let us show that Eq. (4.13) does in fact cause $J(\xi)$ to be minimum. To this end we shall assume that instead of Eqs. (4.9) and (4.13) we have

$$\dot{\eta} = b\eta + m\xi, \quad \xi = q\eta$$

where q is as yet an unknown. Then

$$\eta = \eta_0 e^{(b+qm)t}$$

and, consequently, for a stable system, $(b + qm < 0)$

$$\Psi(\eta_0) = -\frac{(a + cq^2)\eta_0^2}{b + qm}.$$

We shall seek its extremum with respect to q. We have

$$\frac{d\Psi}{dq} = -\frac{cm\eta_0^2}{(b+qm)^2}\;(q - q_1)(q - q_2)$$

$$q_1, q_2 = -\frac{b \mp k}{m}$$

$$\frac{d^2\Psi}{dq^2} = -\frac{\eta_0^{\ 2}}{(b+qm)^3}[cm(2q - q_1 - q_2)(b + qm) - 2m^2c(q - q_1)(q - q_2)].$$

The expression $2m^2c(q - q_1)(q - q_2)$ does not affect the sign of $d^2\psi/dq^2$; on the other hand

$$\frac{cm(2q - q_1 - q_2)(b + qm)}{(b + qm)^3} = \frac{cm(2q - q_1 - q_2)}{(b + qm)^2} = \frac{2[q + (b/m)]cm}{(b + qm)^2}.$$

When $q = q_1$

$$2\left(q + \frac{b}{m}\right)cm = \frac{2kc}{1}.$$

When $q = q_2$

$$2\left(q + \frac{b}{m}\right)cm = -\frac{2kc}{1}.$$

Consequently

$$\frac{d^2\Psi}{dq^2} = \mp \frac{2\eta_0^{\ 2}k}{(b + qm)^2}$$

and the root $q_2 = -\dfrac{b + k}{m}$ ensures that $\psi(\eta_0)$ has minimum.

For what follows, it is important to write the form of the functional $\psi(\eta)$. After eliminating ξ from Eqs. (4.11) we find

$$a\eta^2 + b\eta\frac{\partial\Psi}{\partial\eta} = \frac{m^2}{4c}\left(\frac{\partial\Psi}{\partial\eta}\right)^2. \tag{4.14}$$

This nonlinear differential equation is satisfied by the integral

$$\Psi(\eta) = \frac{(b \pm k)c}{m^2}\eta^2 + B \tag{4.15}$$

where B is an arbitrary constant, which should be set equal to zero.

Let us return to Eqs. (4.9) and (4.10). Now, however, we shall study their solutions in the closed region $\bar{N}(\xi, \eta)$, which is characterized by the relation

$$|\xi| \leqslant \bar{\xi} \tag{4.16}$$

where $\bar{\xi}$ is a given positive number. Here we shall assume that the functions of comparison belong to class C, since the optimal solution of the problem can be on the boundary of the region (4.16). The case when η is continuous and ξ has discontinuities at a finite number of points is examined in Letov [20].

So we shall consider the single-valued nonlinear transformation

$$\xi = \varphi(\zeta). \tag{4.17}$$

The function $\varphi(\zeta)$ is continuous, differentiable, and thus defined:†

$$\varphi(\zeta) = \begin{cases} +\bar{\xi} & \text{when } \zeta > \zeta_* \\ \varphi(\zeta) & \text{when } |\zeta| \leqslant \zeta_* \\ -\bar{\xi} & \text{when } \zeta < -\zeta_* \end{cases} \tag{4.18}$$

The number ζ_* is defined by the form of $\varphi(\zeta)$. Transformation (4.17) translates the closed region $\bar{N}(\zeta, \eta)$ into the open region $N(\zeta, \eta)$, in which ζ takes over the role of control function, thus getting round the considerable difficulties involved in studying the functional equations, owing to the impossibility of differentiating with respect to ξ when $\xi = \bar{\xi}$.

The functional equations (4.11) will in the given case have the form

$$\begin{aligned} a\eta^2 + c\varphi^2(\zeta) + (b\eta + m\varphi(\zeta))\frac{\partial\psi}{\partial\eta} &= 0 \\ \left(2c\varphi(\zeta) + m\frac{\partial\psi}{\partial\eta}\right)\frac{\partial\varphi}{\partial\zeta} &= 0. \end{aligned} \tag{4.19}$$

The second of these equations breaks down into two equations:

$$2c\varphi(\zeta) + m\frac{\partial\psi}{\partial\eta} = 0 \tag{4.20}$$

$$\frac{\partial\varphi}{\partial\zeta} = 0. \tag{4.21}$$

Obviously, when $c \neq 0$, Eq. (4.20), in combination with the first equation (4.19), gives the already known solution (4.13). By force of Eqs. (4.17) and (4.18), this solution holds when

$$\left| -\frac{k+b}{m}\eta \right| \leqslant \zeta_*. \tag{4.22}$$

From Eq. (4.21) we find

$$\varphi(\zeta) = \pm\bar{\xi}. \tag{4.23}$$

Then the first equation (4.19) becomes the normal differential equation for the functional ψ, and has the following solution

$$\Psi = -\frac{a}{2b}\eta^2 + \frac{2ma\bar{\xi}}{b^2}\eta - \frac{am^2 + cb^2}{b^3}\bar{\xi}^2 \log|b\eta + m\bar{\xi}| + D. \tag{4.24}$$

For the purpose of analytic design, the expression for the functional (4.24) is needed only in order to make sure that it is continuous everywhere in $\bar{N}$. Before doing this, however, let us write the equation we have found

† We do not write any form of $\varphi(\zeta)$ precisely when $|\zeta| \leqslant \zeta_*$ as this is not necessary to our purpose.

for the regulator. It is

$$\xi = \begin{cases} +\bar{\xi} & \text{when} \quad -\dfrac{k+b}{m}\eta > \bar{\xi} \\ -\dfrac{k+b}{m}\eta & \text{when} \quad \left|-\dfrac{k+b}{m}\eta\right| \leqslant \bar{\xi} \\ -\bar{\xi} & \text{when} \quad -\dfrac{k+b}{m}\eta < -\bar{\xi}. \end{cases} \tag{4.25}$$

Now assume that the initial condition η_0 has sufficiently large absolute value and that the system has gone outside the boundary of the region $\bar{N}$. It is assumed that the system is stable.† For this case, the expression for the functional is given by Eq. (4.24), where D is an arbitrary constant. Then the functional $\psi(\eta)$ is a bounded and continuous function of η, since nowhere on the boundary does the expression $b\eta + m\xi$ become zero. When $|\eta| = \left|\dfrac{m}{k+b}\right|\bar{\xi}$, the function $\psi(\eta)$ of Eq. (4.15) must take the same value that is taken by the function $\psi(\eta)$ of (4.24) at this point. It is obvious that this can always be ensured by proper choice of the constant D.

Let us consider the general case, in which the disturbed motion of the plant is described by the equations

$$\dot{\eta}_k = \sum b_{k\alpha}\eta_\alpha + m_k\xi \qquad (k = 1, \ldots, n) \tag{4.26}$$

and we are looking for a function ξ that shall minimize the functional

$$J(\xi) = \int_0^\infty V\, dt, \quad \eta_k(0) = \eta_{k0} \tag{4.27}$$

where V is the positive definite quadratic form

$$V = \sum a_k\eta_k^2 + c\xi^2. \tag{4.28}$$

The functional is minimized in the class of functions C_1.

Bellman's general functional equation has the form

$$\Psi(\eta_{10}, \ldots, \eta_{n0}) = \min_{\xi}\int_0^\infty V(\eta_1, \ldots, \eta_n, \xi)\, dt. \tag{4.29}$$

As in the previous case, we arrive at Bellman's functional equation

$$0 = V + \sum_k\left(\sum_\alpha b_{k\alpha}\eta_\alpha + m_k\xi\right)\frac{\partial\psi}{\partial\eta_k}. \tag{4.30}$$

† See footnote, page 308.

Since the function ξ has to ensure minimum for the expression on the right side of Eq. (4.30), we have also

$$2c\xi + \sum m_k \frac{\partial \psi}{\partial \eta_k} = 0. \tag{4.31}$$

Thus the function ψ must satisfy the partial differential equation (4.30), and moreover we have to choose an integral such that relation (4.31) is fulfilled. In order to find such an integral, we shall simplify Eq. (4.30), making use of (4.31). We get

$$\sum a_k \eta_k^{\ 2} + \sum_k \sum_\alpha b_{k\alpha} \eta_\alpha \frac{\partial \psi}{\partial \eta_k} = \frac{1}{4c} \left(\sum_k m_k \frac{\partial \psi}{\partial \eta_k} \right)^2. \tag{4.32}$$

It is easily ascertained that this nonlinear partial differential equation is satisfied by the following integral

$$\Psi = \sum_k \sum_\alpha A_{k\alpha} \eta_k \eta_\alpha + B. \tag{4.33}$$

Here the $A_{k\alpha}$ are completely defined numbers, which can be found by substituting Eq. (4.33) into (4.32) and by matching the coefficients, B being an arbitrary constant.

Substitution of Eq. (4.33) into (4.31) determines the equation of the optimum controller

$$\xi = \sum p_\alpha \eta_\alpha. \tag{4.34}$$

We shall show that Eq. (4.34) is that same equation of the optimum controller which is given by methods based on the Calculus of Variations. To this end, we return to Eqs. (4.30) and (4.31).

Let us denote the right side of (4.30) by U. Taking (4.34) into consideration, we assume

$$U = U(\eta_1, \ldots, \eta_n) = \text{constant}. \tag{4.35}$$

Hence

$$dU = \sum_k \frac{\partial U}{\partial \eta_k} d\eta_k = 0. \tag{4.36}$$

Since Eqs. (4.26) and (4.34) define a set of independent solutions η_k, (4.36) will only hold when the following equations are satisfied

$$\frac{\partial U}{\partial \eta_k} = 0. \qquad (k = 1, \ldots, n) \tag{4.37}$$

Now let us denote

$$\lambda_k = -\frac{\partial \psi}{\partial \eta_k} \qquad (k = 1, \ldots, n) \tag{4.38}$$

and Eqs. (4.37) are written as

$$2a_k \eta_k - \sum_\alpha b_{\alpha k} \lambda_\alpha - \left[\sum_\alpha (b_{k\alpha} \eta_\alpha + m_k \xi) \right] \frac{\partial \lambda_k}{\partial \eta_k} = 0.$$

But taking into account Eq. (4.26)

$$\left[\sum_{\alpha}(b_{k\alpha}\eta_{\alpha}+m_k\xi)\right]\frac{\partial\lambda_k}{\partial\eta_k}=\dot{\lambda}_k \qquad (k=1,\ldots,n)$$

and thereafter (4.30), we find

$$\begin{aligned}\dot{\lambda}_k &= -\sum b_{k\alpha}\lambda_{\alpha}+2a_k\eta_k\\ 0 &= 2c\xi-\sum m_k\lambda_k.\end{aligned} \tag{4.39}$$

It follows from what has been said that the set of equations (4.39) is equivalent to the set of equations (4.30) and (4.31). But Eq. (4.39), in combination with (4.26), forms the equations of the variational problem solved in Letov [17]. The conclusion which has been drawn concerning (4.34) follows from this. We can now reach a second and no less important conclusion, namely, that Eqs. (4.26) and (4.31), as is shown in Letov [17], form in general a stable control system, optimizing the functional (4.27).

Let us return to Eqs. (4.26) and (4.27), assuming that the ξ coordinate shall be restricted by the inequality (4.16), and that the functional (4.27) is minimized for the class of functions C_1. Repeating the argument of page 307, we obtain the general functional equations in the form

$$\begin{aligned}&V+\sum_k\left(\sum_{\alpha}b_{k\alpha}\eta_{\alpha}+m_k\varphi(\zeta)\right)\frac{\partial\psi}{\partial\eta_k}=0\\ &\left[2c\varphi(\zeta)+\sum m_k\frac{\partial\psi}{\partial\eta_k}\right]\frac{\partial\varphi(\ )}{\partial\zeta}=0.\end{aligned} \tag{4.40}$$

As before, we obtain two solutions; the first, Eq. (4.34), for points such that $|\Sigma\, p_{\alpha}\eta_{\alpha}|\leqslant\bar{\xi}$ and the second solution is $\xi=\pm\bar{\xi}$ for points such that $|\Sigma\, p_{\alpha}\eta_{\alpha}|>\bar{\xi}$. In order to make certain that the first equation of (4.40) defines a continuous functional in both cases, we must find, in addition to solution (4.33), the solution of yet one more partial differential equation

$$\sum a_k\eta_k^{\ 2}+c\bar{\xi}^2+\sum_k\left(\sum_{\alpha}b_{k\alpha}\eta_{\alpha}\pm m_k\bar{\xi}\right)\frac{\partial\psi}{\partial\eta_k}=0. \tag{4.41}$$

We shall not dwell upon this.

It is evident from this comparison that the method of Dynamic Programming gives the same result as methods based on the Calculus of Variations. It enables us to obtain the law of control straight away in the form in which it is usually implemented with transducers, amplifiers, and servomotors.

In the case when we want to allow for velocity saturation of the servomotor in the class of functions A', we shall add to (4.26) the equation

$$\dot{\xi}=f(\sigma),\quad |f(\sigma)|\leqslant\bar{f} \tag{4.42}$$

where $f(\sigma)$ is a function of the class (A').

It is necessary for the function $f(\sigma)$ and its argument $\sigma = \sigma(\eta_1, \ldots, \eta_n, \xi)$ to be chosen so as to minimize the functional

$$J(\xi) = \int_0^\infty (V + \alpha\xi^2)\, dt, \quad \eta_k(0) = \eta_{k0}, \quad \xi(0) = \xi_0 \tag{4.43}$$

in class C of the functions $\eta_1, \ldots, \eta_n, \xi$.

Proceeding as before, we find Bellman's equations:

$$\begin{aligned} 0 &= V + \alpha f^2(\sigma) + f(\sigma)\frac{\partial\psi}{\partial\xi} + \sum_k \left(\sum_\alpha b_{k\alpha}\eta_\alpha + m_k\xi\right)\frac{\partial\psi}{\partial\eta_k} \\ 0 &= \left(2\alpha f(\sigma) + \frac{\partial\psi}{\xi}\right)\frac{\partial f}{\partial\sigma}. \end{aligned} \tag{4.44}$$

The solution sought consists of two parts. The first part is determined by a restriction, on speed $\partial f/\partial\sigma = 0$. This means that

$$f(\sigma) = \pm\bar{f}, \quad |\sigma| \geqslant \sigma^* \tag{4.45}$$

where σ^* is a positive number to be determined.

To find the second part of the solution we have

$$f(\sigma) = -\frac{1}{2\alpha}\frac{\partial\psi}{\partial\xi}. \tag{4.46}$$

In combination with the first equation (4.44), this gives a partial differential equation

$$V + \sum_k \left(\sum_\alpha b_{k\alpha}\eta_\alpha + m_k\xi\right)\frac{\partial\psi}{\partial\eta_k} = \frac{1}{4\alpha}\left(\frac{\partial\psi}{\partial\xi}\right)^2 \tag{4.47}$$

which is satisfied by the function

$$\Psi = \sum_k \sum_j A_{kj}\eta_k\eta_j + \xi\sum_k B_k\eta_k + R\xi^2. \tag{4.48}$$

We can find the coefficients of Eq. (4.48) by the method already described. Equation (4.46) gives a linear function $f(\sigma)$ when $|\sigma| < \sigma^*$, that is,

$$f(\sigma) = h\sigma, \quad \sigma = -\frac{1}{2\alpha h}\left[2R\xi + \sum_k B_k\eta_k\right]. \tag{4.49}$$

The quantity σ^* is determined from the condition $h\sigma^* = \bar{f}$.

As in the previous case, it can be shown that this solution of the problem exactly coincides with the solution obtained in Letov [17].

We shall now show that the connection between Liapunov functions and the present problem of optimization of the integrated square error is patently established by the equations derived in this chapter. Indeed, using Eq. (4.34), we shall calculate the total derivative of the ψ-function corresponding to (4.34). This function must be positive wherever $\Sigma\, \eta_k^2 \neq 0$. It will so be and will have meaning if the system of Eqs. (4.26) and (4.34) is stable.

Then the general functional equation (4.30) turns into our familiar equation in partial derivatives for the construction of Liapunov functions. The total derivative of the ψ-function is now determined by the formula

$$\frac{d\psi}{dt} = -V \tag{4.50}$$

so that ψ is a Liapunov function for our problem.

Conversely, assume that we have found the functional ψ of Eq. (4.33) by applying Dynamic Programming methods. If we are somehow able to ascertain that the ψ function is positive definite when $\Sigma\, \eta_k^2 \neq 0$, then it is a Liapunov function of the problem, and the conditions for which ψ is positive form the criterion of stability of the optimal system. This fact is particularly interesting to us, since it means that the method of Dynamic Programming enables us to solve at one and the same time the problems of optimization of a system with respect to the criterion (4.27) and of stability of the optimal system.

This is specially important in the case when the system to be optimized is nonlinear

$$\dot{\eta}_k = \Xi_k\, (\eta_1, \ldots, \eta_n, \xi) \tag{4.51}$$

as Bellman's general functional equation will be

$$0 = V + \sum_k \Xi_k \frac{\partial \psi}{\partial \eta_k} \tag{4.52}$$

and Eq. (4.50) will remain valid.

BIBLIOGRAPHY

1. Barbashin, E. A., "On Constructing Liapunov Functions for Nonlinear Systems," *Proceedings of the IFAC, Moscow, 1960*, Butterworths, 1961.
2. Barbashin, E. A., and Krasovskii, N. N., "On stability of motion as a whole," Doklady Akad. Nauk USSR **36**, No. 3 (1953).
3. Bellman, R., *Stability Theory of Differential Equations*, McGraw-Hill, 1953.
4. Bellman, R., *Dynamic Programming*, Princeton, 1957.
5. Chetaev, N. G., *Stability of Motion* (Ustoichivost' dvizheniya), Gostekhizdat, 1955, translation, Pergamon, 1961.
6. Chzhan Zhen' Wei, "Stability of a control system having two nonlinear elements," Avtomat. i telemekh. (1960).
7. Duboshin, G. N., *Foundations of the Theory of Stability of Motion* (Osnovy teorii ustoichivosti dvizheniya), Moscow State University, 1952.
8. Erugin, N. P., "A problem of the theory of stability of automatic control systems," Priklad. mat. i mekh. **16,** No. 5 (1952).

9. Kalman, R. E., and Bertram, J. E., "Control system analysis and design via the second method of Liapunov," J. Basic Eng. (June, 1960).
10. Krasovskii, N. N., "Stability in the case of large initial disturbances," Priklad. mat. i mekh. **21,** No. 3 (1957).
11. Krasovskii, N. N., "A problem of optimal control," Priklad. mat. i mekh. **23,** No. 1 (1959).
12. Krasovskii, N. N., "Some problems of the theory of stability of motion (Nekotorye zadachi teorii ustoichivosti dvisheniya)," Fizmatgiz (1959).
13. Krasovskii, N. N., "The Choice of Parameters for Optimal Stable Systems," *Proceedings of the IFAC, Moscow, 1960*, Butterworths, 1961.
14. LaSalle, J. P., and Lefschetz, S., *Stability by Liapunov's Direct Method with Applications*, Academic, 1961.
15. Letov, A. M., "Inherently unstable control systems," Priklad. mat. i mekh. 14, No. 2 (1950).
16. Letov, A. M., "Die Stabilität von Regelsystemen mit nachgebender Rückführung," *Regelunstechnik, Moderne Theorien und ihre Verwendbarkeit*, Munich, 1957.
17. Letov, A. M., "The analytical design of control systems, I, II, III," Avtomat. i telemekh. **21,** Nos. 4, 5, 6 (1960).
18. Letov, A. M., *Stability in Nonlinear Control Systems* (Ustoichivost' nelineinykh reguliruemykh sistem), Gostekhizdat, 1955; translation, Princeton, 1961.
19. Letov, A. M., "The analytic design of regulators. Method of dynamic programming, IV," Avtomat. i telemekh. **22,** No. 4 (1961).
20. Letov, A. M., "The analytic design of regulators of discontinuous characteristics, VI," Avtomat. i telemekh. **22,** No. 10 (1961).
21. Letov, A. M., and Lur'e, A. I., "The present state and problems of the development of the theory of stability of automatic control systems. Fundamental problems of automatic control and regulation (Sostoyanie i zadachi razvitiya teorii ustoichivosti sistem avtomaticheskogo regulirovaniya. Osnovhye problemy avtomaticheskogo upravleniya i regulirovaniya)," Izvest. Akad. Nauk SSSR (1957).
22. Liapunov, A. M., *The General Problem of Stability of Motion* (Obshchays zadacha ob ustoichivosti dvizheniya), Gostekhizdat, 1950.
23. Lur'e, A. I., *Some Nonlinear Problems in the Theory of Automatic Control* (Nekotorye nelineinye zadachi teorii avtomaticheskogo regulirovaniya), Gostekhizdat, 1951.
24. Malkin, I. G., *Theory of Stability of Motion* (Teoriia ustoichivosti dvizhemiia), Gostekhizdat, 1952.
25. Tsypkin, Ya. A., and Bromberg, P. V., "On the degree of stability of linear systems (o stepeni ustoichivosti lineinykh sistem)," Izvest. Akad. Nauk SSSR OTN, No. 12 (1945).
26. von Hahn, W., *Theorie und Anwendung der Direkten Methode von Liapunov*, Springer, 1959.
27. Zubov, V. I., "Some sufficient conditions of stability of nonlinear systems of differential equations," Priklad. mat. i mekh. **17,** No. 4 (1953).
28. Zubov, V. I., *The Methods of A. N. Liapunov and Their Application* (Metody A. N. Liapunov iikh primenenie), Leningrad State University, 1957.

CHAPTER VII

Optimal Systems

ALEXANDER A. FELDBAUM

CONTENTS

1. Types of Optimal Systems

At the present time, problems of the design of optimal systems, that is, systems which are the best in some particular sense, are becoming crucial in the theory and technology of automatic control. Any scientifically based system is optimal, since in choosing a system we are, *ipso facto*, preferring it to others; we regard it, then, as better in some respect than other systems. The criteria which dictate our choice, which we shall call in future the criteria of optimality, can be various. When any choice is made, however, there must always be, in the last resort, a criterion of optimality: otherwise, rational choice is impossible.

Before automatic control had been introduced into industry, while technology was still based to a considerable extent on people's experience and skill, and measurement and computation techniques were less developed than they are today, attempts to determine precise criteria of optimality and to construct optimal systems were often useless. But we are now entering upon a new epoch—the epoch of scientifically designed automated industrial processes, and problems of optimal control are becoming central.

Figure 1 is the block diagram of an automatic control system. A is the controller, and B the plant. The plant can be of any kind; it can be, for instance, a rolling mill or a chemical reactor; it may be a whole industrial process, or it may be a single motor. At the output of B there appears the quantity x which may represent the production parameters of the plant, or, in the general case, the parameters characterizing its state. Generally there are several such parameters $x_1, \ldots, x_n$. It is convenient to regard these quantities as the coordinates of a vector $\mathbf{x}$:

$$\mathbf{x} = (x_1, \ldots, x_n). \tag{1.1}$$

We shall call $\mathbf{x}$ the output vector or output quantity of B. It is also called the controlled quantity.

A plant input u is supplied to B by the controller A. If there are several such inputs $u_1, u_2, \ldots, u_r$, we shall unify them in a vector $\mathbf{u}$ with coordinates u_j $(j = 1, \ldots, r)$:

$$\mathbf{u} = (u_1, \ldots, u_r). \tag{1.2}$$

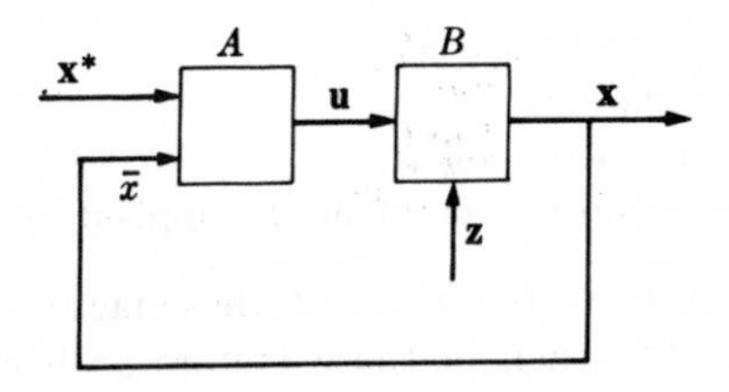

FIGURE 1.

A command signal x^* is applied to the input of the controller A. This is an instruction as to what the output x of the plant must be. The instruction may be a collection of n-quantities $x_1^*, \ldots, x_n^*$, which we shall agree to regard as the coordinates of a vector $\mathbf{x}^*$:

$$\mathbf{x}^* = (x_1^*, \ldots, x_n^*). \tag{1.3}$$

For instance, it may be required that in the ideal case the conditions $x_1 = x_i^*$ $(i = 1, \ldots, n)$ be satisfied, where x_i^* are specified functions of time. The x_i^* are also called desired outputs.

In the general case, the controller A obtains information, by way of a feedback line, on the actual value of $\mathbf{x}$. If this does not answer to the requirements, the device A acts upon the plant B in such a way as to bring $\mathbf{x}$ closer to these requirements.

A departure of $\mathbf{x}$ from the requirements may occur, perhaps, as the result of the effect on B of some unforeseen and uncontrollable disturbance z, which affects $\mathbf{x}$. If different parts of B are affected by disturbances $z_1, \ldots, z_l$, we shall represent them by a vector $\mathbf{z}$:

$$\mathbf{z} = (z_1, \ldots, z_l). \tag{1.4}$$

Usually the plant B is given, and its properties must not vary. The controller A, however, is entirely unspecified, and its properties can be selected from within a very wide range. It is required to design a controller A which shall act upon a given plant B in what is, in some known sense, the best possible way.

In practice, a number of separate requirements, having no direct bearing upon B, are usually made upon the device A. For instance, it may be required that A be sufficiently reliable and not too complex, or that its weight and over-all size not be too great. To render calculation easier, or for other reasons, A may be assumed to be linear, or its general structure may be specified beforehand, leaving only the parameters of individual elements as unknowns. We shall consider below, however, only those theories in which requirements and restrictions concerned directly with the device A are lacking. We shall assume that, if required, this device can be of any kind—extremely complex, for instance. But in this case the operation of the optimal device is determined solely by the following factors relating to the plant B and to the nature of its connection with A:

(1) the characteristics of B;
(2) the requirements made upon B;
(3) the nature of the information about B supplied to the controller A.

If the problem is to be stated in detail, these factors must be examined in detail. We can visualize each of these factors as being measured along a coordinate axis orthogonal to the other two, as is shown in Fig. 2.

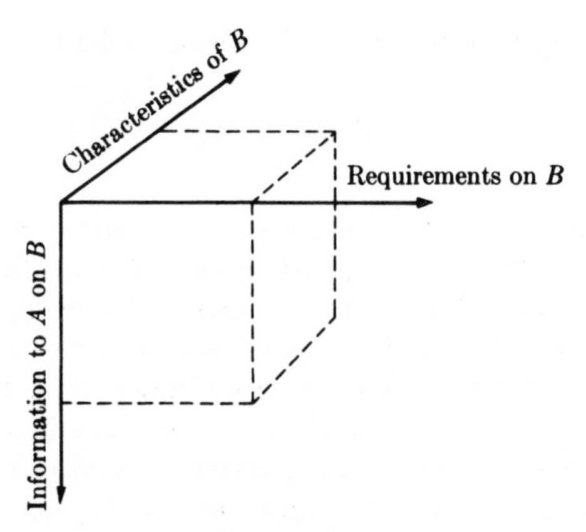

FIGURE 2.

Optimal systems may be classified according to these coordinate axes. A classification of this kind is useful in that it allows the nature of every type of optimal system to be correctly determined with reference to the other types. Examination of all possible types of optimal systems from general viewpoints discloses the unity of the fundamental concepts of the theory, in spite of differences between the individual types.

The first axis shown in Fig. 2 is the classification by the characteristics of the plant. It is obvious from Fig. 1 that a plant is characterized by the dependence of its output quantity $\mathbf{x}$ on the input quantities $\mathbf{u}$ and $\mathbf{z}$. We shall represent this dependence symbolically by

$$\mathbf{x} = \mathbf{F}(\mathbf{u}, \mathbf{z}). \tag{1.5}$$

In the general case, $\mathbf{F}$ is an operator, i.e., the law of correspondence between two sets of functions. For instance, in Eq. (1.5) the vector function $\mathbf{x}$ is dependent on the forms of the vector functions $\mathbf{u}$ and $\mathbf{z}$. The operator $\mathbf{F}$ of the plant B can be specified in various ways—using equations, graphs, or tables. Often this dependence is given in the form of differential equations, such as

$$\begin{aligned} \frac{dx_1}{dt} &= f_1(x_1, \ldots, x_n; u_1, \ldots, u_r; t), \\ &\cdots\cdots\cdots\cdots\cdots\cdots \\ \frac{dx_n}{dt} &= f_n(x_1, \ldots, x_n; u_1, \ldots, u_r; t). \end{aligned} \tag{1.6}$$

Here the f_i are, in the general case, nonlinear functions of $x_1, \ldots, x_n$, $u_1, \ldots, u_r$, and of time t. Introducing the vector notation

$$\frac{d\mathbf{x}}{dt} = \left(\frac{dx_1}{dt}, \ldots, \frac{dx_n}{dt}\right); \quad \mathbf{f} = (f_1, \ldots, f_n) \tag{1.7}$$

we can rewrite Eq. (1.6) in the more compact and all-encompassing vector form

$$\frac{d\mathbf{x}}{dt} = \mathbf{f}(\mathbf{x}, \mathbf{u}, t). \tag{1.8}$$

Here the vector $\mathbf{f}$ is a vector function of the vectors $\mathbf{x}$ and $\mathbf{u}$ and of the scalar t. Equations (1.6) or (1.8), with given initial conditions $x_i(0)$, $(i = 1, \ldots, n)$, enable us to find $\mathbf{x}(t)$, provided that $\mathbf{u}(t)$ be given.

The operators of plants can be classified in various very different ways. We shall touch upon only a few lines of classification here. First of all, let us consider the division into continuous, discrete-continuous, and discrete systems. In the first of these types of systems, quantities are considered at any instant of time; they can vary continually, and can, in general, have any level. Thus these quantities are not quantized with respect to either time or level. The solutions $x_1, \ldots, x_n$ of Eq. (1.6), which are functions of the continuous time t, are such quantities.

Not all types of system are like this, however. In pulsed and digital systems, and also when pulsed modulation is used for the transmission of signals, only the values of the quantities at discrete instants of time $t = t_0, t_1, t_2, \ldots$ are of interest. If all levels of the variables are admissible, the latter are quantized for time, but not for level. Such systems are said to be discrete-continuous.

Finally, in systems of the third type, only discrete levels are admitted. These levels may equal, for instance, la where a is a constant and l is an integer number. Systems in which the magnitudes are quantized for both time and level are called discrete (or purely discrete).

The majority of the specialized literature is devoted to continuous optimal systems [2, 8, 10–12, 14, 28–31, 40, 41, 44, 45, 49, 51, 53–56, 63, 64, 66], etc.† Discrete-continuous systems are considered [3, 4, 21, 25, 26, 33, 34, 46, 48, 60, 61, 65, 70–72]. Eaton and Zadeh [27] deal with purely discrete optimal systems.

Plants can also be classified according to the types of their equations. In most of the papers dealing with optimal systems, plants with lumped parameters are examined; the motion of such plants is described by ordinary differential equations. However, a number of problems have been stated [15] and solved [16, 33], for plants with distributed parameters, which are described by partial differential equations or integral equations.

The characteristics of the plant B also include *restrictions* of a different kind. The plant inputs $u_1, \ldots, u_r$ composing the vector $\mathbf{u}$ (see Fig. 1) cannot have unrestricted values. They cannot or must not exceed certain limits. Very often the restrictions have the form

$$|u_1| \leqslant U_1; \ldots |u_r| \leqslant U_r. \tag{1.9}$$

† Numbers in brackets refer to the bibliography at the end of this chapter.

The case where the functions of several plant inputs are restricted is possible, for example,

$$\sum_{\nu=1}^{r} \lambda_\nu^2 u_\nu^2 \leqslant N \tag{1.10}$$

where λ_ν^2 and N are constants.

Let us imagine an r-dimensional space with Cartesian coordinates $u_1, \ldots, u_r$, and a vector $\mathbf{u}$ in this space. Conditions (1.9) or (1.10) are special cases of the conditions restricting the location of the vector $\mathbf{u}$ to a certain admissible region $\Omega(\mathbf{u})$ of this r-dimensional space. The expression $\mathbf{u}$ belongs to the region $\Omega(\mathbf{u})$ and is written symbolically as

$$\mathbf{u} \in \Omega(\mathbf{u}). \tag{1.11}$$

In the particular case (1.9), the vector $\mathbf{u}$ is restricted to an r-dimensional parallelepiped, and in the case of Eq. (1.10), to an r-dimensional ellipsoid in the $\mathbf{u}$-space.

Constraints can be laid not only on the plant inputs u_j, but also on the coordinates x_i, $(i = 1, \ldots, n)$, of B. Certain specified functions of these coordinates, $H_\mu(\mathbf{x})$, must not exceed certain limits, which, without restriction of generality, we can accept as being zero

$$H_\mu(\mathbf{x}) \leqslant 0. \qquad (\mu = 1, \ldots, m) \tag{1.12}$$

The functions $H_\mu(\mathbf{x})$ may be regarded as the coordinates of an m-dimensional vector $\mathbf{H}(\mathbf{x})$. Conditions (1.12) lay restrictions on the location of this vector. If $\mathbf{H}$ is a single-valued function of $\mathbf{x}$, then conditions (1.12) mean that the vector $\mathbf{x}$ too is restricted within the $\mathbf{x}$-space to a certain admissible region $\Omega(\mathbf{x})$

$$\mathbf{x} \in \Omega(\mathbf{x}). \tag{1.13}$$

In the most general case, what is restricted is a certain operator L of $\mathbf{u}(t)$ and $\mathbf{x}(t)$

$$L[\mathbf{u}(t), \mathbf{x}(t), t] \in \Omega(L) \tag{1.14}$$

where $\Omega(L)$ is the admissible region of variation of the operator. The restriction may be, perhaps

$$\int_0^T u^2(t)\, dt \leqslant N \tag{1.15}$$

where T and N are constants.

This and other more complex restrictions are considered by Rozenman [64]. The discrete-continuous variant of constraint (1.15) is examined by Kalman and Koepcke [46] and Tsypkin [71].

Restrictions of the type (1.11) or (1.13) are of the greatest importance in the design of control systems. For example, suppose that we are required to construct a servomechanism using a dc motor in which the time of the transient process shall be minimum. In theory, by applying voltages as great as is desired to the armature circuit, we can create currents, torques, and accelerations as great as is desired, and can make the time of the transient process as small as is desired. However, the only admissible processes are those in which the armature current and the velocity of the motor shaft do not exceed certain known limits. This very fact creates a lower limit for the time of the transient process. It is usually the presence of restrictions which gives meaning, in most cases, to the problem of the optimal system. The solution of this problem has to answer the question: how are the best results to be attained with limited resources?

Only restrictions of the type (1.11) are considered in the following. The case of constraint (1.13), which is of great practical importance, can be investigated with the aid of the theory presented by Gamkrelidze [42].

The characteristics of a disturbance $\mathbf{z}$ acting upon the plant can also be referred to the characteristics of B; see Fig. 1 and Eqs. (1.4) and (1.5). Sometimes the characteristics of the disturbance are simply included in the plant operator. If, for instance, the $\mathbf{z}_\nu$ are known functions of time, $(\nu = 1, \ldots, l)$, the expressions for them can be substituted in the equation of the plant B, so that these equations will depend explicitly on time; see, for example, Eq. (1.6). For methodological purposes, it is convenient to consider the unforeseen disturbances z_ν as extraneous signals applied to the plant from without, and to include all those disturbances which are assumed to be known into the operator.

The disturbances z_ν can combine with other signals, such as the u_j applied to an element of B. But they can also act in another way, by altering the coefficients of the equations of the elements, or their parameters. Signals of this kind are called parametric. Both kinds are considered in the theory. In nonlinear systems, there is usually no clear-cut difference between these types of signals.

We shall assume that the disturbances z_ν are unforeseen, that is, random. They can be random quantities or random processes. In the first case, the z_ν are constant throughout one process in the system; in the second, the z_ν are random functions of time.

It sometimes happens that the random disturbances z_ν do not enter explicitly into the conditions of a problem. But if $\mathbf{z}$ is random, then for a given $\mathbf{u}$ [see Eq. (1.5)] the output of B will be a random quantity or a random process. The probability characteristics of this process can be calculated, superseding the specification of both the operator $\mathbf{F}$ and the characteristics of the random disturbance $\mathbf{z}$. The plant is characterized in this way in Eaton and Zadeh [27], for instance.

Let us return to the classification by the requirements imposed upon B; see Fig. 2. The purpose of control can be formulated, in every case, as the requirement that some quantity Q should attain an extremum. This will be either a maximum or a minimum, depending on the requirement. In the general case, the criterion of optimality Q is dependent on both the command input $\mathbf{x}^*$ and the plant output $\mathbf{x}$ (and sometimes also on $\mathbf{u}$ and $\mathbf{z}$). To fix ideas, let it be required that $Q(\mathbf{x}, \mathbf{x}^*)$ be minimal

$$Q(\mathbf{x}, \mathbf{x}^*) = \min. \tag{1.16}$$

This expression is an analytic statement of the purpose of control. We note that Q is a functional, that is, a number depending on the form of the functions $\mathbf{x}$ and $\mathbf{x}^*$. For example, in a particular case, let

$$Q = \int_0^T [x(t) - x^*(t)]^2 \, dt \tag{1.17}$$

where T is a fixed quantity. It is obvious that Q depends on the form of the curves $x(t)$ and $x^*(t)$.

Various technical or economic indices can be selected as the criterion Q—such as the productivity of the plant, or the quality of the production, the consumption of raw material or of electrical energy, etc. The choice of a criterion of optimality Q, which is dictated by the actual technical and economic conditions, lies outside the scope of a theory of optimal systems, and will not be discussed in this chapter.

From the equation for Q, we can not only learn the possible minimum value $Q_{\min}$, but we can also evaluate the deterioration of the system as it departs from the ideal. The difference $(Q - Q_{\min})$ is the measure of deterioration.

According to the nature of the criterion Q, three main types of optimal systems can be distinguished:

(1) uniformly optimal systems;
(2) statistically optimal systems;
(3) minimax optimal systems.

In systems of the first type, every individual process is optimal. In minimum response time systems [10, 29–31, 51] the plant arrives at the required state in minimum time, whatever the initial conditions or command signals (the latter must belong to some given class of admissible signals).

It can be said that the uniformly optimal system copes with its problem in the best possible way in every individual case.

In systems of the second type, the best possible behavior is not required, or cannot be guaranteed, in every individual process. The criterion of optimality Q corresponding to this type of system is of a statistical nature. Such systems have to be best on the average. Statistical criteria are applicable to systems in which random factors are present. A simple special case leading to a system of this kind is the problem of choosing the parameters $a_1, \ldots, a_k$ of a controller A, whose the general structure is given. Let us assume the primary criterion of quality to be some scalar function

$$Q_1 = Q_1(\bar{a}_1, \ldots, a_k, x_1^0, \ldots, x_n^0) = Q_1(\mathbf{a}, \mathbf{x}^0) \tag{1.18}$$

where $\mathbf{x}^0 = (x_1^0, \ldots, x_n^0)$ is the vector of the initial conditions x_i^0 of a plant B of Eq. (1.6), and $\mathbf{a} = (a_1, \ldots, a_k)$ is the vector of the parameters.

The criterion Q_1 cannot be used directly for the selection of the parameters a_i, since values of $\mathbf{a}$ which are the best for one type of initial conditions $\mathbf{x}_0$ may not be the best for another type. However, if we know the *a priori* probability density $P(\mathbf{x}^0)$ for the initial condition vector, then the expected value of Q_1 can serve as the criterion Q. We shall denote the expected value by E. Then

$$Q = E\{Q_1\} = \int_{\Omega(\mathbf{x}^0)} Q_1(\mathbf{a}, \mathbf{x}^0)P(\mathbf{x}^0)\, d\Omega(\mathbf{x}^0) \tag{1.19}$$

In this equation, $\Omega(\mathbf{x}^0)$ is the region of variation of the vector $\mathbf{x}^0$, and $d\Omega(\mathbf{x}^0)$ is an infinitesimally small portion of it. With this statement of the problem, we shall consider that system optimal whose parameters a_i correspond to a minimum of Q (allowing, in the general case, for supplementary restrictions as well). Optimal systems with statistical criteria are considered [1, 4, 5, 9, 27, 33, 34, 37, 39, 50, 61].

Systems of the third type, which we are calling minimax optimal systems, secure a better result compared with another system only in the worst case, i.e., under the most adverse conditions. In other words, the worst result in a minimax optimal system is better than the worst result in any other system. This statement of the problem is sometimes appropriate in the case when *a priori* probability distributions are lacking. Some examples of problems of this kind are given by Bellman [4].

The nature of the requirements made of the system is determined to a considerable extent by the form of the function $\mathbf{x}^*$ [see Eq. (1.14)] into which enters all that is unforeseen in the purpose of control. If $\mathbf{x}^*$ is a regular function known beforehand, it can enter into the composition of the functional Q, and will not appear in explicit form. However, in practice, the purpose of control is often not known beforehand. This is the situation, for instance, when a target, the future movements of which are unknown, is being tracked.

An important axis of classification is the nature of the information on the plant B supplied to the controller A. In any automatic system, the controller has to solve two closely connected problems, which are, however, different in kind. In the first place, on the basis of the information supplied, it learns the properties and the state of B. In the second place, on the basis of properties of the plant found by studying, it decides what action must be taken for successful control. The first problem is that of *studying* the plant; the second is that of *forcing* the plant to behave as required. In systems of the simplest types, solution of one of these problems may be lacking, or may have a very elementary form. In complex cases, the controller has to solve both problems.

An analogy can be drawn between the operation of the controller A and man, who interacts with his environment. Man studies the environment in order to act upon it in a sense useful to himself. But sometimes he acts upon the environment not in order to obtain immediate benefit, but with the aim of studying it better. Thus his action upon his environment and study of it are closely interconnected.

The process of studying B is clearly similar to the process of acquiring new knowledge and understanding by man. This knowledge can be received ready-made in the form of information supplied by somebody else; it can be acquired by observation; finally, it can be obtained as the result of an experiment. Optimal systems can also be divided into three types, according to the methods of obtaining knowledge indicated above:

(1) optimal systems with complete (or maximal) information on the plant;
(2) optimal systems with incomplete information on the plant, and with independent, or passive, accumulation of information during the control process;
(3) optimal systems with incomplete information on the plant, and with active accumulation of information during the control process (dual control).

To understand this classification, it is essential to define what we mean by "information on the plant." From what has been said (see also Fig. 1), it is clear that the information on the plant is the sum of the following:

(1) information on its operator, i.e., on Eq. (1.5);
(2) information on the disturbance $\mathbf{z}$ acting upon B;
(3) information on the state of B, for instance, on the coordinates of a point, representing this state, in the phase space;
(4) information on the purpose of control, i.e., on the functional Q; see Eq. (1.16);
(5) information on the command signal $\mathbf{x}^*$.

Complete information on any relation implies that it is known with absolute accuracy. For instance, complete information on some function of time $f(\tau)$ means that its values are known for $-\infty < \tau < \infty$. In the existing theories of optimal systems, it is assumed that complete information is on hand concerning the operator $\mathbf{F}$ of the plant and the purpose of control, i.e., concerning the form of the functional Q. However, the remaining three kinds of information can take very various forms. Consider, for instance, open-loop systems. In these systems, the output $\mathbf{x}$ of the plant B (see Fig. 1) is not supplied to the input of the controller A; in such a case, information on the state of B is lacking.

Until recently, the different groups of theories of optimal systems have been developed sometimes completely independently and in isolation from one another. The first group consists of theories of optimal systems in which the controller holds complete information on the plant. In these works [2, 7, 10, 11, 14, 28–31, 40–42, 44–46, 48, 49, 51, 53–56, 62, 64–66], and others,

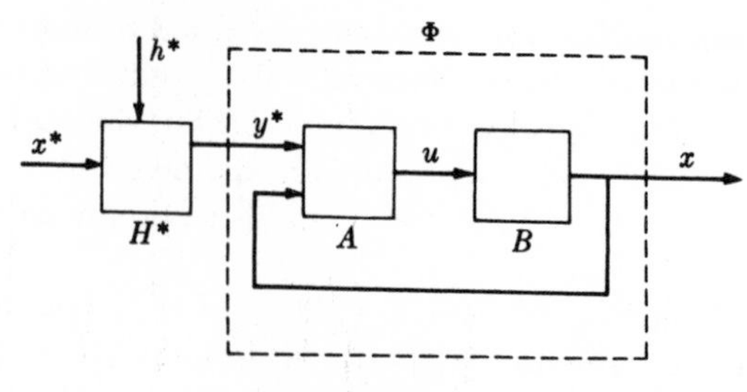

FIGURE 3.

it is assumed either that the controller receives complete information on the signals **z** and **x***, or that **z** and **x*** are known beforehand. In addition, A obtains from B, by way of a feedback loop, complete information on the current state of the plant. When the input signals **u** and **z** are known, this is equivalent to complete information on the future behavior of the plant.

In the second group of theories of optimal systems, only the statistical characteristics of the input signals are assumed to be known. The fundamental problem considered in these theories has reference to the system shown in the block diagram of Fig. 3. First the system as a whole is regarded as a filter Φ. A command input x^* enters this filter, not directly, but by way of a communication channel, or, in general, by way of some system H^*, where it is mixed with a random disturbance or noise h^*. Thus, what arrives at the input of the filter Φ is a mixture of signal and noise, y^*. The filter's problem is to deliver at its output a quantity x which shall be as close as possible, in some statistical sense, to x^* or to the result of some stated transformation of x^*.

If an optimal filter Φ from the class of linear systems is specified, its subsequent breakdown into the controller A and the plant B does not generally present any theoretical difficulties, especially if A and B are connected in a closed-loop system, see Fig. 3. If the filter Φ is nonlinear, the problem of breakdown becomes more complicated.

The second group of optimal systems is characterized by the fact that the process of accumulating information on a signal x^* does not depend on the strategy, or, as it is sometimes called, the algorithm (law of operation) of the controller A. Accumulation of information is effected by *observing* the values of y^* and constructing a hypothesis concerning the process x^* in accordance with these observations. Such systems may be called optimal systems with passive or independent accumulation of information.

It is useful to distinguish the following variant ways of specifying the characteristics of the signal x^*.

(1) $x^*(t)$ is a regular function belonging to some class of known functions, and h^* is a random function whose probability characteristics are known. In this case, the longer the observation of y^* at the output of the channel H^* is carried on, the more precise will be the prediction of the future behavior of $x^*(t)$.

(2) $x^*(t)$ is a random function with given probability characteristics. In this case, it is only possible to make a prognosis of a statistical nature concerning the future behavior of $x^*(t)$; observation of $y^*(t)$ helps to make these prognoses more accurate.

(3) $x^*(t)$ is a random function with unknown or partly known probability characteristics. In this case, observation of $y^*(t)$ should result in the discovery of closer definition of the probability characteristics of $x^*(t)$, which enables prognosis of the future behavior of $x^*(t)$ to be more accurate [9, 37].

We shall not consider theories of the second group, as they concern open-loop systems (see Fig. 3), whereas in this chapter we are investigating feedback systems.

In Feldbaum [33, 34], some problems belonging to the third group are considered. This group has features common to the first and second groups, and thus unifies them to a certain extent. However, the third group has its own specific features, which are absent from the first two groups.

The block diagram considered in Feldbaum [33, 34] is shown in Fig. 4. The control signal u enters the plant B by way of the transmission channel G, where it mixes with the random noise g. Thus the signal v at the input of B is not, as a rule, equal to u. Furthermore, information on the state of the plant, x, passes through the transmission channel H, where it mixes with the random noise h and, transformed into y, enters the input of the controller A.

In the closed-loop system of Fig. 4, processes which have no analogs in open loop systems are possible. In the diagram of Fig. 4, the disturbance $\bar{z}$, that is, essentially, the unpredictably varying characteristics of B, can be studied not by passive observation, but actively, by means of rational experiments. The plant is, as it were, excited by a signal of a perceptual nature, and the results of these excitations, y, are analyzed by the controller A. The purpose of these signals is to promote faster and more accurate investigation of the characteristics of the plant, leading to the development of a better law for its control.

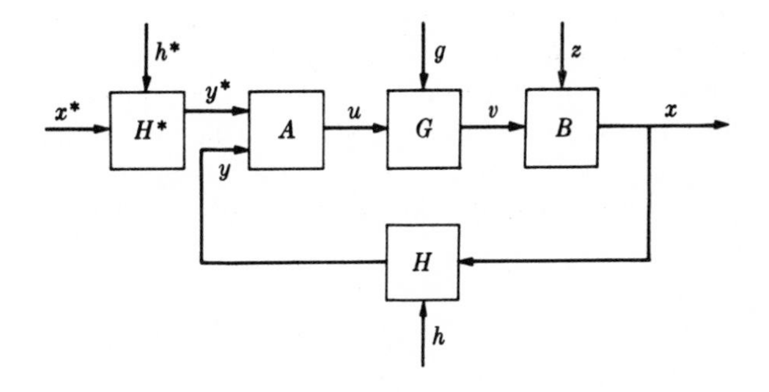

FIGURE 4.

However, a control signal is necessary not only in order to *investigate* the plant, but also in order to *direct* it into the required state. Thus in the diagram of Fig. 4, the control signals have to be of double, *dual* nature; to some extent they are investigatory, but also to some extent directing. It is for this reason that the theory of such systems is called [34] the theory of dual control. The twofold nature of the control is the fundamental physical fact distinguishing the third group of theories of optimal systems from the first two. In the first of these, dual control is not necessary, since the controller has complete information on the plant without this. In the second group, dual control is impossible, since information is accumulated by observation only, and the tempo of its accumulation is entirely independent of the strategy of the controller.

If signals arrive by several channels, the quantities in Fig. 4 can be replaced by vectors [34]. The extraneous signals $\mathbf{x}^*$ and $\mathbf{z}$ can be distinguished as in open-loop systems; see above.

It is evident from what has been said that the kaleidoscopic diversity of the types of optimal systems is no bar to their systematization within the framework of a classification of modest size. This unifies the approach to the problems of optimal systems. It is now even becoming possible to construct a single general theory of optimal systems, based on variational methods—Dynamic Programming and the Maximum Principle. It would be a useful preliminary, however, to construct a rather narrow particular class of problems in the theory of continuous minimum-response time systems, when complete information on the plant B is held in the controller A.

2. Minimum Response Time Systems

This class of closed-loop systems, owing to its great practical importance, was the first to be studied. As early as 1935 a patent [57] was taken out for a system for reversing the rollers of a rolling mill, whose maximum acceleration was succeeded by maximum braking; this system secured, for the case in question, shortest time of the transient processes. A similar principle was applied somewhat later in the Speedomax potentiometer made by Leeds and Northrup (United States). Theoretical works began to appear later. It was proved [28], for a linear plant of the second order (the roots of its characteristic equation are assumed zero), that the optimal policy in eliminating the initial error consisted of two intervals. In the first, the plant input u, restricted by the condition

$$|u| \leqslant U \tag{2.1}$$

is held at one of its limits, let us say, $u = +U$. In the second interval, u is held at the other limit level, $u = -U$. The optimal trajectories in the phase plane are examined by Feldbaum [28].

In Hopkin [44], optimal trajectories for various initial conditions are considered in the phase plane; also the theoretical results are compared with the results obtained by simulation.

In Lerner [55], the problem is stated generally for an nth order system eliminating an initial error (one type of initial condition), and it is suggested that in this case, too, the absolute value of the plant input should be held at the maximum admissible level.

In Feldbaum [29], the general concept of an optimal process in an n-dimensional space is stated for any initial conditions and admissible plant inputs. In the same paper, the theorem of the n-intervals is formulated and proved; see the following. This method made it possible for a method to be devised [31] for synthesizing a given class of optimal systems of the nth order. The presentation in this section is based on Feldbaum [28, 29, 31].

Also, in 1953, Bushaw carried out work, not published at that time [14], in which he determined the optimal policy for a second-order plant whose characteristic equation has complex-conjugate roots.

Beginning in 1954, the flow of papers on the theory of optimal systems of the type indicated above began to swell rapidly [8, 19, 23, 43, 54, 56, 68]. At the same time, methods of creating systems close to the optimal were being developed. We shall not concern ourselves with these methods, since an account of them would involve an excessive lengthening of this chapter; see, for instance, Feldbaum [32].

We shall present the problem in detail. Let a plant be described by Eqs. (1.6) or (1.8). Moreover, let the ideal process be one for which the equalities

$$x_i(t) = x_i^*(t) \tag{2.2}$$

hold. Here, the $x_i(t)$ are the coordinates of the plant, and the $x_i^*(t)$ are given functions of time, subject to certain restrictions which are formulated below. Consider the n-dimensional phase space of the vector $\mathbf{x}$, see Fig. 5, with

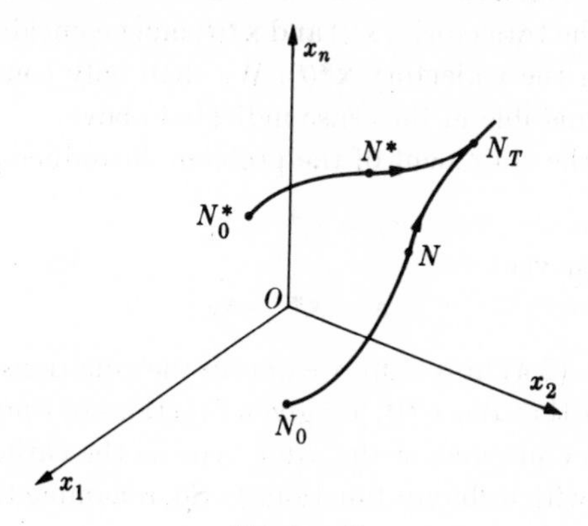

FIGURE 5.

coordinates $x_1, \ldots, x_n$. If the state of the plant changes in exact correspondence with the ideal conditions (2.2), the phase trajectory, the hodograph of the vector $\mathbf{x}^*$, will be, let us say, the trajectory $N_0{}^*N^*N_T$. Let N^* be the position of the representative point at the current instant of time $t > 0$, and let $N_0{}^*$ be its position at the initial instant of time $t = 0$. We shall assume, however, that the actual state of the plant at the instant of time $t = 0$ is given by the representative point N_0, not coinciding with $N_0{}^*$, and the actual state at the instant $t > 0$ by the point N, and that the phase trajectory of the plant has the form of the curve N_0NN_T. The control system operates in such a way as to reconcile the actual state N with the required state N^*. Let the points N and N^* be coincident when $t = T$ at the position N_T, and let their motion thereafter be identical. This means that when $t > T$ the state of the plant is exactly equal to the required state. The transient process, that is, the process of transition from the initial state of the plant to the required state, thus lasts during an interval of time equal to T. A system is called "minimum response time" when the time of the transient process is *minimal*

$$T = \min. \tag{2.3}$$

In such a system, the process $\mathbf{x}(t)$ is called an optimal process, and the control signal $\mathbf{u}(t)$ is called optimal. To find the optimal process, we must solve the problem of the swiftest meeting of the points N and N^* in the phase space.

Why should not the points meet after an infinitesimally small time interval? This is impossible, owing to the restrictions present in any actual system. The restrictions, see Eq. (1.9), (1.11), etc., do not allow infinitely great speeds of transposition of the representative point within the phase space to develop. The restrictions imposed upon $\mathbf{u}$, let us say, must, therefore, be introduced into the formulation of the problem. But it follows from this that not every trajectory $\mathbf{x}(t)$ can be realized with our limited resources of control. We shall call the trajectories which can be realized "admissible." Since at the end of the transient process, the trajectories $\mathbf{x}(t)$ and $\mathbf{x}^*(t)$ must coincide, we shall lay the same restriction on the trajectory $\mathbf{x}^*(t)$. We shall only consider trajectories $\mathbf{x}^*(t)$ which are admissible in the sense indicated above.

We can modify the statement of the problem, introducing the errors

$$\epsilon_i = x_i{}^* - x_i \tag{2.4}$$

or, considering their vector

$$\boldsymbol{\epsilon} = \mathbf{x}^* - \mathbf{x}. \tag{2.5}$$

Substituting Eq. (2.4) into (1.6), we obtain the equations for the errors ϵ_i. We shall not forget that the $x_i{}^*(t)$ are given functions of time. In so doing, we obtain for the $\epsilon_i(t)$ equations of the same type as the earlier equation (1.6), though, of course, with different functions f_i. So, renaming the ϵ_i as x_i, we can again consider equations of the type (1.6).

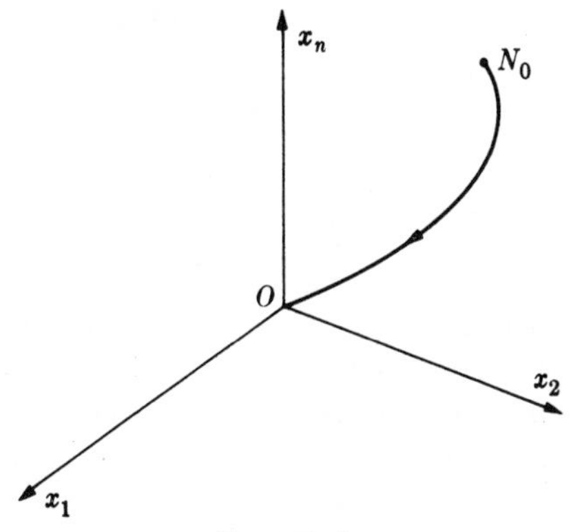

FIGURE 6.

The only difference between this view of the problem and the previous one is that now, at the end of the transient process, all the errors ϵ_i become zero. So in the new phase space (see Fig. 6) the representative point passes from some initial position N_0 to a fixed point, the origin of the coordinate system. Of course, it is possible to consider transition from N_0 to some fixed point other than the origin, but this is not a useful generalization.

Let us now state the problem in a narrower form. Let there be only one control signal u, which is subject to the restriction (2.1). Moreover, let the motion of the plant be given by the linear differential equation

$$a_0 \frac{d^n x}{dt^n} + a_1 \frac{d^{n-1} x}{dt^{n-1}} + \cdots + a_n x = u \tag{2.6}$$

where $a_0 > 0$, while the roots of the characteristic equation

$$a_0 p^n + a_1 p^{n-1} + \cdots + a_n = 0 \tag{2.7}$$

are real and nonpositive (that is, may be either negative or zero). Then we find from Eqs. (2.1) and (2.6) that the restriction can be written† in the following form:

$$a_0 \left| \frac{d^n x}{dt^n} + a_1 \frac{d^{n-1} x}{dt^{n-1}} + \cdots + a_n x \right| \leqslant U. \tag{2.8}$$

With these conditions, the following theorem of the n-intervals applies:

The optimal process $x(t)$ consists of n-intervals and is described by the equation

$$a_0 \frac{d^n x}{dt^n} + a_1 \frac{d^{n-1} x}{dt^{n-1}} + \cdots + a_n x = \sigma U \tag{2.9}$$

† It can happen that a restriction (2.8), the left side of which does not coincide with the equation of the plant, may be imposed on a system. We shall not consider this more general case [32].

that is

$$u = \sigma U \tag{2.10}$$

where

$$\sigma = \pm 1. \tag{2.11}$$

Here the sign of σ alternates in neighboring intervals.

The proof of this theorem was obtained in 1953 [29], without the use of complicated mathematical apparatus. However, it is rather cumbersome, so, in order to give at least the basic principle of the proof, we shall here confine ourselves to the simplest special case, which was considered in 1949 [28].

In this special case, let the equation of the plant (2.6) have the form

$$a_0 \frac{d^2x_1}{dt^2} = u \tag{2.12}$$

and let u be subject to restriction (2.1). Furthermore, let the initial conditions be

$$(x_1)_{t=0} = 0; \quad \left(\frac{dx_1}{dt}\right)_{t=0} = 0. \tag{2.13}$$

We shall assume that it is required to bring the plant in the minimum possible time $T_{\min}$ to the state

$$x_1 = x_{1k} = \text{constant} \neq 0 \qquad \frac{dx_1}{dt} = 0. \tag{2.14}$$

It turns out that it is necessary to first implement maximum acceleration, $u = +U$. Then [see Eq. (2.12)] dx_1/dt will increase linearly with time

$$\frac{dx_1}{dt} = \int_0^t \frac{d^2x_1}{dt^2}\, dt = \frac{U}{a_0} t. \tag{2.15}$$

In Fig. 7a, curve 1 represents the velocity dx_1/dt of the optimal process. Thereafter, maximum braking must be implemented, that is, in the second interval, $u = -U$. Thus the optimal curve dx_1/dt has a "triangular" form.

Since

$$x_1 = \int_0^t \frac{dx_1}{dt}\, dt \tag{2.16}$$

the curve $x(t)$, see Fig. 7b, has the form of two segments of parabolas when $t < T_{\min}$, and becomes the horizontal straight line $x_1 = x_{1k} = \text{const}$ when $t \geqslant T_{\min}$.

In order to prove the optimality of curve 1 in Fig. 7a, we observe that the area under any curve dx_1/dt of the transient process must have a constant magnitude equal to x_{1k}. For, if the time of the transient process be T, and if

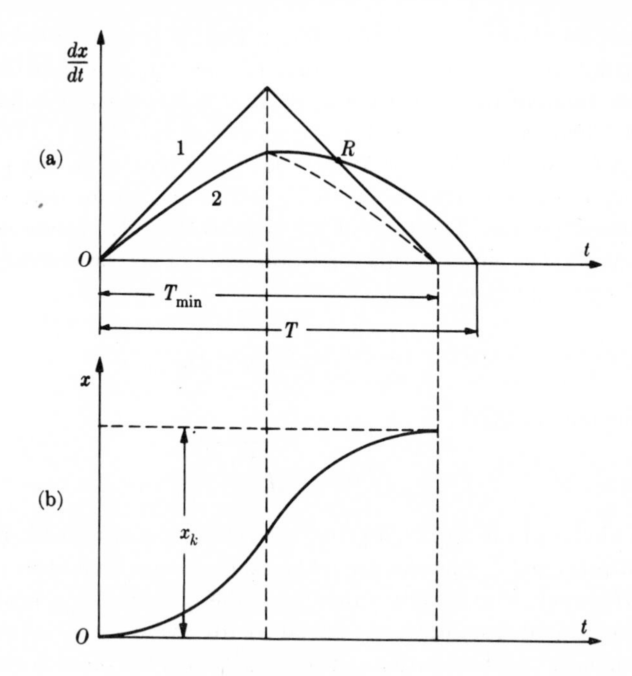

FIGURE 7.

at the end of it $x_1 = x_{1k}$, it follows from Eq. (2.16) that

$$\int_0^T \frac{dx_1}{dt}\,dt = x_{1k}. \tag{2.17}$$

This condition must also hold for the "triangular" curve 1 of Fig. 7a.

Let us consider some curve 2 of dx/dt, different from the "triangular" curve 1. By virtue of restriction (2.1), the condition

$$\left|\frac{d^2x_1}{dt^2}\right| = \left|\frac{u}{a_0}\right| \leqslant \frac{U}{a_0} = \text{const} \tag{2.18}$$

is valid.

Thus in the first interval of change (when $0 \leqslant t \leqslant T_{\min}/2$), curve 2 lies either on or below (but *not* above) curve 1, or its derivative is less than or equal to the derivative of curve 1. Hence it follows that the integral

$$\int_0^{T_{\min}/2} \frac{dx_1}{dt}\,dt$$

for curve 2 is less than that for curve 1. But the integrals (2.17) are identical for both curves. Therefore in the second interval, $(t > T_{\min}/2)$, dx/dt cannot take the path shown by the broken line in Fig. 7a. It must intersect curve 1 at some point R. A second intersection of curve 1 is impossible, since the absolute value of the derivative of curve 2 is less than or equal to that of curve 1. Therefore curve 2 reaches the horizontal axis when $t = T$, $T > T_{\min}$. Hence it follows that the time T of the transient process for any process other than that of curve 1 is greater than $T_{\min}$. This also means that curve 1 gives the optimal process. The time of the process is easily calculated from condition (2.17). For curve 1, this condition means that the area of the triangle formed by it equals x_{1k}

$$\frac{U}{a_0}\frac{T_{\min}}{2}\frac{1}{2}T_{\min} = x_{1k}. \tag{2.19}$$

Hence it follows that

$$T_{\min} = \sqrt{\frac{4x_{1k}a_0}{U}}. \tag{2.20}$$

It is obvious from Eq. (2.20) that the greater the admissible maximum of the control signal U, the smaller is the time of the optimal transient process $T_{\min}$. However, with a finite value for U the quantity $T_{\min}$ is also finite.

In the general case, when the initial conditions for x, the admissible command signal x^*, and the order n of the equation of the plant are all arbitrary, the optimal control signal u has the form shown in Fig. 8, according to the theorem of the n-intervals.

The example shown is of the case when σ is $+1$ in the first and last intervals, i.e., $u = +U$. The whole process of variation of $u(t)$ consists of n-intervals, usually of different lengths, while in each interval $\sigma =$ const, and the signs of σ in neighboring intervals are opposite. This means that "full speed ahead," when $u = +U$, is replaced by "full speed astern," when $u = -U$, and so on. The signs of and the durations of the intervals have to be chosen in such a way that some specified state, say the origin of the coordinate system, is attained from a given initial state (see Fig. 6) if the errors ϵ_i are regarded as x_i.

By itself the theorem of the n-intervals does not give a rule for the selection of the sign of σ in the first interval or of the duration of the intervals; using this theorem, however [29, 31], we can synthesize the structural scheme (or algorithm) of an optimal controller A which will itself automatically make the required selection.

Let us state briefly the essentials of the problem of synthesis in a system with complete information on the plant. The optimal control vector $\mathbf{u}$ must be chosen with the state of the plant, $\mathbf{x}$, in mind. Data on $\mathbf{x}$ enter the input of the controller A together with the command signal $\mathbf{x}^*$. In the general case, the control algorithm can vary with time in a manner laid down beforehand; if, for instance, the dependence on t in Eqs. (1.6) is given, then

$$\mathbf{u} = \mathbf{u}(\mathbf{x}^*, \mathbf{x}, t). \tag{2.21}$$

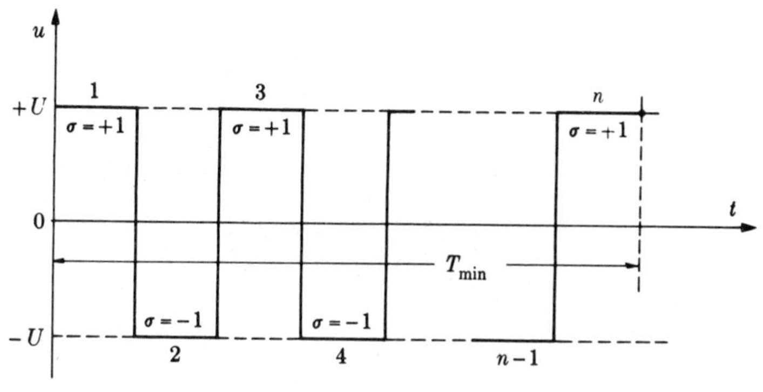

FIGURE 8.

If, within the error space (see Fig. 6) it is required that a fixed point be attained, and if the equations of the plant B do not depend on time, then, in the case of one control signal u, it is required to find the law of control

$$u = u(\mathbf{x}). \tag{2.22}$$

Synthesis of the device A reduces to the determination of this relation. If Eq. (2.22) is known, it is easy to derive from it the structure of the controller. This relation gives, for any state $\mathbf{x}$ of the plant, the corresponding optimal control signal u.

In order to find Eq. (2.22), we shall consider an error phase space of the type shown in Fig. 6. By virtue of the theorem of the n-intervals, every optimal phase trajectory will consist of n-intervals, in which the values $\sigma = +1$ and $\sigma = -1$ alternate. To every ordinary point of the phase space, regarded as an initial point, there corresponds at every instant of time either the value $\sigma = +1$ or the value $\sigma = -1$. This means that for an optimal process starting from a given initial state, it is only necessary to know, at the initial instant of time, which value σ must have, $+1$ or -1; this simplifies the nature of the relation (2.22). Thus, at every instant of time the whole phase space is split into two regions characterized by the values $\sigma = +1$ and $\sigma = -1$. The example shown in Fig. 9 corresponds to a three-dimensional phase space, with two regions, $\sigma = +1$ and $\sigma = -1$. These regions are separated by the boundary surface S. If the space in question is n-dimensional, the boundary between the regions $\sigma = +1$ and $\sigma = -1$ will be an $(n - 1)$-dimensional hypersurface S. The problem of synthesis reduces to knowing this hypersurface at any instant of time. Provided that it be known, we can indicate for any point of the phase space which sign must be chosen for σ. S is sometimes called "switching hypersurface".

In the general case, the hypersurface S is different at different instants of time. Hypersurfaces of this kind are called nonstationary. In a more restricted class of cases, the hypersurface S is fixed, but its form depends on the

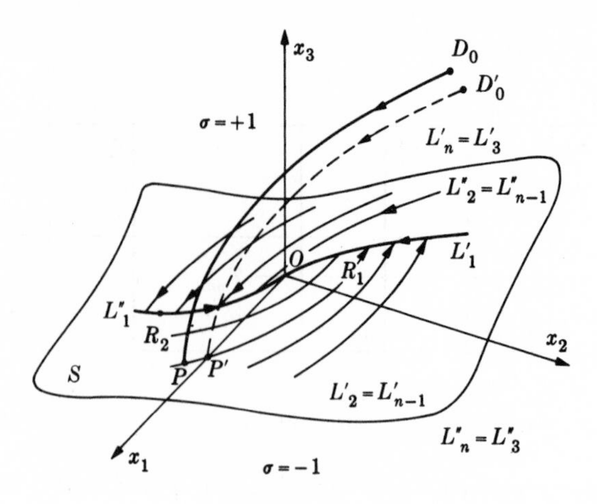

FIGURE 9.

parameters of the function $x^*(t)$. We shall call a hypersurface of this kind quasi-stationary. In an even more exceptional class of cases, the form of the hypersurface S is entirely independent of the parameters of $x^*(t)$; in this case the hypersurface S is called stationary.

The optimal phase trajectory for the example $n = 3$ in Fig. 9 is composed of three sections. The first section D_0P corresponds, let us say, to the value $\sigma = +1$; the second section PR corresponds to $\sigma = -1$, and, finally, the third section RO answers to the value $\sigma = +1$. It is important to observe that it is possible to reach the point O *by moving along either of two trajectories*— R_1O when $\sigma = +1$ and R_2O when $\sigma = -1$. But one may hit upon these trajectories—let us call them L_1' and L_1''—in various ways. It is possible to reach some given point of the trajectory L_1' by moving along one trajectory of the type PR_1 corresponding to $\sigma = -1$. We shall denote by L_2' the set of points of the trajectories corresponding to $\sigma = -1$ and leading to points of the L_1'. In its turn, one trajectory with $\sigma = +1$ leads to each point of the trajectory belonging to L_2'. We shall denote by L_3' the set of points of all trajectories leading to L_2', and so on. In exactly the same way, we shall denote the set of points of trajectories leading to L_1'' by L_2'', the set of points of trajectories leading to L_2'' by L_3'', and so on. It is obvious that L_n' and L_n'' are parts of the space characterized by different signs of σ. The boundary between them is precisely that $(n - 1)$-dimensional hypersurface, the two parts of which consist of the sets of points L'_{n-1} and L''_{n-1}. This is also the hypersurface S [31, 32].

It follows from Fig. 9 that the n-dimensional "streams" of optimal phase trajectories become $(n - 1)$-dimensional after the first change of sign of σ; after the next change, they become $(n - 2)$-dimensional, and so on; finally, in the nth interval a one-dimensional "stream" appears, flowing to the origin.

There are two such one-dimensional "streams" in all, L_1' and L_1''. After the first change of sign, the optimal phase trajectories run along the hypersurface S.

So the construction of S reduces to the formation of families of trajectories L_{n-1}' and L_{n-1}'' (in Fig. 9, these are L_2' and L_2''). It is convenient to construct such families with time reversed, that is, moving toward the time $t' = T - t$. Then the representative point will start from position O along a trajectory of the L_1 type; when $t' = t_1'$ at the point R_1, it will switch to a trajectory of the L_2 type, R_1P; when $t' = t_2'$, it will switch to a type L_3 trajectory; and so on. Integrating Eq. (2.9) and writing the equations $x_i = x_i(t_1', t_2', \ldots, t_{n-2}')$ for those "retreating" motions where $t_j', (j = 1, \ldots, n-2)$, are the instants of switching, and eliminating t_j' from these equations, we obtain the relation between the x_i, which is the equation of the hypersurface S. Assume this equation to have the form

$$\psi(x_1, \ldots, x_n) = 0. \tag{2.23}$$

Moreover, we shall assume that on that side of this hypersurface where $\psi > 0$, the sign of σ must be positive, and on the side where $\psi < 0$ the sign of σ must be negative. Then the control signal, in accordance with Eq. (2.10), must have the form

$$u = \sigma U = U \operatorname{sign} \psi(x_1, \ldots, x_n) \tag{2.24}$$

where

$$\sigma = \operatorname{sign} \psi = \begin{cases} +1, & \psi > 0 \\ -1, & \psi < 0. \end{cases} \tag{2.25}$$

If the function ψ is known, then, using Eq. (2.24), it is easy to devise the diagram of the controller; see Fig. 10. We remember that here $x_1, \ldots, x_n$ are errors which we are required to determine, in accordance with Eq. (2.4); for this purpose, both the command vector $\mathbf{x}^*$ and the output of the plant B, by way of the feedback line OO', are fed to the block Σ which calculates these errors. The calculated errors $x_1, \ldots, x_n$ enter the input of the nonlinear converter NC, which usually converts them into a nonlinear function ψ. This is

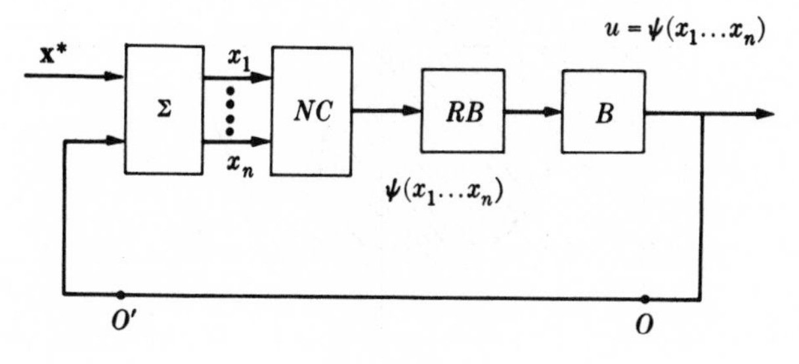

FIGURE 10.

fed to the input of the relay block RB, whose output u is subject to the law $u = U \text{ sign } \psi$, that is, to Eq. (2.24). The control signal u is applied to the input of B.

We shall show how the function ψ and the surface S are determined, using the very simple example of a second-order plant. In this case, the phase space of the errors becomes a phase plane (see Fig. 11) and the surface S is one-dimensional, that is, a switching curve which divides the phase plane into two regions, $\sigma = +1$ and $\sigma = -1$.

Let the plant B be characterized by Eq. (2.12) and by restriction (2.1). The command signal shall have the form

$$x_1^*(t) = A_0 + A_1(t) + A_2t^2 \tag{2.26}$$

where A_0, A_1, and A_2 can have various values; but in each individual transient process, they are constants. The admissible functions, in accordance with Eqs. (2.1) and (2.12), are restricted by the condition

$$\left| \frac{d^2x_1}{dt^2} \right| \leqslant \frac{|u|_{\max}}{a_0} = \frac{U}{a_0}. \tag{2.27}$$

Therefore, the same restrictions must be laid also on $x_1^*(t)$, where it follows that

$$|2A_2| < \frac{U}{a_0}. \tag{2.28}$$

If the function $x_1^*(t)$ is to be admissible, then, instead of $\leqslant$, we must put $<$. Under these conditions, the state N^* (see Fig. 5) is always attainable for points N in a finite interval of time.

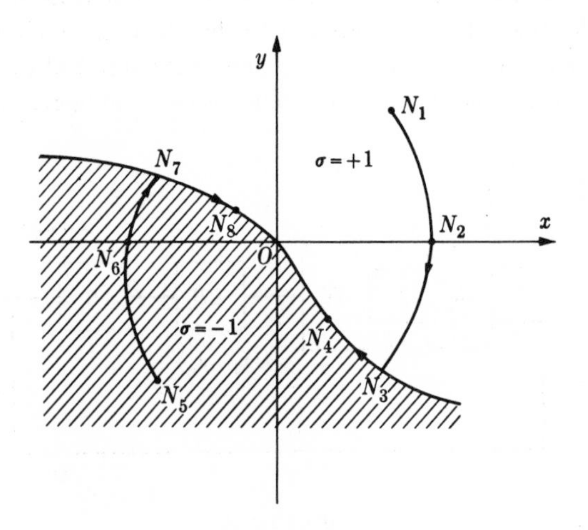

FIGURE 11.

For the example in question, an equation of type (2.9) takes the form

$$\frac{d^2x_1}{dt^2} = \frac{\sigma U}{a_0}. \tag{2.29}$$

We shall denote the error $(x_1{}^* - x_1)$ by x, and its derivative by y. Then

$$\frac{d^2x}{dt^2} = \frac{d^2x_1{}^*}{dt^2} - \frac{d^2x_1}{dt^2} = 2A_2 - \frac{\sigma U}{a_0}\,\mu_0. \tag{2.30}$$

In every interval, $\mu_0 = \text{const}$, since $\sigma = \text{const}$.

Let us now reverse the time, putting $t' = T - t$.

Then

$$\frac{d^2x}{dt'^2} = \frac{d}{dt'}\left(\frac{dx}{dt'}\right) = -\frac{d}{dt}\left(-\frac{dx}{dt}\right) = \frac{d^2x}{dt^2} = \mu_0. \tag{2.31}$$

Moreover

$$y = \frac{dx}{dt} = -\frac{dx}{dt'} = -\int \frac{d^2x}{dt'^2}\,dt' = -\mu_1 - \mu_0 t' \tag{2.32}$$

and

$$x = -\int y\,dt' = \mu_2 + \mu_1 t' + \mu_0\,\frac{(t')^2}{2} \tag{2.33}$$

where μ_1 and μ_2 are constants. Let us find the curves L_1' and L_2', which, in the example in question, form the switching curve. Since, when $t' = 0$, the quantities x and y equal zero, we find from Eq. (2.32) that $\mu_1 = \mu_2 = 0$ and

$$x = \mu_0\,\frac{(t')^2}{2}; \quad y = -\mu_0 t'. \tag{2.34}$$

Let us first find the curve L_1', for which $\sigma = -1$. From Eq. (2.30) and from condition (2.28) it is obvious that the sign of μ_0 is determined by the sign of σ

$$\operatorname{sign}\mu_0 = -\operatorname{sign}\sigma. \tag{2.35}$$

From the second equation of (2.34) it follows that

$$\operatorname{sign} y = -\operatorname{sign}\mu_0 = \operatorname{sign}\sigma. \tag{2.36}$$

Consequently, when $\sigma = -1$, $\mu_0 > 0$ and $y < 0$. Eliminating t' from the two equations (2.34), we find the equation of the curve L_1' in the form

$$\begin{gathered} x = \frac{y^2}{2\mu_0} > 0 \\ \operatorname{sign}\sigma = \operatorname{sign} y = -1. \end{gathered} \tag{2.37}$$

For the curve L_1'', $\sigma = +1$; consequently $\operatorname{sign}\mu_0 = -1$ and $y > 0$. In this case, we find from Eq. (2.34)

$$\begin{gathered} x = \frac{y^2}{2\mu_0} < 0 \\ \operatorname{sign}\sigma = \operatorname{sign} y = 1 \end{gathered} \tag{2.38}$$

It is obvious that the equations of both curves, L_1' and L_1'', can be united in the form of a single equation representing the set of points L_1

$$x = \frac{y^2}{2\mu_0} = \frac{y^2}{2[(2A_2 - (U/a_0)\operatorname{sign} y]} \tag{2.39}$$

since $\sigma = \operatorname{sign} \sigma = \operatorname{sign} y$. Equation (2.39) is the equation of the switching curve, which can also be written in a form analogous to (2.23), i.e., in the form $\psi = 0$, where

$$\begin{aligned} \psi(x, y) &= x + \frac{y^2}{2[(U/a_0)\operatorname{sign} y - 2A_2]} \\ &= x + \frac{y^2 \operatorname{sign} y}{2[(U/a_0) - 2A_2 \operatorname{sign} y]}. \end{aligned} \tag{2.40}$$

Figure 11 shows the switching curve and phase trajectories in the phase plane. The switching curve comprises the points N_3, N_4, O, N_8, N_7. The representative point moves along a parabolic trajectory $N_1N_2N_3$, which is easily obtained by solving Eq. (2.30) for $\sigma = +1$, and reaches the switching curve at the point N_3. After switching, the representative point moves to the origin along the switching curve itself, N_3N_4O. However, if the representative point is located, at the initial instant of time, at N_5 in the shaded region, where $\sigma = -1$, it moves along the parabolic trajectory $N_5N_6N_7$ [the solution of Eq. (2.30) for $\sigma = -1$] as far as that part of the switching curve which lies in the second quadrant, N_7N_8O, and thereafter along the switching curve to the origin of the coordinate system.

Since $\psi(x, y)$ depends on the parameter A_2 of the command signal $x_1^*(t)$, the switching curve S is quasi-stationary according to the definition given above.

3. Dynamic Programming

During the fifties, R. Bellman and a number of his colleagues developed a new general method for solving variational problems, which they called Dynamic Programming. The method of Dynamic Programming was applied to an extensive class of optimal control systems [1, 3–5, 7, 9, 33, 34, 37, 46, 47, 58, 71].

Let the motion of a plant B be given by Eqs. (1.6) or (1.8), and let the plant input be subject to certain restrictions of the type (1.11). Assume that the criterion of optimality Q [see Eq. (1.16)], which is required to be minimized, is expressed by the integral

$$Q = \int_0^T g[\mathbf{x}(t), \mathbf{u}(t), t]\, dt \tag{3.1}$$

where g is a certain function

$$g[\mathbf{x}(t), \mathbf{u}(t), t] = g(x_1, \ldots, x_n; u_1, \ldots, u_r; t) \tag{3.2}$$

and $T > 0$ is some number either known beforehand and fixed, or not fixed. To begin with, we shall regard T as fixed. The problem of minimizing the integral (3.1) easily reduces to the problem of minimizing the value of some coordinate at the instant of time $t = T$. We introduce, supplementary to the variables $x_1, \ldots, x_n$, a new variable x_{n+1}

$$x_{n+1}(t) = \int_0^t g(\mathbf{x}, \mathbf{u}, t)\, dt \tag{3.3}$$

where $x_{n+1}(0) = x_{n+1}^0 = 0$. Then, adding to the set of equations (1.6) yet one more equation

$$\frac{dx_{n+1}}{dt} = g(x_1, \ldots, x_n; u_1, \ldots, u_r; t). \tag{3.4}$$

We can consider the set of $(n + 1)$ equations (1.6) and (3.4). The problem of minimizing the integral Q [see Eq. (3.1)] reduces to the problem of minimizing $x_{n+1}(T)$. If we introduce the $(n + 1)$-dimensional vectors

$$\begin{aligned} \tilde{\mathbf{x}} &= (x_1, \ldots, x_n, x_{n+1}) \\ \frac{d\tilde{\mathbf{x}}}{dt} &= \left(\frac{dx_1}{dt}, \ldots, \frac{dx_n}{dt}, \frac{dx_{n+1}}{dt}\right) \\ \tilde{\mathbf{f}} &= (f_1, \ldots, f_n, g) \end{aligned} \tag{3.5}$$

the vector equation (1.8) for the n-dimensional vector $\mathbf{x}$ will be replaced by a new vector equation for the $(n + 1)$-dimensional vector $\tilde{\mathbf{x}}$

$$\frac{d\tilde{\mathbf{x}}}{dt} = \tilde{\mathbf{f}}(\tilde{\mathbf{x}}, \mathbf{u}, t) \tag{3.6}$$

where $\mathbf{u}$, as before, is an r-dimensional vector.

The problem of the minimum time of transition from one state to the other can likewise be reduced to a problem of this kind; for, assume that in Eqs. (3.1) and (3.3), $g = 1$. Then $x_{n+1}(t) = t$, and minimizing $x_{n+1}(T)$ reduces to minimizing the time T, which in this case is not known beforehand, and therefore is not fixed.

We also observe that various restrictions (boundary conditions) can be laid on the final state of the system at the instant $t = T$. For instance, in the problems considered in Section 2, when $t = T$ (see Fig. 6), the representative point of the system can be in a fixed position, or on a fixed trajectory, or else must hit upon a certain set P of points of the phase space. In a special case, the set P can coincide with the whole of the phase space. This means that no conditions are laid upon the final state. Problems of this kind are called free-end-trajectory problems.

It is possible, without restricting generality, to leave out of consideration the dependence on time t in Eqs. (1.6) or (3.4). For we can always introduce a

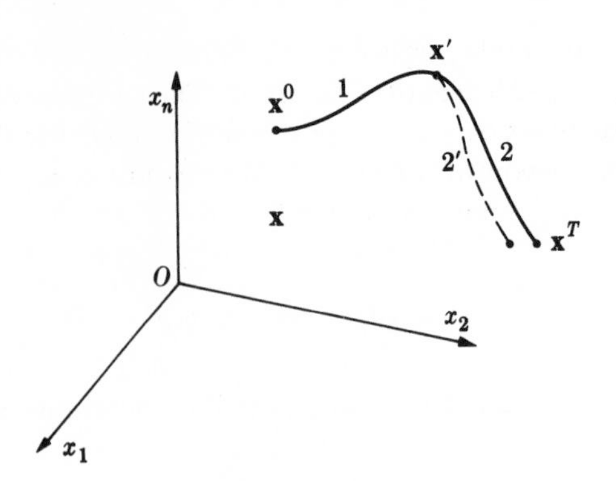

FIGURE 12.

new variable $x_{n+1}(t) = t$ and a new $(n + 1)$th equation $dx_{n+1}/dt = 1$ with the initial condition $x_{n+1}(0) = x^0_{n+1} = 0$. Then t is replaced everywhere by x_{n+1}. Therefore, it is sufficient to consider Eqs. (1.6) in which there is no explicit dependence on time.

The method of Dynamic Programming is based on the principle of optimality formulated by R. Bellman. Let us consider an optimal trajectory in a phase space (see Fig. 12), the initial and final values of whose vector $\mathbf{x}$ are $\mathbf{x}^0$ and $\mathbf{x}^T$, respectively.

We shall mark some intermediate point of the trajectory, $\mathbf{x}'$, corresponding to $t = t'$, and shall call the section of the trajectory from $\mathbf{x}^0$ to $\mathbf{x}'$ the first section, and that from $\mathbf{x}'$ to $\mathbf{x}^T$ the second. These sections are numbered 1 and 2 in Fig. 12. The principle of optimality can be stated thus:

The second section of an optimal trajectory is, in its turn, an optimal trajectory.

This means that in the case when the initial state of a system is $\mathbf{x}'$ and the initial instant $t = t'$, then independently of the previous history of the system, its subsequent optimal motion will be trajectory 2. Let us assume the contrary. Then the criterion (3.1), taken for the interval of time from t' to T, will be smaller, not for trajectory 2, but for some other trajectory 2′ starting from the point $\mathbf{x}'$ and shown by the broken line. But in this case it would be possible to construct a "better" trajectory than the trajectory 1-2 for the original problem as well. For this, it is only necessary to choose the control signal $\mathbf{u}$ in such a way that trajectory 1 is described, and then 2′. However, we started from the hypothesis that trajectory 1-2 was optimal. The contradiction proves the impossibility of the existence of a trajectory 2′ which ensures a smaller value for Q than does trajectory 2. So trajectory 2 is optimal.

The principle of optimality stated above is a very general necessary condition of optimality, valid not only for continuous, but also for discrete systems.

Although the principle of optimality appears to be trivial and, at first glance, poor in content, it is possible, as Bellman has shown, to derive from it, by methodical argument, the necessary conditions for an optimal trajectory, which are by no means of a trivial nature. The fact that the principle of optimality is not at all as trivial as it first seems is also clear from the untruth, generally speaking, of the following assertion, seemingly a generalization of it: "Any section of an optimal trajectory is an optimal trajectory." For example, the first section of the trajectory $\mathbf{x}^0 - \mathbf{x}' - \mathbf{x}^T$ in Fig. 12 cannot by itself be an optimal trajectory†; that is, it cannot ensure minimum of criterion (3.1) for the interval of time from 0 to t'. Let us explain this statement by means of an elementary example. How does a good runner deploy his forces when running a considerable distance? Does he act on the principle: "In every section, run as fast as you can!"; that is, "Cover the maximum distance in every small interval of time!" Of course not. He would be exhausted long before he reached the finishing post. Using his resources sensibly, in accordance with his ultimate goal, the runner at first economizes his strength in order to spurt ahead, or at least not to be exhausted, at the end of the distance. In the same way, control must not be "short-sighted"; it should not be influenced only by the desire to obtain an effect which is momentarily, locally, the best. It must be "far-seeing;" it should be subordinate to the ultimate aim, that is, to minimizing the value of Q [see Eq. (3.1)] over the whole of the interval from O to T.

The principle of optimality can also be formulated thus:

Optimal strategy does not depend on the "prehistory" of the system, but is determined only by the state of the system at the initial instant of time and by the ultimate goal.

It is obvious that this formulation is equivalent to the former one, if we understand by the "prehistory" of the system the trajectory 1 by which the representative point has arrived at $\mathbf{x}'$ (see Fig. 12). In this case, the "state of the system" is understood to mean the state corresponding to the point $\mathbf{x}'$.

Let us illustrate R. Bellman's method of argument by means of the simple example of a plant, the motion of which is given by an equation of the first order

$$\frac{dx}{dt} = f_1(x, u) \tag{3.7}$$

where x is the sole coordinate of the system, and u is the sole control signal, restricted to some region; see (1.11). Let the initial condition $x(0) = x^0$. It is required to find a law of control such as shall minimize the integral

† Every section of an optimal trajectory is itself an optimal trajectory only in the case when not only the initial, but also the final point of such a section is fixed.

$$Q = \int_0^T g_1(x, u)\, dt + \varphi_1[x(T)] \tag{3.8}$$

where, for simplicity, we shall assume the value of T to be fixed.

First of all we shall discretize the problem; that is, we shall substitute for the continuous system a discrete-continuous approximation. The grounds for this are as follows: first, discretization is an unavoidable stage in the preliminary "trimming" of the problem in preparing it for solution on a digital computer. Secondly, the reasoning is more easily explained at first by the example of a discrete-continuous system. But the discrete form is not obligatory, and in what follows equations will be derived for continuous systems too.

We shall break the interval (O, T) down into N equal small portions Δ, and shall consider only discrete values of $x = x_k$ and $u = u_k$ at the instants of time $t = 0, \Delta, 2\Delta, \ldots, k\Delta, \ldots, (N - 1)\Delta, N\Delta = T$.

Then the differential equation of the plant (3.7) can be approximately replaced by the difference equation

$$\frac{x_{k+1} - x_k}{\Delta} = f_1(x_k, u_k) \tag{3.9}$$

or by

$$x_{k+1} = x_k + f(x_k, u_k) \tag{3.10}$$

where

$$f(x_k, u_k) = \Delta f_1(x_k, u_k). \tag{3.11}$$

The initial condition remains as before

$$x(0) = [x]_{t=0} = x^0. \tag{3.12}$$

The integral of Eq. (3.8) is approximately replaced by the sum

$$Q = \sum_{n=0}^{N-1} g(x_k, u_k) + \varphi(x_N) \tag{3.13}$$

where

$$\begin{aligned} g(x_k, u_k) &= g_1(x_k, u_k) \cdot \Delta t \\ \varphi(x_N) &= \varphi_1[x(N\Delta)] = \varphi_1[x(T)]. \end{aligned} \tag{3.14}$$

The problem is to determine the sequence of discrete values of the control signal u, that is, of the quantities $u_0, u_1, \ldots, u_{N-1}$ which minimize the sum (3.13) when conditions (1.11), (3.10), and (3.12) are imposed upon the system.

To solve the problem, we shall make use of the trick which consists of "retrograde" motion. We shall "retreat" from the end of the process, that is, from the instant $t = T$. Assume that all the values of u_i $(i = 0, 1, \ldots, N - 2)$ except the last, u_{N-1}, have already been selected by some means, and that the value of x_{N-1} is fixed. From the principle of optimality, the signal u_{N-1} does not depend on the "prehistory" of the system, but is determined by the state x_{N-1} at the instant of time in question and by the purpose of control. Consider the last portion from $t = (N-1)\Delta$ to $t = N\Delta$. The quantity u_{N-1} affects only those terms of the sum (3.13) which have reference to this portion. We shall denote the sum of these terms by Q_{N-1}

$$Q_{N-1} = g(x_{N-1}, u_{N-1}) + \varphi(x_N). \tag{3.15}$$

From Eq. (3.10) we get

$$x_N = x_{N-1} + f(x_{N-1}, u_{N-1}). \tag{3.16}$$

Consequently, x_N also depends on u_{N-1}. Let us find an admissible value of u_{N-1} which satisfies Eq. (1.11) and minimizes Q_{N-1}. We shall denote the minimal value found for Q_{N-1} by S_{N-1}. This quantity obviously depends on what value of x_{N-1} enters into Eqs. (3.15) and (3.16). So

$$\begin{aligned} S_{N-1}(x_{N-1}) &= \min_{u_{N-1}\in\Omega(u)} Q_{N-1} = \min_{u_{N-1}\in\Omega(u)} \{g(x_{N-1}, u_{N-1}) + \varphi(x_N)\} \\ &= \min_{u_{N-1}\in\Omega(u)} \{g(x_{N-1}, u_{N-1}) + \varphi[x_{N-1} + f(x_{N-1}, u_{N-1})]\}. \end{aligned} \tag{3.17}$$

We notice that to find S_{N-1}, it is necessary to minimize with respect to only one variable, u_{N-1}. Having carried out this process, we obtain a function S_{N-1} of x_{N-1}, which we are required to store (perhaps in some memory system), before going on to the succeeding stages of the solution.

Let us now turn to the penultimate interval of time. Considering the two intervals—the last and the one before the last—together, we can see that the choice of u_{N-2} and u_{N-1} only affects terms in Eq. (3.13) which enter into the expression

$$Q_{N-2} = g(x_{N-2}, u_{N-2}) + \{g(x_{N-1}, u_{N-1}) + \varphi(x_N)\}. \tag{3.18}$$

We shall regard x_{N-2} as fixed. It follows from the principle of optimality that only the value of x_{N-2} and the aim of control, minimization of Q_{N-2} determine the optimal control signal in the interval of time in question. Let us find the minimum of Q_{N-2} with respect to u_{N-2} and u_{N-1}. But the minimum of the term between the braces has already been found for every value of x_{N-1}, as has also the best value of u^*_{N-1} in every case, in minimizing Q_{N-1} and obtaining S_{N-1}, see (3.17). Therefore Q_{N-2} in Eq. (3.18) can be minimized as follows:

$$\begin{aligned} S_{N-2}(x_{N-2}) &= \min_{\substack{u_{N-2}\in\Omega(u) \\ u_{N-1}(u)}} Q_{N-2} = \min_{u_{N-2}\in\Omega(u)} \{g(x_{N-2}, u_{N-2}) + S_{N-1}(x_{N-1})\} \\ &= \min_{u_{N-2}\in\Omega(u)} \{g(x_{N-2}, u_{N-2}) + S_{N-1}[x_{N-2} + f(x_{N-2}, u_{N-2})]\} \end{aligned} \tag{3.19}$$

since, from (3.10)

$$x_{N-1} = x_{N-2} + f(x_{N-2}, u_{N-2}). \tag{3.20}$$

We note that in Eq. (3.19), too, minimization is carried out with respect to only one variable u_{N-2}. Moreover, we have found u^*_{N-2}—the optimal value of u_{N-2}, and S_{N-2}—the minimum of the function Q_{N-2}. Both u^*_{N-2} and S_{N-2} are functions of x_{N-2}. We can store the function S_{N-2} in a cell of the memory, and "erase" the function $S_{N-1}(x_{N-1})$ previously stored there, as it is now no longer needed.

It is interesting to note that the optimal value found, u^*_{N-2}, minimizes the *whole* of the expression in the braces in Eq. (3.19), but is far from being the result of minimizing *only one* term $g(x_{N-2}, u_{N-2})$. The strategy in which every u_{N-j} is chosen by the method of minimization of its "own" term $g(x_{N-j}, u_{N-j})$ of the sum in Eq. (3.13) is not optimal at all—it is too "shortsighted" as has been said above.

We continue in the same way, "retreating" from the end of the interval (O, T) to its origin. For example, to calculate the antepenultimate interval we have to consider a certain part of Q, namely, the sum

$$Q_{N-3} = g(x_{N-3}, u_{N-3}) + \{g(x_{N-2}, u_{N-2}) + g(x_{N-1}, u_{N-1}) + \varphi(x_N)\}. \quad (3.21)$$

The minimum S_{N-3} of this part is

$$\begin{aligned} S_{N-3}(x_{N-3}) &= \min_{u_{N-3}\in\Omega(u)} \{g(x_{N-3}, u_{N-3}) + S_{N-2}(x_{N-2})\} \\ &= \min_{u_{N-3}\in\Omega(u)} \{g(x_{N-3}, u_{N-3}) + S_{N-2}[x_{N-3} + f(x_{N-3}, u_{N-3})]\} \end{aligned} \quad (3.22)$$

since from Eq. (3.10)

$$x_{N-2} = x_{N-3} + f(x_{N-3}, u_{N-3}) \quad (3.23)$$

and so on. Proceeding in this way to S_{N-k}, we obtain the recurrence formula for the determination of $S_i(x_i)$

$$S_{N-k}(x_{N-k}) = \min_{u_{N-k}\in\Omega(u)} \{g(x_{N-k}, u_{N-k}) + S_{N-k+1}[x_{N-k} + f(x_{N-k}, u_{N-k})]\} \quad (3.24)$$

In parallel with the process of minimizing the right side of Eq. (3.24), we find the optimal value $u^*_{N-k} = u^*_{N-k}(x_{N-k})$.

Calculating S_{N-k} from Eq. (3.24) successively for $k = 1, 2, \ldots, N$, we come at last to the optimal value $u_0{}^*$, that is, to the value of the control signal required at the given initial instant of time. At the same time, S_0 is determined, that is, the minimum value of Q obtained by the optimal process.

In some very simple cases it is possible to carry out all this procedure analytically, provided that we succeed in finding an analytic expression for $S_{N-k}(x_{N-k})$ and $u^*_{N-k}(x_{N-k})$. Generally, however, an analytic expression for the results of minimization is impossible, and this procedure can be considered only as a program for calculations to be carried out manually in simple cases, and in more complex cases by a digital computer.

The whole solution process is immediately applicable to a plant with Eq. (1.6) of any order n, and to any number r of control signals. It is only necessary to replace the scalar quantities x, u, and f in the equations of this section by the vectors $\mathbf{x}$, $\mathbf{u}$, and $\mathbf{f}$. In this case, however, one must, at each stage, minimize the function

$$g(\mathbf{x}_{N-k}, \mathbf{u}_{N-k}) + S_{N-k+1}[\mathbf{x}_{N-k} + \bar{\mathbf{f}}(\mathbf{x}_{N-k}, \mathbf{u}_{N-k})]$$

with respect to $\mathbf{u}_{N-k}$, that is, find the minimum of the function of r variables $u_{1,N-k}, u_{2,N-k}, \ldots, u_{r,N-k}$, where $u_{j,N-k}$ is the jth signal at the instant of time $t = (N-k)\Delta$. Furthermore, the optimal quantities, the scalar S_{N-k} and vector $\mathbf{u}^*_{N-k}$, are functions of $\mathbf{x}_{N-k}$, that is, of the n-variables $x_{1,N-k}, \ldots, x_{n,N-k}$, where $x_{i,N-k}$ is the ith coordinate of the plant at the instant of time $t = (N-k)\Delta$.

In general, the solution is obtained by numerical calculation, carried out either by hand or by digital computer. The method of finding the solution is, in actual fact, a program for such a calculation. The better the method, the simpler is the calculation procedure. The Dynamic Programming method is a substantial rationalization compared with, for instance, the direct method of solving a problem. Assume that we are engaged in the solution of the problem of minimizing the sum (3.13), by finding the minimum of the function N of the variables $u_0, u_1, \ldots, u_{N-1}$. To do this, it is first necessary to express every x_k in the form of a function of *all* the previous values of the control signals $u_0, u_1, \ldots, u_{k-1}$, using Eq. (3.10). After this, Eq. (3.13) becomes impossibly complex, and only in simple cases can it be brought to a form which is not too unwieldy. Moreover, we will have to seek out the most minimal of the minima (and there may be several!) of the resulting complex function in a great many variables, which is, in most cases, a practically impossible task. In addition to this, the minimum must be on the boundary of the admissible region for $\bar{u}$, and in this case it cannot be found by equating the derivatives to zero.

Dynamic Programming allows the minimization of a complex function of many variables to be replaced by a *sequence of minimizations*, where in every process of the minimization, as has been stressed above, there is a minimum of a relatively less complex function of one variable (or of n-variables, for an nth-order plant.) So by using Dynamic Programming we can solve a number of problems which cannot be solved by direct methods.

It should be observed, however, that in general the solution of problems by the method of Dynamic Programming can, all the same, be exceedingly cumbrous. At every stage of the calculation, the functions $S_{N-k}(\mathbf{x})$ and $S_{N-k+1}(\mathbf{x})$ have to be found and stored, that is, in the general case, two functions of n-variables. To store such functions for large values of n requires a memory of mammoth proportions, and is a practical possibility, in complex cases, only with the aid of approximations of some kind. Some tricks of calculation, together with references to the literature, are to be found in Bellman and Dreyfus [7].

The method described can be applied, without changes in principle, to optimal systems with random processes. As an illustration, let us consider the case when a first-order plant is affected by a random disturbance z. Then Eq. (3.10) is replaced by

$$x_{k+1} = x_k + f(x_k, u_k, z_k) \tag{3.25}$$

where the z_k are discrete values of the disturbance. Since x_k and the criterion (3.13) are now random quantities, we shall take as the new criterion requiring to be minimized the expected value of (3.13), where, for generality, g also contains z

$$Q = E\left\{\sum_{n=0}^{N-1} g(x_k, u_k, z_k) + \varphi(x_N)\right\}. \tag{3.26}$$

It is easy to write this equation in explicit form, provided that the probability densities $P(z_0), P(z_1), \ldots, P(z_N)$ of the z_k be known. They need not be identical. (For simplicity, we shall assume that z_i and z_j are independent when $i \neq j$.) Using the method described above, we find first

$$\begin{aligned} S_{N-1}(x_{N-1}) &= \min_{u_{N-1}\in\Omega(u)} Q_{N-1} = \min_{u_{N-1}\in\Omega(u)} \\ &\quad \times E\{g(x_{N-1}, u_{N-1}, z_{N-1}) + \varphi[x_{N-1} + f(x_{N-1}, u_{N-1}, z_{N-1})]\} \\ &= \min_{u_{N-1}\in\Omega(u)} \int_{-\infty}^{\infty} P(z_{N-1})\{g(x_{N-1}, u_{N-1}, z_{N-1}) \\ &\quad + \varphi[x_{N-1} + f(x_{N-1}, u_{N-1}, z_{N-1})]\}\, dz_{N-1} \cdots . \end{aligned} \tag{3.27}$$

Simultaneously with the minimization, the optimal value $u^*_{N-1}(x_{N-1})$ is found. Storing $S_{N-1}(x_{N-1})$, we go on to find

$$\begin{aligned} S_{N-2}(x_{N-2}) &= \min_{u_{N-2}\in\Omega(u)} E\{g(x_{N-2}, u_{N-2}, z_{N-2}) + S(x_{N-1})\} \\ &= \min_{u_{N-2}\in\Omega(u)} \int_{-\infty}^{\infty} P(z_{N-2})\{g(x_{N-2}, u_{N-2}, z_{N-2}) \\ &\quad + S_{N-1}[x_{N-2} + f(x_{N-2}, u_{N-2}, z_{N-2})]\, dz_{N-2} \end{aligned} \tag{3.28}$$

and so on. An analogous method can be applied to a plant of any order. It is possible to examine even more general cases, in which the $P(z_i)$ are not known beforehand, and some optimal procedure for processing observations enables information on probability densities to accumulate [9, 37].

Let us turn to the derivation of the relations for continuous systems. Let the motion of the plant be given by Eqs. (1.6) or (1.8), and let the criterion of optimality Q be expressed by (3.1). Assume that the optimal trajectory, starting from point $\mathbf{x}^0$ and arriving at point $\mathbf{x}^T$, has already been found; see Figs. 12 and 13.

We shall denote the minimal value of Q corresponding to this trajectory by $S(\mathbf{x}^0, t = 0)$. From the principle of optimality, the section of the trajectory

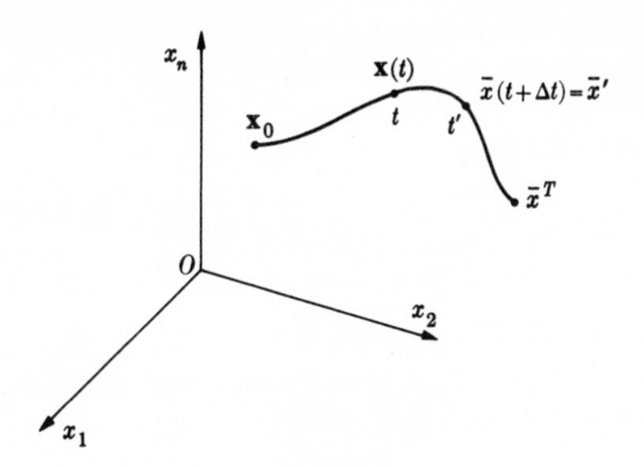

FIGURE 13.

from the point $\mathbf{x}$ at the instant of time t to $\mathbf{x}^T$ (see Fig. 13) is also an optimal trajectory, and that part of Q which corresponds to this section and to the interval of time $T - t = \tau$ has, in consequence, the minimum possible value, which we shall denote by $S[\mathbf{x}(t), t]$.

Let Δt be a small interval of time, and let $S[\mathbf{x}(t + \Delta t), t + \Delta t] = S[\mathbf{x}', t']$ be the minimum value of that part of Q which corresponds to the section of the optimal trajectory from the point $\mathbf{x}(t + \Delta t)$ to $\mathbf{x}^T$, see Fig. 13. The relation between $S[\mathbf{x}', t']$ and $S[\mathbf{x}, t]$ is completely analogous to Eq. (3.24). It is only necessary to substitute $S[\mathbf{x}, t]$ for $S_{N-k}(x_{N-k})$, $S[\mathbf{x}', t']$ for $S_{N-k+1}[x_{N-k+1}]$ and $g[\mathbf{x}(t), \mathbf{u}(t), t]\ \Delta t$ for $g(x_{N-k}, u_{N-k})$. This last substitution has, indeed, been carried out in the first of equations (3.14). Since Δt is a small but finite interval of time, we must add to one of the sides of the equation yet another expression, $O_1(\Delta t)$, that is, a quantity of a higher order of smallness than Δt. Thus

$$\lim_{\Delta t \to 0} \frac{O_1(\Delta t)}{\Delta t} = 0. \tag{3.29}$$

So we now write instead of Eq. (3.24)

$$S[\mathbf{x}, t] = \min_{\mathbf{u}(t) \in \Omega(\mathbf{u})} \{g[\mathbf{x}, \mathbf{u}, t]\, \Delta t + S[\mathbf{x}', t']\} + O_1(\Delta t). \tag{3.30}$$

Just as in Eq. (3.24), it must be borne in mind that $\mathbf{x}(t + \Delta t)$ depends on $\mathbf{u}(t)$. From Eq. (1.8), we find, for small Δt

$$\mathbf{x}' = \mathbf{x}(t + \Delta t) = \mathbf{x}(t) + \mathbf{f}[\mathbf{x}(t), \mathbf{u}(t), t]\Delta t + O_2(\Delta t) \tag{3.31}$$

where $O_2(\Delta t)$ is of a higher order of smallness than Δt. Equation (3.31) is analogous to (3.23) or (3.10). Let us substitute (3.31) into $S[\mathbf{x}', t']$. Supposing that S has partial derivatives with respect to x_i and t, that is, that all $\partial S/\partial x_i$, $(i = 1, \ldots, n)$, and $\partial S/\partial t$ exist, we can† expand $S[\mathbf{x}', t']$ into a Taylor

† This supposition is, as yet, without mathematical foundation, so that the derivation of Eq. (3.36) has only a heuristic meaning. But, for a number of practical cases, the resulting optimal strategy, derived by means of this supposition, is quite correct.

series in the vicinity of the point $\mathbf{x}t$

$$\begin{aligned} S[\mathbf{x}', t'] &= S[\mathbf{x}(t+\Delta t), t+\Delta t] \\ &= S[\mathbf{x}(t) + \mathbf{f}[\mathbf{x}(t), \mathbf{u}(t), t]\Delta t + O_2(\Delta t), t+\Delta t] \\ &= S[\mathbf{x}, t] + \sum_{i=1}^{n} \frac{\partial S[\mathbf{x}(t), t]}{\partial x_i} f_i[\mathbf{x}(t), \mathbf{u}(t), t] \cdot \Delta t + \frac{\partial S[\mathbf{x}(t), t]}{\partial t} \cdot \Delta t + O_3(\Delta t) \end{aligned} \tag{3.32}$$

where $O_3(\Delta t)$ is of a higher order of smallness than Δt. This equation can be rewritten in more compact form if we introduce the gradient of the function $S[x, t]$—a vector with coordinates $\partial S/\partial x_i$, $(i = 1, \ldots, n)$

$$\operatorname{grad} S = \left(\frac{\partial S}{\partial x_1}, \ldots, \frac{\partial S}{\partial x_n}\right). \tag{3.33}$$

Then Eq. (3.32) takes the form

$$\begin{aligned} S[\mathbf{x}', t'] &= S[\mathbf{x}(t+\Delta t), t+\Delta t] \\ &= S[\mathbf{x}, t] + \langle \operatorname{grad} S[\mathbf{x}, t] \cdot \mathbf{f}[\mathbf{x}(t), \mathbf{u}(t), t]\rangle \Delta t + \frac{\partial S[\mathbf{x}, t]}{\partial t} \Delta t + O_3(\Delta t) \end{aligned} \tag{3.34}$$

Here the brackets $\langle\quad\rangle$ denote the scalar product of the vector grad S and $\mathbf{f}$. Let us substitute Eq. (3.34) into (3.30) and remove $S[\mathbf{x}, t]$ and $\partial S/\partial t$ from the braces in the right side, since they do not depend on $\mathbf{u}(t)$. Then it becomes obvious that $S[\mathbf{x}, t]$ in the left and right sides can be shortened, and the equation takes the form, after division by Δt

$$-\frac{\partial S[\mathbf{x}, t]}{\partial t} = \min_{\mathbf{u}(t)\in\Omega(\mathbf{u})} \{g[\mathbf{x}(t), \mathbf{u}(t), t] + \langle \operatorname{grad} S[\mathbf{x}, t] \cdot \mathbf{f}[\mathbf{x}(t), \mathbf{u}(t), t]\rangle\} + \frac{O_4(\Delta t)}{\Delta t} \tag{3.35}$$

where $O_4(\Delta t)$ is of a higher order of smallness than Δt. If Δt is now made to tend toward zero, in view of the condition of the type of (3.29), the last term in the right side of (3.35) vanishes, and finally we obtain

$$-\frac{\partial S[\mathbf{x}, t]}{\partial t} = \min_{\mathbf{u}(t)\in\Omega(\mathbf{u})} \{g[\mathbf{x}(t), \mathbf{u}(t), t] + \langle \operatorname{grad} S[\mathbf{x}, t] \cdot \mathbf{f}[\mathbf{x}(t), \mathbf{u}(t), t]\rangle\}. \tag{3.36}$$

This expression is a rather peculiar partial differential equation since as a result of minimizing with respect to $\mathbf{u}$, this quantity vanishes from the right side at every instant of time. As an illustration, let us consider a simple example [65]. In a particular case, let Eq. (3.36) have the form (writing for brevity, S for $S[\mathbf{x}, t]$)

$$-\frac{\partial S}{\partial t} = \min_{u} \left\{g(x_1, x_2) + \frac{\partial S}{\partial x_1}(ux_1 + x_2) + \frac{\partial S}{\partial x_2} u^2\right\} \tag{3.37}$$

that is, in the case in question, $n = 2$, $r = 1$, and $f_1 = ux_1 + x_2$, $f_2 = u^2$. Then, assuming that $\partial S/\partial x_2 > 0$, we find the minimum with respect to u of the expression enclosed in the braces by equating its derivative with respect to u to zero. The optimal value u^* minimizing the figured brackets is

$$u^* = -\tfrac{1}{2}x_1 \frac{\partial S}{\partial x_1} \frac{1}{\partial S/\partial x_2}. \tag{3.38}$$

Substituting this expression into Eq. (3.37), we get a partial differential equation of the "usual" form

$$-\frac{\partial S}{\partial t} = g(x_1, x_2) + \frac{\partial S}{\partial x_1} x_2 - x_1{}^2 \frac{(\partial S/\partial x_1)^2}{4\partial S/\partial x_2}. \tag{3.39}$$

The partial differential equation (3.36) can be solved, since the boundary conditions for it are known; for $S[\mathbf{x}, T]$ is a known function. For instance, in the case of the criterion (3.8), this function is $\varphi_1[x(T)]$ which is totally independent of the control signal. For criterion (3.1) the function $S[\mathbf{x}, T]$ equals zero. Knowing this boundary function, we can integrate the partial differential equation (3.36) by known methods. The usual method consists of discretizing the problem and solving it by the means described above; see Eq. (3.24). However, in some cases an approximate solution of Eq. (3.36) can be found in another way—in the form of a series, see for instance [58].

4. The Maximum Principle

In 1956, Pontriagin published, together with his pupils Boltianskii and Gamkrelidze, a short paper [12] in which they presented as a hypothesis a principle leading to the solution of the general problem of finding the minimum response time transient process. The discovery of this principle was the result of work by Pontriagin and his co-authors on the solution of the general problems stated by the present author in a number of reports concerning the theory of optimal systems in 1954, at a seminar presided over by Pontriagin [30]; at this seminar, the statement of the general problems presented at the Second All-Union Conference on the Theory of Automatic Control in 1953 was repeated. This again confirmed that contacts between engineers and mathematicians are fruitful. The Maximum Principle has been established as a necessary and sufficient criterion of an optimal process for linear systems, and a necessary criterion for nonlinear systems, and has also been generalized for the case of the minimization of an integral in a number of papers by Pontriagin, Boltianskii, and Gamkrelidze [11, 13, 40–42, 62]. Other proofs of the principle were worked out [65–67], where, too, the connection between the Maximum Principle and Dynamic Programming was established [24] and [63]. There are at present only a few examples of the application of the Maximum Principle to the solution of automatic control problems [16, 17, 69]. The Maximum Principle is generalized [16, 17] for a given class of integral equations. The potentialities of this principle are very great, and cannot be rated too highly.

The proofs of the validity of the Maximum Principle given in the papers of Pontriagin and his co-authors have no relation to Bellman's principle of optimality or to Dynamic Programming. However, from considerations concerned with methodology, it is convenient to derive the Maximum Principle from Eq. (3.36). We shall rewrite it in more compact form. For this, we shall introduce a supplementary coordinate $x_{n+1} = t$, such that $x_{n+1}(0) = 0$. Obviously, the equation for this coordinate has the form

$$\frac{dx_{n+1}}{dt} = f_{n+1} = 1. \tag{4.1}$$

Then instead of $\partial S/\partial t$ we can write $\partial S/\partial x_{n+1}$. If there is no explicit dependence of S on time, (which is the case when the time t does not enter explicitly into g and $\mathbf{f}$), then $\partial S/\partial t = 0$ and there is no need to introduce the coordinate $x_{n+1} = t$.

Let us also introduce a coordinate x_{n+2}, such that $x_{n+2}(0) = 0$, and the equation has the same form as in (3.4)

$$\frac{dx_{n+2}}{dt} = f_{n+2} = g(x_1, \ldots, x_n; u_1, \ldots, u_r; x_{n+1}). \tag{4.2}$$

Here x_{n+1} is written instead of t. Then minimizing Q [see Eq. (3.1)] reduces to minimizing $x_{n+2}(T)$. We shall now introduce the generalized vectors in the $(n + 2)$-dimensional space†

$$\begin{aligned} \tilde{\mathbf{f}} &= (f_1, \ldots, f_n, f_{n+1}, f_{n+2}) \\ \tilde{\mathbf{x}} &= (x_1, \ldots, x_n, x_{n+1}, x_{n+2}) \end{aligned} \tag{4.3}$$

and

$$\tilde{\boldsymbol{\Psi}} = \left(-\frac{\partial S}{\partial x_1}, \ldots, -\frac{\partial S}{\partial x_n}, -\frac{\partial S}{\partial x_{n+1}}, -1\right). \tag{4.4}$$

We transfer $\partial S/\partial t$ in Eq. (3.36) to the right side of the equation, and then assume that the minimum of this right side stands for the maximum, with the minus sign, of the expression opposite to it in sign, since $\max(-\Psi) = -\min \Psi$. Now, substituting the coordinates $\tilde{f}_i$ and $\tilde{\Psi}_i$ of the vectors $\tilde{\mathbf{f}}$ and $\tilde{\boldsymbol{\Psi}}$ in Eq. (3.36) and taking (4.2) into account, we can rewrite (3.36) in the following form

$$0 = \max_{\mathbf{u}(t)\in\Omega(\mathbf{u})} \{\langle \tilde{\boldsymbol{\Psi}} \tilde{\mathbf{f}} \rangle\}. \tag{4.5}$$

† It should be noted that the validity of the Maximum Principle, unlike that of Dynamic Programming, has been rigorously proved for a wide class of continuous systems and also for some types of discrete system. However, the Maximum Principle in its "powerful" formulation cannot be extended to any discrete-continuous or discrete systems [21]. Therefore continuous systems form the principal region of application of the Maximum Principle.

We introduce the scalar

$$\tilde{H} = \langle \tilde{\boldsymbol{\Psi}} \tilde{\mathbf{f}} \rangle = \sum_{i=1}^{n+2} \tilde{\Psi}_i \tilde{f}_i. \tag{4.6}$$

Then Eq. (4.5) takes the form

$$0 = \max_{\mathbf{u}(t) \in \Omega(\mathbf{u})} \tilde{H} \tag{4.7}$$

which is also the Maximum Principle of Pontriagin.

What is the meaning of Eq. (4.7)? From it, we draw two conclusions.

(a) If the process is optimal—we started from this assumption, in deriving Eq. (3.36)—then, at any moment of time t, optimal control $\mathbf{u}^*(t)$ is obtained by maximizing the expression for $\tilde{H}$

$$\tilde{H}_{\max} = \max_{\mathbf{u}(t) \in \Omega(\mathbf{u})} \tilde{H} = \max_{\mathbf{u}(t) \in \Omega(\mathbf{u})} \langle \tilde{\boldsymbol{\Psi}} \tilde{\mathbf{f}} \rangle = \max_{\mathbf{u}(t) \in \Omega(\mathbf{u})} \sum_{i=1}^{n+2} \tilde{\Psi}_i \tilde{f}_i. \tag{4.8}$$

It should be pointed out that $\tilde{H}$ depends on $\mathbf{u}$, since $\tilde{\mathbf{f}}$ depends on $\mathbf{u}$. At a given point of the space $\tilde{\mathbf{x}}$, the quantity $\tilde{H}$ is completely determined, as a function of $\mathbf{u}$, as soon as $\tilde{\boldsymbol{\Psi}}$ is known. But this last function is known, if $S[\mathbf{x}, t]$ and, consequently, the derivatives $\partial S / \partial x_i$ $(i = 1, \ldots, n + 1)$ are known.

There follows from Eq. (4.8) the rule for selecting the optimal $\mathbf{u}$: $\mathbf{u}$ must be so selected as to ensure maximum of $\tilde{H}$.

(b) At any point of the optimal trajectory, the maximum of $\tilde{H}$ equals zero.

The Maximum Principle has an obvious geometric meaning. To make this clear, let us introduce the supplementary function

$$\tilde{S} = S(x_1, \ldots, x_n, x_{n+1}) + x_{n+2}. \tag{4.9}$$

Consider, in the $(n + 2)$-dimensional space $\tilde{\mathbf{x}} = (x_1, \ldots, x_n, x_{n+1}, x_{n+2})$ the trajectory of a representative point moving from an initial location $\tilde{\mathbf{x}}_0$ to a final location $\tilde{\mathbf{x}}^T$. $\tilde{S}$ is a function of a point in the space $\tilde{\mathbf{x}}$. Let us visualize in this space the surfaces $\tilde{S} =$ constant. We shall call them iso-surfaces.

Comparing Eqs. (4.4) and (4.9), we can see that the $\tilde{\Psi}_i$, the coordinates of the vector $\tilde{\boldsymbol{\Psi}}$, can be expressed in terms of $\tilde{S}$

$$\tilde{\Psi}_i = -\frac{\partial S}{\partial \tilde{x}_i}. \tag{4.10}$$

Consequently, $\tilde{\boldsymbol{\Psi}}$ is the negative of the gradient of $\tilde{S}$ in the $(n + 2)$-dimensional space $\tilde{\mathbf{x}}$

$$\tilde{\boldsymbol{\Psi}} = -\text{grad}\, \tilde{S}. \tag{4.11}$$

The gradient, as is well known, is orthogonal to the iso-surface $\tilde{S} =$ constant.

We can now interpret the geometrical condition (4.8) as follows: control must be such that the scalar product of the vector

$$\tilde{\mathbf{f}} = \frac{d\tilde{\mathbf{x}}}{dt} \tag{4.12}$$

and the vector $\tilde{\boldsymbol{\Psi}}$ should be as large as possible. In other words, the control signal $\mathbf{u}$ must be so chosen that the projection of the vector $d\tilde{\mathbf{x}}/dt$ of the velocity of the representative point in a direction normal to the iso-surface should be maximum. It is evident from Eq. (4.7) that this projection, in a nonoptimal case, is negative, and that its largest value is zero.

Let us consider the particular case when explicit dependence on time is lacking in Eq. (1.6) and it is required that the time of the transient process should be minimum. In this case, $g = 1$ in Eq. (3.1), and $\partial S/\partial t = 0$. Then, directly from Eq. (3.36) we find

$$\max_{\mathbf{u}\in\Omega(\mathbf{u})} \langle -\text{grad } S \cdot \mathbf{f} \rangle = 1. \tag{4.13}$$

We let

$$H = -\text{ grad } S \cdot \mathbf{f} = \boldsymbol{\Psi}\mathbf{f} \tag{4.14}$$

where

$$\boldsymbol{\Psi} = -\text{ grad } S. \tag{4.15}$$

Then condition (4.13) becomes

$$\max_{\mathbf{u}\in\Omega(\mathbf{u})} H = 1 \tag{4.16}$$

This is the form that the Maximum Principle takes in this particular case. Now we can consider the trajectory of a representative point $\mathbf{x}$ in n-dimensional space. The optimal control signal $\mathbf{u}$ must be so selected that at every instant of time the scalar H is maximized, while the maximum value of H at any point of the trajectory is 1. Since

$$S[\mathbf{x}, t] = \int_t^T 1 \cdot dt = T - t \tag{4.17}$$

where t is the instant of time which is being considered, then S decreases as t increases. Consequently the vector $\boldsymbol{\Psi} = -$ grad S is directed towards the "inside" of the iso-surface S (see Fig. 14) which encompasses the final point $\mathbf{x}^T$. In this particular case the iso-surfaces $S =$ constant are surfaces of equal times $\tau_i = T - t_i$ of attainment of the final point $\mathbf{x}^T$; surfaces of this kind are introduced in Lerner [56], where they are called isochronous surfaces. In the given case, the Maximum Principle requires that $\mathbf{u}$ be so selected that the projection of the velocity $d\mathbf{x}/dt$ of the representative point in the phase space upon the direction $\boldsymbol{\Psi}$ normal to the iso-surface shall be maximal. This is also obvious from purely intuitive physical considerations; for, motion *along* an iso-surface, say, $t_2 =$ constant, has no useful effect, since even after changing its position, the representative point remains in a location whence, at best, the final point x^T can be attained in the very same t_2 seconds. Moreover, the

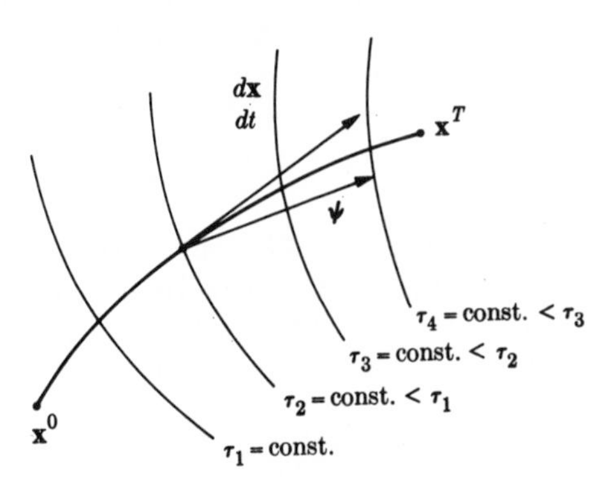

FIGURE 14.

quicker the motion along the *normal* to an iso-surface, the faster does the representative point move to the next iso-surface $t_2 - \Delta t =$ constant, so that an ever lessening time of attaining the final point $\mathbf{x}^T$ becomes possible.

As has been shown above in the Dynamic Programming method, it is required to find the functions $S[\mathbf{x}, t]$ or $\tilde{S}$, which involves very laborious operations—in general, the solution of partial differential equations; whereas when the Maximum Principle is used, all that is necessary is the vector $\tilde{\boldsymbol{\Psi}}$, which is assumed to be on the optimal trajectory, and this vector, as it turns out, can be found without constructing $\tilde{S}$. To find $\tilde{\boldsymbol{\Psi}}$ it is necessary to solve the so-called conjugate equation, which is an ordinary differential equation.

The conjugate equation has been derived by various methods. [13, 18, 24, 40–42, 62, 63, 65, 67]. The derivation given below is that of Butkovskii [63].

Assume that the function $\tilde{S}(\tilde{\mathbf{x}})$ has continuous partial derivatives with respect to all $\tilde{x}_i$ $(i = 1, \ldots, n + 2)$. Let us see how the vector $\tilde{\boldsymbol{\Psi}}$ varies with the motion of the representative point along the optimal trajectory. Since $\tilde{\boldsymbol{\Psi}} = \tilde{\boldsymbol{\Psi}}[\tilde{\mathbf{x}}(t)]$, the vector $\tilde{\boldsymbol{\Psi}}$, depending on $\tilde{\mathbf{x}}$, ultimately depends on time, and we can write

$$\begin{aligned}\frac{d\tilde{\Psi}_i}{dt} &= -\frac{d}{dt}\left(\frac{\partial \tilde{S}}{\partial \tilde{x}_i}\right) = -\sum_{j=1}^{n+2} \frac{\partial}{\partial \tilde{x}_j}\left(\frac{\partial \tilde{S}}{\partial \tilde{x}_i}\right)\frac{d\tilde{x}_j}{dt} \\ &= -\sum_{j=1}^{n+2} \frac{\partial^2 \tilde{S}}{\partial \tilde{x}_i \partial \tilde{x}_j} \tilde{f}_j^*. \end{aligned} \tag{4.18}$$

Here the notation $\tilde{f}_j^*$ indicates that the optimal control signal $\mathbf{u}^*$ has been substituted in the expression for $\tilde{f}$. The last coordinate $\tilde{\Psi}_{n+2}$ always equals (-1), as is evident from Eq. (4.4). Therefore

$$\frac{d\tilde{\Psi}_{n+2}}{dt} = 0. \tag{4.19}$$

If, for $\mathbf{u}(t)$ in Eq. (4.5), we substitute the optimal control signal $\mathbf{u}^*(t)$ along the optimal trajectory in question, we obtain

$$0 = \langle \tilde{\mathbf{\Psi}}\tilde{\mathbf{f}}^* \rangle = \sum_{j=1}^{n+2} \tilde{\Psi}_j \tilde{f}_j^* = \sum_{j=1}^{n+2} \frac{\partial \tilde{S}}{\partial \tilde{x}_j} \tilde{f}_j^*. \tag{4.20}$$

Let us consider the dependence of $\langle \tilde{\mathbf{\Psi}}\tilde{\mathbf{f}}^* \rangle$ on x_i in the case of fixed t. Since the fixed quantity $\mathbf{u}^*(t)$ is an optimal control signal only on the optimal trajectory in question, on it the expression $\langle \tilde{\mathbf{\Psi}}\tilde{\mathbf{f}}^* \rangle$ attains maximum (which is zero). Therefore the partial derivatives of this expression with respect to x_i equal zero.

Differentiating both sides of this equation with respect to $\tilde{x}_i$, we find

$$0 = \sum_{j=1}^{n+2} \frac{\partial^2 \tilde{S}}{\partial \tilde{x}_j \partial \tilde{x}_i} \tilde{f}_j^* + \sum_{j=1}^{n+2} \frac{\partial \tilde{S}}{\partial \tilde{x}_j} \frac{\partial \tilde{f}_j^*}{\partial \tilde{x}_i}. \tag{4.21}$$

Hence we obtain

$$-\sum_{j=1}^{n+2} \frac{\partial^2 \tilde{S}}{\partial \tilde{x}_i \partial \tilde{x}_j} \tilde{f}_j^* = \sum_{j=1}^{n+2} \frac{\partial \tilde{S}}{\partial \tilde{x}_j} \frac{\partial \tilde{f}_j^*}{\partial \tilde{x}_i}. \tag{4.22}$$

Observing that the right side of Eq. (4.18) is identical with the left side of (4.22), we substitute the right side of (4.22) in (4.18). As a result we find

$$\frac{d\tilde{\Psi}_i}{dt} = \sum_{j=1}^{n+2} \frac{\partial \tilde{S}}{\partial \tilde{x}_j} \frac{\partial \tilde{f}_j^*}{\partial \tilde{x}_i} = -\sum_{j=1}^{n+2} \tilde{\Psi}_j \frac{\partial \tilde{f}_j^*}{\partial \tilde{x}_i}. \tag{4.23}$$

It follows from Eq. (4.6) that, inasmuch as $\tilde{\mathbf{f}}$ depends on $\tilde{x}_i$,

$$\frac{\partial \tilde{H}}{\partial \tilde{x}_i} = \sum_{j=1}^{n+2} \tilde{\Psi}_j \frac{\partial \tilde{f}_j}{\partial \tilde{x}_i}. \tag{4.24}$$

So we can rewrite Eqs. (4.23) in compact form

$$\frac{d\tilde{\Psi}_i}{dt} = -\frac{\partial \tilde{H}}{\partial \tilde{x}_i}, \quad (i = 1, \ldots, n+1) \tag{4.25}$$

where the dependence of $\mathbf{u}$ on $\tilde{x}_i$ must be disregarded. We note that it also follows from Eq. (4.6) that

$$\frac{\partial \tilde{H}}{\partial \tilde{\Psi}_i} = \tilde{f}_i \tag{4.26}$$

inasmuch as $\tilde{\mathbf{f}}$ does not depend on $\tilde{\Psi}_i$. Hence Eqs. (1.6) or (1.8) together with (4.1) and (4.2) can be rewritten as

$$\frac{d\tilde{x}}{dt} = \frac{\partial \tilde{H}}{\partial \tilde{\Psi}_i} \tag{4.27}$$

Equations (4.25) and (4.26) are called canonical-conjugate equations. We should note that the conjugate equations (4.23) are linear differential equations for $\tilde{\boldsymbol{\Psi}}$. In them the superscript * can be omitted, as long as we remember that Eqs. (4.23) are valid only for the optimal trajectory.

Thus the values of the vector $\tilde{\boldsymbol{\Psi}}$ are found from Eq. (4.23) or (4.25). Provided that the vector $\tilde{\boldsymbol{\Psi}}$ be known, there is no need to calculate the function $\tilde{S}$. When the Maximum Principle is applied, two sets of equations, the original and the conjugate set are solved jointly. The process of solution is as follows. We assume that the system starts from some point $\tilde{\mathbf{x}} = \tilde{\mathbf{x}}^0$. We also specify the initial value $\tilde{\boldsymbol{\Psi}}^0$ of the vector $\tilde{\boldsymbol{\Psi}}$. The value of the vector $\mathbf{u}$ at the initial instant is selected from condition (4.8) in such a way that the product

$$(\tilde{H})_{\tilde{\mathbf{x}}=\tilde{\mathbf{x}}^0} = \tilde{\Psi}^0\tilde{\mathbf{f}}^0 = \tilde{\Psi}^0 \frac{d\tilde{\mathbf{x}}}{dt}(\tilde{\mathbf{x}} = \tilde{\mathbf{x}}^0, \bar{\mathbf{u}}) \tag{4.28}$$

is maximum. Having chosen the control signal $(\mathbf{u})_{t=0}$, we can find from Eqs. (1.6), (4.1), (4.2), and (4.25) the increments $\Delta\tilde{\Psi}_i$ and $\Delta\tilde{x}_i$ for a sufficiently small interval of time Δt, and so also the values of the vectors $\tilde{\boldsymbol{\Psi}}$ and $\tilde{\mathbf{x}}$ at a new point of the optimal trajectory corresponding to $t = \Delta t$. At this point, the process is repeated; new increments $\Delta\tilde{\Psi}_i$ and $\Delta\tilde{x}_i$ are found; the representative point moves on to a new location, corresponding to the instant $t = 2\Delta t$; and so on. In this way, one step at a time, we can plot the whole optimal trajectory, or, as it is often called, the extremal. At the same time, at every point, by means of minimization of $\tilde{H}$, the optimal control $\mathbf{u}^*$ results.

If explicit dependence on time is lacking in Eq. (1.6), and if it is required that minimum time of the transient process be guaranteed, that is, that $g = 1$ [see (4.16)], we can use H instead of $\tilde{H}$ and the ordinary phase space $\mathbf{x}$ instead of the space $\tilde{\mathbf{x}}$. Then the basic equations take the form

$$\frac{dx_i}{dt} = \frac{\partial H}{\partial \Psi_i}, \qquad (i = 1, \ldots, n) \tag{4.29}$$

and the conjugate equations (4.25) can be written as

$$\frac{d\Psi_i}{dt} = -\frac{\partial H}{\partial x_i}. \qquad (i = 1, \ldots, n) \tag{4.30}$$

In the process we have described for the construction of the extremal, there is one question which is not yet resolved. It is not known how the initial values of the coordinates $\tilde{\Psi}_i^0$ of the vector $(\tilde{\boldsymbol{\Psi}})_{t=0} = \tilde{\boldsymbol{\Psi}}^0$ should be selected. The choice of these values turns out to be closely connected with the boundary conditions of the problem. Let us see how this choice should be made for two particular cases.

(1) The free-end-trajectory problem with fixed time T. The problem of minimizing the functional (3.1) reduces, on introduction of the variable x_{n+2} [see also Eq. (4.2)] to the problem of minimizing the value of $x_{n+2}(T)$.

We already know that for this it is necessary to implement as high an "acceleration" of the representative point along the appropriately chosen vector $\tilde{\mathbf{\Psi}}$ as possible. However, in the "last" interval of time $T - \Delta t$, where Δt is small, the required sign of the maximal "acceleration" can be found from simple considerations. This also means that the vector $\tilde{\mathbf{\Psi}}$ is found for the "last" interval of time, that is (when $\Delta t \to 0$), the quantity $\tilde{\mathbf{\Psi}}(T)$. For in the "last instant" $t = T$, the vector $d\tilde{\mathbf{x}}/dt$ must have a direction such that the increment $x_{n+2}(T)$ shall be as small as possible, that is, that the projection of $d\tilde{\mathbf{x}}/dt$ upon the direction opposite to x_{n+2} shall be as large as possible. So the vector $\tilde{\mathbf{\Psi}}(T)$ must have the direction opposite to x_{n+2}. Since $\tilde{\Psi}_{n+2} = -1$ [see (4.4)] the value of $\tilde{\mathbf{\Psi}}(T)$ comes out as

$$\tilde{\mathbf{\Psi}}(T) = (0, \ldots, 0, -1). \tag{4.31}$$

Thus $\tilde{\Psi}_i(T) = 0$, $(i = 1, \ldots, n + 1)$. This also gives us the final values of $\tilde{\Psi}_i(T)$. The initial values of $\tilde{\Psi}_i^0$ must be so selected that the final values of $\tilde{\Psi}_i$ are those given.

(2) The problem where the end of the trajectory $\mathbf{x}^T$ in the space $\mathbf{x}$ is fixed, and the time T, which is the criterion of optimality, is not fixed beforehand. It is required to control the process so that the representative point $\mathbf{x}$ is brought from a given initial location $\mathbf{x}^0$ to a given final location $\mathbf{x}^T$ in minimum time; see Fig. 14.

In the case of a joint solution of Eqs. (4.29) and (4.30) with parallel selection of u so as to maximize H at every point of the optimal trajectory, there are n known initial values $x_1^0, \ldots, x_n^0$, the coordinates of the point $\mathbf{x}^0$, and n initial values $\Psi_1^0, \ldots, \Psi_n^0$, the coordinates of the vector $\mathbf{\Psi}^0$. The latter are unknown. They have to be selected so as to satisfy n given boundary conditions at the end of the trajectory, that is, the n given conditions $x_1^T, \ldots, x_n^T$ of the coordinates of the vector $\mathbf{x}^T$.

There are no general rules for the selection of the initial value $\mathbf{\Psi}^0$ of the vector $\mathbf{\Psi}$. Let us fix at hazard upon a vector $\mathbf{\Psi}^0$; see Fig. 15. We shall construct the optimal trajectory (extremal) M_0M_1 in the way indicated. Assume that it does not pass through the required point M_T of coordinate $\bar{\mathbf{x}}^T$. We shall then fix upon another value for the vector $\mathbf{\Psi}^0$, and construct another extremal M_0M_2, and

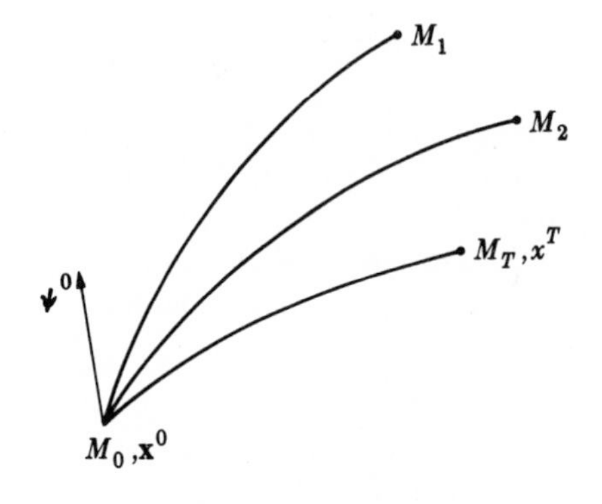

FIGURE 15.

shall continue in this way until the extremal does pass through the point M_T. This process can be rationalized [32] by introducing a measure R of the distance of the extremal M_0M_1 from the required point M_T. This measure can be, for instance, the smallest of the distances of points on the curve M_0M_1 from M_T. Then, by a search carried out in accordance with a well-known procedure, we must choose the coordinates $\Psi_1^0, \ldots, \Psi_n^0$ in such a way as to minimize R. This minimum, of course, should be zero.

Let us consider a simple example of the application of the Maximum Principle to a case with a free end to the trajectory and a fixed time T [65]. It is required to find the control signal minimizing the integral

$$Q = \frac{1}{2}\int_0^T (x^2 + u^2)\, dt \tag{4.32}$$

while the equation of the plant is of the first order

$$\frac{dx}{dt} = -ax + u. \tag{4.33}$$

The value $(x)_{t=0} = x^0$ is given. The control signal u is not restricted in any way. We shall introduce the variables

$$x_1(t) = x(t); \quad x_2(t) = \frac{1}{2}\int_0^t (x_1{}^2 + u^2)\, dt. \tag{4.34}$$

We then obtain a set of two equations

$$\frac{dx_1}{dt} = -ax_1 + u; \quad \frac{dx_2}{dt} = \tfrac{1}{2}x_1{}^2 + \tfrac{1}{2}u^2. \tag{4.35}$$

The second of these is analogous to Eq. (4.2). We now obtain the function $\tilde{H}$ using condition (4.8)

$$\tilde{H} = \tilde{\Psi}_1 \frac{dx_1}{dt} + \tilde{\Psi}_2 \frac{dx_2}{dt} = \tilde{\Psi}_1(-ax_1 + u) + \tilde{\Psi}_2\, \tfrac{1}{2}(x_1{}^2 + u^2). \tag{4.36}$$

We also obtain the conjugate equations for $\tilde{\Psi}_1$ and $\tilde{\Psi}_2$, using Eq.(4.23) or (4.25)

$$\frac{d\tilde{\Psi}_1}{dt} = a\tilde{\Psi}_1 - \tilde{\Psi}_2 x_1; \quad \frac{d\tilde{\Psi}_2}{dt} = 0. \tag{4.37}$$

The second of these equations is analogous to (4.19). Since the initial value $x_2(0) = 0$ [see Eq. (4.2)] and the final values of $\tilde{\Psi}_1$ and $\tilde{\Psi}_2$ [see (4.31)] are $\tilde{\Psi}_1(T) = 0$, $\tilde{\Psi}_2(T) = -1$, (4.35) and (4.37) must be solved with the initial conditions

$$x_1(0) = x^0,\ x_2(0) = 0,\ \tilde{\Psi}_1(T) = 0,\ \tilde{\Psi}_2(T) = -1. \tag{4.38}$$

The control signal u should be so selected, at every instant of time, as to minimize $\tilde{H}$; see Eq. (4.36). By virtue of Eqs. (4.37) and (4.38)

$$\tilde{\Psi}_2(t) = -1 = \text{const.} \tag{4.39}$$

So we find from Eq. (4.36)

$$\tilde{H} = -a\tilde{\Psi}_1 x_1 + \tilde{\Psi}_1 u - \frac{x_1^2}{2} - \frac{u^2}{2}. \tag{4.40}$$

Equating the derivative $\partial\tilde{H}/\partial u$ to zero, we find the optimal value u^*

$$u^* = \tilde{\Psi}_1. \tag{4.41}$$

Substituting this value in the equation for x_1 and $\tilde{\Psi}_1$, we arrive at a set of equations (the function x_2 does not enter into these equations, and does not concern us)

$$\frac{dx_1}{dt} = -ax_1 + \tilde{\Psi}_1, \quad \frac{d\tilde{\Psi}_1}{dt} = a\tilde{\Psi}_1 + x_1. \tag{4.42}$$

The boundary conditions for this set [see Eq. (4.38)] have the form

$$x_1(0) = x^0, \tilde{\Psi}_1(T) = 0. \tag{4.43}$$

The linear equations (4.42) are easily integrated; we get

$$x_1(t) = C_1 e^{pt} + C_2 e^{-pt}, \tilde{\Psi}_1(t) = D_1 e^{pt} + D_2 e^{-pt} \tag{4.44}$$

where

$$p = \sqrt{a^2 + 1} \tag{4.45}$$

is a root of the characteristic equation. From the conditions

$$x^0 = x_1(0) = C_1 + C_2, \quad 0 = \tilde{\Psi}_1(T) = D_1 e^{pT} + D_2 e^{-pT}$$

$$C_1 p - C_2 p = \frac{dx_1}{dt}(0) = -ax_1(0) + \tilde{\Psi}_1(0) = -ax^0 + D_1 + D_2$$

$$D_1 p - D_2 p = \frac{d\tilde{\Psi}_1(0)}{dt} = a\tilde{\Psi}_1(0) + x_1(0) = a(D_1 + D_2) + x^0 \tag{4.46}$$

it is easy to find C_1, C_2, D_1, D_2. In particular,

$$D_1 = \frac{x^0}{(p-a) + (p+a)e^{2pT}}, \quad D_2 = \frac{x^0 e^{2pT}}{(p-a) + (p+a)e^{2pT}} \tag{4.47}$$

whence see [Eqs. (4.41) and (4.44)] it follows that

$$u^*(t) = \tilde{\Psi}_1(t) = \frac{x^0}{(p-a) + (p+a)e^{2pT}} (e^{pt} - e^{2pT-pt}). \tag{4.48}$$

Let us turn to the problem of the minimum response time and to Eq. (2.6); we shall assume the roots of the characteristic equation (2.7) to be real and positive. Let $|u| \leqslant U =$ constant. We assume that $x_1 = x$ and $x_{k+1} = d^k x/dt^k$

($k = 1, \ldots, n - 1$). Then we can replace Eq. (2.6) by a set of n-equations

$$\frac{dx_1}{dt} = x_2, \ldots, \frac{dx_{n-1}}{dt} = x_n; \quad \frac{dx_n}{dt} = \frac{u - a_1 x_n - \cdots - a_n x_1}{a_0}. \tag{4.49}$$

Let us write the expression

$$\begin{aligned} H &= \sum_{i=1}^{n} \Psi_i f_i \\ &= \Psi_1 x_2 + \Psi_2 x_3 + \cdots + \Psi_{n-1} x_n + \Psi_n \frac{u - a_1 x_n - \cdots - a_n x_1}{a_0}. \end{aligned} \tag{4.50}$$

We select u in the range $|u| \leqslant U$ so as to achieve maximum of H. Variation of u only affects the term $\Psi_n u/a_0$. Since $a_0 > 0$, to the maximum of H there corresponds the condition

$$u = U \operatorname{sign} \Psi_n. \tag{4.51}$$

Writing out the conjugate equations (4.30), it is easy to establish that the equation obtained for Ψ_n is linear with constant coefficients and with real roots. But in this case, as is known, whatever the initial conditions, $\Psi_n(t)$ changes sign not more than $(n - 1)$ times. Therefore there are, in the general case, n-intervals in which the sign of u is constant; this also implies the validity of the theorem of the n-intervals.

5. Optimal Systems with Accumulation of Information

In Section 1 of this chapter we have indicated the characteristic features of optimal systems with both passive and active accumulation of information. Systems of the second type have been called systems of dual control [34]. A class of systems is examined below in which both processes of accumulation proceed simultaneously [33]. Information on the command input x^* (see Fig. 4) accumulates passively, and information on the disturbance z, that is, on those characteristics of the plant B which vary, is accumulated actively, by means of rational "experiments" carried out automatically by the controller A.

We shall consider the quantities entering into the block diagram of Fig. 4 only at discrete instants of time $t = 0, 1, \ldots, N$, where N is a fixed instant. In this section, we shall label the symbol for every quantity at the sth discrete instant with the subscript s—for instance, x_s^*, x_s, y_s, etc. Let the discrete value of the noise inputs h_s^*, h_s, g_s form sequences of independent random quantities with invariable probability densities $P(h_s^*)$, $P(h_s)$, $P(g_s)$. Furthermore, let z_s and x_s^* be functions of random vectors of the parameters $\boldsymbol{\mu}$ and $\boldsymbol{\lambda}$, respectively

$$z_s = z(s, \boldsymbol{\mu}); \quad x_s^* = x_s^*(s, \boldsymbol{\lambda}) \tag{5.1}$$

where

$$\boldsymbol{\mu} = (\mu_1, \ldots, \mu_m); \quad \boldsymbol{\lambda} = (\lambda_1, \ldots, \lambda_l). \tag{5.2}$$

For example, let us imagine the functions of time s

$$z_s = \mu_1 + \mu_2 s; \quad x_s^* = \lambda_1 + \lambda_2 s + \lambda_3 s^2 \tag{5.3}$$

or some other functions, not necessarily polynomials in s. We shall assume the *a priori* probability densities $P(\boldsymbol{\mu})$ and $P(\boldsymbol{\lambda})$ of the vectors $\boldsymbol{\mu}$ and $\boldsymbol{\lambda}$ to be given.

We assume the plant B to have no memory. This means that the value of x_s depends only on the values of z and v at the sth instant of time

$$x_s = F_0(z_s, v_s). \tag{5.4}$$

Generalization for plants with memory has been carried out [34].

We define the purpose of control as follows: let the specific loss function (the "cost" of diverging from the ideal) corresponding to the sth instant of time have the form

$$W_s = W_s(s, x_s, x_s^*). \tag{5.5}$$

Furthermore, let the total loss function W for the whole interval of time N equal the sum of the specific loss functions

$$W = \sum_{s=0}^{s=N} W_s(s, x_s, x_s^*). \tag{5.6}$$

We shall call optimal a system for which the average risk R, that is, the expected value of W, is minimum. The value of the risk is expressed by

$$\begin{aligned} R = E\{W\} &= E\left\{\sum_{s=0}^{s=N} W_s(s, x_s, x_s^*)\right\} \\ &= \sum_{s=0}^{s=N} E\{W_s\} = \sum_{s=0}^{s=N} R_s. \end{aligned} \tag{5.7}$$

We shall call $R_s = E\{W_s\}$ the specific risk at the sth sampling time. Here the average risk R acts as the criterion of optimality Q.

We shall assume that the ways in which signal and noise combine in the blocks H^*, H, and G (see Fig. 4) are known and invariable, and that the blocks themselves have no memory. Therefore

$$v_s = v_s(u_s, g_s); \quad y_s^* = y_s^*(h_s^*, x_s^*); \quad y_s = y_s(h_s, x_s). \tag{5.8}$$

We shall assume the random quantities $\boldsymbol{\mu}$, $\boldsymbol{\lambda}$, g_s, h_s, and h_s^* to be independent. Let us introduce the vectors $(0 \leqslant s \leqslant N)$

$$\begin{aligned} &\mathbf{u}_s = (u_0, u_1, \ldots, u_s); \quad \mathbf{x}_s^* = (x_0^*, x_1^*, \ldots, x_s^*); \\ &\mathbf{v}_s = (v_0, v_1, \ldots, v_s); \quad \mathbf{y}_s^* = (y_0^*, y_1^*, \ldots, y_s^*); \\ &\mathbf{x}_s = (x_0, x_1, \ldots, x_s); \quad \mathbf{y}_s = (y_0, y_1, \ldots, y_s). \end{aligned} \tag{5.9}$$

The coordinates of each of these vectors consist of the consecutive values of the variable at different discrete instants of time. We may call such vectors "time vectors."

We shall assume the controller A to possess a memory; besides this, we shall suppose, for the sake of generality, the algorithm of this device to be random. This means that the control signal u_s is an radom function of the y_i and u_i entering the input of A in the preceding instants of time $(0 \leqslant i \leqslant s)$, and also of the y_j^*, $(0 \leqslant j \leqslant s)$.

It is required to find the optimal probability densities—in other words, the optimal random strategies

$$P_s(u_s) = \Gamma_s(u_s \mid \mathbf{u}_{s-1}, \mathbf{y}_{s-1}, y_s^*) \quad (0 \leqslant s \leqslant N). \tag{5.10}$$

Here the vectors $\mathbf{u}_{s-1}$, $\mathbf{y}_{s-1}$, and $\mathbf{y}_s^*$ are shown to the right of the slash; they are assumed to be known in the equation for the conditional probability density. The probability density Γ_s is a function of these vectors. The problem is to find that sequence of functions Γ_s for which the average risk R is minimal. Since Γ_s is a probability density

$$\int_{\Omega(u_s)} \Gamma_s(u_s)\, d\Omega(u_s) = 1 \tag{5.11}$$

where $\Omega(u_s)$ is the region of variation of u_s and $d\Omega(u_s)$ is an infinitesimally small portion of it. We have to find the optimal functions Γ_s when restrictions of the type (5.11) are laid upon these functions, and restrictions of the type (1.11) are imposed upon the values of the control signal u_s. To do this, it is first necessary to derive the equation of the risk R. We shall first work out the equation for the *conditional* specific risk r_s, understanding by this the risk at the sth sampling instant when the "prehistory" of the inputs of the controller A is fixed, that is, when the values of $\mathbf{y}_s^*$, $\mathbf{u}_{s-1}$, $\mathbf{y}_{s-1}$ are fixed. We assume that the previous values of the u_i $(i < s)$ are stored, as also are the y_i and y_i^*, and that they affect the selection of u_s. Using the well-known formulas of probability theory, we can write

$$\begin{aligned} r_s &= E\{W_s \mid \mathbf{y}_s^*, \mathbf{u}_{s-1}, \mathbf{y}_{s-1}\} \\ &= \int_{\Omega(\boldsymbol{\lambda}, x_s)} W_s[s, x_s^*(s, \boldsymbol{\lambda}), x_s] P(\boldsymbol{\lambda}, x_s \mid \mathbf{y}_s^*, \mathbf{u}_{s-1}, \mathbf{y}_{s-1})\, d\Omega(\boldsymbol{\lambda}, x). \end{aligned} \tag{5.12}$$

Here $\Omega(\boldsymbol{\lambda}, x_s)$ is the region of variation of $\boldsymbol{\lambda}$ and x_s with coordinates $(\lambda_1, \ldots, \lambda_l, x_s)$; $d\Omega(\boldsymbol{\lambda}, x_s)$ is an infinitesimally small portion of it, and $P(\boldsymbol{\lambda}, x_s \mid \mathbf{y}_s^*, \mathbf{y}_{s-1}, \mathbf{u}_{s-1})$ is the conditional joint probability density of $\boldsymbol{\lambda}$ and x_s with fixed vectors $\mathbf{y}_s^*$, $\mathbf{u}_{s-1}$, $\mathbf{y}_{s-1}$. From the well-known theorem of probability theory

$$P(\boldsymbol{\lambda}, x_s \mid \mathbf{y}_s^*, \mathbf{u}_{s-1}, \mathbf{y}_{s-1}) = P(\boldsymbol{\lambda} \mid \mathbf{y}_s^*, \mathbf{u}_{s-1}, \mathbf{y}_{s-1}) \cdot P(x_s \mid \boldsymbol{\lambda}, \mathbf{y}_s^*, \mathbf{u}_{s-1}, \mathbf{y}_{s-1}). \tag{5.13}$$

The probability density of $\boldsymbol{\lambda}$ depends on $\mathbf{y}_s^*$, but not on $\mathbf{u}_{s-1}$ or $\mathbf{y}_{s-1}$, as can be seen from Fig. 4. Therefore

$$P(\boldsymbol{\lambda} \mid \mathbf{y}_s^*, \mathbf{u}_{s-1}, \mathbf{y}_{s-1}) = P(\boldsymbol{\lambda} \mid \mathbf{y}_s^*) = P_s(\boldsymbol{\lambda}). \tag{5.14}$$

Here the notation $P_s(\boldsymbol{\lambda})$ is used, since this expression is the *a posteriori* probability density for $\boldsymbol{\lambda}$, calculated at the sth instant of time on the basis of the observed values of $y_0, y_1, \ldots, y_s$.

The probability density for x_s with fixed $\mathbf{y}_s^*$, $\mathbf{y}_{s-1}$, $\mathbf{u}_{s-1}$ does not vary, provided $\boldsymbol{\lambda}$ has been fixed. Therefore

$$P(x_s \mid \boldsymbol{\lambda}, \mathbf{y}_s^*, \mathbf{y}_{s-1}, \mathbf{u}_{s-1}) = P(x_s \mid \mathbf{y}_s^*, \mathbf{u}_{s-1}, \mathbf{y}_{s-1}). \tag{5.15}$$

Substituting Eqs. (5.14) and (5.15) into (5.13), and (5.13) into (5.12), we obtain

$$r_s = \int_{\Omega(\boldsymbol{\lambda}, x_s)} W_s[s, x_s^*(s, \boldsymbol{\lambda}), x_s] P_s(\boldsymbol{\lambda}) P(x_s \mid \mathbf{y}_s^*, \mathbf{u}_{s-1}, \mathbf{y}_{s-1})\, d\Omega(\boldsymbol{\lambda}, x_s). \tag{5.16}$$

At the sth instant of time, let the *a posteriori* probability density of the vector $\boldsymbol{\mu}$ be $P_s(\boldsymbol{\mu})$; we shall denote the conditional probability density of x_s with fixed $\boldsymbol{\mu}$ and u_s by $P(x_s \mid \boldsymbol{\mu}, u_s)$. Figure 4 shows that

$$P(x_s \mid \mathbf{y}_s^*, \mathbf{u}_{s-1}, \mathbf{y}_{s-1}) = \int_{\Omega(\boldsymbol{\mu}, u_s)} P(x_s \mid \boldsymbol{\mu}, u_s) P(\boldsymbol{\mu}) \Gamma_s(u_s \mid \mathbf{y}_s^*, \mathbf{u}_{s-1}, \mathbf{y}_{s-1})\, d\Omega(\boldsymbol{\mu}, u_s). \tag{5.17}$$

Substituting this expression into Eq. (5.16), we find

$$r_s = \int_{\Omega(\boldsymbol{\lambda}, \boldsymbol{\mu}, x_s, u_s)} W_s[s, x_s^*(s, \boldsymbol{\lambda}), x_s] \times P_s(\boldsymbol{\lambda}) P(x_s \mid \boldsymbol{\mu}, u_s) P_s(\boldsymbol{\mu}) \Gamma_s(u_s \mid \mathbf{y}_s^*, \mathbf{u}_{s-1}, \mathbf{y}_{s-1})\, d\Omega(\boldsymbol{\lambda}, \boldsymbol{\mu}, x_s, u_s). \tag{5.18}$$

In article III of Feldbaum [34] we derive the expression

$$P_s(\boldsymbol{\mu}) = P(\boldsymbol{\mu}) \frac{\prod_{i=0}^{s-1} P(y_i \mid \boldsymbol{\mu}, i, u_i) \cdot \prod_{i=0}^{s-1} \Gamma_i}{P(\mathbf{y}_{s-1}, \mathbf{u}_{s-1} \mid \mathbf{y}_s^*)} \tag{5.19}$$

where Γ_i is the strategy at the ith instant of time, $P(y_i \mid \boldsymbol{\mu}, i, u_i)$ is the conditional probability density for y_i in the case of fixed $\boldsymbol{\mu}$ and u_i at the ith instant of time, and $P(\mathbf{y}_{s-1}, \mathbf{u}_{s-1})$ is the joint probability density of the vectors $\mathbf{y}_{s-1}$ and $\mathbf{u}_{s-1}$. The *a posteriori* probability density $P_s(\boldsymbol{\lambda})$ can be obtained with the aid of Bayes' formula, which is well known in probability theory. Let us recall the derivation of this formula. Since the joint probability density is

$$P(\boldsymbol{\lambda}, \mathbf{y}_s^*) = P(\boldsymbol{\lambda}) P(\mathbf{y}_s^* \mid \boldsymbol{\lambda}) = P(\boldsymbol{\lambda} \mid \mathbf{y}_s^*) \cdot P(\mathbf{y}_s^*) \tag{5.20}$$

it follows that

$$P_s(\boldsymbol{\lambda}) = P(\boldsymbol{\lambda} \mid \mathbf{y}_s^*) = P(\boldsymbol{\lambda}) \frac{P(\mathbf{y}_s^* \mid \boldsymbol{\lambda})}{P(\mathbf{y}_s^*)}. \tag{5.21}$$

Inasmuch as the h_i^* are independent for different i, we can write

$$P(\mathbf{y}_s^* \mid \boldsymbol{\lambda}) = \prod_{i=0}^{s} P(y_i^* \mid \boldsymbol{\lambda}). \tag{5.22}$$

Let us consider the difference in principle between Eqs. (5.19) and (5.21). The accumulation of information on z or $\boldsymbol{\mu}$, that is, essentially, on the unpredictable varying characteristics of B, is expressed by the fact that the *a priori* probability density $P(\boldsymbol{\mu})$ is superseded at every sampling instant by the *a posteriori* densities $P_s(\boldsymbol{\mu})$, which characterize $\boldsymbol{\mu}$ with ever increasing precision. It is clear from Eq. (5.19) that the functions $P_s(\boldsymbol{\mu})$, and, consequently, the rate of information accumulation, too, depend on all the preceding strategies Γ_i, $(0 \leqslant i \leqslant s)$. In other words, the rate of identifying the plant depends on how appropriate the experiment used in the analysis of the plant, i.e., the control signals u_i and the evaluation of the plant reactions y_i to these signals, are. In Eq. (5.21), on the other hand, for $P_s(\boldsymbol{\lambda})$ the rate of accumulation of information does not depend on the strategies Γ_i, that is, the information accumulation process is passive or independent.

For different processes taking place in the system, the vectors $\mathbf{y}_s^*$, $\mathbf{u}_{s-1}$, and $\mathbf{y}_{s-1}$, which are not, in general, known beforehand, can take different values. Let $P(\mathbf{y}_s^*, \mathbf{u}_{s-1}, \mathbf{y}_{s-1})$ be the joint density of these vectors. Then the specific average risk R_s, which is the average value of r_s when mass tests of the system are carried out, is defined by

$$R_s = \int_{\Omega(\mathbf{y}_s^*, \mathbf{u}_{s-1}, \mathbf{y}_{s-1})} r_s P(\mathbf{y}_s^*, \mathbf{u}_{s-1}, \mathbf{y}_{s-1})\, d\Omega(\mathbf{y}_s^*, \mathbf{u}_{s-1}, \mathbf{y}_{s-1}). \tag{5.23}$$

Let us now assume that

$$\begin{aligned} P(\mathbf{y}_s^*, \mathbf{u}_{s-1}, \mathbf{y}_{s-1}) &= P(\mathbf{u}_{s-1}, \mathbf{y}_{s-1} \mid y_s^*) \cdot P(\mathbf{y}_s^* \mid \mathbf{u}_{s-1}, \mathbf{y}_{s-1}) \\ &= P(\mathbf{u}_{s-1}, \mathbf{y}_{s-1}) \cdot P(\mathbf{y}_s^*) \end{aligned} \tag{5.24}$$

Substituting Eqs. (5.24) and (5.18) into (5.23), and taking into account (5.19), (5.21), and (5.22), we obtain the expression for R_s in the following form

$$\begin{aligned} R_s = &\int_{\Omega(\boldsymbol{\lambda}, \boldsymbol{\mu}, x_s, \mathbf{y}_s^*, \mathbf{u}_s, \mathbf{y}_{s-1})} W_s[s, x_s^*(s, \boldsymbol{\lambda}), x_s] P(\boldsymbol{\lambda}) \left[\prod_{i=0}^{s} P(y_i^* \mid \boldsymbol{\lambda}) P(x_s \mid \boldsymbol{\mu}, u_s)\right] \\ &\times P(\boldsymbol{\mu}) \left[\prod_{i=0}^{s-1} P(y_i \mid \boldsymbol{\mu}, i, u_i)\right] \left[\prod_{i=0}^{s} \Gamma_i\right] d\Omega(\boldsymbol{\lambda}, \boldsymbol{\mu}, x_s, \mathbf{y}_s^*, \mathbf{u}_s, \mathbf{y}_{s-1}). \end{aligned} \tag{5.25}$$

It should be noted that, although in the case in question the plant B has no memory, the risk R_s at the sth instant of time depends on all the strategies Γ_i at the instants of time $t = 0, 1, \ldots, s$. The physical reason for this property, which does not hold in an open-loop system, is, precisely, the duality of control. The control signal at the kth instant of time must be designed not only to decrease R_k, that is, the risk corresponding to the given instant of time; it must also, by means of a better study of the plant, promote diminution of the risks R_i, $(i > k)$, in the succeeding instants of time. Let us consider S_k, a part of the total risk [see Eq. (5.7)] depending on the strategy Γ_k

$$S_k = \sum_{i=k}^{N} R_i = R_k + \sum_{i=k+1}^{N} R_i. \tag{5.26}$$

With respect to Γ_k, the first term of the right side may be called the *risk of action*, and the second, the *risk of study*. The primitive strategy which selects the signal u_s (or its probability density Γ_s) in such a way as to minimize only the risk of action, is not optimal. On the other hand, to ignore the risk of action and to minimize only the risk of study, that is, to select u_s with the aim of making the best use of the result of the study in the succeeding actions, is also not optimal behavior. The optimal strategy minimizes the sum S_k of the risks of action and study.

In determining the optimal strategy, we shall make use of the ideas of Dynamic Programming. Let us first consider the risk R_N for the last instant of time $t = N$, assuming the strategies $\Gamma_0, \ldots, \Gamma_{N-1}$ to have been obtained by some means. From Eq. (5.25) it follows that

$$\begin{aligned} R_N = & \int\limits_{\Omega(\boldsymbol{\lambda}, \boldsymbol{\mu}, x_N, \mathbf{y}_N^*, \mathbf{u}_N, \mathbf{y}_{N-1})} W_N[N, x_N^*(N, \boldsymbol{\lambda}), x_N] P(\boldsymbol{\lambda}) \left[\prod_{i=0}^{N} P(y_i^* \mid \boldsymbol{\lambda}) P(x_N \mid \boldsymbol{\mu}, u_N)\right] P(\boldsymbol{\mu}) \\ & \times \left[\prod_{i=0}^{N-1} P(y_i \mid \boldsymbol{\mu}, i, u_i)\right]\left[\prod_{i=0}^{N-1} \Gamma_i\right] \cdot \Gamma_N(u_N \mid \mathbf{y}_N^*, \mathbf{u}_{N-1}, \mathbf{y}_{N-1}) \\ & \times d\Omega(\boldsymbol{\lambda}, \boldsymbol{\mu}, x_N, \mathbf{y}_N^*, \mathbf{u}_N, \mathbf{y}_{N-1}). \end{aligned} \tag{5.27}$$

Let us introduce the auxiliary functions

$$\begin{aligned} \alpha_k = & \int\limits_{\Omega(\boldsymbol{\lambda}, \boldsymbol{\mu}, x_k)} W_k[k, x_k^*(k, \boldsymbol{\lambda}), x_k] \cdot P(\boldsymbol{\lambda}) \left[\prod_{i=0}^{k} P(y_i^* \mid \boldsymbol{\lambda})\right] P(x_k \mid \boldsymbol{\mu}, u_k) P(\boldsymbol{\mu}) \\ & \times \left[\prod_{i=0}^{k-1} P(y_i \mid \boldsymbol{\mu}, i, u_i)\right] d\Omega(\boldsymbol{\lambda}, \boldsymbol{\mu}, x_k) \end{aligned} \tag{5.28}$$

and

$$\beta_k = \prod_{i=0}^{k} \Gamma_i. \tag{5.29}$$

Then

$$\begin{aligned} R_N &= \int\limits_{\Omega(\mathbf{u}_N, \mathbf{y}_{N-1}, \mathbf{y}_N^*)} \alpha_N(\mathbf{u}_N, \mathbf{y}_{N-1}, \mathbf{y}_N^*) \beta_{N-1} \Gamma_N \, d\Omega(\mathbf{u}_N, \mathbf{y}_{N-1}, \mathbf{y}_N^*) \\ &= \int\limits_{\Omega(\mathbf{u}_{N-1}, \mathbf{y}_{N-1}, \mathbf{y}_N^*)} \beta_{N-1} \mathscr{H}_N(\mathbf{u}_{N-1}, \mathbf{y}_{N-1}, \mathbf{y}_N^*) \, d\Omega(\mathbf{u}_{N-1}, \mathbf{y}_{N-1}, \mathbf{y}_N^*) \end{aligned} \tag{5.30}$$

where

$$\begin{aligned} & \mathscr{H}_N(\mathbf{u}_{N-1}, \mathbf{y}_{N-1}, \mathbf{y}_N^*) \\ & \quad = \int\limits_{\Omega(u_N)} \alpha_N(u_N, \mathbf{u}_{N-1}, \mathbf{y}_{N-1}, \mathbf{y}_N^*) \Gamma_N(u_N, \mathbf{u}_{N-1}, \mathbf{y}_{N-1}, \mathbf{y}_N^*) \, d\Omega(u_N). \end{aligned} \tag{5.31}$$

On the basis of the mean value theorem, and taking Eq. (5.11) into account, we can write

$$\mathscr{H}_N = (\alpha_N)_{cp} \int_{\Omega(u_N)} \Gamma_N \, d\Omega(u_N) = (\alpha_N)_{cp} \geqslant (\alpha_N)_{\min} \tag{5.32}$$

We have to select Γ_N so as to minimize R_N. This can be done if for *any* $\mathbf{u}_{N-1}, \mathbf{y}_{N-1}, \mathbf{y}_N^*$; we select Γ_N in such a way that the function $\mathscr{H}_N$ is minimum. Let us select the values $u_N = u_N^*$ so as to minimize the function α_N. We shall also introduce the notation $\gamma_N = \alpha_N$ and shall write

$$\gamma_N^* = \alpha_N(u_N^*, \mathbf{u}_{N-1}, \mathbf{y}_{N-1}, \mathbf{y}_N^*) = \min_{u_N \in \Omega(u_N)} \alpha_N(u_N, \mathbf{u}_{N-1}, \mathbf{y}_{N-1}, \mathbf{y}_N^*). \tag{5.33}$$

Obviously, u_N^* is a function of $\mathbf{u}_{N-1}, \mathbf{y}_{N-1}, \mathbf{y}_N^*$

$$u_N^* = u_N^*(\mathbf{u}_{N-1}, \mathbf{y}_{N-1}, \mathbf{y}_N^*). \tag{5.34}$$

We shall show that the optimal strategy Γ_N^* is given by

$$\Gamma_N^* = \delta(u_N - u_N^*) \tag{5.35}$$

where δ is the unit-impulse function (delta function). Since it follows from Eq. (5.35) that $\Gamma_N^* = 0$ when $u_N \neq u_N^*$, then Γ_N^* is a *regular*, not a random, strategy. The optimal value of u_N is u_N^* [see Eq. (5.34)] and is chosen as a function of the values of $u_s, y_s, (s = 0, \ldots, N-1)$ and $y_i^*, (i = 0, \ldots, N)$ previously fed to the controller A.

The proof of the validity of expression (5.35) is very simple. Substituting it into Eq. (5.31), we obtain, by virtue of the well-known property of the delta function.

$$\mathscr{H}_N = \min_{u_N \in \Omega(u_N)} \alpha_N(u_N, \mathbf{u}_{N-1}, \mathbf{y}_{N-1}, \mathbf{y}_N^*) = (\alpha_N) \min. \tag{5.36}$$

But it follows from Eq. (5.32) that this value is the smallest possible value of $\mathscr{H}_N$. Therefore Γ_N^* is the optimal strategy.

To find the optimal strategies Γ_i^* for $i < N$, we must proceed step by step from the instant $t = N$ to the origin. For instance, to find Γ_{N-1}^*, we consider the two last terms of the risk R, i.e., the sum

$$\begin{aligned} S_{N-1} = R_{N-1} + R_N &= \int_{\Omega(\mathbf{y}_{N-2}, \mathbf{u}_{N-1}, \mathbf{y}_{N-1}^*)} \alpha_{N-1}\beta_{N-1} \, d\Omega(\mathbf{u}_{N-1}, \mathbf{y}_{N-2}, \mathbf{y}_{N-1}^*) \\ &\quad + \int_{\Omega(\mathbf{u}_N, \mathbf{y}_{N-1}, \mathbf{y}_N^*)} \alpha_N\beta_N \, d\Omega(\mathbf{u}_N, \mathbf{y}_{N-1}, \mathbf{y}_N^*) \\ &= \int_{\Omega(\mathbf{u}_{N-2}, \mathbf{y}_{N-2}, \mathbf{y}_{N-1}^*)} \beta_{N-2}\mathscr{H}_{N-1}(\mathbf{u}_{N-2}, \mathbf{y}_{N-2}, \mathbf{y}_{N-1}^*) \; d\Omega(\mathbf{u}_{N-2}, \mathbf{y}_{N-2}, \mathbf{y}_{N-1}^*) \end{aligned} \tag{5.37}$$

where

$$\mathscr{H}_{N-1}(\mathbf{u}_{N-2}, \mathbf{y}_{N-2}, \mathbf{y}_{N-1}^*) = \int\limits_{\Omega(u_{N-1})} \Bigg\{\Gamma_{N-1}\alpha_{N-1} + \int\limits_{\Omega(y_{N-1}, y_N^*)} \Gamma_{N-1}\alpha_N \, d\Omega(y_{N-1}, y_N^*)\Bigg\} d\Omega(u_{N-1}). \quad (5.38)$$

Let us consider the function

$$\gamma_{N-1} = \gamma_{N-1}(\mathbf{u}_{N-1}, \mathbf{y}_{N-2}, \mathbf{y}_{N-2}^*) = \alpha_{N-1} + \int\limits_{\Omega(y_{N-1}, y_N^*)} \gamma_N^*(u_N^*, \mathbf{u}_{N-1}, \mathbf{y}_{N-1}, \mathbf{y}_{N-1}^*) \times d\Omega(y_{N-1}, y_N^*). \quad (5.39)$$

Let us find the value u_{N-1}^* which minimizes this function. Obviously it depends, in general, on $\mathbf{u}_{N-2}, \mathbf{y}_{N-2}, \mathbf{y}_{N-1}^*$

$$u_{N-1}^* = u_{N-1}^*(\mathbf{u}_{N-2}, \mathbf{y}_{N-2}, \mathbf{y}_{N-1}^*). \quad (5.40)$$

Then the optimal strategy, that is

$$\Gamma_{N-1}^* = \delta(u_{N-1} - u_{N-1}^*) \quad (5.41)$$

is also regular. The proof of the validity of this result is analogous to that given above for Γ_N^*. Continuing this process, we come to the following rule for obtaining the optimal strategy: let

$$\gamma_N = \alpha_N$$

and

$$\gamma_{N-k} = \alpha_{N-k} + \int\limits_{\Omega(y_{N-k}, y_{N-k+1}^*)} \gamma_{N-k+1}(u_{N-k+1}^*, \mathbf{u}_{N-k}, \mathbf{y}_{N-k}, \mathbf{y}_{N-k+1}^*) \times d\Omega(y_{N-k}, y_{N-k+1}^*) \quad (5.42)$$

and let u_{N-k}^* be the value of u_{N-k} which minimizes γ_{N-k}.

Obviously, in the general case

$$u_{N-k}^* = u_{N-k}^*(\mathbf{u}_{N-k-1}, \mathbf{y}_{N-k-1}, \mathbf{y}_{N-k}^*). \quad (5.43)$$

Then Eq. (5.43) gives an optimal strategy which is regular. It can be shown that in the expression for α_0 we must set $\prod_{i=0}^{s-1} P(y_i \mid \boldsymbol{\mu}, i, u_i) = 1$. Here $u_0^* = u_0^*(y_0^*)$.

It should be noted that in the optimal algorithm (5.43), which must be built into the controller A, the value of u_{N-k}^* depends only on the quantities u, y, and y^* having been fed to A in the past, and on y_{N-k}^*. Therefore a device of this kind can be realized physically.

In Feldbaum [33] a simple example is considered, in which

$$v_s = u_s + g_s \tag{5.44}$$

and

$$y_s^* = x_s^* + h_s^* \tag{5.45}$$

and the equation of the plant has the form

$$x_s = v_s + \mu = u_s + g_s + \mu. \tag{5.46}$$

The command input is

$$x_s^* = \lambda = \text{const} \tag{5.47}$$

and the loss function is

$$W_s = W_s(s, x_s, x_s^*) = (x_s - x_s^*)^2 = (x_s - \lambda)^2. \tag{5.48}$$

Let the random quantities λ, μ, g_s, and h_s^* have normal distributions

$$\begin{aligned} P(\mu) &= \frac{1}{\sigma_\mu\sqrt{2\pi}} \exp\left\{-\frac{\mu^2}{2\sigma_\mu^{\,2}}\right\}; \qquad P(\lambda) = \frac{1}{\sigma_\lambda\sqrt{2\pi}} \exp\left\{-\frac{(\lambda-\lambda_0)^2}{2\sigma_\lambda^{\,2}}\right\} \\ P(g_s) &= \frac{1}{\sigma_g\sqrt{2\pi}} \exp\left\{-\frac{g_s^{\,2}}{2\sigma_g^{\,2}}\right\}; \quad P(h_s^*) = \frac{1}{\sigma_h\sqrt{2\pi}} \exp\left\{-\frac{(h_s^*)^2}{2\sigma_h^{\,2}}\right\}. \end{aligned} \tag{5.49}$$

The application of Eqs. (5.42) and (5.43), in this example, leads to the following optimal algorithm of control at the sth sampling time

$$u_s^* = \frac{\lambda_0}{1 + (\sigma_\lambda/\sigma_h)^2(s+1)} + \frac{\sum_{i=0}^{s} y_i^*}{(\sigma_h/\sigma_\lambda)^2 + (s+1)} - \frac{\sum_{i=0}^{s-1} (x_i - u_i)}{s + (\sigma_g/\sigma_\mu)^2}. \tag{5.50}$$

All the terms of this expression have precise physical meaning. For, if the disturbances g_s and h_s^* were to be missing, then, to ensure the condition $x_s = x_s^*$, it would be necessary to establish [see Eq. (5.46)] $u_s = x_s^* - \mu = \lambda - \mu$.

In Eq. (5.50), the two first terms also give an evaluation of λ, and the last term, of $(-\mu)$; see also Feldbaum [34]. For small s, the value of λ_0 can have substantial weight in the evaluation of λ. For large s, the sum of the first two terms of Eq. (5.50) approaches the arithmetic mean of y_i^*, which fully corresponds to intuitive considerations. The last term, for large s, approaches the arithmetic mean of $(x_i - u_i)$, $(i = 0, \ldots, s-1)$. Indeed, we can find out the value of $(\mu + g_i)$ by measuring this difference [see Eq. (5.46)] just as if the value of μ were to be measured with the error g_i. Thus, the last term, in the case of large s, also corresponds to intuitive considerations.

In more complex cases, the calculations become exceedingly complicated, and only approximate methods can be used to solve the problem.

6. Conclusion

In this chapter we have outlined the theory of optimal systems, and have summarized the fundamental ideas of this theory and some trends of its development. We have left untouched a number of important questions—questions concerning, for instance, nearly optimal systems, or the mutual relationship of optimal systems and automatic optimization systems (which are self-adjusting systems), and others. The task of this chapter has been to inform the reader on the fundamental concepts, and also to give an idea of the methods of the theory, the unity of which appears ever more clearly through the diversity of its multitudinous ramifications.

Why do we need a theory of optimal systems?

First, it is impossible to create optimal or nearly optimal systems without such a theory, since the engineer's intuition is inadequate for this purpose, even in relatively simple cases. Secondly, knowing the performance attainable only in the best, optimal, system, and comparing it with that of an existing system, we can decide whether it is worthwhile to develop a new system, or whether it is reasonable to content ourselves with the one we have.

BIBLIOGRAPHY

1. Aoki, M., "Stochastic-time optimal systems," Applications and Industry (May, 1961).
2. Bass, R. W., "Equivalent Linearization, Nonlinear Circuit Synthesis and the Stabilization and Optimization of Control Systems," Proceedings of the Symposium on Nonlinear Circuit Analysis, Polytechnic Institute of Brooklyn, New York, April, 1956.
3. Bellman, R., "On the Application of the Theory of Dynamic Programming to the Study of Control Processes," Proceedings of the Symposium on Nonlinear Circuit Analysis, Polytechnic Institute of Brooklyn, New York, April, 1956.
4. Bellman, R., *Dynamic Programming*, Princeton, 1957.
5. Bellman, R., "Dynamic programming and stochastic control processes," Information and Control No. 3 (September, 1958).
6. Bellman, R., *Adaptive Control Systems: a Guided Tour*, Princeton, 1961.
7. Bellman, R., and Dreyfus, S., "Functional approximations and dynamic programming," Math. Tables and Other Aids to Comput. **13,** No. 68 (October, 1959).
8. Bellman, R., Glicksberg, I., and Gross, O., "On the bang-bang control problem," Quart. Appl. Math. **14,** 11 (1956).
9. Bellman, R., and Kalaba, R., "On adaptive control processes," IRE Natl. Convention Record Part 4 (1959).
10. Bogner, I., and Kazda, L. F., "An investigation of the switching criteria for higher order saturating servomechanisms," Trans. AIEE **73,** Part II (1954).

11. Boltianskii, V. G., "The maximum principle in the theory of optimal processes," Doklady Akad. Nauk SSSR **123,** 2 (1958).
12. Boltianskii, V. G., Gamkrelidze, R. V., and Pontriagin, L. S., "Toward a theory of optimal processes," Doklady Akad. Nauk SSSR **110,** 1 (1956).
13. Boltianskii, V. G., Gamkrelidze, R. V., and Pontriagin, L. S., "Theory of optimal processes, I," Izvest. Akad. Nauk SSSR Ser. Mat. **24,** 1 (1960).
14. Bushaw, D. W., "Optimal Discontinuous Forcing Terms," and "Contribution to Nonlinear Oscillations," *Annals of Mathematical Study*, Volume 41, Princeton, 1958.
15. Butkovskii, A. G., and Lerner, A. Ia., "Optimal control of systems with distributed parameters," Avtomat. i telemekh. **21,** 6 (1960).
16. Butkovskii, A. G., "Optimal processes in systems with distributed parameters," Avtomat. i telemekh. **22,** 1 (1961).
17. Butkovskii, A. G., "The maximum principle for optimal systems with distributed parameters," Avtomat. i telemekh. **22,** 10 (1961).
18. Chan Su-in, "Toward a theory of optimal control," Priklad. mat. i mekh. **25,** 4 (1961).
19. Chandaket, P., and Leondes, C. T., "Optimum nonlinear bang-bang control systems with complex roots," Applications and Industry (May, 1961).
20. Chandaket, P., and Leondes, C. T., "Synthesis of quasi-stationary nonlinear control systems; Part I, Synthesis considerations; Part II, Extensions in mechanization concepts," Applications and Industry 313–319, 319–324 (January, 1962).
21. Chang, S. S. L., "Computer optimization of nonlinear control systems by means of the discrete maximum principle," IRE Natl. Convention Record Part 4. 48–55 (1961).
22. Chang, S. S. L., *Synthesis of Optimum Control Systems*, McGraw-Hill, 1961.
23. Desoer, C. A., "The bang-bang servo problem treated by variational techniques," Information and Control **2** (1959).
24. Desoer, C. A., "Pontriagin's maximum principle and the principle of optimality," J. Franklin Inst. **271,** 5 (May, 1961).
25. Desoer, C. A., and Wing, J., "An optimal strategy for a saturating sampled-data system," IRE Trans. on Automatic Control **AC-6,** 1 (February, 1961).
26. Desoer, C. A., and Wing, J., "A minimal-time discrete system," IRE Trans. on Automatic Control **AC-6,** 2 (May, 1961).
27. Eaton, T. H., and Zadeh, L. A., "Optimal Pursuit Strategies in Discrete-State Probabilistic Systems," Paper No. 61-JAC-11.
28. Feldbaum, A. A., "The simplest relay system of automatic control," Avtomat. i telemekh. **10,** 4 (1949).
29. Feldbaum, A. A., "Optimal processes in automatic control systems," Avtomat. i telemekh. **14,** 5 (1953).
30. Feldbaum, A. A., "An approach to the problem of the synthesis of optimal automatic control systems," Proceedings of the II All-Union Conference on the Theory of Automatic Control (Trudy II Vsesoiuznogo soveshchaniia po teorii avtomaticheskogo regulirovaniia), Volume II, Izvest, Akad. Nauk SSSR (1955).

31. Feldbaum, A. A., "Synthesis of optimal systems by means of the phase space," Avtomat. i telemekh. **16,** 2 (1955).
32. Feldbaum, A. A., "Computers in automatic systems (Vychislitel'nyie ustroistva v avtomaticheskikh sistemakh)," Fizmatgiz (1959).
33. Feldbaum, A. A., "The accumulation of information in closed loop automatic control systems," Izvest. OTN Akad. Nauk SSSR Ser. Energet. i avtomat. No. 4 (1961).
34. Feldbaum, A. A., "The theory of dual control, I, II, III, IV," Avtomat. i telemekh. **21,** Nos. 9 and 11 (1960); **22,** Nos. 1 and 2 (1961).
35. Feldbaum, A. A., "Optimal control of Markovian plants," Avtomat. i telemekh. **23,** No. 8 (1962).
36. Florentin, J. J., "Optimal control of continuous time, Markov, stochastic systems." J. Electronics and Control Ser. 1, **10,** No. 6 (June, 1961).
37. Freimer, M. A., "Dynamic programming approach to adaptive control processes," IRE Natl. Convention Record Part 4 (1959).
38. Friedland, B., "The structure of optimum control systems," J. Basic Eng. (March, 1962).
39. Fuller, A. T., "Optimization of nonlinear control systems with random inputs," J. Electronics and Control Ser. 1, **9,** No. 1 (July, 1960).
40. Gamkrelidze, R. V., "A theory of minimum response time processes in linear systems," Izvest. Akad. Nauk SSSR Ser. Mat. **22,** 4 (1958).
41. Gamkrelidze, R. V., "Toward a general theory of optimal processes," Doklady Akad. Nauk SSSR **123,** 2 (1958).
42. Gamkrelidze, R. V., "Minimum response time processes with constrained phase coordinates," Doklady Akad. Nauk SSSR **125,** 3 (1959).
43. Gosiewski, A., "Optymalne servomechanizmy przekaznikowe drugiego rzedu," Rozprawy elektrotechen. Polska Akad. Nauk **7,** 1 (1961).
44. Hopkin, A. M., "A phase-plane approach to the compensation of saturating servomechanisms," Trans. AIEE **70,** Part 1 (1951).
45. Hopkin, A. M., and Iwama, M., "A study of a predictor type 'Air-Frame' controller designed by phase-space analysis," Applications and Industry No. 23 (March, 1956).
46. Kalman, R. E., and Koepcke, R. W., "Optimal synthesis of linear sampling control systems, using generalized performance indexes," Trans, ASME **80** (1959).
47. Kramer, T. D. R., "On control of linear systems with time lags," Information and Control **3** (1960).
48. Krasovskii, N. N., "On a problem of automatic control," Priklad. mat. i mekh. **21,** 5 (1957).
49. Krasovskii, N. N., "Toward a theory of optimal control," Avtomat. i. telemekh. **18,** 11 (1957).
50. Krasovskii, N. N., and Lidskii E. A., "Analytic design of regulators in systems with random properties," Avtomat, i telemekh. **22,** 9 (1961).
51. Kuba, R. E., and Kazda, L. F., "A phase-space method for the synthesis of nonlinear servomechanisms," Applications and Industry No. 27 (November, 1956).

52. Kulikowski, R., "Concerning a class of optimum control systems," Bull. acad. pol. sci. **8,** No. 10 (1960).
53. LaSalle, J. P., "Basic principles of the bang-bang servo," Bull. Am. Math. Soc. **60** (1954).
54. LaSalle, J. P., "Time optimal control systems," Proc. Natl. Acad. Sci. U.S. **45** (1959).
55. Lerner, A. Ia., "Improvement of the dynamic properties of automatic compensators with the aid of nonlinear networks, I, II," Avtomat. i telemekh. **13,** Nos. 2 and 4 (1952).
56. Lerner, A. Ia., "Minimum response time in automatic control systems," Avtomat. i telemekh. **15,** 6 (1954).
57. Mar'ianovskii, D. I., and Svecharnik, D. V., U.S. Patent No. 77,023, Claim 181,007, February 25, 1935.
58. Merriam, C. W., "A class of optimum control systems," J. Franklin Inst. **267,** No. 4 (April, 1959).
59. Neustadt, L., "Time optimal control systems with position and integral limits," J. Math. Anal. and Applications **3,** No. 3 (December, 1961).
60. Novosel'tsev, V. N., "The optimal process in second-order sampled relay system," Avtomat. i telemekh. **21,** 5 (1960).
61. Novosel'tsev, V. N., "Optimal control in a sampled second-order relay system in the case of random disturbances," Avtomat. i telemekh. **22,** 7 (1961).
62. Pontriagin, L. S., "Optimal control processes," Uspekh. mat. nauk **14,** 1 (1959).
63. Pontriagin, L. S., Boltianskii, B. H., Gamkrelidze, R. V., and Mishchenko, E. F., *A Mathematical Theory of Optimal Processes* (Matematicheskaia teoriia optimal'nykh protsessov), Fizmatgiz, 1961; translation, Interscience and Wiley, 1962.
64. Rozenman, E. A., "Optimal transient processes in systems with limited power," Avtomat. i telemekh. **18,** 6 (1957).
65. Rozonoer, L. I., "L. A. Pontriagin's maximum principle in the theory of optimal systems, I, II, III," Avtomat. i telemekh. **20,** Nos. 10, 11, and 12 (1959).
66. Rozonoer, L. I., "The sufficient conditions of optimality," Doklady Akad. Nauk SSSR **127,** 3 (1959).
67. Rozonoer, L. I., "Quality of Analysis of Automatic Control Systems," *Proceedings of the IFAC Moscow, 1960*, Butterworths, 1961.
68. Smith, F. B., "Time-optimal control of higher-order systems," IRE Trans. on Automatic Control **AC-6,** 1 (February, 1961).
69. Sun Tsian', "Optimal control in a certain nonlinear system," Avtomat. i telemekh. **21,** 1 (1960).
70. Tsypkin, Ia. Z., "Optimal processes in pulsed automatic systems," Doklady Akad. Nauk SSSR **134,** 2 (1960).
71. Tsypkin, Ia, A., "Optimal processes in pulsed automatic systems," Izvest. OTN Akad. Nauk SSSR Ser. Energet. i avtomat. No. 4 (1960).
72. Yu-Chi ho, "Solution Space Approach to Optimal Control Problems," Paper No. 60 JAC-11.

CHAPTER VIII

Reference Stabilization and Inertial Guidance Systems

CONNIE L. McCLURE

CONTENTS

1. Introduction and Conceptual Foundations

Despite the inexorable stimuli of the natural cosmic environment, of which one terrestrial manifestation is the inherent biological compulsion to procreate, it is apparent that expanding *knowledge* and *technique* are increasingly significant stimuli affecting the variable morphology of terrestrial society. Recapitulating with greater specific delineation; *systematized knowledge* and *organized physical technique*, as manifest through the arts, sciences, crafts, and gross industrial mechanizations, are emerging as prime factors configuring the destiny of man. This observation is of particular significance when considered vis-a-vis the statistical extrapolation which already predicts eras wherein gross technology *must* allay the population pressures attending biological compulsion, or perish with the species as another mere object of cosmic caprice. Apart from the dire implications of an angry utilization of nuclear energy, and dismissing the consideration of some celestial cataclysm, the ponderable destiny of terrestrial man is otherwise irrevocably interwoven with his science and technology. The nature of this destiny first depends on the wisdom employed in adjusting traditions and emotions in accord with the social responsibilities of exploding technology, and ultimately depends upon the capacity of technology in relation to the exploding terrestrial population. Although philosophical discussion may give credence to an ethical suppression of the cause of the population peril, it is obvious that, short of a final solution by nuclear holocaust, salvation must be at least partially technologic. Giving rein to speculation, one concludes that in the early eras of the "great congestion" technology must satisfy the ever expanding demands for sustenance and waste disposition. Passing beyond these early eras, technology must, under any humane solution, provide the vehicular means for extraterrestrial migration.

An examination of the amazing growth of scientific discipline and technical capability which has occurred since the turn of the century may indicate that it is *not* completely fantastic to ponder the possibility of extraterrestrial migration. Indeed, given sufficient time and supposing a dedication attending cognizance of urgency, it is quite reasonable to extrapolate the known time variations of knowledge and capability into eras wherein there is indication of the comprehension and technology commensurate with extraterrestrial migration. It must be admitted, of course, that currently unknown properties of the physical cosmos may render such extrapolation meaningless. However, the Van Allen belts notwithstanding, nature has, as yet, erected no insurmountable barriers before a determined advance of man's technique, or before a tenacious expansion of man's domain of mobility. Rather, it would appear that it is the rigidly pessimistic disciplinarian who ultimately founders on his highly cherished and supposedly impassable obstacle. Perhaps some distant chronicle will record that man's greatest discovery was that human achievement is limited only by the limitations of human imagination. If so, the same distant chronicle may also then record that the sciences and techniques, which are now, currently, solidifying into a primitive extraterrestrial capability, were the crude beginnings of a massive technologic mechanism (and also a world view) which ultimately preserved the species and truly emancipated human experience. Apart from any prognostic accuracy, the foregoing peripheral speculation may lend additional fascination to the intrinsically interesting topics which are reviewed in this chapter.

Thus, within the *in toto* expansion of human technical capability, there are certain sciences and technologies which convey rather fascinating implications both in relation to the immediate future and to the ultimate destiny of man. These specific sciences and technologies concern the conception, construction, inhabitancy, operation, maintenance, and utilization of the *vehicles* without which there can be no execution of extraterrestrial missions and excursions. Such sciences and technologies, and also those topics of the foundation sciences which are directly pertinent (which would seem to eventually include most of science), have, in the current era, acquired a collective identification variously conveyed by the terms: "astronautics," "space technology," "cosmonautics," "Aerospace technology," etc. Here, it is elected that the collective identification be conveyed by the word "cosmonautics." Significant specific technologies, vitally involved in the implementations and objectives of current and future cosmonautics, relate to the areas of *vehicle operation* and *utilization* and concern the disciplines and instrumentations of *guidance* and *control*. Basic concepts and foundation analytical description relating to a particular subdivision of the technology of vehicular guidance, known as *inertial guidance*, constitute the principal topics of this chapter.

Though closely related by mechanical concepts and in analytical description, it is, nevertheless, usually convenient to identify *vehicular guidance* and *vehicular control* as subjects of *separate* technologies. Guidance technology is usually defined to be that pertaining to the *analytical disciplines* and *physical instrumentations* of *guidance intelligence generation*. In other words, a guidance system functions to generate physical effects (shaft rotations, voltages, electronic displays, etc.) which represent: *present position, velocity, heading, attitude*, etc., as *measured between vehicle* and *some coordinate reference frame* which is pertinent to some expedition or mission. On the other hand, vehicular control technology is usually defined as that concerned with the *analytical disciplines* and *physical mechanisms* (the latter usually involves components of the vehicle per se) which utilize *guidance intelligence* to *implement directional* and *translational control* of a vehicle such that *desired guidance is achieved*. In short, a vehicular control system functions to *implement* the *guidance commands generated by a guidance system*. Guidance intelligence supplied to a vehicular control system may emanate from an automatic guidance system (which may be an inertial guidance system), from a preprogramed set of instructions, or from a human operator.

By basic concept and function, inertial directional reference systems and complete inertial guidance systems are transported by the guided vehicle and do *not* necessarily involve remote communication. As the employment of devices which provide remote communication (usually electromagnetic devices, such as radar or radio) often simultaneously afford easy hostile detection, there are important military justifications for inertial guidance, particularly in applications to the operation of terrestrial vehicles such as aircraft and undersea craft. In this connection it may be of interest to recall that the genesis of inertial guidance, as a technology, was provided by the development of the gyrocompass and its applications to terrestrial (nautical) navigation. Although the gyrocompass, per se, is only a directional device, it provided a point of departure for Schuler, Draper, and others, to subsequently expand an inertial systems technology to the implementation of complete guidance systems and, also, to apply the basic principles to other mechanizations in the areas of vehicle control and automatic tracking and gun direction. Though these latter applications are closely related to concepts and descriptions of this chapter, their explicit consideration would be presented at the expense of the principal topics.

Vehicular guidance may be implemented by composite guidance systems which involve both *inertial features* and *external monitors* or *sensors*. Common examples of external sensing, employed in composite guidance, are those of stellar observation and radio sensing. Other guidance systems, which are *not*, by essential function, inertial guidance systems, frequently involve *inertially stabilized directional reference elements*. Thus, though *not* inertial guidance systems, these implementations still utilize the concepts and techniques of inertial guidance technology. In general, vehicular guidance systems entail the implementation of two or more modes of functional operation. One of these modes of operation may be that of a pure inertial system, while alternate modes may involve various systematic combinations of inertial sensors, external monitors, and computational programs.

Inertial guidance systems, inertial directional reference systems, and the *inertial* motion *sensors* which render the entire technology a reality, all acquire the adjective "*inertial*" in their literal designations from the concept of *inertial space*, which is a foundation concept of Newtonian classical mechanics. It is in this connection that inertial systems and inertial guidance are endowed with a certain intrinsic attraction not so directly apparent in the analytical disciplines of technology in general. *Primary inertial space* is defined as a coordinate frame of reference which is at *absolute rest*, and as such, provides the conceptual environment for the Newtonian analytical link relating applied force and the induced change of *kinetic state* of a *mass point* existing within an *empty medium* enveloping the inertial reference frame. Other inertial reference frames (or spaces) are *nonrotating* coordinate systems which move with *constant velocity* relative to primary inertial space. Such unaccelerated nonrotating reference systems may be denoted as secondary inertial spaces, or as *Galilean* reference systems. Under Newtonian description the rectilinear force which is reacted by a *free mass point* of mass m is proportional to the *time rate of change of the inertial rectilinear momentum*, (mv), of the mass point. Thus, when expressed in terms of *suitable units*,

$$F_m = \frac{d}{dt}(mv) = m\frac{dv}{dt} + \frac{dm}{dt}v \tag{1.1}$$

where v is the *rectilinear velocity* of the mass point as measured relative to an *inertial reference system* (an inertial space). As a *constant velocity* measured relative to a reference frame which *is moving with a constant inertial velocity* is just *another constant velocity relative to primary inertial space*, it follows that expression (1.1) is just as valid in *all Galilean reference systems*. If the mass of the mass point is measured in *grams*, the displacement (primary or inertial Galilean) measured in *centimeters*, and the time measured in *seconds* (usually mean solar), then the force, F_m, is in dynes, and has the units:

$$(\text{dyne}) = \frac{(\text{gm})(\text{cm})}{(\text{sec})^2}.$$

In particular, if the mass m of the mass point is *invariant*, it then follows from expression (1.1) that

$$F_m = m\frac{dv}{dt} = m\frac{d^2x}{dt^2} = m\ddot{x} = ma$$

and the rectilinear acceleration, $a = \ddot{x}$, is of necessity and inevitably an acceleration measured with respect to an *inertial reference system* (primary or Galilean).

Foregoing recapitulation indicates that an elemental *accelerometer*, which is a basic inertial *motion sensor* that provides a force reaction to an applied change in rectilinear momentum, *must*, under *omission of mass attraction* (gravity) *influences*, supply a *signal* which is a measure of *inertial kinetic* acceleration (primary or Galilean).

It is then one of the essential functions of an inertial guidance system to convert signals representing inertial kinetic acceleration to signals indicating *relative* kinetic acceleration, *relative velocity*, and *relative position* in a local *moving* (and rotating) *reference frame*, such as those fixed to the earth or the solar system. This is achieved through system generated corrections (including mass attraction corrections) of accelerometer signals, and involves corrective inputs fed back to accelerometers, or is elsewhere implemented in the data processing program of the system.

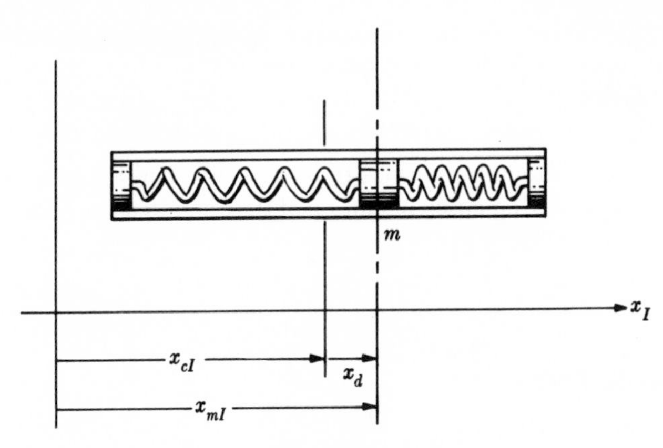

FIGURE 1.

Although *not* the usual physical configuration of real accelerometers, the fundamental concept of a rectilinear accelerometer is most conveniently introduced by employment of the discussional device depicted by Fig. 1. This figure indicates a *constant* mass m (essentially a mass point) which is constrained by linear springs and supported within a tube (or case) such that linear deflection of the mass occurs along the tube axis which is parallel to an inertial axis (primary or Galilean), x_I. An acceleration of the entire device, along x_I, deflects the mass in accord with expression (1.1), while the reaction afforded by the springs provides the functional feature of an accelerometer. A reference mark on the tube identifies the location of the mass when the springs are undeflected, while the coordinate x_{cI} of the same mark is the inertial displacement of the entire device. A *positive* displacement of the mass relative to the null reference mark is defined in the same direction (to the right) as positive x_I (even though a positive acceleration actually depresses the mass negatively). Thus, as is indicated by Fig. 1, the instantaneous inertial coordinate (primary or Galilean) of the disturbed mass is; $x_{mI} = x_{cI} + x_d$, where x_d is the relative deflection of the mass. In addition to the reaction supplied by the linear springs, which generate a force $F_s = k_s x_d$ (being directly proportional to x_d), it is functionally practical to provide a reactive force proportional to the *relative velocity* of the mass (it is otherwise assumed that the system is frictionless). This *damping* is characterized by

$$F_d = f_d \frac{dx_d}{dt}$$

and is implemented by immersing the mass in a viscous fluid such that the mass may move through the fluid (perhaps by longitudinal holes through the mass). It is observed that the constants k_s and f_d have the cgs units:

$$k_s = \frac{(\text{dyne})}{(\text{cm})} = \frac{(\text{gm})}{(\text{sec})^2} \qquad f_d = \frac{(\text{dyne})(\text{sec})}{(\text{cm})} = \frac{(\text{gm})}{(\text{sec})}.$$

Clearly, then, assuming the springs to be massless, and the viscous damping to be truly linear, the equation of motion of the disturbed mass, based directly on expression (1.1), is

$$m\frac{d^2x_{mI}}{dt^2} = m\left(\frac{d^2x_{c1}}{dt^2} + \frac{d^2x_d}{dt^2}\right) = -k_s x_d - f_d\frac{dx_d}{dt}$$

which may be written

$$\frac{d^2x_d}{dt^2} + \frac{f_d}{m}\frac{dx_d}{dt} + \frac{k_s}{m}x_d = -\frac{d^2x_{cI}}{dt^2} = -a(t)$$

where $a(t)$ is the rectilinear inertial acceleration impressed on the accelerometer (as defined by the motion of the reference mark on the case). Under null initial conditions (no relative displacement or velocity of the mass at the initial instant, $t = 0$) and an application of a *constant* inertial acceleration $a(t) = a_k$, $t > 0$, the solution of the foregoing differential equation is easily found to be

$$x_d(t) = -\frac{a_k m}{k_s}\left(1 - \frac{e^{-\zeta\omega_n t}}{\sqrt{1-\zeta^2}}\sin\left(\omega_n\sqrt{1-\zeta^2}t + \beta\right)\right)$$

where

$$\omega_n = \sqrt{\frac{k_s}{m}} \qquad \zeta = \frac{f_d}{2\sqrt{k_s m}} \qquad \beta = \text{arc cos}\,\zeta$$

and the response (mass deflection) is that of an *underdamped* system, defined by:

$$\zeta < 1 \qquad f_d^2 - 4k_s m < 0.$$

Appearance of the external minus sign in the solution merely indicates that a *positive* inertial kinetic acceleration deflects the mass in the *negative* direction, as should be expected. Inspection of the function $x_d = x_d(t)$ reveals that (under an adequate suppression of the transient by suitable selection of constants) the deflection of the mass is essentially proportional to the impressed acceleration, a_k. Consequently, as the deflection settles to a constant for a constant acceleration, it follows that, within the operating range of the device, the deflection of the mass is essentially a measure of the impressed acceleration $a(t)$. If a linear potentiometer is built into the case such that a voltage proportional to the relative displacement x_d is generated, then the accelerometer functions to supply a signal which is a measure of inertial kinetic acceleration. Polarity of the voltage may be reversed so that a positive signal represents a positive acceleration. The effect of mass attraction (or gravity) on this primitive accelerometer has not been considered.

Foregoing discussion has recapitulated the fundamental significance of the concept of inertial space (primary or Galilean) as the point of departure in the Newtonian descriptions of mechanics, and consequently, also as the point of departure for the conceptual foundations of inertial guidance. However, as is well known, more recent inquiry and evidence have relegated Newtonian description to a status of *approximation*. Although generally undisputed as exact description of nature for some two centuries, twentieth century physics and astronomy have provided other theory and specific evidence which impugn the *philosophical integrity* of Newtonian mechanics. To recall one particular feature of modern discipline: the special theory of relativity has been verified in its indication that the *intrinsic mass* of an elemental mass point is *not* a *kinetic invariant* (*not* constant under a changing state of motion). Rather, as characterized in the special theory, the instantaneous inertial mass of a moving elemental mass point is

$$m = m_0\left(1 - \frac{v^2}{c^2}\right)^{-1/2} = m(v)$$

where c is the free-space velocity of light, and m_0 is the rest mass of the mass point (particle). There is consequently a relativistic *dilatation* of elemental mass which becomes arbitrarily large as velocity approaches that of light. Relativistic dilatation of the mass of an elemental mass point should *not* be confused with a gross variation of the mass of a ponderable body; for example, the variation of the mass of a rocket which occurs as the fuel is expended. This latter mass variation involves an application of expression (1.1) in the elementary sense wherein the gross mass is chemically dissipated as an explicit function of time, $m = m(t)$. On the other hand, the foregoing relativistic expression for mass, $m = m(v)$, and its first time derivative may be substituted into expression (1.1) to characterize force as includes the kinetic dilatation of inertial mass. Further operations applied to the force expression so derived provides the celebrated energy expression†; $E = mc^2$.

It is of philosophical interest to observe that Newton may have anticipated that elemental inertial mass might be a function of kinetic state when he hypothesized that kinetic force is proportional to the rate of change of momentum. Otherwise, he could have merely stated that force is proportional to the product of mass and inertial acceleration. However, it should be appreciated that the philosophical invalidity of Newtonian description is related to the basic concept of inertial space as such, and not from the fact that in many Newtonian descriptions intrinsic inertial mass is regarded as constant. Moreover, it is further recalled that the theories of relativity also involve a *dilatation of the time variable t*, while in Newtonian mechanics

† See Sokolnikoff, I., *Tensor Analysis*, Wiley, p. 271.

time is a completely inelastic independent variable of which the continuous flow is unaltered by any physical phenomenon. An observation of fundamental import herein is that it is only velocities which are appreciable fractions of the velocity of light which induce detectable dilatations of mass (or time). For example, if v is one-tenth of the velocity of light, which is a *tremendous* velocity for ponderable masses, then the inertial mass is $m \cong 1.005\, m_0$, which is still a small dilatation. Consequently, relativistic dilatations are generally inconsequential in relation to vehicular relative motion in the current and foreseeable eras of technology. Thus, the unqualified utilization of the concept of inertial space and the employment of Newtonian mechanics induces virtually no error in current vehicular guidance and control technology.

Thus far, only *one* basic type of inertial motion sensor has been mentioned. This is the *rectilinear sensor*, exemplified by the rudimentary accelerometer of Fig. 1, which was utilized for conceptual introduction. Rectilinear inertial sensors (of which there are several types) constitute but one of the *two basic categories of inertial sensors* involved in the implementations of inertial systems and inertial guidance. In addition to rectilinear (or curvilinear) motion sensing, which may be achieved by several different specific rectilinear inertial sensors, there is also, in general, the systematic requirement for the detection of *angular inertial kinetic state*. Analytical demonstrations, revealing the very fundamental physical necessities of inertial *angular* motion detection, are an integral part of the dynamics reviewed presently. Thus the other basic category of inertial sensors is that of *inertial angular sensors*, of which there are several types. As even the *constant* inertial *angular velocity* of a point rotating about an axis (at a radius $r > 0$) *involves an inertial acceleration* (centripetal-centrifugal), there is *no angular equivalent of the Galilean* (constant rectilinear velocity) *reference frame*.

This fundamental is here recalled to emphasize that even a rectilinear sensor, the sensitive axis of which is *not* along the axis of rotation, will sense an acceleration (centripetal) due to *any* angular velocity, constant or other. Thus, in this sense, a rectilinear sensor is also an angular sensor.

Centripetal-centrifugal effects constitute one of the error sources which must be considered in the inertial implementation of rectilinear (and curvilinear) motion sensing.

A common implementation in past and current inertial systems and inertial guidance is that of the *directional* (angular) *stabilization* of a *reference platform*, or *stable element*, which is affixed within a vehicle *but, by virtue of the stabilization, is isolated from the angular behavior of the vehicle*. Such a platform is analytically defined by a right-handed orthogonal triad (of axes) fixed to the stable element, and may be directionally stabilized with respect to an inertially fixed triad, or may be slaved to the changing directions of some desired rotating reference triad.

In many inertial guidance systems the *rectilinear sensors are mounted on a platform*, with their sensitive (input) axes respectively along the platform triad. In this manner the *rectilinear sensors* may be *subjected to a controlled angular behavior* while being simultaneously *isolated from undesired angular motions of the vehicle.*

Reference stabilization is the term employed herein to denote the directional (angular) stabilization of a controlled triad (the platform) with respect to an inertially fixed triad of orthogonal directions, or with respect to a rotating orthogonal reference triad. In the usual implementation of *inertial directional stabilization*, it is the *angular sensors* which supply the outputs which are the *error signals* in the (gimbal) servo-control loops which achieve the stabilization. Here the inertial reference triad, to which the platform is slaved, may be defined by the *initial directions* of the platform axes, or the platform may be initially *erected* to some local reference which is then stipulated to thereafter remain directionally fixed in inertial space. On the other hand, in an implementation of *rotating reference stabilization*, *rectilinear sensors* usually supply the signals which are suitably processed and then employed to rotate the platform with respect to the directional inertial stabilization simultaneously achieved by the angular sensors and the platform stabilization servos (gimbal control servos). *Angular sensors* are essential components in inertial guidance systems of several configurations.

A rudimentary inertial angular sensor could be evolved from the elementary torsional pendulum. However, in behalf of consistency with common current practice, one may consider the *angular precession* of the spinning rotor of an elemental *gyroscope* (which is dynamically related to a disturbing imput inertial angular velocity) as the source of signal generation in a rudimentary angular motion sensor. Among the implementations based on the detection of *gyroscopic precession*, the following are of particular significance in the mechanization of vehicular inertial guidance systems:

(1) measurement of inertial angular velocity,
(2) inertial directional (angular) stabilization of a reference line or platform axis;
(3) angular stabilization of a reference line or platform axis with respect to a *rotating angular reference*.

The latter mechanism, involving the use and control of gyro precession in the angular stabilization or enslavement of a platform axis with respect to a *rotating reference line*, also entails the participation of *rectilinear sensors*, and is fundamental in the *attitude control* of a reference platform. Stabilized and controlled reference platforms operate with some *required rotational behavior* (for example, the rotation needed to maintain a *moving vertical*, of some definition, with respect to a planet) while simultaneously achieving *isolation* from undesired *angular perturbations* of the vehicle.

Other philosophies and implementations of inertial guidance may involve angular sensors of a *different nature*. Opposed to an *intended generation* of the *precession* of a rotating symmetrical mass as the signal generating mechanism of an angular sensor, there may be employed an *electrostatically* or *cryogenically* suspended freely rotating sphere which is *not* intended to precess. Rather, in implementations which employ such angular sensors, the rotations of a platform or a vehicle are measured against an inertially fixed set of reference directions which are (ideally) maintained by the spin axes of the freely suspended and undisturbed rotating spheres. Detection of such rotations may be geometrically based on the variable angle subtended by a circular *equatorial* line (equatorial band) *inscribed* within the cavity surrounding the free sphere and an *equatorial* line (or band) *circumscribed* around the surface of the free sphere (in the equatorial plane normal to the spatially fixed axis of rotation). Angular sensors of this type (based on sensor case rotation about the spatial fixity of an electrostatically or cryogenically suspended freely rotating sphere) may be employed in the directional stabilization of a reference platform, or may be fixed rigidly to the vehicle in an implementation of a "*vehicle oriented*" (or so-called "strapped-down") inertial guidance system. In further reference to the latter philosophy of inertial guidance implementation, it must be recalled that the previously mentioned *gyroscopic angular sensors* (inertial angular sensors based on the precession phenomenon) may *also be used* in *vehicle oriented* inertial guidance systems.†

A little more cursory contemplation of the *vehicle oriented* inertial guidance system reveals that as there is *no directionally stabilized reference platform* upon which to mount the *rectilinear sensors*, such a system can provide *no angular motion isolation* for the rectilinear sensors. Consequently, as *all* sensors are rigidly *fixed to the vehicle*, and as the rectilinear sensors are then *disturbed by angular perturbations of the vehicle* (and also by gravitation in a variable manner), a vehicle oriented inertial system must include a computer of sufficient capacity to continually isolate and evaluate the guidance variables from sensor signals, which include the spurious effects of vehicle angular perturbations, variable gravitational bias, and certain other structural and dynamic anomalies. Decision concerning the selection of an implementation philosophy (platform system vis-a-vis vehicle oriented

† See McClure, C., *Theory of Inertial Guidance*, Prentice-Hall, pp. 284–291.

system) is thus based on a comparison of the mechanical complications of a platform system with the mechanical complications and additional computer complexity of a vehicle oriented system. Most inertial guidance systems to date have involved a stabilized (or stabilized and controlled) reference platform.

Recapitulating the salient features of this introductory section, it is first recalled that *vehicular guidance* is herein the identification applied to the collective sciences and technologies relating to *guidance intelligence generation*. On the other hand, *vehicular control* is the term employed to identify the physical control of vehicle attitude, trajectory, and state of motion as are required by guidance objectives and *guidance intelligence*. That is, a vehicular control system utilizes guidance intelligence to implement directional and translational control of the vehicle such that the desired guidance is achieved. Transmission of guidance commands to the vehicular control system constitutes an essential functional link in the over-all guidance-control mechanism which may be implemented by a human operator, by integral mechanization of guidance intelligence generation and vehicular control systems, or by a combination of human participation and automatic interconnection. *Inertial guidance* (including reference stabilization and other supplementary vehicular applications) is the technology of *guidance intelligence generation* conceptually founded on the inertial principles of Newtonian mechanics. Inertial guidance systems thus utilize the detection of inertial kinetic state (primary or Galilean) and gravitational influence to implement the generation of required guidance and attitude variables as measured in *relative coordinates*.

2. Foundational Mechanics and Salient Dynamical Descriptions of Inertial Guidance

A pure ballistic trajectory, which is the spatial trace of the relative motion of a material object as governed only by the *innate interactions* between *inertial* and *gravitational* forces, provides a manifestation of inertial guidance in the most rudimentary natural form. This statement is, of course, merely a declaration that the foundation concepts and descriptions of Newtonian celestial mechanics, Newtonian particle and rigid body dynamics, and (current) inertial guidance are synonymous. Consequently, a recapitulation of the elemental hypotheses and descriptions of Newtonian mechanics defines the theoretical foundations of inertial guidance, and also recalls basic features of other disciplines which are intimately related to inertial guidance in the larger technology of cosmonautics.

In addition to the laws of (inertial) motion, which are partially characterized by expression (1.1)

$$F_m = m\frac{dv}{dt} + \frac{dm}{dt}v = m\frac{dv}{dx}\frac{dx}{dt} + \frac{dm}{dv}\frac{dv}{dx}\frac{dx}{dt}v = mv\frac{dv}{dx} + v^2\frac{dm}{dv}\frac{dv}{dx}.$$

Newton also postulated that material objects have a *mutual affinity* due only to their respective amounts of matter (mass) and spatial separation. This fundamental postulate is analytically described by the celebrated *inverse square law of mass attraction*:

$$F = \frac{km_1m_2}{\rho^2}. \tag{2.1}$$

Here F is a *mutual* attraction (force) in dynes, while m_1 and m_2 represent the respective masses (in grams) of two *mass points* separated by a distance of ρ (rho) centimeters. The constant of proportionality, k, is the (Newtonian) universal gravitational constant which has the value and units:

$$k = 6.670(\pm 0.005) \cdot 10^{-8} \frac{(\text{cm})^3}{(\text{gm})(\text{sec})^2}.$$

Expressions (1.1) and (2.1) provide the genesis of Newtonian dynamics, which, though subject to relativistic impugnation, is otherwise the current conceptual foundation for most of celestial mechanics, inertial guidance, and other topics of cosmonautics.

Stipulating mass points of *constant mass* and a medium of motion which is *frictionless empty space*, an equating of orthogonal components of the *inertial* and *gravitational* forces characterized by expressions (1.1) and (2.1) may be employed in connection with a certain *differencing* of *inertial coordinates* and *derivatives* to derive the basic Newtonian equations of *relative* ballistic motion.† These equations are

$$\begin{aligned} \frac{d^2x}{dt^2} + \frac{\mu_2}{\rho^3}x &= \frac{\partial R}{\partial x} \\ \frac{d^2y}{dt^2} + \frac{\mu_2}{\rho^3}y &= \frac{\partial R}{\partial y} \\ \frac{d^2z}{dt^2} + \frac{\mu_2}{\rho^3}z &= \frac{\partial R}{\partial z} \end{aligned} \tag{2.2}$$

$$\rho^2 = x^2 + y^2 + z^2 \qquad \mu_2 = k(m_N + m_v)$$

being nonlinear differential equations of the motion of a mass point, m_v, *relative to a moving mass point*, m_N, as characterized in terms of coordinates measured in a *nonrotating* orthogonal reference frame with axes x, y, z, the origin of which is *fixed* to m_N (or vice versa). It is emphasized that the cardinal condition of the derivation is that although the origin of the xyz system (fixed to m_N) is in curvilinear motion (is *not* a Galilean frame), the axes, x, y, and z remain *directionally fixed* in *inertial space*. The function R, being explicitly

† See Smart, W. M., *Celestial Mechanics*, Longmans, Green and Co., 1953, Article 1.07.

$$R = k \sum_{i=1}^{n} m_i \left(\frac{1}{\rho_{vi}} - \frac{xx_i + yy_i + zz_i}{{\rho_{Ni}}^3} \right)$$
$${\rho_{vi}}^2 = (x_i - x)^2 + (y_i - y)^2 + (z_i - z)^2 \tag{2.3}$$
$${\rho_{Ni}}^2 = {x_i}^2 + {y_i}^2 + {z_i}^2$$

is the *disturbing function* which accounts for *perturbing effects* of other mass points, $m_1, m_2, \ldots, m_n$, having the *relative* coordinates (measured in x, y, z) $x_1, y_1, z_1, x_2, y_2, z_2, \ldots, x_n, y_n, z_n$. By way of specific example; the *four point* equations of motion (the so-called four-body problem), involving *two* disturbing mass points m_1 and m_2, are readily seen to be:

$$\frac{d^2x}{dt^2} + \frac{\mu_2}{\rho^3} x = km_1 \left(\frac{x_1 - x}{{\rho_{v1}}^3} - \frac{x_1}{{\rho_{N1}}^3} \right) + km_2 \left(\frac{x_2 - x}{{\rho_{v2}}^3} - \frac{x_2}{{\rho_{N2}}^3} \right)$$
$$\frac{d^2y}{dt^2} + \frac{\mu_2}{\rho^3} y = km_1 \left(\frac{y_1 - y}{{\rho_{v1}}^3} - \frac{y_1}{{\rho_{N1}}^3} \right) + km_2 \left(\frac{y_2 - y}{{\rho_{v2}}^3} - \frac{y_2}{{\rho_{N2}}^3} \right)$$
$$\frac{d^2z}{dt^2} + \frac{\mu_2}{\rho^3} z = km_1 \left(\frac{z_1 - z}{{\rho_{v1}}^3} - \frac{z_1}{{\rho_{N1}}^3} \right) + km_2 \left(\frac{z_2 - z}{{\rho_{v2}}^3} - \frac{z_2}{{\rho_{N2}}^3} \right).$$

Of particular historic, conceptual, and utilitarian interest is the case of Eqs. (2.2) which involve *no disturbing mass points*. In this case, which defines the so-called *two-body problem*, the right-hand side of each equation is *zero*, and suitable manipulations† may be employed to show that the relative motion is *coplanar* in *some plane passing through the origin* of the nonrotating frame. Further transformation then gives the coplanar nonlinear polar equations

$$\frac{d^2\rho}{dt^2} - \rho \left(\frac{d\theta}{dt} \right)^2 + \frac{\mu_2}{\rho^2} = 0 \qquad \rho^2 \frac{d\theta}{dt} = c_1 \tag{2.4}$$

which may readily be solved to give ρ as a function of θ and a θ_0 (where θ_0 locates the line of apsides). Solutions so obtained specify the relative trajectory of m_v, with respect to m_N (or vice versa), to be *elliptic*, *parabolic*, or *hyperbolic*, depending, respectively, on the conditions

$$ {v_L}^2 < \frac{2\mu_2}{\rho_L} \qquad {v_L}^2 = \frac{2\mu_2}{\rho_L} \qquad {v_L}^2 > \frac{2\mu_2}{\rho_L}$$

where v_L is the initial ballistic (injection) velocity magnitude (relative), and ρ_L is the initial distance from m_N to m_v. For example, if ${v_L}^2 < 2\mu_2 {\rho_L}^{-1}$, the relative trajectory

$$\rho = \frac{{c_1}^2/\mu_2}{1 + (({c_1}^2/\mu_2\rho_0) - 1) \cos (\theta - \theta_0)} = \frac{\rho_0(1 + e_c)}{1 + e_c \cos (\theta - \theta_0)}$$

is an ellipse

† See Smart, W. M., *Celestial Mechanics*, Longmans, Green and Co., 1953, Article 2.01.

$$\rho = \frac{a(1 - e_c^2)}{1 + e_c \cos(\theta - \theta_0)}$$

of eccentricity, $|e_c| < 1$, symmetrical about the line of apsides which is located by θ_0 with respect to a coplanar two-space reference frame pertinent to the initial ballistic conditions. The eccentricity e_c, for all three cases, may be expressed by

$$e_c = \pm\sqrt{\sin^2 \alpha_L + ((\rho_L v_L^2/\mu_2) - 1)^2 \cos^2 \alpha_L}$$

where α_L is the angle of ballistic injection measured at m_v between a line perpendicular to the distance ρ_L and the direction of v_L. Eccentricity is positive or negative according to whether m_N is at the right or left focus of the trajectory. In particular, if $v_L^2 = 2\mu_2\rho_{-L}^1$ this expression gives $e_c = \pm 1$, as is required for a *parabolic trajectory.*

Elementary analysis may be applied to the foregoing description to associate any two-point (so-called two-body) relative trajectory with the relative initial ballistic conditions which establish it in the selected relative coordinates (the origin of the coplanar polar reference system being coincident with one of the mass points). Of further interest; other elementary manipulations may be employed to verify Kepler's laws of two-point elliptic relative motion.

Preceding recapitulations are of rudimentary significance in ballistic flight (nature's own inertial guidance), and also as a point of departure for a heuristic development of the principles of instrumented inertial guidance (the inertial generation of guidance intelligence). Instrumented inertial guidance functions by virtue of an identification of *relative kinetic state* (motion relative to the coordinates in which guidance is desired) from physical signals which, *before systematic correction,* reflect *inertial kinetic state* (relative to a primary of Galilean inertial frame) and *mass attraction disturbance.* An accelerometer, for example, detects total inertial-gravitational acceleration. Consequently, a cardinal description in inertial guidance is that of the *total acceleration* impressed along the axes of a (right-handed) orthogonal sensor triad as that triad moves in an *arbitrary manner* relative to a *gravitating guidance environment* (the earth and terrestrial coordinates, for example) *which is itself in motion relative to a primary or Galilean inertial* frame. If all contributions to the total acceleration component along each axis of the sensor triad may be analytically identified, then the *kinetic acceleration relative to the guidance environment may be isolated,* and velocity, position, heading, etc., *with respect to the guidance environment* may be implemented. An identification of the individual kinematic and gravitational contributions to the total velocity and acceleration components along the axes of a reference triad, under the *condition of compound relative motion,* is

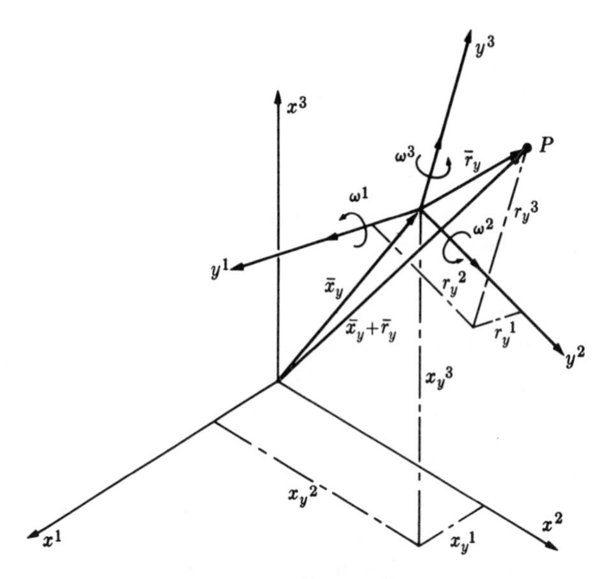

FIGURE 2.

most readily achieved by *vectorial description*,† of which salient features are reviewed in the following paragraphs.

An initial recollection concerning the vectorial treatment of the analytical kinematics and dynamics pertinent to *compound relative motion* is that of the definition of a *right-handed three-space orthogonal* reference frame. Denoting the orthogonal axes of such a frame, ϕ_y, by y^1, y^2, y^3, where the *superscripts are axial indices* and are *not power exponents*, its right-handedness is defined by associating a *rotation about a positive axis with the positive direction along that axis* in accord with the rotational-translational relation of a *right-handed screw*. Thus, if one positively rotates the axes of a right-handed frame with respect to their initial orthogonal directions, the following cyclic order is revealed

$$y^1 \to y^2 = +y^3 \quad y^2 \to y^3 = +y^1 \quad y^3 \to y^1 = +y^2$$

indicating that a right-handed (positive) rotation of the y^1 axis from its initial direction toward the initial direction of the y^2 axis is a *positive rotation about* the y^3 axis in accord with the *positive direction along* that axis, etc. Two such right-handed frames, ϕ_y and ϕ_x, are depicted by Fig. 2, which also indicates a point, P, that moves relative to ϕ_y (axes y^1, y^2, y^3) while ϕ_y is in motion relative to ϕ_x (axes x^1, x^2, x^3). It is again emphasized that the superscripts are *not* power exponents [the square of a coordinate y^2, for example,

† See McClure, C., *Theory of Inertial Guidance*, Prentice-Hall, Chap. 4.

is written $(y^2)^2$]. Denoting the coordinates of P, with respect to the y-axes of ϕ_y, by; $r_y^{\,1} = r_y^{\,1}(t)$, $r_y^{\,2} = r_y^{\,2}(t)$, and $r_y^{\,3} = r_y^{\,3}(t)$, it is then recalled that these coordinates are the instantaneous *projections of the position vector*, $\bar{r}_y$, of P, as measured in ϕ_y. That is, P is located in ϕ_y by the *vector*

$$(\bar{r}_y)_y = r_y^{\,1}\hat{\imath}_y + r_y^{\,2}\hat{\jmath}_y + r_y^{\,3}\hat{k}_y \tag{2.5}$$

where $\hat{\imath}_y$, $\hat{\jmath}_y$, and $\hat{k}_y$ are the *fundamental unit vectors* as are associated with ϕ_y (measured respectively along y^1, y^2, and y^3 as unit projections from the origin), and the notation $(\bar{r}_y)_y$ denotes that the vector from the origin of ϕ_y to P is measured in terms of projections in ϕ_y. If the *same* vector were specified by projections in ϕ_x this would then be denoted by $(\bar{r}_y)_x$. While the location and motion of P relative to ϕ_y may be described by an explicit behavior of the position vector $\bar{r}_y$, the motion of the entire frame ϕ_y relative to the frame ϕ_x is yet required to complete a systematization of compound relative motion. A cardinal feature of the dynamical descriptions required in inertial guidance, most readily achieved by vectorial description, is that all contributions to total kinetic-gravitational state be *expressed in terms of projections measured along local sensor axes*. This will be repeatedly emphasized in subsequent discussion.

Description of the total kinetic state of P (Fig. 2) relative to the frame ϕ_x, in terms of projections measured along the moving axes of ϕ_y, is initiated by consideration of the *total relative velocity*. Under completely general motion, the *origin of* ϕ_y has a *curvilinear trajectory* relative to ϕ_x, while the axes y^1, y^2, and y^3 are in *general angular motion about each other* relative to the space of ϕ_x. A general angular motion of the frame, ϕ_y, may be characterized by the *angular velocity projections*: $\omega^1 = \omega^1(t)$, $\omega^2 = \omega^2(t)$, and $\omega^3 = \omega^3(t)$, measured respectively along the rotating axes y^1, y^2, and y^3. That is, ω^1 is the instantaneous angular rate, in radians per unit time, at which the y^2 and y^3 axes are sweeping around the mutually orthogonal axis y^1, etc. Or, in other words, ω^1 is a *right-handed* projection *along* y^1 which is proportional to the instantaneous angular velocity of ϕ_y *about that axis* with respect to the space of ϕ_x, and so also for ω^2 and ω^3. Thus, the angular velocity of ϕ_y relative to ϕ_x may be described by the *vector*

$$(\bar{\omega}_{yx})_y = \omega^1\hat{\imath}_y + \omega^2\hat{\jmath}_y + \omega^3\hat{k}_y \tag{2.6}$$

which is defined by projections *along the same moving axes about which the component angular velocities occur*. Suppose first that P is *fixed* in ϕ_y ($(\bar{r}_y)_y$ is constant), and also that the *only motion* of ϕ_y relative to ϕ_x is the *general angular motion* indicated by $(\bar{\omega}_{yx})_y$ (for the present there is no curvilinear or translational motion of the origin of ϕ_y). Now *even though fixed* in ϕ_y, P has a *positive linear velocity* in the *instantaneous direction* of y^1 (with respect to the space of ϕ_x) due to the *angular velocity* ω^2 *about* y^2. An examination of Fig. 2 reveals that this linear velocity is $\omega^2 r_y^{\,3}$. *Simultaneously, however, there is also an instantaneous negative linear velocity along* y^1 (with respect to ϕ_x) due to the *angular velocity* ω^3 about y^3. This is viewed in the y^1y^2 plane and is, of course, $\omega^3 r_y^{\,2}$. Consequently, the *net linear velocity* in the *instantaneous direction* of y^1 (with respect to ϕ_x), due to the *angular velocity* of the frame ϕ_y (with respect to ϕ_x), is: $\omega^2 r_y^{\,3} - \omega^3 r_y^{\,2}$. An application of this fundamental reasoning to all three axes of ϕ_y, which thus far involves no knowledge of vectors, reveals that the *linear velocity* of P (for the moment fixed in ϕ_y) with respect to ϕ_x, *due only to the angular velocity* of ϕ_y, is expressed by the three projections

$$v_\omega^{\,1} = \omega^2 r_y^{\,3} - \omega^3 r_y^{\,2}$$
$$v_\omega^{\,2} = \omega^3 r_y^{\,1} - \omega^1 r_y^{\,3}$$
$$v_\omega^{\,3} = \omega^1 r_y^{\,2} - \omega^2 r_y^{\,1}$$

which are measured along the respective *moving axes* y^1, y^2, and y^3. Utilizing now the recollections of elementary vector algebra, it is observed that these projections are *exactly those of the vector product* (cross product); $(\bar{v}_\omega)_y = \bar{\omega}_{yx} \times \bar{r}_y$, as expresed in the frame ϕ_y. That is

$$\bar{\omega}_{yx} \times \bar{r}_y = \begin{vmatrix} \hat{\imath}_y & \hat{\jmath}_y & \hat{k}_y \\ \omega^1 & \omega^2 & \omega^3 \\ r_y^{\,1} & r_y^{\,2} & r_y^{\,3} \end{vmatrix}$$

gives the velocity projections $v_\omega^{\,i}$ $(i = 1, 2, 3)$ previously derived by elementary reasoning based on the geokinematics of Fig. 2.

Relaxing the condition that P be fixed in ϕ_y, *but still retaining the condition that there is no translational motion of the origin of* ϕ_y *relative to* ϕ_x, it is readily concluded that the projections $v_\omega^{\,i}$ are *still valid* in accounting for the linear velocity of P due to the relative angular velocity $\bar{\omega}_{yx}$, but must now be augmented by the *velocity projections, along the axes of* ϕ_y, due to the *local relative motion* (with respect to ϕ_y). These projections are just

$$\frac{dr_y^{\,1}}{dt}, \text{ along } y^1 \qquad \frac{dr_y^{\,2}}{dt}, \text{ along } y^2 \qquad \frac{dr_y^{\,3}}{dt}, \text{ along } y^3$$

and the total velocity of P, relative to the space of ϕ_x, is now expressed by the projections

$$v^1_{x)y} = \frac{dr_y^{\,1}}{dt} + \omega^2 r_y^{\,3} - \omega^3 r_y^{\,2}$$

$$v^2_{x)y} = \frac{dr_y^{\,2}}{dt} + \omega^3 r_y^{\,1} - \omega^1 r_y^{\,3}$$

$$v^3_{x)y} = \frac{dr_y^{\,3}}{dt} + \omega^1 r_y^{\,2} - \omega^2 r_y^{\,1}$$

measured respectively along y^1, y^2, and y^3. A vectorial equation which implies these projections is then immediately seen to be

$$\bar{v}_{x)y} = \left(\frac{d\bar{r}}{dt}\right)_{x)y} = \left(\frac{d\bar{r}}{dt}\right)_y + \bar{\omega}_{yx} \times \bar{r}_y \tag{2.7}$$

which is known as the *theorem of Coriolis*, and may be employed to describe the rate of change of *any vector* (defined in a rotating frame) with respect to the frame against which the angular velocity of the rotating frame is measured. The significant feature here is that the projections are measured along the moving axes themselves.

In addition to the motion of P in ϕ_y and the rotation of ϕ_y, suppose now that the origin of ϕ_y has a *general translational motion* with respect to ϕ_x. That is, the condition that the coordinates $x_y^{\,i}(t)$ (Fig. 2) are constants is now relaxed. The time derivatives of these coordinates specify the translational velocity projections of the origin of ϕ_y with respect to ϕ_x, *but measured in* ϕ_x. To achieve a moving frame description of total velocity, these projections must be *resolved* onto the axes of ϕ_y and added to the respective projections $v^i_{x)y}$, vectorially expressed by Eq. (2.7). Required resolutions are given by the transformation

$$\begin{bmatrix} \dfrac{dy_x^{\,1}}{dt} \\[2ex] \dfrac{dy_x^{\,2}}{dt} \\[2ex] \dfrac{dy_x^{\,3}}{dt} \end{bmatrix} = \begin{bmatrix} a_1^{\,1} & a_2^{\,1} & a_3^{\,1} \\[2ex] a_1^{\,2} & a_2^{\,2} & a_3^{\,2} \\[2ex] a_1^{\,3} & a_2^{\,3} & a_3^{\,2} \end{bmatrix} \cdot \begin{bmatrix} \dfrac{dx_y^{\,1}}{dt} \\[2ex] \dfrac{dx_y^{\,2}}{dt} \\[2ex] \dfrac{dx_y^{\,3}}{dt} \end{bmatrix} \tag{2.8}$$

where the *direction cosines*, $a_j^{\,i}$ (the elements of the direction cosine matrix), are defined according to the arrangement

$$\begin{array}{c} \\ y^1 \\ y^2 \\ y^3 \end{array} \begin{array}{c} \begin{array}{ccc} \qquad x^1 \qquad & \qquad x^2 \qquad & \qquad x^3 \qquad \end{array} \\ \begin{bmatrix} a_1^{\,1} = \cos(x^1, y^1) & a_2^{\,1} = \cos(x^2, y^1) & a_3^{\,1} = \cos(x^3, y^1) \\ a_1^{\,2} = \cos(x^1, y^2) & a_2^{\,2} = \cos(x^2, y^2) & a_3^{\,2} = \cos(x^3, y^2) \\ a_1^{\,3} = \cos(x^1, y^3) & a_2^{\,3} = \cos(x^2, y^3) & a_3^{\,3} = \cos(x^3, y^3) \end{bmatrix} \end{array}$$

and are, in general, time functions $a_j^{\,i} = a_j^{\,i}(t)$. The projections specified by an expansion of matric equation (2.8) are those of a vector

$$\bar{v}_y = \frac{dy_x^{\,1}}{dt}\,\hat{\imath}_y + \frac{dy_x^{\,2}}{dt}\,\hat{\jmath}_y + \frac{dy_x^{\,3}}{dt}\,\hat{k}_y$$

which represents the instantaneous velocity of translation of the frame ϕ_y with respect to ϕ_x, and is instantaneously the same for all points in ϕ_y. Consequently, the total velocity of P with respect to ϕ_x, *in terms of projections along the moving axes* y^1, y^2, and y^3, is

$$\bar{v}_{x)y} = \bar{v}_y + \left(\frac{d\bar{r}}{dt}\right)_y + \bar{\omega}_{yx} \times \bar{r}_y \tag{2.9}$$

being simultaneously due to contributions of the velocity of P in ϕ_y, the angular velocity of ϕ_y, and the velocity of translation of ϕ_y.

Although the total *velocity* of a point moving with respect to a rotating *and translating* reference frame has been recalled by the presentation of expression (2.9), it is *most frequently* necessary to consider the total kinetic state of a point or system which moves (in an arbitrary manner) relative to a reference frame which has *only a general rotation* relative to an inertial frame (usually Galilean). For example, in the case of *terrestrial inertial guidance*, the total inertial motion of the earth may usually be characterized in terms of an inertial *angular velocity only*. This is *not* to imply that rectilinear velocities and accelerations relative to the earth, and rectilinear velocities and accelerations *due to the inertial angular velocity of the earth*, are not cardinal in the fundamental analytical descriptions of terrestrial inertial guidance. Rather, it is to be inferred that the theorem of Coriolis, particularized by expression (2.7), enjoys much more frequent application than expression (2.9) because in many important descriptions (in dynamics and in inertial guidance) *a suitable selection of moving axes affords an isolation of rotational dynamics from simultaneous translational dynamics.*† In other words, by a suitable selection of moving reference axes, and judicious identifications and analysis, rotational and translational dynamics are isolated; and the theorem of Coriolis

$$\left(\frac{d\bar{A}}{dt}\right)_{x)y} = \left(\frac{d\bar{A}}{dt}\right)_y + \bar{\omega}_{yx} \times \bar{A}_y \tag{2.10}$$

where $\bar{A} = \bar{A}(t)$ is any vector (variable or constant), describes the *interframe time differentiation* of vector quantities which is essential in the *moving frame description* of relative rotational mechanical phenomena.

It is understood, of course, that while the theorem of Coriolis gives the time derivative of a vector measured in a *rotating frame*, with respect to the frame against which the rotation of the rotating frame is reckoned (and in terms of projections *in the rotating frame*), the vector, *as measured in the rotating frame, may be constant, or may vary in an arbitrary manner*. For example, if $\bar{A}$ is a translational relative velocity vector, $\bar{v}_{yR}$, there is curvilinear translation of the *moving point* with respect to both ϕ_y and ϕ_x, but the origin of ϕ_y is either *not translating* (relative to ϕ_x), *or the omission of translation is justified by other stipulations.*

† See McClure, C., *Theory of Inertial Guidance*, Prentice-Hall, pp. 88, 89, 95.

Particular examples of the varied applications of the theorem of Coriolis can convey segments of the foundations of analytical mechanics. A recapitulation of some of these applications here affords a concise presentation of certain salient analytical topics of reference stabilization and inertial guidance systems.

2.1 Total Kinetic Acceleration in a Rotating Frame. If the total velocity of a point P moving relative to a rotating frame ϕ_y is

$$\bar{v}_{x)y} = \left(\frac{d\bar{r}}{dt}\right)_{x)y} = \left(\frac{d\bar{r}}{dt}\right)_y + \bar{\omega}_{yx} \times \bar{r}_y$$

then the *total kinetic acceleration* of P, with respect to ϕ_x, in terms of projections along the axes of ϕ_y, is vectorially specified by a second application of the theorem of Coriolis. Thus

$$\bar{a}_{x)y} = \left(\frac{d^2\bar{r}}{dt^2}\right)_{x)y} = \frac{d}{dt}(\bar{v}_{x)y}) + \bar{\omega}_{yx} \times \bar{v}_{x)y}$$

which, after expansion, becomes:

$$\bar{a}_{x)y} = \left(\frac{d^2\bar{r}}{dt^2}\right)_y + 2\bar{\omega}_{yx} \times \left(\frac{d\bar{r}}{dt}\right)_y + \frac{d\bar{\omega}_{yx}}{dt} \times \bar{r}_y + \bar{\omega}_{yx} \times (\bar{\omega}_{yx} \times \bar{r}_y) \quad (2.11)$$

where $\bar{r}_y$ and $\bar{\omega}_{yx}$ are given, respectively, by expressions (2.5) and (2.6). Individual terms of $\bar{a}_{x)y}$ have the following designations and expansions.

Relative Acceleration, with respect to ϕ_y:

$$\bar{a}_R = \left(\frac{d^2\bar{r}}{dt^2}\right)_y = \frac{d^2r_y^{\,1}}{dt^2}\,\hat{\imath}_y + \frac{d^2r_y^{\,2}}{dt^2}\,\hat{\jmath}_y + \frac{d^2r_y^{\,3}}{dt^2}\,\hat{k}_y$$

which, in general, involves centripetal and tangential resolutions.

Coriolis Acceleration (not to be confused with the theorem of Coriolis):

$$\bar{a}_{c0} = 2\bar{\omega}_{yx} \times \left(\frac{d\bar{r}}{dt}\right)_y = 2\left(\omega^2\frac{dr_y^{\,3}}{dt} - \omega^3\frac{dr_y^{\,2}}{dt}\right)\hat{\imath}_y + 2\left(\omega^3\frac{dr_y^{\,1}}{dt} - \omega^1\frac{dr_y^{\,3}}{dt}\right)\hat{\jmath}_y + 2\left(\omega^1\frac{dr_y^{\,2}}{dt} - \omega^2\frac{dr_y^{\,1}}{dt}\right)\hat{k}_y$$

which engenders some very interesting and important interpretations. First, the meaning and nature of Coriolis acceleration depends directly on the *constraint* imposed on the motion of P relative to the rotating frame ϕ_y. If P *is* constrained to move relative to ϕ_y, then the Coriolis acceleration is with respect to ϕ_x (still in terms of projections in ϕ_y), and is an acceleration needed to achieve the constrained motion in ϕ_y. This is the Coriolis acceleration *directly* described by the preceding expression. On the other hand, if P is *not constrained* relative to ϕ_y, then the Coriolis acceleration is relative to ϕ_y and does *not exist* relative to ϕ_x. Physical understanding of Coriolis acceleration is readily achieved by consideration of a projectile fired from the equator northward along a meridian. At the instant the projectile is fired it has an eastward inertial velocity component due to the rotation of the earth. Under no external retardation, this eastward component of inertial velocity is *retained* as the projectile moves northward. Meanwhile, points on the meridian (fixed to the earth) have eastward linear velocity components (due to the constant angular velocity of the earth) *which diminish with increasing latitude*. Consequently, in retaining the state of eastward inertial velocity, the projectile *must move east of points in the meridian* as it moves generally northward. The *Coriolis drift*, associated with the Coriolis acceleration, thus is here *to the right relative to the earth* and has no existence in inertial space (here Galilean). Conversely, a projectile fired from the North Pole southward along a meridian has *no* linear inertial velocity due to the rotation of the earth, and points in the meridian must thus move *east of the projectile* as the projectile moves generally southward. Coriolis *drift* is thus again *to the right with respect to the direction of motion*. In the southern hemisphere the kinematical situation is reversed.

If the right-handed rotating frame ϕ_y is fixed in the earth with $+y^3$ along the north polar axis, and y^1 and y^2 in the plane of the equator, and ϕ_x is a right-handed (Galilean) inertial frame with $+x^3$ along $+y^3$, and x^1 and x^2 coplanar with y^1 and y^2, then the inertial angular velocity of ϕ_y relative to ϕ_x is specified by: $\omega^1 = 0$, $\omega^2 = 0$, and $\omega^3 = \omega_{EI}$, where ω_{EI} is the constant magnitude of the inertial angular velocity of the earth (by the right-hand rule, $\bar{\omega}_{EI}$ is along the north polar axis). The Coriolis acceleration of *a point constrained to move in the northern meridian* in the y^1y^3 plane with a *constant* tangential velocity, v (magnitude), at a *constant* geocentric radius, $r = |\bar{r}_y|$, is easily shown (as a special case of the preceding expression) to be

$$\bar{a}_{c0} = (-2\omega_{EI} v \sin \lambda)\hat{\jmath}_y, \quad \text{parallel to } -y^2 \text{ for } v \text{ northward.}$$

$$\bar{a}_{c0} = (2\omega_{EI} v \sin \lambda)\hat{\jmath}_y, \quad \text{parallel to } +y^2 \text{ for } v \text{ southward.}$$

where λ is the geocentric latitude. In both cases $\bar{a}_{c0}$ is the inertial acceleration, to the *left with respect to the direction of motion, needed to stay in the specified earth fixed meridian*. If these inertial accelerations are *not* applied, then the point P moves with the velocity v in a Galilean plane *but drifts with respect to the earth fixed meridian with the accelerations*:

$$a_{c0} = +2\omega_{EI} v \sin \lambda, \quad \text{being to the east for northward motion.}$$

$$a_{c0} = -2\omega_{EI} v \sin \lambda, \quad \text{being to the west for southward motion.}$$

In particular, if the point P departs from the *North Pole* and has a southward constant tangential velocity v, which is then in the rotating y^1y^3 plane *only at the instant of departure* $t = 0$, points in the y^1y^3 plane fixed to the rotating earth then drift to the east of the Galilean plane of v, defined by the initial conditions (P appears to drift to the west to observers in the earth fixed

y^1y^3 meridian). Under these conditions, the eastward drift (displacement) of points in the y^1y^3 meridian, with respect to the Galilean plane of v (or the apparent westward displacement of the point with respect to the y^1y^3 meridian), is easily shown to be:

$$d_s = r\omega_{EI}t \sin \frac{vt}{r} .$$

It should be remembered that v is constant and is measured in the Galilean plane with respect to which the y^1y^3 plane rotates. Moreover, it has been implicitly assumed that mass attraction, or some other vertical plane constraint, keeps v tangent to a circular trajectory of constant geocentric radius r (the trajectory in the vertical plane).

Coriolis acceleration, drift, and corrections are important topics in all vehicular guidance. An example which readily reveals the basic significance of Coriolis phenomena is directly available in *terrestrial inertial guidance.* If Coriolis *drift* is *uncorrected*, a vehicle with a northward velocity of 800 feet per second will drift to the east about 148 feet per minute when in north latitude of 45°. However, if the drift *is* corrected (vehicle constrained to the meridian), *this then imposes a westward inertial acceleration on system accelerometers which must then be recorrected so that signals measuring relative terrestrial acceleration are generated.*

Another interesting situation relating to Coriolis phenomena concerns the contribution of the Coriolis term in expression (2.11) under the condition of *directly eastward terrestrial motion around a small circle of constant latitude* λ_k. An explicit development of all the terms of expression (2.11) for the conditions of constant r, ω_{EI}, λ, and relative velocity magnitude v, with v directly eastward, gives an acceleration directly toward the polar axis y^3, in the plane of the small circle (parallel to the equatorial plane), and of the magnitude.

$$|\bar{a}_{x)y}| = a_k = \frac{(v)^2}{r \cos \lambda_k} + 2\omega_{EI}v + r(\omega_{EI})^2 \cos \lambda_k$$

where the $2\omega_{EI}v$ comes directly from the Coriolis term, and the total acceleration is all of a *centripetal nature*. Significance of the Coriolis acceleration in this case of directly eastward terrestrial motion is revealed by a direct consideration of the total centripetal acceleration due to the *total angular velocity* of P *relative to inertial space*. That is, as a centripetal acceleration is also the radius of motion multiplied by the square of the angular velocity, and as the total inertial angular velocity is here

$$\frac{v}{r \cos \lambda_k} + \omega_{EI}$$

while the radius of motion is $r \cos \lambda_k$, it thus follows that the total centripetal acceleration is

$$r \cos \lambda_k \left(\frac{v}{r \cos \lambda_k} + \omega_{EI}\right)^2 = \frac{(v)^2}{r \cos \lambda_k} + 2\omega_{EI} v + r(\omega_{EI})^2 \cos \lambda_k = a_k.$$

Thus, while $r(\omega_{EI})^2 \cos \lambda_k$ is the centripetal acceleration of a point *fixed to the earth*, and

$$\frac{(v)^2}{r \cos \lambda_k}$$

is the centripetal acceleration of a point *moving relative to a nonrotating earth, the Coriolis term here accounts for the middle term introduced by squaring the sum of the two angular velocities which give the total angular velocity of P relative to inertial space*. Thus, even in directly eastward motion, the Coriolis term is directly required in describing the total inertial acceleration of the point P.

Tangential Acceleration Due to Frame Rotation:

$$\bar{a}_T = \frac{d\bar{\omega}_{yx}}{dt} \times \bar{r}_y = \left(\frac{d\omega^2}{dt} r_y{}^3 - \frac{d\omega^3}{dt} r_y{}^2\right)\hat{\imath}_y + \left(\frac{d\omega^3}{dt} r_y{}^1 - \frac{d\omega^1}{dt} r_y{}^3\right)\hat{\jmath}_y + \left(\frac{d\omega^1}{dt} r_y{}^2 - \frac{d\omega^2}{dt} r_y{}^1\right)\hat{k}_y.$$

For a *constant* $\bar{\omega}_{yx}$, such as the $\bar{\omega}_{EI}$ employed in the preceding discussion of terrestrial Coriolis phenomena, the tangential acceleration due to frame rotation, $\bar{a}_T$, is zero.

Centripetal Acceleration Due to Frame Rotation (not to be confused with the centripetal acceleration usually inherent in the relative acceleration):

$$\begin{aligned}\bar{a}_c = \bar{\omega}_{yx} \times (\bar{\omega}_{yx} \times \bar{r}_y) &= [-r_y{}^1((\omega^2)^2 + (\omega^3)^2) + \omega^1(\omega^2 r_y{}^2 + \omega^3 r_y{}^3)]\hat{\imath}_y \\ &+ [-r_y{}^2((\omega^1)^2 + (\omega^3)^2) + \omega^2(\omega^1 r_y{}^1 + \omega^3 r_y{}^3)]\hat{\jmath}_y \\ &+ [-r_y{}^3((\omega^1)^2 + (\omega^2)^2) + \omega^3(\omega^1 r_y{}^1 + \omega^2 r_y{}^2)]\hat{k}_y.\end{aligned}$$

It is apparent that this centripetal acceleration, $\bar{a}_c$, due to the rotation of ϕ_y, is present even though P is fixed in ϕ_y. In particular, if P is fixed to the earth in the y^1y^3 plane at a geocentric latitude, λ_k, then, with $\omega^1 = \omega^2 = 0$, $\omega^3 = \omega_{EI}$, the foregoing expression reduces to just $\bar{a}_c = (-r(\omega_{EI})^2 \cos \lambda_k)\hat{\imath}_y$, being of a magnitude which is synonymous with the corresponding acceleration magnitude revealed by the prior example pertaining to directly eastward relative terrestrial motion (as must be expected).

It may be of interest here to recall that the acceleration specified by the last two terms of expression (2.11), taken collectively as a vector sum, is frequently called the *acceleration of transport*. One may note that if $\bar{\omega}_{yx}$ is *not constant*, then the acceleration of transport is *not perpendicular* to the spatial trajectory of P due to the rotation of ϕ_y.

2.2 Salient Descriptions in the Rotational Dynamics of Rigid Bodies. Recalling that a *rigid body* is defined as a system of *mass points* of which the mutual orientations are in *no way altered by any applied forces or torques*, one may utilize the theorem of Coriolis in an organized summation of effects over all the mass points of a rigid body to establish the salient features of the rotational dynamics of rigid bodies.† First, if the rotating frame ϕ_y (Fig. 2), is *fixed in a rigid body with the origin at the mass centroid*, then it may be shown that the *inertial moment of momentum* (general angular momentum) of the body, *in terms of projections along body axes* y^1, y^2, and y^3, is

$$\begin{aligned}\bar{h}_{I)y} = (J_1\omega^1 - K_{12}\omega^2 - K_{13}\omega^3)\hat{\imath}_y \\ + (J_2\omega^2 - K_{12}\omega^1 - K_{23}\omega^3)\hat{\jmath}_y \\ + (J_3\omega^3 - K_{13}\omega^1 - K_{23}\omega^2)\hat{k}_y\end{aligned} \tag{2.12}$$

where the ω^i are the *inertial angular velocities* of the body about the indicated axes, the J_i are the *polar moments of inertia* about the same respective axes, and:

K_{12} = the *product of inertia* with respect to planes y^1y^3 and y^2y^3;

K_{13} = the *product of inertia* with respect to planes y^1y^2 and y^2y^3;

K_{23} = the *product of inertia* with respect to planes y^1y^2 and y^1y^3.

It is conceptually significant to note here that the analytical separation of rotational and translational dynamics attends the specific location of the *origin* of the body frame ϕ_y at the *mass centroid*. A cardinal description in rigid body rotational dynamics concerns the *applied torques*, about the body axes y^i, which are reacted only by the induced change of rotational inertial kinetic state. Vectorially symbolized (and in suitable units), the applied torque kinetically reacted by a rigid body (through compound rotational response) is the time rate of change, with respect to inertial space (directional), of the inertial moment of momentum, $\bar{h}_I$. That is, in terms of the body axes y^i, about which the torques are applied,

$$\bar{\tau}_{a)y} = \left(\frac{d\bar{h}_I}{dt}\right)_{I)y} = \left(\frac{d\bar{h}_I}{dt}\right)_y + \bar{\omega}_{yI} \times \bar{h}_{I)y}$$

which reveals another important application of the theorem of Coriolis. Consequently, respective applied torques, about the y^i axes, are

$$\tau_{ay}{}^1 = \frac{dh^1}{dt} + \omega^2h^3 - \omega^3h^2$$

† See McClure, C., *Theory of Inertial Guidance*, Prentice-Hall, pp. 84–94.

$$\tau_{ay}{}^{2} = \frac{dh^2}{dt} + \omega^3 h^1 - \omega^1 h^3$$

$$\tau_{ay}{}^{3} = \frac{dh^3}{dt} + \omega^1 h^2 - \omega^2 h^1$$

where h^1, h^2, and h^3 are, respectively, the angular momentum magnitudes associated with the $\hat{\imath}_y$, $\hat{\jmath}_y$, and $\hat{k}_y$ terms of expression (2.12). i.e.,

$$h^1 = J_1\omega^1 - K_{12}\omega^2 - K_{13}\omega^3,$$

etc. Indicated operations in the preceding expressions for the $\tau_{ay}{}^{i}$ then specify these applied torques to be

$$\tau_{ay}{}^{1} = J_1\frac{d\omega^1}{dt} - (J_2 - J_3)\omega^2\omega^3 - \left(K_{12}\frac{d\omega^2}{dt} + (K_{13}\omega^1 + K_{23}\omega^2)\omega^2\right) - \left(K_{13}\frac{d\omega^3}{dt} - (K_{12}\omega^1 + K_{23}\omega^3)\omega^3\right)$$

(about y^1)

$$\tau_{ay}{}^{2} = J_2\frac{d\omega^2}{dt} - (J_3 - J_1)\omega^1\omega^3 - \left(K_{23}\frac{d\omega^3}{dt} + (K_{12}\omega^2 + K_{13}\omega^3)\omega^3\right) - \left(K_{12}\frac{d\omega^1}{dt} - (K_{13}\omega^1 + K_{23}\omega^2)\omega^1\right)$$

(about y^2)

$$\tau_{ay}{}^{3} = J_3\frac{d\omega^3}{dt} - (J_1 - J_2)\omega^1\omega^2 - \left(K_{13}\frac{d\omega^1}{dt} + (K_{12}\omega^1 + K_{23}\omega^3)\omega^1\right) - \left(K_{23}\frac{d\omega^2}{dt} - (K_{12}\omega^2 + K_{13}\omega^3)\omega^2\right)$$

(about y^3)

where the *body fixed axes* y^i are thus far restricted in location *only to the extent that the origin of the reference frame is located at the mass centroid of the body*. Units applicable to these expressions could be those of the cgs system with torque in (dyne) (cm), polar moments of inertia and products of inertia in (gm) (cm)^2, and the ω^i in radians per second.

Although explicit, the foregoing nonlinear differential expressions relating applied torques to inertial angular velocities and the six body constants are of a complexity which justifies a search for some simplification. Appreciable simplification is achieved by selecting the body fixed axes y^i with origin at mass centroid, *such that they are also the principal axes of the body*. Fixed to (or within) *any rigid body* there is *at least one triad* of *mutually orthogonal axes* the coordinate planes of which are *so oriented that the products of inertia of the body with respect to these planes are all zero*. Such orthogonal axes, for which the *products of inertia vanish*, are the *principal axes* of a rigid body.

While an identification of the principal axes of an arbitrary rigid body is frequently difficult,† symmetry is significant. In particular, an axis of circular symmetry of a homogeneous body is always a principal axis. It is evident that if the body axes y^i *are further selected along the principal axes*, then the rather formidable foregoing expressions for the applied torques, ${\tau_{ay}}^i$, reduce to just

$$\begin{aligned} {\tau_{ay}}^1 &= J_1 \frac{d\omega^1}{dt} - (J_2 - J_3)\omega^2\omega^3 \\ {\tau_{ay}}^2 &= J_2 \frac{d\omega^2}{dt} - (J_3 - J_1)\omega^1\omega^3 \\ {\tau_{ay}}^3 &= J_3 \frac{d\omega^3}{dt} - (J_1 - J_2)\omega^1\omega^2 \end{aligned} \tag{2.13}$$

which are the celebrated expressions known as *Euler's dynamical equations.* Euler's dynamical equations, or the preceding general equations from which they are deduced, provide Newtonian foundations for description of the rotational behavior of rigid bodies about the points defined by the mass centroids of such bodies (being simultaneously the treatment which separates rotational and translational dynamics). *Directional* inertial axes, x^i (or I^i), which radiate from the moving mass centroid, being of common origin with the body fixed axis y^i, constitute the first reference frame against which the angular behavior of a rigid body (identified by the angular behavior of the y^i) is reckoned. Other reference frames of known angular behavior relative to the directional inertial axes may then be utilized in a relative reckoning of the angular dynamics of the body. Description of the fundamental and rather sophisticated *cross-coupled rotational mechanisms* usually identified by the term *gyroscopic phenomena* is greatly simplified by the concepts and definitions of the *rigid body*, the *mass centroid*, and *principal axes*. These *cross-coupled rotational phenomena, manifest by axially reciprocal excursions and/or oscillations* which are identified by such words as *precession*, *nutation*, etc., are cardinal not only in the implementation of many inertial sensors and systems, but are inexorable in the inherent behavior of physical entities ranging from elemental particles to the major bodies of the cosmos. Although all ponderable bodies are *to some extent elastic*, and thus *not* rigid in the strict sense of the definition, Euler's dynamical equations nevertheless provide descriptions which are of sufficient accuracy in significant analytical predictions in vehicular technology, inertial guidance, celestial mechanics, and other areas of cosmonautics.

It is first observed that *if* there are *no applied torques*, ${\tau_{ay}}^i$, impressed about the principal axes of a rigid body, then, under an *initial state* of compound inertial rotation, Euler's dynamical equations give the relations

† See Whittaker, E. T., *Analytical Dynamics*, Dover, 1944, Chap. V.

$$\left.\begin{aligned} J_1 \frac{d\omega^1}{dt} &= (J_2 - J_3)\omega^2\omega^3 \\ J_2 \frac{d\omega^2}{dt} &= (J_3 - J_1)\omega^1\omega^3 \\ J_3 \frac{d\omega^3}{dt} &= (J_1 - J_2)\omega^1\omega^2 \end{aligned}\right| \tag{2.14}$$

which indicate the respective axial inertial reactions to the cross-coupled mechanism characterized by the terms on the right. In particular, if the rigid body is a *wheel* symmetrical about the y^2 axis with $J_1 = J_3 = J_N < J_2$, and $\omega^3 = \Omega = a$ constant, then

$$J_N \frac{d\omega^1}{dt} = (J_2 - J_N)\Omega\omega^3$$

$$J_2 \frac{d\omega^2}{dt} = 0, \quad J_2\Omega = h_k^{\ 2}$$

$$J_N \frac{d\omega^3}{dt} = -(J_2 - J_N)\Omega\omega^1$$

which may be manipulated to provide the *simultaneous linear* differential equations

$$\frac{d^2\omega^1}{dt^2} + \left(\frac{J_2}{J_N} - 1\right)^2 (\Omega)^2\omega^1 = 0$$

$$\frac{d^2\omega^3}{dt^2} + \left(\frac{J_2}{J_N} - 1\right)^2 (\Omega)^2\omega^3 = 0$$

that clearly convey the *axial reciprocity* of the *precession mechanism*, and, moreover, indicate that it must *cease* if $J_1 = J_2 = J_3$. While an *exact* realization of the condition $J_1 = J_2 = J_3$ is extremely improbable in a real body (due to elasticity, if for no other reason), this discussion does place in evidence the basic significance of *mass distribution* in gyroscopic phenomena. In this connection, it is understood that a *perfect sphere* (geometrically perfect, homogeneous, and rigid) under *mechanically free* spatial rotation can *not precess*. If there were such an ideal body, then torques applied about its principal axes (of which there would be an infinitude) would be inertially reacted only be accelerations (change of angular momentum) *about those axes*. That is, if $J_1 = J_2 = J_3$ then Euler's dynamical equations become

$$\tau_{ay}^{\ 1} = J_1 \frac{d\omega^1}{dt} \qquad \tau_{ay}^{\ 2} = J_1 \frac{d\omega^2}{dt} \qquad \tau_{ay}^{\ 3} = J_1 \frac{d\omega^3}{dt}.$$

Returning to the symmetrical rigid body exemplified by the wheel, wherein $J_1 = J_3 = J_N < J_2$, *if there are applied torques* $\tau_{ay}^{\ 1}$ and $\tau_{ay}^{\ 3}$, they may each be regarded as consisting of *two parts*

$$\tau_{ay}{}^1 = \tau_{aa}{}^1 + \tau_{aG}{}^1 = J_N \frac{d\omega^1}{dt} - (J_2 - J_N)\Omega\omega^3$$

$$\tau_{ay}{}^3 = \tau_{aa}{}^3 + \tau_{aG}{}^3 = J_N \frac{d\omega^3}{dt} + (J_2 - J_N)\Omega\omega'$$

where the $\tau_{aG}{}^1$ and $\tau_{aG}{}^3$ are those torques reacting the cross-coupled gyroscopic torques. Equating like parts, one obtains expressions relating the precessional angular velocities to the corresponding applied torques;

$$\omega^1 = \frac{\tau_{aG}{}^3}{\Omega(J_2 - J_N)} \qquad \omega^3 = \frac{-\tau_{aG}{}^1}{\Omega(J_2 - J_N)}$$

$$J_2 > J_N$$

which again depict the axial reciprocity of the precessional mechanism, and also indicate that the spin axis (the y^2-axis) precesses toward the applied torque axes according to the right-hand rule (ω^1 carries y^2 toward the initial direction of y^3, and ω^3 carries y^2 toward the initial direction of $-y^1$, both in accord with the right-hand rule). Recalling again

$$\bar{\tau}_{a)y} = \left(\frac{d\bar{h}_I}{dt}\right)_y + \bar{\omega}_{yI} \times \bar{h}_{I)y}$$

it is apparent that the precession mechanism is described by that part of the expression which is the vector product

$$\bar{\tau}_{aG} = \bar{\omega}_{yI} \times \bar{h}_{I)y}$$

an expansion of which gives the second terms of Euler's dynamical equations.

In contemplation of the foregoing dynamics, it must be remembered that the discussion has concerned *only* freely rotating rigid bodies which *are completely unlinked or ungimbaled with respect to other bodies or structures.* Although Euler's dynamical equations provide the foundation for the classical description of the compound behavior of the *gyroscope*,† the inclusion of a gimbal system, etc., introduces factors not necessarily implicit in the equations per se. Engineering and inertial guidance applications of precession devices and gyros often permit considerable analytical simplification in relation to the nonlinear differential equations of the classical gyroscope† (derived by starting with Euler's dynamical equations). Such circumvention is achieved by component configuration and by analytical simplification which often attends the merging of sensors and over-all system (gyro precession is suppressed, etc.).

† See Webster, A. G., *The Dynamics of Particles and of Rigid Elastic, and Fluid Bodies*, Hafner.

2.3 Total Kinetic Acceleration Descriptions in Terms of Guidance Variables. Other significant applications of the theorem of Coriolis are those which yield the *total kinetic acceleration* of the origin of a *directionally controlled* or *computationally identified* vehicular *reference triad* as is *expressed in terms of projections along its own axes* where each projection is;

(1) identifiably partitioned according to the *relative*, *Coriolis*, and *transport* accelerations, and;
(2) expressed in terms of the *guidance variables*.

Such descriptions permit the identification and *isolation* of the *relative acceleration*, being the *desired part* of the total acceleration sensed by accelerometers with input axes along the axes of the reference triad, respectively. That is, the expressions now of interest specify the *instrumental* or *computational corrections* which *isolate* the *relative acceleration signals* (from the total acceleration signals) required for the *inertial generation of guidance intelligence* in the designated relative coordinates (terrestrial, terra-lunar, etc.). This characterization of total acceleration in terms of local projections (along transported reference axes) and guidance variables is in marked contradistinction to the prior examples depicting total acceleration in terms of projections measured along axes *fixed in the earth*.

Relative geokinematics of the situation now of interest is depicted by Fig. 3. This figure indicates a right-handed orthogonal relative reference frame ϕ_R with axes R^i, of which the inertial angular motion is described by the inertial angular velocity $\bar{\omega}_{RI}$, where the characteristic projection is along R^3. The origin of a right-handed vehicular reference frame ϕ_P (transported by vehicle but *not* here directionally fixed to the vehicle) with axes P^i is located relative to the frame ϕ_R by a position vector $\bar{\rho}_R$ of instantaneous magnitude ρ (rho). While the origin of ϕ_P (the vehicle) is instantaneously so located relative to the rotating frame ϕ_R, its axes P^i are *physically controlled* (being then a directionally stabilized reference platform) *or* are *computationally remembered* (in this implementation ϕ_P is a "*phantom*" *reference platform*, maintained in the system computer) such that $+P^1$ is *eastward*, $+P^2$ is *northward*, and $+P^3$ is along a *positive extension* of $\bar{\rho}_R$ ($+P^3$ is geocentrically vertical). *Relative velocity* of the origin of the reference triad ϕ_P (being almost exactly the relative velocity of the vehicle with respect to ϕ_R), as expressed in terms of projections *measured along the* P^i, is readily shown to be

$$\bar{v}_{R)P} = \left(\rho \frac{d\phi}{dt} \cos \lambda\right)\hat{\imath}_P + \left(\rho \frac{d\lambda}{dt}\right)\hat{\jmath}_P + \left(\frac{d\rho}{dt}\right)\hat{k}_P \tag{2.15}$$

where $\phi(t)$ and $\lambda(t)$ are, respectively, the relative longitude and latitude as depicted by Fig. 3 and the unit vectors; $\hat{\imath}_P$, $\hat{\jmath}_P$, $\hat{k}_P$, are, respectively, measured along P^1, P^2, and P^3. Simultaneously, the *inertial velocity* of the origin of ϕ_P

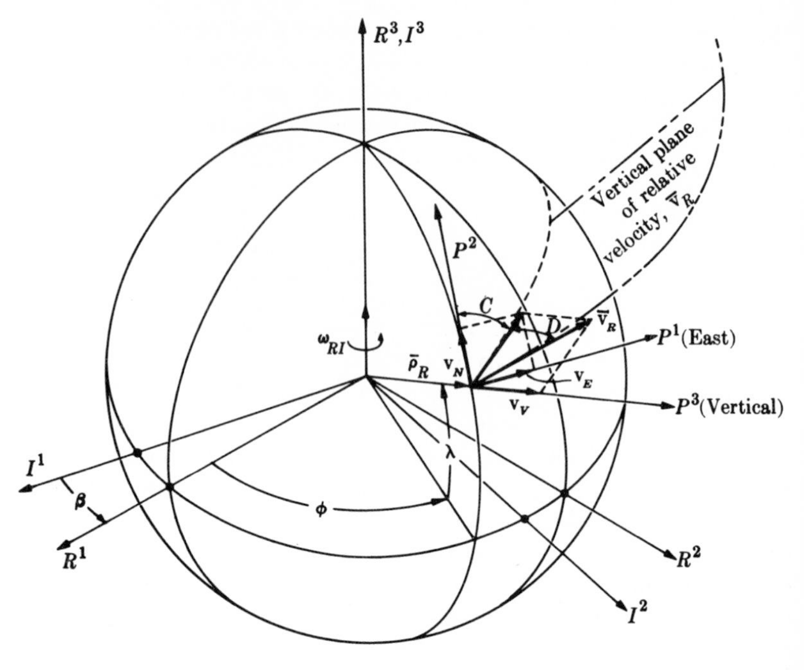

FIGURE 3.

in terms of projections along the same P^i axes is easily shown to be

$$\bar{v}_{I)P} = \left(\rho\left(\frac{d\beta}{dt} + \frac{d\phi}{dt}\right)\cos\lambda\right)\hat{\imath}_P + \left(\rho\frac{d\lambda}{dt}\right)\hat{\jmath}_P + \left(\frac{d\rho}{dt}\right)\hat{k}_P \tag{2.16}$$

where $|\bar{\omega}_{RI}| = \omega_{RI} = d\beta/dt$. At the same time, the *relative angular velocity* of the axes of ϕ_P (about each other relative to the space of ϕ_R) as expressed by projections along these axes is

$$\bar{\omega}_{PR)P} = \left(-\frac{d\lambda}{dt}\right)\hat{\imath}_P + \left(\frac{d\phi}{dt}\cos\lambda\right)\hat{\jmath}_P + \left(\frac{d\phi}{dt}\sin\lambda\right)\hat{k}_P \tag{2.17}$$

while the *inertial angular velocity* of the same vehicular triad is:

$$\bar{\omega}_{PI)P} = \left(-\frac{d\lambda}{dt}\right)\hat{\imath}_P + \left(\left(\frac{d\beta}{dt} + \frac{d\phi}{dt}\right)\cos\lambda\right)\hat{\jmath}_P + \left(\left(\frac{d\beta}{dt} + \frac{d\phi}{dt}\right)\sin\lambda\right)\hat{k}_P. \tag{2.18}$$

Another application of the theorem of Coriolis, being here

$$\bar{a}_{I)P} = \left(\frac{d\bar{v}_{I)P}}{dt}\right)_{I)P} = \left(\frac{d\bar{v}_{I)P}}{dt}\right)_P + \bar{\omega}_{PI} \times \bar{v}_{I)P}$$

then gives the total kinetic acceleration of the origin of ϕ_P in terms of projections along the axes of ϕ_P. As all projections are here already along the P^i axes, there is no differentiation of the unit vectors involved in this expansion. In particular, if $\omega_{RI} = d\beta/dt$ is *constant*, the total *kinetic* acceleration, $\bar{a}_{I)P}$, is found to have the projections

$$\left.\begin{aligned} a_P{}^1 &= \rho \frac{d^2\phi}{dt^2} \cos \lambda + 2\left(\omega_{RI} + \frac{d\phi}{dt}\right)\left(\frac{d\rho}{dt} \cos \lambda - \rho \frac{d\lambda}{dt} \sin \lambda\right) \\ a_P{}^2 &= \rho \frac{d^2\lambda}{dt^2} + 2 \frac{d\lambda}{dt}\frac{d\rho}{dt} + \rho\left(\omega_{RI} + \frac{d\phi}{dt}\right)^2 \frac{\sin 2\lambda}{2} \\ a_P{}^3 &= \frac{d^2\rho}{dt^2} - \rho\left(\frac{d\lambda}{dt}\right)^2 - \rho\left(\omega_{RI} + \frac{d\phi}{dt}\right)^2 \cos^2 \lambda \end{aligned}\right| \tag{2.19}$$

which are, respectively, associated with $\hat{\imath}_P$, $\hat{\jmath}_P$, and $\hat{k}_P$ (are, respectively, along P^1, P^2, and P^3).

Expressions (2.19) constitute a *particular* description of the total *kinetic* acceleration (does *not* include the effect of *mass attraction* or *gravitation*) impressed along the axes of the vehicular reference triad ϕ_P, which is directionally controlled in a specified particular manner. While further discussion here is required to explicitly identify relative, Coriolis, and transport acceleration contributions, the projections $a_P{}^i$ *are* directly expressed in terms of the *relative position variables* $\phi(t)$, $\lambda(t)$, and $\rho(t)$, which may be defined as the basic *guidance variables* in the relative reference frame ϕ_R. Thus, omitting for the moment the dynamic effects of gravitation, expressions (2.19) may otherwise be employed to indicate the configuration of a *block diagram* of implemented mathematical operations which systematically isolates the second derivatives,

$$\ddot{\phi} = \frac{d^2\phi}{dt^2} \qquad \ddot{\lambda} = \frac{d^2\lambda}{dt^2} \qquad \ddot{\rho} = \frac{d^2\rho}{dt^2}$$

from the total projections $a_P{}^i$, and successively integrates these derivatives to provide $\phi(t)$, $\lambda(t)$, and $\rho(t)$. That is, a *system functional schematic* (thus far *not* including gravitation) of the *signal processing* which generates signals proportional to ϕ, λ, and ρ, from signals generated by accelerometers respectively along the P^i axes (being signals respectively proportional to the $a_P{}^i$) may be constructed from expressions (2.19). Moreover, an implementation of the *directional control* of the reference triad ϕ_P, the control assumed in the derivation of expressions (2.19), may be simultaneously evolved with the generation of the signal processing (computer) schematic. The cardinal participation of mass attraction and gravitation in the inertial generation of guidance intelligence is described in subsequent discussion.

Opposed to the preceding description, which specifies the total kinetic acceleration projections $a_P{}^i$ directly in terms of the position variables ϕ, λ, and ρ, one may rather begin by showing that the *relative velocity* $\bar{v}_R$ is also

$$\left(\frac{d\bar{\rho}_R}{dt}\right)_{R)P} = \bar{v}_{R)P} = (v_R \sin C \cos D)\hat{\imath}_P + (v_R \cos C \cos D)\hat{\jmath}_P + (v_R \sin D)\hat{k}_P \quad (2.20)$$

where C is the relative north heading of the vertical plane containing $\bar{v}_R$, and D is the elevation of $\bar{v}_R$ relative to the P^1P^2 plane. See again Fig. 3. If $\omega_{RI} = d\beta/dt$ is again *constant*, as is usually the case, then time differentiation, *here involving the theorem of Coriolis applied to the differentiation of the unit vectors* $\hat{\imath}_P$, $\hat{\jmath}_P$, $\hat{k}_P$,† produces the $a_P{}^i$ in terms of $v_R = |\bar{v}_R| = v_R(t)$, $C = C(t)$, $D = D(t)$, $\lambda = \lambda(t)$, and some of their time derivatives. Explicitly, it may be shown that the projections $a_P{}^i$ are also:

$$a_P{}^1 = \frac{dv_R}{dt}\sin C \cos D + v_R \cos C \cos D \times \left(\frac{dC}{dt} - \frac{v_R}{\rho}\sin C \cos D \tan \lambda - 2\omega_{RI}\sin\lambda\right) + 2\omega_{RI}v_R \sin D \cos\lambda - v_R \sin C \sin D\left(\frac{dD}{dt} - \frac{v_R}{\rho}\cos D\right) \quad (2.21)$$

$$a_P{}^2 = \frac{dv_R}{dt}\cos C \cos D - v_R \sin C \cos D \times \left(\frac{dC}{dt} - \frac{v_R}{\rho}\sin C \cos D \tan \lambda - 2\omega_{RI}\sin\lambda\right) + \rho(\omega_{RI})^2 \sin\lambda\cos\lambda - v_R \cos C \sin D\left(\frac{dD}{dt} - \frac{v_R}{\rho}\cos D\right) \quad (2.22)$$

$$a_P{}^3 = \frac{dv_R}{dt}\sin D + v_R\frac{dD}{dt}\cos D - \frac{(v_R)^2}{\rho}\cos^2 D - 2\omega_{RI}v_R \sin C \cos D \cos\lambda - \rho(\omega_{RI})^2\cos^2\lambda. \quad (2.23)$$

Expressions (2.21) through (2.23) provide the basis for the construction of other computational and implementational schematics for the inertial generation of guidance intelligence (again, not yet including the cardinal gravitational effects). Signal processing based on these expressions may produce the direct outputs $v_R(t)$, $C(t)$, $D(t)$, $\lambda(t)$, and $\rho(t)$. That expressions (2.19) are *respectively equivalent* to (2.21), (2.22), and (2.23) may be demonstrated by starting with

$$v_E = v_R \sin C \cos D \qquad v_N = v_R \cos C \cos D \qquad v_v = v_R \sin D$$

which then lead to:

† See McClure, C., *Theory of Inertial Guidance*, Prentice-Hall, p. 173.

$$\frac{d\phi}{dt} = \frac{v_E}{\rho \cos \lambda} = \frac{v_R \sin C \cos D}{\rho \cos \lambda} \qquad \frac{d\lambda}{dt} = \frac{v_N}{\rho} = \frac{v_R \cos C \cos D}{\rho}.$$

These expressions, with their time derivatives (where all symbols are variables), may then, with others, be substituted into the expressions of (2.19) to complete the demonstration. In the process of the derivation of expressions (2.21) through (2.23) it is established that the *relative acceleration* is

$$\begin{aligned}\bar{a}_{R)P} = & \left(\frac{dv_R}{dt} \sin C \cos D + v_R \cos C \cos D\left(\frac{dC}{dt} - \frac{v_R}{\rho} \sin C \cos D \tan \lambda\right)\right. \\ & \left. - v_R \sin C \sin D\left(\frac{dD}{dt} - \frac{v_R}{\rho} \cos D\right)\right)\hat{\imath}_P \\ & + \left(\frac{dv_R}{dt} \cos C \cos D - v_R \sin C \cos D\left(\frac{dC}{dt} - \frac{v_R}{\rho} \sin C \cos D \tan \lambda\right)\right. \\ & \left. - v_R \cos C \sin D\left(\frac{dD}{dt} - \frac{v_R}{\rho} \cos D\right)\right)\hat{\jmath}_P \\ & + \left(\frac{dv_R}{dt} \sin D + v_R \frac{dD}{dt} \cos D - \frac{(v_R)^2}{\rho} \cos^2 D\right)\hat{k}_P \end{aligned} \tag{2.24}$$

while the *Coriolis acceleration* is revealed to be:

$$\begin{aligned}\bar{a}_{c0)P} = & (2\omega_{RI} v_R(\sin D \cos \lambda - \cos C \cos D \sin \lambda))\hat{\imath}_P \\ & + (2\omega_{RI} v_R \sin C \cos D \sin \lambda)\hat{\jmath}_P \\ & + (-2\omega_{RI} v_R \sin C \cos D \cos \lambda)\hat{k}_P. \end{aligned} \tag{2.25}$$

Remaining terms of expressions (2.21) through (2.23) reflect the *acceleration of transport* which, as $\bar{\omega}_{RI}$ is *constant*, is here just the *centripetal acceleration* due to *frame rotation*.

3. Rudimentary Features of Directional Reference Stabilization

As previously indicated, the somewhat sophisticated analysis pertaining to the classical treatment of gyroscopic phenomena may frequently be circumvented in the applications of gyro precession to the angular motion sensing and directional control implemented in inertial guidance. A so-called "*single degree of freedom*" *gyro*, which has been of common application in inertial guidance, is depicted by Fig. 4, which is a figure that also conveys the basic components of a *uniaxial* stabilization and directional control mechanism which may be based on such an angular motion sensor. Although *not* depicted by the figure, the gyro and gyro drive are mounted on a base such that the gyro may be driven in rotation about the I^3 (or c^3) axis, *relative to the base*, while the base itself may be rotated about I^3 relative to the *directional* inertial frame ϕ_I. It is here understood that the mechanism is

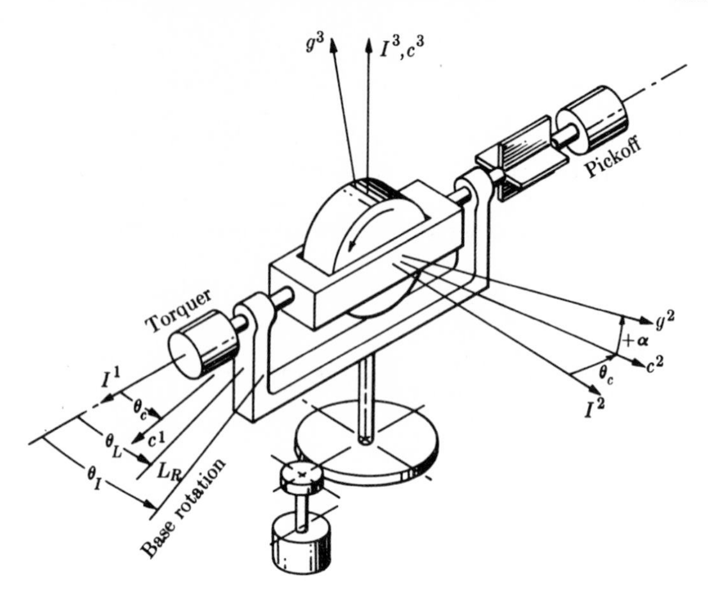

FIGURE 4.

uniaxial in the sense that angular disturbance, directional stabilization, and control of a *reference line on the gyro,* say the c^1 axis, all occur about I^3, while the precession $\alpha(t)$ and signal generation due to $\alpha(t)$ occur about the moving c^1 axis. That is, the reference line to be *stablized or controlled,* here the c^1 axis, rotates about I^3 (sweeps though an angle θ_c, measured in a plane which is perpendicular to I^3) so that I^3 (or c^3) is the single axis about which the *disturbing base rotation,* the *stabilizing angular restoration,* or *control rotation,* all occur. Although introduced in the foregoing uniaxial sense, the mechanism to be reviewed may, by further complication, be extended to the angular stabilization and directional control of an *orthogonal reference triad* or *gimbaled reference platform,* such as the ϕ_P frame of prior discussion.

Rudimentary functional features of the uniaxial angular stabilization and directional control mechanism implied by Fig. 4 attend the fact that a *net* input *inertial angular velocity, impressed on the gyro about* I^3 (or c^3), being

$$\omega_c = \frac{d\theta_c}{dt} = \dot{\theta}_c$$

causes the gyro to generate a *precessional torque* $\tau_{cG}{}^1$, measured about (projection along) its moving output axis c^1. Another application of the theorem of Coriolis, here to the projections of the *angular* (moment of) *momentum* of the gyro wheel $h_w = J_w\omega_w$ along the *case axes* c^1, c^2, and c^3, being $h_w{}^1 = 0$, $h_w{}^2 = h_w \cos\alpha$, $h_w{}^3 = h_w \sin\alpha$, then gives the *applied torques*

$\tau_{aG}{}^{i}$. Recognizing that $\omega_c{}^1 = \omega_c{}^2 = 0$, $\omega_c{}^3 = \omega_c = \dot{\theta}_c$, it is found that the precessional torque $\tau_{cG}{}^1$ about the case axis c^1 (being in *opposition* to the *applied torque* $\tau_{aG}{}^1$) is

$$\tau_{cG}{}^1 = h_w \frac{d\theta_c}{dt} \cos \alpha$$

where $\alpha = \alpha(t)$ is the instantaneous value of the precessional rotation about c^1. Again, see Fig. 4. Now even though the axis c^1 sweeps about in the plane (I^1I^2) perpendicular to I^3, the only rotation *about* c^1 is the dynamic response of the precessing assembly (wheel and inner gimbal structure) to the torque $\tau_{cG}{}^1$. Thus, under an assumption that the yet to be discussed precession control is very tight, so that $\alpha(t)$ remains small ($\cos \alpha \cong 1$), the scalar equation of motion of the precessing assembly about the c^1 axis is

$$J_\alpha \frac{d^2\alpha}{dt^2} + f_\alpha \frac{d\alpha}{dt} = h_w \frac{d\theta_c}{dt} \tag{3.1}$$

where J_α is the polar moment of inertia of the precessing assembly about c^1, and f_α is an intentionally imposed *damping coefficient* which has the cgs units

$$f_\alpha = (\text{dyne})(\text{cm})(\text{sec}) = \frac{(\text{gm})(\text{cm})^2}{(\text{sec})}$$

which are the same as those of the angular momentum $h_w = J_w\omega_w$. Under null initial conditions (dependent variables and their time derivatives are zero at $t = 0$), the Laplace transform of expression (3.1) may be written:

$$A(s) = \frac{h_w/f_\alpha}{J_\alpha/f_\alpha s + 1}\, \Theta_c(s). \tag{3.2}$$

A *simplified* description of the uniaxial stabilization and control mechanism attends the condition that the damping coefficient f_α is *large* relative to the polar moment of inertia J_α of the precessing assembly. This is frequently an induced physical condition (in single degree of freedom gyros) which justifies a reduction of expression (3.2) to

$$A(s) = \frac{h_w}{f_\alpha}\, \Theta_c(s) = k_G \Theta_c(s) \tag{3.3}$$

That is, *if* f_α is large relative to J_α, then the coefficient of s is *small*, and the relation between $\alpha(t)$ and $\theta_c(t)$ is described by a *dimensionless gain* (constant) k_G. In short, *if* $f_\alpha \gg J_\alpha$ (say 1000 to 1, or greater), then *gyro output axis dynamics are circumvented* in the derivation of the stabilization and control (system) equations. On the other hand, if this condition is *not* present, then the differential equations describing the closed-loop stabilization and directional control system are increased by at least one order (increased by more than one order if compensation circuits are then required).

In contemplation of the uniaxial angular stabilization and directional control system based on the angular motion sensing afforded by the "single degree of freedom" gyro, it is cardinal to appreciate the following.

Inertial angular stabilization of the reference line defined by the c^1 axis means that this line should *remain along its initial inertial direction* I^1 despite an arbitrary rotation $\theta_I(t)$ (about I^3, and here also c^3) of the base on which the entire mechanism is mounted.

Such inertial directional stabilization is here implemented by a pickoff signal voltage $e_P = k_P\alpha$ (proportional to α), which is amplified and applied to a drive motor which rotates the gyro case about I^3 (or here c^3) *relative to the base and in opposition to the base rotation* $\theta_I(t)$. Thus, the net inertial angular velocity applied about the gyro input axis c^3 (here along I^3) is the angular velocity *difference* $\omega_c = \dot{\theta}_c = \dot{\theta}_I - \dot{\theta}_0$, resulting from the base rotation $\theta_I(t)$, and the system restoration rotation $\theta_0(t)$. Thus an integral property of the mechanism is that the precession $\alpha(t)$ is *restrained to small values* while generating the activation (error) signal, $e_P = k_P\alpha$. An *additional term* is added to the left side of expression (3.1) to induce *rotational control* of c^1 (as opposed to the current directional inertial stabilization), and also to represent a *spurious torque* (about c^1) which induces *unwanted angular drift* of c^1 (about I^3). These features of the mechanism will be considered presently.

In further consideration of the *inertial* directional stabilization of a mass (such as the gyro of Fig. 4) supported by bearings (in a base which rotates relative to inertial space), it is first understood that the *inertia* of the mass provides an *inherent directional inertial stabilization*. That is, *in the absence of bearing friction* a mass supported about a single axis, and otherwise unconnected to the base, *would receive no applied torque due to base rotation*, and its own inertia would then keep the mass directionally fixed in inertial space. On the other hand, if there is off-set gearing, such as depicted by Fig. 4, then *even if there is no friction*, the inertia of the otherwise directionally stable mass can *not* provide complete directional stabilization. This is understood by consideration of the situation which occurs when the drive motor is *not* energized. Clearly, the axis of the pinion is carried by the rotating base and thus the *pinion orbits about the base gear*. As the pinion meshes with the gyro base gear, a rotation of the base from rest, or any change in the inertial angular velocity of the base, causes the pinion to experience *angular acceleration* about its own (orbiting) axis (parallel to I^3). Torque associated with this pinion angular acceleration is reacted by an angular acceleration of the gyro base gear (and gyro), about I^3, and the reference line c^1 thus does *not* remain directionally fixed in inertial space, even though there be *no friction* in gears or bearings. A rigorous description of even the uniaxial directional stabilization and control mechanism involves sophistications not considered here (self-stabilization, and others). Rather, it is here stipulated that the drive system gear ratio is of such a magnitude that base rotation is directly transmitted to the gyro (about I^3) when the stabilization system is *not* operating. That is, it is stipulated that the inertia torque of the inert gyro (and base gear) mass is completely ineffective in driving the "wrong way" through the large gear ratio to the motor shaft, and thus that the gyro is *locked to the base* when the drive motor is *not* operating. Under such implementation there is no *self-stabilization* of the reference line c^1 due to the inertia of the gyro system about I^3.

Recalling that base rotation about I^3 is denoted by $\theta_I(t)$, while *net* inertial rotation of the reference line c^1 is $\theta_c(t)$, it is then observed that under the condition of *no self-stabilization* the drive motor torque is dynamically reacted such that

$$\tau_M = J_\Sigma\left(\frac{d^2\theta_I}{dt^2} - \frac{d^2\theta_c}{dt^2}\right) + f_\Sigma\left(\frac{d\theta_I}{dt} - \frac{d\theta_c}{dt}\right)$$

where $\theta_0 = \theta_I - \theta_c$ is the inertial restoration (opposition) rotation of c^1 supplied by the drive system. Constants J_Σ and f_Σ, respectively, denote *reflected inertia and damping* of the drive system measured first at the motor shaft and then retransferred back to the final restoration rotation† of the reference line c^1. Simultaneously, as electrically developed, this same stabilization and control torque is assumed to be proportional to the applied control voltage e_M, which is an amplification of the gyro pickoff voltage e_P. Thus

$$\tau_M = k_M(k_A e_P) = k_A k_M k_P \alpha = k_\Sigma \alpha$$

or $T_M(s) = k_\Sigma\, A(s)$, where:

$$k_A = \frac{\text{volts}}{\text{volt}} \qquad k_M = \frac{\text{(dyne)(cm)}}{\text{volt}} \qquad k_P = \frac{\text{volts}}{\text{rad.}}$$

Employment of the heavily damped gyro, characterized in the Laplace domain by expression (3.3), or in the time domain by $\alpha(t) = k_G\theta_c(t)$, then leads to the stabilization system equation

$$J_\Sigma \frac{d^2\theta_c}{dt^2} + f_\Sigma \frac{d\theta_c}{dt} + k_G k_\Sigma \theta_c = J_\Sigma \frac{d^2\theta_I}{dt^2} + f_\Sigma \frac{d\theta_I}{dt} \tag{3.4}$$

which is established by elimination of τ_M and $\alpha(t)$ between the foregoing equations. A simple *test* forcing function $\theta_I(t)$, which specifies the disturbing base rotation as a function of time, is provided by $\theta_I(t) = \omega_I t$, $(t > 0)$.

† See McClure, C., *Theory of Inertial Guidance*, Prentice-Hall, pp. 129–134.

That is, the uniaxial angular stabilization system, as characterized by Eq. (3.4), is evaluated by supposing that at $t = 0$ the base starts rotating at the constant angular velocity ω_I (radians per second). Perfect response of the stabilization mechanism would be: the reference line c^1 remains along the initial inertial direction I^1 despite the angular motion of the base. In other words, under *perfect* angular stabilization, the *stabilization error* θ_c *would remain equal to zero.* The explicit solution of Eq. (3.4) for the disturbance $\theta_I(t) = \omega_I t$ and *null initial conditions* is easily found to be

$$\theta_c(t) = \frac{f_\Sigma \omega_I}{k_G k_\Sigma}\left[1 - \frac{e^{-\zeta\omega_n t}}{\sqrt{1-(\zeta)^2}} \sin\left(\omega_n \sqrt{1-(\zeta)^2}\,t + \psi\right)\right] \tag{3.5}$$

where

$$\omega_n = \sqrt{\frac{k_G k_\Sigma}{J_\Sigma}} \qquad \zeta = \frac{f_\Sigma}{2\sqrt{J_\Sigma k_G k_\Sigma}} \qquad \psi = \operatorname{arc\,cos} \zeta.$$

Although involving the angular velocity ω_I, expression (3.5) is, of course, readily seen to be *dimensionless* (the stabilization error $\theta_c(t)$ is an angle in radians as a function of time). Consequently, after the transient has decayed, the reference line c^1 comes to rest at the inertial angle

$$\lim_{t\to\infty} \theta_c(t) = \frac{f_\Sigma \omega_I}{k_G k_\Sigma} = \frac{f_\alpha f_\Sigma \omega_I}{h_w k_\Sigma} \quad \text{(radians)}$$

being measured from the initial inertial direction of c^1, along I^1. Thus, after sufficient time and a small angular displacement, $\theta_c(\infty)$ (above), c^1 *thereafter remains directionally fixed in inertial space despite the continued constant angular velocity* ω_I *of the base upon which the system is mounted.* The steady-state stabilization error $\theta_c(\infty)$ may be reduced by reducing f_Σ [but *not* f_α, as this would violate expression (3.3)], and directional inertial stabilization of the reference line c^1 is (according to this description) achieved.

The foregoing rudimentary description is based on the condition $f_\alpha \gg J_\alpha$, which is frequently the actual situation in single degree of freedom gyros as here employed. On the other hand, if the gyro is *not* heavily damped about the output axis c^1, then Eq. (3.1) must be employed in the derivation of the stabilization error equation. In this more general case, which otherwise retains the prior assumptions ($\alpha(t)$ is small, e_P directly proportional to $\alpha(t)$ etc.), it is readily shown that the stabilization error equation is

$$J_\alpha J_\Sigma \frac{d^3\theta_c}{dt^3} + (f_\alpha J_\Sigma + f_\Sigma J_\alpha)\frac{d^2\theta_c}{dt^2} + f_\alpha f_\Sigma \frac{d\theta_c}{dt} + h_w k_\Sigma \theta_c$$
$$= J_\alpha J_\Sigma \frac{d^3\theta_I}{dt^3} + (f_\alpha J_\Sigma + f_\Sigma J_\alpha)\frac{d^2\theta_I}{dt^2} + f_\alpha f_\Sigma \frac{d\theta_I}{dt} \tag{3.6}$$

which, being of the *third order*, immediately poses the question of *systematic stability*. As the angular momentum of the gyro wheel, $h_w = J_w\omega_w$, should, in general, be *large*, the stability condition

$$(f_\alpha J_\Sigma + f_\Sigma J_\alpha) f_\alpha f_\Sigma > h_w J_\alpha J_\Sigma k_\Sigma$$

may be difficult to satisfy. *Compensating circuits* may thus be required to achieve systematic stability or desired stabilization performance. If such equalization circuits (signal processing electrical networks) are included in the system, then Eq. (3.6) *is no longer the system equation.*

Whereas the rudimentary angular stabilization considered above concerned the directional stabilization of the reference line c^1 relative to an *inertial direction* defined by the I^1 axis, the stabilization (or enslavement) of the reference line c^1 with respect to a *rotating reference line*, L_R, defined by $\theta_L(t)$ (measured from I^1), is now considered. That is, instead of stabilizing c^1 to I^1 (or to a small angular displacement from I^1), it is now desired that c^1 be *rotated* (about I^3) *such that it remains along the rotating reference line* L_R, defined by $\theta_L(t)$. This behavior is implemented by supplying the gyro an *artificial precession* by activating a *torque generator* (called a torquer) mounted such that the *induced torque occurs about the precession axis* c^1 (being also again the controlled line). Under application of the *artificially induced precessional torque*, Eq. (3.1) becomes

$$J_\alpha \frac{d^2\alpha}{dt^2} + f_\alpha \frac{d\alpha}{dt} + k_\tau \tau_s(t) = h_w \frac{d\theta_c}{dt} \tag{3.7}$$

where $\tau_s(t)$ is a time-varying signal (of a nature yet to be specified), and k_τ is a *dimensional constant* related to the *torquer* (torque generator) which gives the term the units of a torque. If, for example, $\tau_s(t)$ is a voltage, then k_τ has the cgs units, (dyne) (cm) per volt. For null initial conditions the Laplace transform of Eq. (3.7) gives:

$$A(s) = \frac{h_w/f_\alpha}{J_\alpha/f_\alpha s + 1}\,\Theta_c(s) - \frac{k_\tau/f_\alpha}{s(J_\alpha/f_\alpha s + 1)}\,T_s(s).$$

If the gyro is again *heavily damped* about the output axis, such that $f_\alpha \gg J_\alpha$, then

$$A(s) = k_G \Theta_c(s) - \frac{k_\tau}{f_\alpha}\frac{T_s(s)}{s}$$

or, in the time domain

$$\alpha(t) = k_G \theta_c(t) - \frac{k_\tau}{f_\alpha}\int_0^t \tau_s(t)\,dt. \tag{3.8}$$

Elimination of τ_M and $\alpha(t)$ between foregoing equations then provides the equation:

$$J_\Sigma \frac{d^2\theta_c}{dt^2} + f_\Sigma \frac{d\theta_c}{dt} + k_G k_\Sigma \theta_c = J_\Sigma \frac{d^2\theta_I}{dt^2} + f_\Sigma \frac{d\theta_I}{dt} + \frac{k_\Sigma k_\tau}{f_\alpha}\int_0^t \tau_s(t)\,dt.$$

If the *torquer control signal*, $\tau_s(t)$, is *made proportional to the angular velocity of the reference line* L_R *that* c^1 *is intended to follow*, being expressed by

$$\tau_s(t) = k_L \frac{d\theta_L}{dt}$$

then the foregoing system equation becomes:

$$J_\Sigma \frac{d^2\theta_c}{dt^2} + f_\Sigma \frac{d\theta_c}{dt} + k_G k_\Sigma \theta_c = J_\Sigma \frac{d^2\theta_I}{dt^2} + f_\Sigma \frac{d\theta_I}{dt} + \frac{k_L k_\Sigma k_\tau}{f_\alpha} \theta_L.$$

Suppose first that it is desired that $\theta_c(t)$ be equal to $\theta_I(t)$ (c^1 is slaved to base rotation). In this case; $\theta_L(t) = \theta_I(t)$, and the foregoing equation *may be made an identity* by setting

$$k_G k_\Sigma = \frac{h_w k_\Sigma}{f_\alpha} = \frac{k_G k_\Sigma k_\tau}{f_\alpha}$$

which gives

$$k_L k_\tau = h_w \tag{3.9}$$

which is dimensionally homogeneous. Consequently, if the product $k_L k_\tau$ is numerically adjusted to be equal to h_w, then with $\theta_L(t) = \theta_I(t)$, the left and right sides of the system differential equation are identical which dictates that $\theta_c(t) = \theta_I(t)$ (that is, c^1 is slaved to base motion).

The foregoing exercise establishes the parametric requirement, $k_L k \;= h_w$, for the stabilization of the reference line c^1 to the rotating reference line L_R, defined by $\theta_L(t)$. Under the required adjustment the system equation is rewritten:

$$J_\Sigma \frac{d^2\theta_c}{dt^2} + f_\Sigma \frac{d\theta_c}{dt} + k_G k_\Sigma \theta_c = J_\Sigma \frac{d^2\theta_I}{dt^{\,2}} + f_\Sigma \frac{d\theta_I}{dt} + k_G k_\Sigma \theta_L. \tag{3.10}$$

A simple test situation is provided by supposing that the base is again in rotation such that $\theta_I(t) = \omega_I t$, while it is desired that c^1 follow L_R as defined by: $\theta_L(t) = \omega_L t$, $t > 0$. Equation (3.10) is a linear differential equation and thus *superposition is applicable*. Solution for the first two terms of the forcing function is again exactly expression (3.5), while solution for the forcing function term $k_G k_\Sigma \theta_L(t) = k_G k_\Sigma \, \omega_L t$ is

$$\theta_{cL}(t) = \omega_L t - \frac{f_\Sigma \omega_L}{k_G k_\Sigma} + \frac{e^{-(f_\Sigma/2J_\Sigma)t}}{\sqrt{4J_\Sigma k_G k_\Sigma - (f_\Sigma)^2}} \sin(\beta_L t - \psi_L) \tag{3.11}$$

where:

$$\beta_L = \frac{\sqrt{4J_\Sigma k_G k_\Sigma - (f_\Sigma)^2}}{2J_\Sigma} \qquad \psi_L = 2 \operatorname{arc\,tan} \frac{-\sqrt{4J_\Sigma k_G k_\Sigma - (f_\Sigma)^2}}{f_\Sigma}$$

Being a linear system, the total solution of Eq. (3.10) for null initial conditions and the stipulated forcing functions is thus the *sum* of expressions (3.5) and (3.11). Steady-state response indicated by this total solution is easily seen to be:

$$\theta_c(\infty) = \theta_c(t)_{ss} = \omega_L t + \frac{f_\alpha f_\Sigma}{h_w k_\Sigma}(\omega_I - \omega_L). \tag{3.12}$$

Thus, after the decay of transient terms of expressions (3.5) and (3.11), $\theta_c(t)$ follows $\theta_L(t)$ (the line c^1 follows the rotating reference line L_R) with a constant angular displacement error which may be made small by making f_Σ small.

Of cardinal significance in the foregoing description is the revelation that the example reference line c^1 (being here also the output axis of the gyro) is *stabilized with respect to the rotating reference line L_R, while being isolated from the base rotation $\theta_I(t)$*. Although described here in terms of rudimentary implementation and simple rotational forcing functions, these are the cardinal features of directional stabilization and control systems.

Recapitulating: a directional reference system must physically or computationally isolate a reference line (or a triad of axes) from undesired angular perturbations (such as oscillations of the vehicle) while stabilizing the same reference line (or triad) with respect to *directional inertial space* or with respect to some *desired rotating reference*.

A *rotating reference line* of particular significance is that which defines (in some suitable manner) the *vertical*, as is measured with respect to the earth (or other gross bodies). Rotational control of a reference line as involved in vertical indication is an integral feature of subsequent discussion.

Performance of a directional stabilization mechanism, operating in either the inertial directional or rotational mode, is *degraded* by the presence of undesired or *spurious torques* about the output axes of its gyros. Continuing the current uniaxial discussion, based on Fig. 4, a *spurious torque* (which may be due to several physical effects or anomalies) *about the gyro output axis* is denoted by τ_E. Under inclusion of this spurious torque Eq. (3.1) now becomes:

$$J_\alpha \frac{d^2\alpha}{dt^2} + f_\alpha \frac{d\alpha}{dt} + \tau_E(t) = h_w \frac{d\theta_c}{dt}. \tag{3.13}$$

Dynamically, τ_E is of *exactly the same nature* as the implemented torque, $k_\tau \tau_s(t)$, supplied by the torque generator (torquer) to induce stabilization of c^1 with respect to the rotating reference line L_R. Thus, in the same way that torquer torque induces a desired rotation of the controlled reference line c^1, the *spurious torque τ_E induces an undesired rotation or angular drift of c^1 away from its intended angular behavior* (inertial directional or rotating). Operational transformation of Eq. (3.13) plus a stipulation that the gyro is again heavily damped ($f_\alpha \gg J_\alpha$) provides the Laplace domain expression

$$A(s) = k_G\Theta_c(s) - \frac{1}{f_\alpha}\frac{T_E(s)}{s}$$

where $T_E(s)$ is the Laplace transform of the spurious torque $\tau_E(t)$, measured about the output axis c^1. Rudimentary description of the stabilization error due to the spurious torque is most conveniently established by supposing that there is *no base rotation* $\theta_I(t)$. Under this stipulation and the condition that the spurious torque is a *constant* $\tau_E(t) = \tau_{Ek}$, which gives

$$T_E(s) = \mathscr{L}[\tau_{Ek}] = \frac{\tau_{Ek}}{s}$$

it is readily established that the transform of the *drift rate* of the reference line c^1 is:

$$s\Theta_c(s) = \Omega_D(s) = \frac{k_\Sigma\tau_{Ek}/f_\alpha}{s(J_\Sigma s^2 + f_\Sigma s + (h_w k_\Sigma/f_\alpha))} \tag{3.14}$$

An application of the final value theorem then indicates that the *steady-state drift rate* of c^1 (angular drift rate away from the desired directional stabilization, either inertial or rotating) due to a *constant spurious torque* (here about c^1) is:

$$\omega_D = \frac{\tau_{Ek}}{h_w}\,. \tag{3.15}$$

Thus, in the steady state (and for the rudimentary system under discussion) a constant spurious torque about the gyro output axis induces a constant drift rate of the stabilized line c^1 (which here also is the axis about which the spurious torque is measured).

A torquer torque exactly equal and opposite to the spurious torque τ_E could, in theory, stop the drift. However, as torquer torque is intended to cause rotation of a reference line in accord with some rotational stabilization requirement, *its absorption in opposing spurious torque immediately generates a drift rate with respect to the desired rotational behavior of the reference line.* For a given constant spurious torque τ_{Ek}, the drift rate is smaller for greater values of the gyro wheel angular momentum h_w, as should be expected. In particular, if $h_w = 10^5$(gm)(cm)^2(sec)$^{-1}$, which is typical for certain gyros, then a constant spurious torque of 0.02 (dyne)(cm), measured about c^1, induces a drift rate of c^1 (about I^3 or c^3) of about 0.04 degree per hour. Although apparently small, such a drift rate value may be *very significant* in error generation in an inertial guidance system.

Spurious torques effective about the output axes of the stabilization and control gyros of an inertial guidance system are *cardinal anomalies* or *error sources which generally degrade the accuracy* of the guidance or reference variables generated by such implementations.

Much of the mechanical technology devoted to the physical fabrication of inertial sensors and systems involves techniques specifically developed to suppress performance degrading drifts due to spurious torques and forces.

Some specific physical anomalies which induce spurious torques about the output axes of gyros are: *mass unbalance* (under translational acceleration), *anisoelastic deflection* of gyro gimbal structure (under vibration and translational acceleration), *output axis bearing friction, thermal variations* within components and damping fluids, and *drifts in electrical excitations and signals*. It may be recalled here that the damping fluid, utilized to achieve the heavy damping (such that $f_\alpha \gg J_\alpha$) about the output axes of single degree of freedom gyros, is frequently simultaneously employed to *"float" the precessing assembly so as to reduce the effective friction of the output axis support bearings.*

The preceding description concerns the inertial directional and rotational stabilization of a line c^1 (which, for convenience, is also the precessional axis of the gyro) about a single directionally fixed axis I^3 (or c^3), and also indicates an undesired angular drift of the controlled line away from the intended stabilizations. As the stabilized and controlled reference line c^1 rotates in one single plane perpendicular to a single directionally fixed axis I^3, the mechanisms are referred to as *uniaxial*. It is here understood that the *single axis* implied by the word *uniaxial* is the axis about which the stabilization, control, and drift of the reference line occur, being specifically the I^3 axis (not to be confused with the reference line itself, here the c^1 axis). Basic concepts and implementation introduced by the uniaxial descriptions are fundamental to the more sophisticated *three-axis mechanisms* of the stabilization and control (and drift) of *an orthogonal triad of reference axes*. Previous discussion has indicated the participation of a controlled triad of reference axes in the inertial generation of guidance intelligence. Recapitulating: under specified directional control of an orthogonal triad of accelerometers the *relative acceleration components* (projections) of the origin of the triad (with respect to the reference frame of guidance, and in terms of projections along the controlled axes of the triad) *may be identified within the total acceleration impressed on the origin*. It is here understood that this involves corrections for gravitational effects as well as those for undesired kinetic acceleration contributions. Subsequent integrations of the relative kinetic acceleration signals then simultaneously participate in maintaining the directional control of the triad and in the generation of guidance intelligence.

Physical realization of a stabilized and controlled reference triad (usually right-handed) is implemented by employment of a *gimbaled reference platform* of which a particular configuration is indicated by Fig. 5. Reference

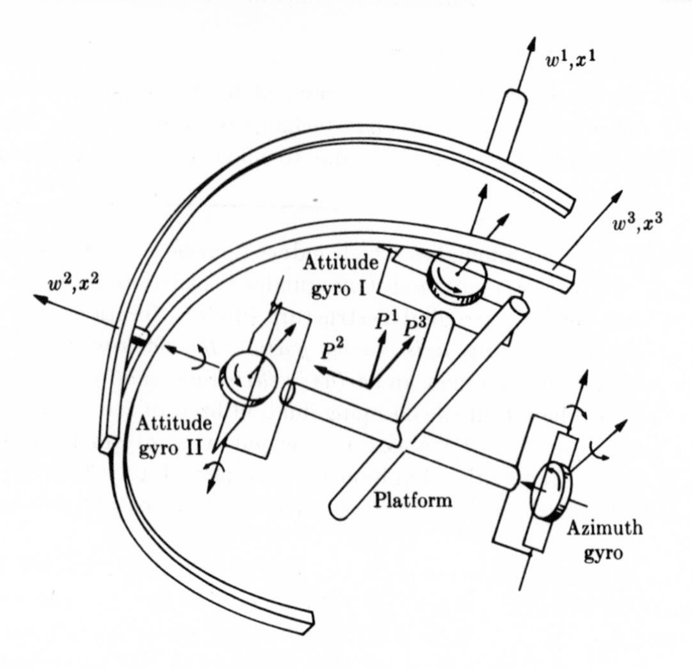

FIGURE 5.

axes of the platform (the reference triad ϕ_P) are here denoted by P^1, P^2, and P^3, and are colinear, respectively, with gimbal axes and vehicle axes at the instant which is depicted. Input axes of a rectilinear accelerometer and a "single degree of freedom" gyro are fixed along or are fixed parallel to each of the platform (reference triad) axes. Accelerometers are not shown in the figure. It is realized, of course, that the gyro input axes along (or parallel to), respectively, P^1, P^2, and P^3 are *case* input axes, each synonymous with the c^3 axis of Fig. 4, while the actual input axis of any gyro rotates under precession and remains mutually perpendicular to the spin axis and the precession axis (c^1). See the axis g^3 in Fig. 4. Also, in contemplation of the complete platform mechanism, the gimbals of the gyros must *not* be confused with the larger gimbals: *roll* (outer) and *pitch* (inner) which support the platform (triad) per se.

In further consideration of the reference platform depicted by Fig. 5, it is understood that the gyro with *case* input axis along (or parallel to) P^1, being *attitude gyro I*, is the angular sensor which measures the rotation of P^2 and P^3 *about* P^1 (in the same manner as the case input axis is along c^3 for the stabilization and control of c^1 in the uniaxial mechanisms of Fig. 4. Simultaneously, the gyros with case input axes along P^2 and P^3, respectively, sense the rotation of P^1 and P^3 about P^2, and the rotation of P^1 and P^2

about P^3. In the typical platform arrangement depicted by Fig. 5, the platform is servo driven about P^3 with respect to the inner (pitch) gimbal. That is, the *physical rotational axis* of the central element (being the triad to which the gyros and accelerometers are fixed) is the P^3 axis, which, under terrestrial guidance, is nominally *vertical*, and is mounted within the pitch (inner) gimbal by upper and lower trunnion bearings. Orthogonal axes P^1 and P^2 (perpendicular to P^3) are fixed in the physical platform to define the P^1P^2 plane, which is nominally horizontal under terrestrial guidance. Simultaneously, the pitch (inner) gimbal is itself servo controlled about the (rotating) x^2 axis with respect to the roll (outer) gimbal. Again see Fig. 5. Meanwhile, the roll (outer) gimbal is servo controlled in rotation about the w^1 (longitudinal) axis with respect to the vehicle. Rotation of the vehicle disturbs the platform (completely, or with some residual rotation) through rotations which are sensed by the gyros with case input axes along P^1, P^2, and P^3, respectively. Pickoff signals, generated by rotations about the output (precession) axes of the respective gyros, are employed to servo drive the platform and gimbals (with respect to their respective supporting members) in opposition to the residual angular disturbances so as to achieve directional stabilization and control of the reference triad (platform).

An *absolutely essential feature* of the directional stabilization and control of a gimbaled platform is the *continuous* (or digitally continuous) *transformational resolution* of the signals generated by the gyros. That is, as the platform axes P^i (along which the gyro case input axes and accelerometer axes are aligned) *rotate in an arbitrary manner relative to vehicle and gimbal axes* (or vice versa), *each gyro* (in general) *detects angular velocities which occur about all three vehicle axes*. Thus, the stabilization and control servo drives; one between platform and inner gimbal, one between inner gimbal and outer gimbal, and one between outer gimbal and vehicle, must, in general, *accept signals from all three gyros* to achieve stabilization and control of the triad (platform). Consequently, *appropriate trigonometric resolution* of gyro signals is an essential requirement in platform directional stabilization and control.†

While the particular gimbal arrangement of Fig. 5 provides a basic mechanical scheme for directional stabilization and control, it is easily seen that the use of *only two gimbals* in platform suspension entails certain *vehicle attitude restrictions*. That is, one may easily observe that the *terrestrial horizontal stabilization* of the P^1P^2 plane introduces indeterminacy when the w^1 (vehicle) axis is in a vertical attitude (vehicle in a vertical dive or climb). In such attitude, a P^3 gyro, which is otherwise an azimuth rotation sensor, senses roll motion, while the other two gyros (case input axes perpendicular to P^3), normally employed to achieve horizontal stabilization of the P^1P^2 plane, can *not* sense roll of the vehicle. Stabilization singularities of this

† See McClure, C., *Theory of Inertial Guidance*, Prentice-Hall, pp. 149–152.

nature may be circumvented by use of a *third* or so-called *redundant gimbal* in the platform suspension system.†

Certain *terrestrial leveling systems* (which slave the P^1P^2 plane of a platform to a horizontal plane of some definition) function in such a manner that the *generation of guidance intelligence is an integral feature of the leveling mechanism.* A *horizontal* enslavement of a P^1P^2 plane is, of course, synonymous with an enslavement of the P^3 axis to the corresponding *vertical*. As here the inertial generation of guidance intelligence is integral with the particular platform directional control of vertical indication, such systems are logically included under the topic of directional reference stabilization. Such *terrestrial leveling* or *vertical indication* is implemented by rotating the platform away from inertial directional stabilization by *suitable torquing* of the attitude gyros (case input axes along P^1 and P^2, respectively). This implementation, of necessity, involves the *signal resolution* previously mentioned.

Rudimentary analytical discussion of the inertial generation of guidance intelligence is frequently conducted in terms of the so-called *single-channel* approach. Single-channel description of an inertial guidance system usually involves an analysis based on *a single rectilinear inertial motion sensor* which is constrained to move along an *idealized trajectory*, and the mating *angular sensor* (gyro) of which the input axis is perpendicular to the *input axis* of the rectilinear sensor *and the plane of the trajectory*. Moreover, the dynamical environment assumed in a single-channel treatment is usually greatly simplified. Single-channel descriptions (the single channel, or control loop, is usually that closed around the rectilinear sensor) provide a background for the cross-connection of two or more single-channel systems and a subsequent relaxation of the ideal dynamical environment. As many important properties of inertial guidance systems may be evaluated and discussed by the single channel technique, the method is both a first approximation to more sophisticated behavior and a *useful comparative criterion*. A single-channel description is employed in the following review of an ideal inertial terrestrial leveling and guidance system known as the *Schuler‡ system*.

An idealized dynamical environment is employed to yield an uncomplicated description of the Schuler leveling mechanism and attending guidance outputs. Geometrical conditions upon which this ideal dynamical environment is based are depicted by Fig. 6. It is assumed that the system moves along a *great circle* trajectory at a *constant geocentric* radius r, measured from the center of a *nonrotating homogeneous spherical* planet such that an accelerometer input axis P^1 (of the triad ϕ_P) is nominally along the direction of motion. Being homogeneous and nonrotating, the gravitational field of

† See Savant, C., Howard, R., Solloway, C., and Savant, C. A., *Principles of Inertial Navigation*, McGraw-Hill, pp. 109–112.

‡ After M. Schuler, whose original paper (1923) introduced basic natural features of the mechanism.

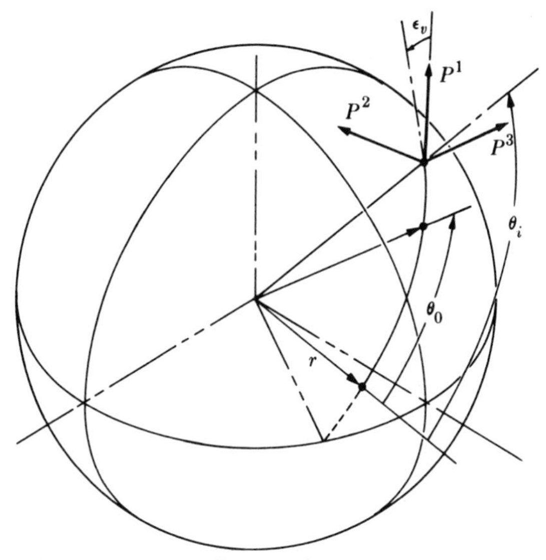

FIGURE 6.

this hypothetical spherical planet is truly radial and is characterized by a *constant acceleration* of magnitude g at the constant radial distance r. Variable velocity of the platform system ϕ_P (and vehicle) along the great circle trajectory is assumed to be less than the orbital velocity at the distance r so that the centrifugal effect associated with the centripetal acceleration is small relative to g, or so that the change in effective g due to variation in velocity is negligible. It is fundamental to appreciate that with the P^1-axis in the plane of the great circle trajectory, which is also the vertical plane, the platform (triad) is further oriented such that the case input axis of the mating gyro, along P^2, is right-handed perpendicular to the great circle plane containing P^1 and P^3. It is this gyro, with case input axis along P^2, that is *torqued* (a signal applied to the output axis torque generator) so as to *rotate the platform* (about P^2) away from its (otherwise) inertial directional stabilization in an attempt to keep P^3 vertical as the platform moves along the trajectory.

It is again recalled that a gyro torquing signal which rotates a reference line or platform with respect to inertial directional stabilization in accord with some desired rotation, $\theta_L = \theta_L(t)$, *must be proportional to the desired angular velocity* $\dot{\theta}_L$. This recollection indicates that here the required torquing signal, to keep the platform level, may be generated by operations performed on the *accelerometer output*. That is, a continuous time integration of the P^1-accelerometer signal, which thus provides a measure of *linear velocity* V_0, may be divided by the geocentric radius r to implement a measure of *angular velocity* around the spherical shell as a function of time. A gyro torquing signal (applied to the torque generator on the output axis of the gyro with input axis along P^2) proportional to this angular velocity is then employed to rotate the platform (about P^2) so as to remain level as the system moves along the circular trajectory.

Reference to Fig. 6 indicates that at a time t (after departure from an initial point) the system has displaced the actual great circle angle $\theta_i(t)$ (measured at the geocenter) while indicating the angular displacement $\theta_0(t)$. In other words, admitting that the system is *not* perfect, the vertical axis P^3 is along the radial line located by $\theta_0(t)$, which is the system generated vertical, while the platform origin is actually located by $\theta_i(t)$. Consequently, the error in the indicated vertical, being the unseen error in the apparent normal to the spherical shell, measured in the great circle plane of $\theta_i(t)$ and $\theta_0(t)$, is here directly:

$$\epsilon_v(t) = \theta_i(t) - \theta_0(t). \tag{3.16}$$

A rudimentary single-channel system to generate the vertical indication $\theta_0(t)$ in error by $\epsilon_v(t)$, and the related output velocity $V_0(t)$ and displacement $d_0(t)$ (along the great circle trajectory), is schematically implemented by starting with the accelerometer (with input axis along the P^1-axis). Admitting that the physical system is not perfect and has at time t generated a vertical indication (the direction of the P^3-axis) with a *positive* error defined by $\epsilon_v = \theta_i - \theta_0$, the acceleration impressed on the accelerometer along the P^1-axis is then

$$a = \frac{dV_i}{dt} \cos \epsilon_v + g \sin \epsilon_v \tag{3.17}$$

where V_i is the actual velocity magnitude along the circular trajectory, and g is the magnitude of the acceleration due to the geocentric gravity. Expression (3.17) is justified by thinking of the accelerometer as a spring mounted mass which is deflected along P^1 by the total acceleration (inertial) impressed along that axis. When the error ϵ_v, defined by $\epsilon_v = \theta_i - \theta_0$, is *positive*, a *positive kinetic acceleration* presses the mass *back*, *negatively along* P^1, while the component of force due to g and ϵ_v deflects it in the *same* direction. Consequently, if the accelerometer is implemented to provide a *positive signal* when the mass is so deflected, expression (3.17) is unambiguous. As $\epsilon_v = \epsilon_v(t)$ must remain small, the system is linearized by the small angle relations $\sin \epsilon_v \simeq \epsilon_v$, $\cos \epsilon_v \simeq 1$. Expression (3.17) is thus used as:

$$a = \frac{dV_i}{dt} + g\epsilon_v. \tag{3.18}$$

Realizing that a system block diagram may be drawn for a kinetic input specified by: a distance function, $d_i(t)$, a velocity function, $V_i(t)$, or an acceleration function, $a_i(t)$ (all specifying the true instantaneous state of motion along the great circle trajectory), it is recognized that for an input state of

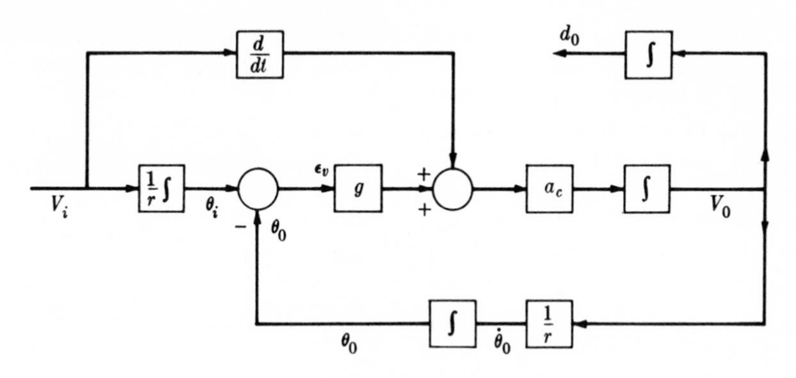

FIGURE 7.

motion at the *velocity level*, $V_i(t)$, the single channel block diagram is as depicted by Fig. 7. Proceeding from left to right, across the figure, *the first actual physical component is the accelerometer*, denoted by a_c. Preceding the accelerometer are the *environmental blocks*, one of which is that containing the symbol for time differentiation. This block reflects the fact that an accelerometer senses acceleration, and is schematically necessitated by the input being specified as a *velocity* function $V_i(t)$. Actual environmental generation of the true angular position, $\theta_i(t)$, is schematically incorporated by the environmental block indicating integration and division by the constant r, as is readily understood from the elementary relation between circular arc length and radian measure.

Effect of the gravitational acceleration on the P^1 axis accelerometer when *not* exactly perpendicular to the radius r is represented by the block containing g. This block accounts for the second term in expression (3.18). It is here understood that the *summation point* which gives $\epsilon_v = \theta_i - \theta_0$ does *not* represent any physical component, but rather merely *characterizes the tilt of the platform* in terms of the actual and indicated angular displacements, $\theta_i(t)$ and $\theta_0(t)$.

Following the accelerometer is an *integrator, which is a physical component* that accepts the accelerometer signal and provides an output signal *which is the system generated linear velocity* $V_0(t)$. Division of $V_0(t)$ by r, indicated by the next block and implemented by a computer, then provides the system generated angular velocity $\dot{\theta}_0(t)$, *which is the signal to which the gyro torquing signal is proportional*. Torquing of the P^2 gyro (signal applied to the output axis torquer) causes the platform to rotate about P^2 (as previously developed in the uniaxial sense) *through the angle* $\theta_0(t)$, *being then in effect an integration of* $\dot{\theta}_0(t)$, indicated by the integration in the feedback path of Fig. 7. Continuous rotation of the platform thus establishes the system indication of the vertical by the direction of the P^3 axis.

If the P^1 axis accelerometer is assumed to be *perfect, and if all scaling problems are ignored,* then, under the linearization indicated by expression (3.18), Fig. 7 is employed to write:

$$\theta_0(t) = \frac{1}{r} \int\int \left(\frac{dV_i}{dt} + g\epsilon_v\right) dt\, dt.$$

Simultaneously, by definition and the specified trajectory:

$$\theta_i(t) = \frac{1}{r} \int V_i(t)\, dt.$$

Substitution of these two expressions into expression (3.16) and two successive time differentiations then give the differential equation

$$\frac{d^2\epsilon_v}{dt^2} + \frac{g}{r}\,\epsilon_v = 0 \tag{3.19}$$

which is the equation which describes the behavior of the *vertical error,* $\epsilon_v(t)$, for the stipulated ideal situation and system (the ideal single-channel Schuler system).

Equation (3.19) indicates the basic property of the ideal Schuler system. This is *under the ideal stipulations, the vertical error* $\epsilon_v(t)$ *is independent of the velocity forcing function* $V_i(t)$.

If Eq. (3.19) is to have a solution other than the trivial solution $\epsilon_v(t) = 0$, it is required that there be *at least one nonzero initial condition.* If the two principal initial conditions are $\epsilon_v(0) = \epsilon_{v0}$, $\dot{\epsilon}_v(0) = \dot{\epsilon}_{v0}$, the solution for Eq. (3.19) is easily found to be

$$\epsilon_v(t) = \sqrt{(\epsilon_{v0})^2 + \left(\frac{\dot{\epsilon}_{v0}}{\omega_s}\right)^2} \cos\,(\omega_s t - \psi_s) \tag{3.20}$$

where:

$$\omega_s = \sqrt{\frac{g}{r}} \qquad \tan\psi_s = \frac{\dot{\epsilon}_{v0}}{\epsilon_{v0}\omega_s}.$$

Employment of $r = 6.37 \times 10^8$(cm) (an approximate mean radius of the earth) and $g = 981$ (cm)(sec)$^{-2}$ establishes the radian frequency ω_s as about: $\omega_s = 1.24 \times 10^{-3}$ radian per second. The corresponding period T_{sc} is about

$$T_{sc} = 2\pi\sqrt{\frac{r}{g}} \cong 84.4 \text{ min (time)}.$$

This radian frequency ω_s and the corresponding period T_{sc} are known as the *Schuler frequency* and *Schuler period*. Expression (3.20) indicates that under the ideal stipulations, the error in the indicated vertical (direction of the P^3 axis) is *independent* of $V_i(t)$ *but rather undulates periodically* at the Schuler frequency with an amplitude and phase which depend only on the *initial conditions* on ϵ_v and on the Schuler frequency. Clearly, if the second initial condition is zero ($\dot{\epsilon}_v(0) = 0$), then the error in the indicated vertical is just

$$\epsilon_v(t) = \epsilon_{v0} \cos \omega_s t \tag{3.21}$$

which is a cosine wave of which the amplitude depends only on the *initial error in the vertical.*

Error functions describing the errors in indicated velocity and indicated position are readily established by elementary analysis based directly on the block diagram, Fig. 7. Thus, under the same ideal stipulations, it is easily established that the *error in the system generated measure of velocity* is

$$V_\epsilon(t) = V_{\epsilon 0} \cos \omega_s t + \frac{\dot{V}_{\epsilon 0}}{\omega_s} \sin \omega_s t \tag{3.22}$$

where $V_{\epsilon 0} = V_\epsilon(0)$, and $\dot{V}_{\epsilon 0} = \dot{V}_\epsilon(0)$. Simultaneously, the *error in indicated position* is

$$d_\epsilon(t) = \frac{V_{\epsilon 0}}{\omega_s} \sin \omega_s t - r\epsilon_{v0}(1 - \cos \omega_s t) \tag{3.23}$$

where it has been assumed that the initial error in indicated distance is zero ($d_\epsilon(0) = 0$). Clearly, if $V_\epsilon(0)$ is also zero, then:

$$d_\epsilon(t) = -r\epsilon_{v0}(1 - \cos \omega_s t). \tag{3.24}$$

Single-channel description of the Schuler leveling system provides a simple revelation of the major features of this gravitationally oriented inertial guidance mechanism. In this connection, it is observed that the Schuler mechanism is a direct consequence of platform rotation by gyro torquing based on integration of a *relative acceleration which is contaminated by a component of gravitational acceleration.* As the control loop of the basic Schuler mechanism is closed only through the agency of platform rotation by gyro torquing, it is clear that an untorqued platform can*not* (in the current sense) exhibit the Schuler behavior. Other significant properties of the Schuler system which may be evaluated by single channel description relate to the effects of *component anomalies* and other error sources. In particular, the *error in indicated position* which attends the *platform drift* (here about P^2) due to *a constant spurious torque about the output axis of the pertinent gyro* (the gyro with case input axis along P^2) may be shown to be

$$d_{\epsilon D}(t) = r\omega_D\left(t - \frac{1}{\omega_s} \sin \omega_s t\right) \tag{3.25}$$

where ω_D is the *drift rate* of the platform (about P^2) as is specified by expression (3.15). For example, if ω_D is only 0.05 of a degree per hour, and r is again 6.37×10^8 cm, it is found that the distance error due to this drift is over 2000 feet after only 20 minutes. Platform drift is thus revealed to have an extremely degrading effect on the accuracy of inertial guidance implementation. Other significant error sources in the single-channel Schuler mechanism are: *integrator errors* (bias and variable dependent), *accelerometer error* (bias and variable dependent), and *computational* error (in the division by r).

The foregoing discussion concerns an idealized single-channel directional stabilization and control mechanism which functions such that the continuance of terrestrial level attitude (after erection) provides a direct generation of guidance intelligence. Needless to emphasize, the cross-connection of two such single-channel Schuler systems, for leveling and guidance in a real dynamical environment, entails sophistications *not* yet mentioned. Moreover, quite apart from the sophistications of the two-channel Schuler mechanism, the single-channel description may be made *more realistic* by inclusion of *component anomalies* and *error sources*. In particular, if the physical components in the pure Schuler mechanism (single-channel) behave as follows:

accelerometer output $= a_a = a_\beta + (1 + k_a)a$;

integrator output $= V_0 = V_{\beta\epsilon} + (1 + k_I)\int a_a\,dt$;

computer is such that the input is divided by $(r + \epsilon_r)$, instead of r;

platform drifts (about P^2) at the rate ω_D (radians per second);

then the vertical error and velocity error differential equations are, respectively:

$$\frac{d^2\epsilon_v}{dt^2} + \frac{(1 + k_a)(1 + k_I)g}{r + \epsilon_r}\,\epsilon_v = \left(\frac{1}{r} - \frac{(1 + k_a)(1 + k_I)}{r + \epsilon_r}\right)\frac{dV_i}{dt} - \frac{1 + k_I}{r + \epsilon_r}\,a_\beta \tag{3.26}$$

$$\frac{d^2V_\epsilon}{dt^2} + \frac{(1 + k_a)(1 + k_I)g}{r + \epsilon_r}\,V_\epsilon = (1 - (1 + k_a)(1 + k_I))\frac{d^2V_i}{dt^2} - \frac{(1 + k_a)(1 + k_I)g\epsilon_r}{r(r + \epsilon_r)}\,V_i + (1 + k_a)(1 + k_I)g\omega_D + \frac{(1 + k_a)(1 + k_I)g}{r + \epsilon_r}\,V_{\beta\epsilon}, \tag{3.27}$$

For the accelerometer and integrator the constants k_a and k_I characterize output errors which are *proportional to the outputs*, while a_β and $V_{\beta\epsilon}$ are *bias errors*. Equations (3.26) and (3.27) immediately indicate that with component error sources, the output error functions $\epsilon_v(t)$ and $V_\epsilon(t)$ are *not* completely independent of the forcing velocity $V_i(t)$.

Certain other terrestrial leveling and guidance systems which evolve *from* the (all inertial) pure Schuler system are also conveniently introduced by single-channel description. Two particular *quasi-inertial* systems, which are *not* Schuler mechanisms but which may be evolved from the basic Schuler configuration, are the *second-* and *third-order velocity damped* leveling and guidance systems. These systems, which are also both directional reference and guidance systems, *employ an external measurement of the relative velocity* $V_i(t)$ (frequently implemented by Doppler radar) to monitor the inertially generated vertical indication and guidance variables.† Single-channel descriptions (linear) of these two systems give the respective *velocity error* equations

$$\frac{d^2V_\epsilon}{dt^2} + k_1 \frac{dV_\epsilon}{dt} + \frac{(1 + k_2)g}{r} V_\epsilon = k_1(1 - k_D) \frac{dV_i}{dt} - k_2(1 - k_D) \frac{d^2V_i}{dt^2} \quad (3.28)$$

$$\frac{d^3V_\epsilon}{dt^3} + k_1 \frac{d^2V_\epsilon}{dt^2} + \frac{(1 + k_2)g}{r} \frac{dV_\epsilon}{dt} + \frac{k_3 g}{r} V_\epsilon$$
$$= (k_1(1 - k_D) - k_3(1 - k_D)) \frac{d^2V_i}{dt^2} - k_2(1 - k_D) \frac{d^3V_i}{dt^3} \quad (3.29)$$

where $k_1 = (\mathrm{sec})^{-1}$, k_2 is dimensionless, $k_3 = (\mathrm{sec})^{-1}$, and k_D is the dimensionless Doppler radar constant (ignoring Doppler dynamics) which, for a *perfect velocity* sensor of this nature, should be exactly *unity* (a typical value is, say, $k_D = 0.998$). That an incorporation of external velocity sensing (or measurement) introduces damping in the *second-order* system is manifest by the first-order term $k_1 \dot{V}_\epsilon$ in the dependent variable V_ϵ.‡

For *null* initial conditions ($\epsilon_v(0) = V_\epsilon(0) = 0$), and the step-function kinetic input, $V_i(t) = V_k$, $t > 0$, it is easily established that the velocity error function $V_\epsilon(t)$ is

$$V_\epsilon(t) = \frac{k_1(1 - k_D)V_k}{\omega_\beta} e^{-k_1 t/2} \sin \omega_\beta t \quad (3.30)$$

where

$$\omega_\beta = \left(\frac{4(1 + k_2)g - r(k_1)^2}{4r}\right)^{1/2}$$

while, with $d_\epsilon(0) = 0$, the corresponding distance error function is

$$d_\epsilon(t) = r \frac{k_1(1 - k_D)V_k}{(1 + k_2)g} \left(1 - e^{-k_1 t/2}\left(\cos \omega_\beta t + \frac{k_1}{2\omega_\beta} \sin \omega_\beta t\right)\right). \quad (3.31)$$

† See McClure, C., *Theory of Inertial Guidance*, Prentice-Hall, pp. 233 and 249 for block diagrams.

‡ See Appendix VI of the preceding reference for an important note concerning the effective damping coefficient k_1.

An advantage of the *third-order* system is revealed by the order of the derivatives in the forcing terms (on the right) in Eq. (3.29). Observing that these two forcing terms *have the same respective coefficients* as the forcing terms in the second order system (expression (3.28)) but that *the associated derivatives are one order higher*, it is then understood that the third-order system can accept the constant *acceleration* forcing function $V_i(t) = a_k t$, $t > 0$ *and still effect a complete transient suppression of the velocity error.* That is, the third-order system can experience a constant acceleration input and still *drive the velocity error to zero even if k_D is not unity.*

Corresponding to Eq. (3.28) for the velocity error, the *vertical error* equation for the ideal second-order single-channel velocity damped leveling system is:

$$\frac{d^2\epsilon_v}{dt^2} + k_1\frac{d\epsilon_v}{dt} + \frac{(1+k_2)g}{r}\epsilon_v = \frac{k_1(1-k_D)}{r}V_i(t) - \frac{k_2(1-k_D)}{r}\frac{dV_i}{dt}. \quad (3.32)$$

This equation may be derived from the block diagram (see a prior reference), or may be established from Eq. (3.28) by employment of the relation

$$V_\epsilon(t) = r\frac{d}{dt}(\epsilon_v(t))$$

Suppose now that $V_\epsilon(0) = V_{\epsilon 0} = 0$, but that there *is an initial error in the vertical,* $\epsilon_v(0) = \epsilon_{v0}$. If the forcing function is the step-function of velocity, $V_i(t) = V_k$, $t > 0$, then the vertical error function $\epsilon_v = \epsilon_v(t)$ is

$$\epsilon_v(t) = \frac{k_1(1-k_D)V_k}{(1+k_2)g}\left(1 - e^{-k_1t/2}\left(\cos\omega_\beta t + \frac{k_1}{2\omega_\beta}\sin\omega_\beta t\right)\right) + \epsilon_{v0}e^{-k_1t/2}\left(\cos\omega_\beta t + \frac{k_1}{2\omega_\beta}\sin\omega_\beta t\right) \quad (3.33)$$

where, as before:

$$\omega_\beta = \left(\frac{4(1+k_2)g - r(k_1)^2}{4r}\right)^{1/2}.$$

Now the last term of expression (3.33) is that part of $\epsilon_v(t)$ which is due to the *nonzero* initial condition, $\epsilon_v(0) = \epsilon_{v0}$, and is a component of $\epsilon_v(t)$ *which approaches zero with increasing time.*

Thus, with suitable values of k_D, the Doppler mode of operation (velocity damped) provides a means of *erecting* a platform, even though it may thereafter operate in some *other mode*, a pure Schuler mode, for example.

For constant values of g and r, and for the underdamped systems of usual interest, the time constant, $t_c = 2(k_1)^{-1}$, and the period

$$T_\beta = \frac{2\pi}{\omega_\beta} = \frac{2\pi}{\sqrt{(4(1 + k_2)g - r(k_1)^2)/4r}}$$

depend on the selection of k_1 and k_2, which are thus basic design parameters in the implementation of velocity-damped leveling systems. A table of values relating t_c, T_β, and the *damping ratio*

$$\zeta = \frac{k_1}{2\sqrt{((1 + k_2)g)/r}}$$

to k_1 and k_2 may be compiled.† A table of this nature is quite convenient in the design and evaluation of the applicable systems. In this connection, it should be recalled that in some velocity-damped terrestrial leveling systems, the constant k_2 is *zero*, reflecting an omission of the corresponding component. If such is the case, then the damping ratio is just.

$$\zeta = \frac{k_1}{2\sqrt{g/r}} = \frac{k_1}{2\omega_s}$$

where ω_s is again the *pure Schuler frequency*, even though the system is *not* a Schuler system. The aforementioned table is *not* directly applicable to this implementation.

Other directional reference systems, which fall within the general category of terrestrial leveling and guidance systems, may involve *variable coefficient linear* description and/or implementation, or *nonlinear* description and/or implementation.‡ Variable coefficient and nonlinear description may reflect a desire for *more accurate analytical characterization*, or may represent actual variable coefficient or nonlinear *implementation*. Such *implementations* frequently fall with the category of *adaptive control systems*, of which the techniques and configurations are considered elsewhere.

Directional reference systems thus far reviewed concern terrestrial leveling (vertical indication, as yet considered only in the ideal geocentric sense) and relate to the inertial generation of guidance intelligence as implemented aboard vehicles which experience relative velocities *well below* orbital velocities. In this connection it is understood that the Schuler mechanism, and other gravitationally affected guidance mechanisms (velocity-damped leveling, for example), become *increasingly ineffectual* as relative velocity approaches orbital values, and cease to function in orbit. Inertial directional reference and guidance systems transported by hypervelocity kinetically borne vehicles, which operate within and beyond an atmosphere, entail considerations, specifications, and requirements of which many are more stringent than those applicable to low-velocity terrestrial systems. Hypervelocity and extraterrestrial inertial implementations may be subjected to

† See the preceding reference, p. 237.
‡ See the preceding reference, Chap. 9.

more severe dynamical environments, may necessitate a high radiation impunity, or, depending on application, may require high reliability over very long time intervals. In relation to dynamical environments, some of the mechanical error sources in hypervelocity systems are indigenous to all inertial implementations of corresponding natures. In gyro sensors and directionally stabilized and controlled reference platforms the mechanisms of *dynamic drift*, *mass unbalance*, and *anisoelastic torque* are error sources which are enhanced by the severity of the dynamical environment.

Recalling that the actual input axis of a gyro is that axis which remains mutually perpendicular to both the output axis and the spin axis, it is seen that in the *strict sense*, the expression

$$\tau^1{}_{cG} = h_w \frac{d\theta_c}{dt} \cos \alpha$$

(which precedes expression (3.1)) *should be*

$$\tau^1{}_{cG} = (\omega_c{}^3 \cos \alpha - \omega_c{}^2 \sin \alpha) h_w$$

where $\omega_c{}^3 = \dot{\theta}_c$, and ω^2 is an angular velocity about the *case axis* c^2. This expression indicates the genesis of *cross-effects* in the conventional gyro wheel and platform suspension structures which can, under cyclic disturbances or residual vibrations transmitted to the gimbals, cause the gyro or platform to drift away from the intended angular behavior. Such drift is frequently called *dynamic drift*,† and is an error source which must be reckoned, particularly in severe vibrational environments.

If the true *mass centroid* of the precessing element of a gyro is *not* exactly on the output axis, then, depending on its angular orientation about the output axis, a component of acceleration perpendicular to the output axis induces a *spurious torque* about the output axis. Such spurious torque is usually called *mass unbalance torque*. Thus, a mass centroid eccentricity of 10^{-5} cm in a precessing element of 100 gm induces a spurious output axis torque of $10^{-5}10^2 a_P$ (dyne)(cm) where a_P is a component of acceleration (kinetic or gravitational) perpendicular to the output axis and the orientation of the eccentricity. As kinetic and gravitational accelerations here are indistinguishable in effect, a little consideration indicates that under suitable laboratory control, the drift of a platform may be experimentally employed to evaluate gyro anomalies (mass unbalance and frictional torques) and to establish some measure of the gyro mass centroid eccentricity.

Whereas the spurious torque due to gyro mass unbalance, in the preceding, is an anomaly of simple description, the *anisoelastic torque*, which is a spurious output axis torque that is due to the difference in elastic properties in the two orthogonal directions in the gyro wheel suspension (gimbal) structure,

† See the preceding reference, Section 7.5, p. 155.

is of somewhat greater analytical complexity. It may be shown that under rectilinear or cyclic acceleration (the latter pertinent to vibrational environments), and for a given difference in orthogonal elastic properties, this spurious torque is *proportional to the square of the impressed acceleration.*† Suppression of this drift inducing spurious torque is clearly one of the requirements of good gyro design, particularly for those sensors which experience severe changes in kinetic state which attend either vehicular vibration or vehicular transportation.

4. Geodetical Considerations and Certain Features of Terrestrial Inertial Guidance

Prior discussion has included the effect of the mass attraction or of the gravitation of gross bodies only to the extent that a *geocentric* acceleration due to gravity g was involved in the single-channel descriptions of leveling mechanisms. In the proximity of a gross body, and under relative velocities less than orbital velocities, an inertial generation of guidance intelligence must recognize the mass attraction or gravitational field which surrounds the body. Here it is to be noted that there is a *distinction* between mass attraction and gravitation, and that this distinction involves both the inertial angular velocity of the gross body and the relative motion of a test mass point. The gravity of common terrestrial experience includes not only the mass attraction (of the earth) exerted on a test mass, but also involves the centrifugal force due to the inertial angular velocity of the earth (and other effects).

The force of gravity, as defined for a test mass point *fixed to a planet*, or for a test mass point *of which the motion is referred to the planet*, is the vector resultant of the mass attraction of the planet and the planet's rotational centrifugal force at that point.

Corresponding *acceleration due to gravity* $\bar{g}$ is evaluated by defining the test mass to be a *unit mass*, or by dividing the gravitational force by the mass of the test mass point. Meanwhile, *except for certain perfect spheres*, the mass attraction force is itself *not geocentric*, but is the total vector attraction exerted by all the (countless) mass points of the planet on the test mass. Mass attraction thus depends on the mass distribution in the planet and on the relative location of the test mass point. A direct consideration of *mass attraction* acceleration indicates that a vectorial extension of the acceleration implicit in expression (2.1) may be employed to write

† See the preceding reference, pp. 210–215.

$$\bar{g}_{ma} = \sum_{p=1}^{n} \frac{km_p}{(\rho_p)^2} \frac{\bar{\rho}_p}{\rho_p} \tag{4.1}$$

where $\bar{\rho}_p$ (rho) is the vector measured from the pth mass point of the planet to the test mass point, m_p is the mass of the pth mass point, k is again the universal gravitational constant, and the discrete number n is *extremely large* (that which counts, say, all the atoms of the planet). Expression (4.1) does *not* explicitly describe the resultant mass attraction of a planet at a test point unless the location (in a planet fixed reference frame) and mass of all the mass points are explicitly known, which is a practical impossibility. Indeed, in the strict sense, *neither the mass attraction field of the earth or the corresponding gravitational field* (which includes the centrifugal effect due to planet rotation) *are exactly known*. Rather, expression (4.1) provides a conceptual foundation for mass attraction which is then combined with the effect of planet rotation to establish a definition of terrestrial gravity of which the acceleration $\bar{g}$ is then experimentally evaluated with the science of *geodesy*.

Certain instruments employed in geodetic empiricism, called "*gravity meters*," are conceptually and functionally synonymous with the accelerometers employed in inertial guidance. Configuration of the earth as is established by *gravity meter readings* (the figure of the earth so established is not to be confused with visible surface irregularities) is called the *geoid*.

Mass attraction acceleration, $\bar{g}_{ma}$, is considered in connection with the *centripetal acceleration* due to the earth's rotation

$$\bar{a}_c = \bar{\omega}_{EI} \times (\bar{\omega}_{EI} \times \bar{r}_E), \quad |\bar{a}_c| = (-r(\omega_{EI})^2 \cos \lambda)$$

to describe the terrestrial gravity of everyday experience, which is also that effecting a moving test mass *of which the relative motion is referred to the earth*. Consider a test mass point, of mass m_r, which is fixed to *or referred to the earth*. As is indicated by Fig. 8, it may be reasoned that the mass attraction force $\bar{g}_{ma}m_T$, and the *centrifugal force*, $(-\bar{\omega}_{EI} \times (\bar{\omega}_{EI} \times \bar{r}_E))m_T$, are the terrestrially induced forces, and that they are reacted by forces $-\bar{g}_{ma}m_T$ and $(\bar{\omega}_{EI} \times (\bar{\omega}_{EI} \times \bar{r}_E))m_T$. Thus:

$$\bar{F}_E = (-\bar{\omega}_{EI} \times (\bar{\omega}_{EI} \times \bar{r}_E) + \bar{g}_{ma})m_T$$
$$\bar{F}_R = (\bar{\omega}_{EI} \times (\bar{\omega}_{EI} \times \bar{r}_E) - \bar{g}_{ma})m_T.$$

That is, under equilibrium, $\bar{F}_R$ is equal and opposite to the environmental force $\bar{F}_E$. Clearly, then, the *acceleration of gravity* $\bar{g}$ is

$$\bar{g} = -(\bar{\omega}_{EI} \times (\bar{\omega}_{EI} \times \bar{r}_E)) + \bar{g}_{ma} \tag{4.2}$$

and may be incorporated with the *kinetic* acceleration of expression (2.11) in the following manner. First

$$\bar{a}_\sigma = \left(\frac{d^2\bar{r}}{dt^2}\right)_E + 2\bar{\omega}_{EI} \times \left(\frac{d\bar{r}}{dt}\right)_E - (-\bar{\omega}_{EI} \times (\bar{\omega}_{EI} \times \bar{r}_E) + \bar{g}_{ma})$$

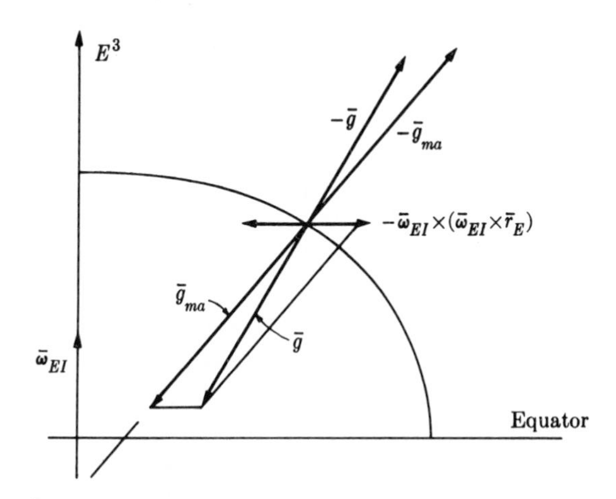

FIGURE 8.

where the subscript σ now denotes *total* acceleration, and here the third term of expression (2.11) is zero because $\bar{\omega}_{EI}$ is *constant* (in magnitude and direction, along E^3). Utilizing expression (4.2) the foregoing expression may be written:

$$\bar{a}_\sigma = \left(\frac{d^2\bar{r}}{dt^2}\right)_E + 2\bar{\omega}_{EI} \times \left(\frac{d\bar{r}}{dt}\right)_E - \bar{g}. \tag{4.3}$$

It may be observed that under *no* motion relative to the earth (test mass fixed to the earth), expression (4.3) reduces to just $\bar{a}_\sigma = -\bar{g}$, which reverifies that if a test mass is to remain fixed relative to the planet it must receive a force equal and opposite to the environmental force $m_T\bar{g}$.

Under recognition that the gravitational acceleration $\bar{g}$ deflects the mass of a vertical accelerometer *downward, which is the same deflection direction as that for an upward kinetic acceleration*, the negative polarity of $\bar{g}$ in expression (4.3) may, for some systems, be taken to indicate that $\bar{g}$ is an undesired acceleration from which the signal is to be nulled. In this connection it may be noted that positive $\bar{g}$ (expression (4.2) and Fig. 8) is defined here in accord with its kinetic manifestation (a body falls downward due to gravity), and that this definition is *systematically arbitrary*. That is, it may sometimes be convenient to define positive $\bar{g}$ as being upward.

Although Fig. 8 employs a quadrant of an ellipse to depict a polar (meridional) section through the level surface which is perpendicular to the gravitational acceleration $\bar{g}$, this is *not* the figure exhibited by the *actual geoid*. Rather, Fig. 8 reflects the fact that the most convenient elementary *reference* figure adaptable to earth measurement is an *ellipsoid of revolution* symmetrical about the polar axis E^3. On the other hand, due to the heterogeneous mass distribution within the earth, the *actual geoid*, which is the

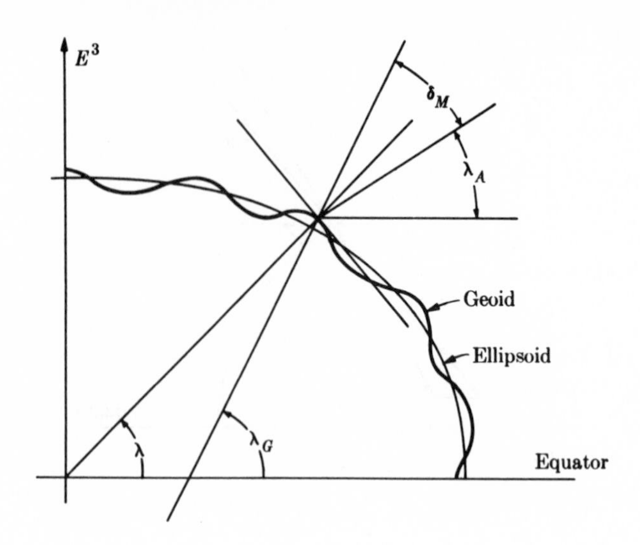

FIGURE 9.

level surface everywhere perpendicular to $\bar{g}$ (established by gravity data and not to be confused with the visible physical surface), *undulates* with respect to the *reference ellipsoid* in the manner indicated by Fig. 9. Needless to state, the eccentricity of the section ellipse and the magnitude of the undulations of the geoid are greatly exaggerated in this figure. Undulations of the geoid relative to the reference ellipsoid define the *gravity deflections* (a meridional projection, δ_M, of which is indicated in Fig. 9) and *magnitude anomalies* (magnitude differences measured at geoid and ellipsoid) which are studied in geodesy. These spurious deviations from the ellipsoid are error sources in terrestrial inertial guidance, and in the applications of inertial guidance to the preballistic control of missiles and extraterrestrial vehicles. Figure 9 also indicates the definitions of *geographic latitude*, λ_G, *geocentric latitude*, λ, and *astronomic latitude*, λ_A. An accepted value of the eccentricity of the polar section of the reference ellipsoid is such that

$$(e_c)^2 = \left(\frac{c}{a}\right)^2 = 6.69259 \cdot 10^{-3}$$

while the semimajor axis (equatorial radius) is about:

$$a = 6.378145 \cdot 10^8 \text{ (cm)}.$$

It may be recalled that the deflections of $\bar{g}$ (deflections of the gravitational vertical) with respect to a reference ellipsoid (of which there are several) are *not*, in general, characterized by simple functions, and, moreover, are *not* completely known for the entire geoid. However, the effects of such deflections (and of gravitational anomalies) in inertial guidance systems may be evaluated under certain idealizing assumptions,† or may be reckoned by statistical techniques for specified trajectories over given regions of the geoid.

Various design and implementation philosophies involve different methods of identifying and correcting the effects of gravitation in the inertial generation of guidance intelligence. For example, if one ignores the spurious effects of the gravitational deflections, above, and otherwise accounts for periodic components attending a Schuler mechanism, then a vertical indicating (leveling) system which slaves an accelerometer (axis) to the *geographic vertical* implicit in expression (4.3) *eliminates gravitational inputs to the attitude accelerometers in the horizontal plane*. Acceleration inputs along the *horizontal accelerometer input axis* are then characterized by an explicit expansion of *just the first two vector terms of expression* (4.3) (in the platform reference frame), if the required reference attitude control is achieved. In such a system the only accelerometer requiring major gravitational correction is that which is along the vertical. On the other hand, if a planet does *not exert a truly geocentric* $\bar{g}$, then a geocentric platform system, with the vertical accelerometer slaved to the *geocentric vertical* indicated in Fig. 9, *necessitates a running correction for gravitational inputs along all three platform axes.*

As previously reviewed, single-channel descriptions of directional reference and guidance systems provide significant conceptual introductions of the mechanisms, and are useful in routine engineering approximations and discussions. However, actual implementation of a real Schuler system, or any *real inertial guidance system* subject to the dynamical environment attending *arbitrary trajectories* and/or *nonidealized gravitational influences*, necessitates spatial description (two- or three-dimensional). In the case of the Schuler leveling and guidance system, *being a particular mode of operation for a reference platform system*, multichannel implementation and description may be evolved by suitably *cross-connecting* two or three single-channel schematics. Cross-connections involved in this design and description technique must be based on a spatial characterization of the actual kinetic and gravitational environment of the platform. In short, when evolving multichannel description and implementation based on the cross-connection of single-channel schematics, the system generated measures of *Coriolis acceleration*, etc., must be derived from the *simultaneous sensing capabilities* of the cross-connected channels. Outputs from the sensors of the orthogonal cross-connected channels are employed in a simultaneous closed-loop operation with *a suitable system computer* to achieve leveling and/or to generate guidance intelligence. Multichannel description and implementation is exemplified here by a two-channel terrestrial Schuler system the discusssion of which is initiated in the following paragraph.

† See McClure, C., *Theory of Inertial Guidance*, Prentice-Hall, Section 8.3, p. 191.

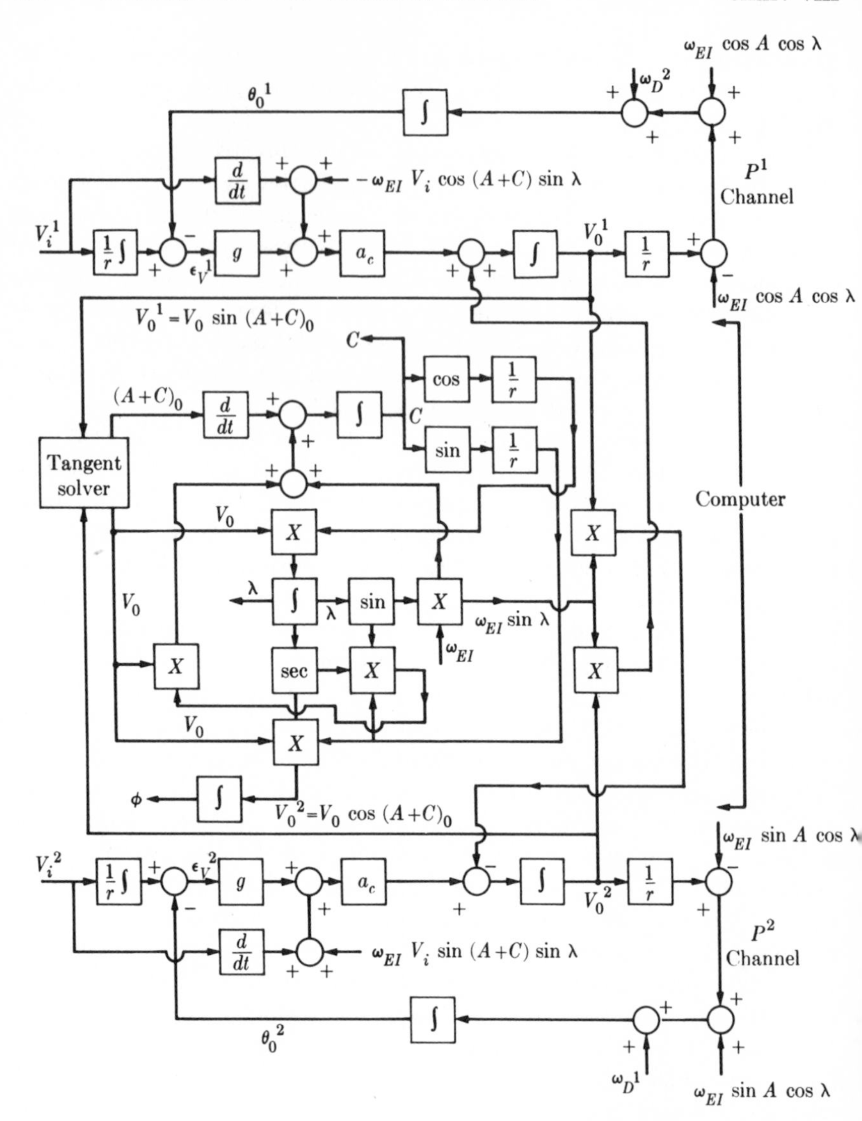

FIGURE 10.

In behalf of discussional simplicity it is here elected to review an inertial guidance system which operates at a *constant geocentric radial distance* r in the presence of a *constant geocentric gravitational acceleration* $\bar{g}$, which is assumed to be *undisturbed* by the inertial angular velocity of the geoid ($\omega_{EI} = 7.2921 \cdot 10^{-5}$ radian per second). This is the hypothetical gravitational environment of the exemplary two-channel Schuler system which is schematically depicted by Fig. 10. The P^1 and P^2 leveling channels are those identified, respectively, with the platform axes P^1 and P^2, which are horizontal after erection, and along each of which is an accelerometer input axis and a s.d.g. gyro case input axis. Again, see Fig. 5. After *adequate erection*, the continuation of the Schuler leveling and guidance mechanism is *essentially independent of the azimuth orientation of the P^1 and P^2 in the horizontal plane*. That is, once *level and operating*, the Schuler oscillations of the P^1 and P^2 axes (small oscillations occurring in perpendicular vertical planes which intersect along the P^3 axis, which is nominally vertical) *are essentially independent of the control enslavement of P^1 and P^2 in rotation about* P^3. That is, the mechanism is independent of the torquing signal applied to the *output* axis torquer of the gyro with case *input axis along* P^3 (independent of platform rotation about P^3).

Simultaneously, the torquing signals supplied to the output axis torquers of the gyros with case *input* axes along the P^1 and P^2 platform axes (the leveling or attitude gyros), respectively, must be proportional to the *sum* of the *angular velocity* components (about these axes) *which are due to vehicle motion relative to the planet and planet motion relative to inertial space*. This is frequently referred to as "*torquing according to vehicle's rate plus earth's rate*."

As the erected and operating Schuler mechanism is independent of the torquing signal applied to the output axis torquer of the *azimuth gyro*, this guidance system *may employ various implementations of the azimuth behavior of the P^1- and P^2*-axes (in rotation about P^3, now vertical). It is here understood that under *any rotational control* of the P^1 and P^2 axes about the (now vertical) P^3-axis, *correct resolution of signals between leveling gyros* (case input axes along P^1 *and* P^2) *and gimbal drives* (resolved by the resolver between platform and inner gimbal) still supplies the signals to gimbal motors to keep the P^1P^2 plane *level* (in the horizontal plane).

A *particular implementation* of azimuth control of the P^1- and P^2-axes. (about P^3) is that wherein *no torquer signal* is applied to the azimuth gyro. Under this control philosophy the platform is *not rotated* about the vertical (P^3-axis) as the system moves along its trajectory. A platform under such control is said to be "*inertial about the vertical*," and an observer watching such an *erected* system *at rest relative to the earth* would witness a *clockwise drift* (when viewed from above) or relative rotation of the P^1 and P^2 axes relative to the local meridian of a rate $\omega_{EI} \sin \lambda$, where λ is the latitude (between P^3 and the equatorial plane), and ω_{EI} is the magnitude of the angular velocity of the earth. This apparent clockwise rotation (in the northern hemisphere) reflects the rotation of the earth itself and demonstrates that P^1 and P^2 are directionally fixed in inertial space, *but about the vertical only*. It is understood, of course, that here P^1, P^2, and P^3 are *not* completely directionally fixed in inertial space, and that P^3 *must rotate* (a rotation of P^3, as opposed to a rotation *about* P^3) to remain vertical to the earth as the earth rotates and as the system moves relative to the earth. In further contemplation of platform axes which are "*inertial about the vertical*," let A denote the positive (counterclockwise) angle (a right-handed rotation about the positive upward P^3 axis) measured *from the eastward* direction *to* the P^1 axis. If the vehicle containing the erected system is *at rest* relative to the earth, then, in the *northern hemisphere*, the angular velocity of drift between the P^1 axis (and P^2 axis) and the *local meridian* is

$$\left(\frac{dA}{dt}\right)_{v_R=0} = -\omega_{EI} \sin \lambda$$

where λ is the measure of the latitude consistent with the vertical employed (geocentric or geographic).

In general, when the origin of the platform axes P^i is in relative terrestrial motion specified by the velocity $\bar{v}_R = \bar{v}_R(t)$, the *total inertial angular velocities* about an *erected* triad of axes respectively along the *instantaneous directions* of the P^i-axes are

$$\omega_{Pd}{}^1 = -\frac{v_R}{r_M} \cos A \cos C \cos D + \frac{v_R}{r_N} \sin A \sin C \cos D + \omega_{EI} \sin A \cos \lambda$$

$$\omega_{Pd}{}^2 = \frac{v_R}{r_M} \sin A \cos C \cos D + \frac{v_R}{r_N} \cos A \sin C \cos D + \omega_{EI} \cos A \cos \lambda$$

$$\omega_{Pd}{}^3 = \frac{v_R}{r_p} \sin C \cos D \sin \lambda + \omega_{EI} \sin \lambda$$

where

$$r_M = \frac{a(1 - e_c{}^2)}{(1 - e_c{}^2 \sin^2 \lambda)^{3/2}}, \quad r_N = \frac{a}{(1 - e_c{}^2 \sin^2 \lambda)^{1/2}}, \quad r_P = \frac{a \cos \lambda}{(1 - e_c{}^2 \sin^2 \lambda)^{1/2}}$$

if the instantaneous level surface perpendicular to the direction of P^3 is an *ellipsoid of revolution* (about E^3) of eccentricity e_c and equatorial radius a. For such an ellipsoidal surface the latitude is the *geographic latitude* $\lambda = \lambda_G$.† Again, see Figs. 3 and 4, and the expressions following expression (4.3). Strictly speaking, if $\bar{v}_R$ has a *vertical* component, as is implied by $D \neq 0$, then the foregoing expressions involve a *variable* eccentricity e_c and equatorial radius a. However, near the surface of an ellipsoidal geoid, e_c and a, as utilized in r_M, r_N, and r_P, are essentially constant. On the other hand, if the planet is assumed to be a *homogeneous sphere*, then

$$e_c = 0, \quad r_M = r_N = a = r, \quad r_P = r \cos \lambda$$

and the total inertial angular velocity projections $\omega_{Pd}{}^i$ become

† See the preceding reference, expression (1-16), p. 15.

$$\omega_{Pd}{}^1 = -\frac{v_R}{r}\cos(A + C)\cos D + \omega_{EI}\sin A\cos\lambda$$

$$\omega_{Pd}{}^2 = \frac{v_R}{r}\sin(A + C)\cos D + \omega_{EI}\cos A\cos\lambda$$

$$\omega_{Pd}{}^3 = \frac{v_R}{r}\sin C\cos D\tan\lambda + \omega_{EI}\sin\lambda$$

where the latitude λ is now the *geocentric* latitude. Next, if there is *no* vertical velocity component, which is the environmental situation upon which the two-channel system depicted by Fig. 10 is directly based, then $D = 0$, and the $\omega_{Pd}{}^i$ reduce to

$$\omega_{Pd}{}^1 = -\frac{v_R}{r}\cos(A + C) + \omega_{EI}\sin A\cos\lambda \tag{4.4}$$

$$\omega_{Pd}{}^2 = \frac{v_R}{r}\sin(A + C) + \omega_{EI}\cos A\cos\lambda \tag{4.5}$$

$$\omega_{Pd}{}^3 = \frac{v_R}{r}\sin C\tan\lambda + \omega_{EI}\sin\lambda. \tag{4.6}$$

Finally, if the P^1 and P^2 axes are *controlled* about P^3 such that they are respectively *slaved* to the *east* and *north* directions, then $A = 0$, and the $\omega_{Pd}{}^i$ become

$$\omega_{Pd}{}^1 = -\frac{v_R}{r}\cos C$$

$$\omega_{Pd}{}^2 = \frac{v_R}{r}\sin C + \omega_{EI}\cos\lambda$$

$$\omega_{Pd}{}^3 = \frac{v_R}{r}\sin C\tan\lambda + \omega_{EI}\sin\lambda$$

which, for $D = 0$, are exactly the angular velocities about the P^i axes for the situation depicted by Fig. 3 (with $D = 0$, there being then no vertical velocity). In all cases of the $\omega_{Pd}{}^i$ above, the variable C is, of course, the magnitude of the velocity heading with respect to terrestrial north.

With the foregoing angular velocity descriptions as background, the two-channel leveling and guidance intelligence system depicted by Fig. 10 may be anatomized. Recalling that this system is such that the leveling axes (horizontal axes) P^1 and P^2 are "*inertial about the vertical*," which means that *no torquing signal* is applied to the azimuth gyro (case input axis along P^3), consider first the behavior of the angle $A = A(t)$ under this implementation (operation at a constant r, no vertical velocity). Expression (4.6) immediately indicates that

$$\frac{dA}{dt} = -\omega_{Pd}{}^3 = -\frac{v_R}{r}\sin C\tan\lambda - \omega_{EI}\sin\lambda \tag{4.7}$$

where positive $A(t)$ is defined from east to north (counterclockwise) while for a net eastward inertial velocity component the *apparent* rotation of the P^1 (and P^2) axis must be clockwise in the Northern Hemisphere (where λ is positive). Expression (4.7) reflects both the vehicle's rate and the earth's rate. Simultaneously, the inertial angular velocities about the leveling axes of the platform P^1 and P^2, are, respectively, given by expressions (4.4) and (4.5). The inertial angular velocity $\omega_{Pd}{}^2$, projection along P^2, is that of the P^1 and P^3 axes about P^2 *if the platform remains level as the system moves relative to the rotating earth.* Similarly, the angular velocity $\omega_{Pd}{}^1$ (projection along P^1) is the inertial angular velocity of the P^2 and P^3 axes about P^1 under the continuance of level attitude. Thus, the torquing signal applied to the *output axis torquer* of the gyro with case *input* axis along P^1 rotates the platform (under proper signal resolution) about P^1 to keep the P^2 axis level. Consequently, as the leveling channels are identified by their *rectilinear accelerometers,* $\omega_{Pd}{}^2$ is involved in the P^1 channel system dynamics, while $\omega_{Pd}{}^1$ is involved in the system dynamics of the P^2 channel.

Now the P^1 channel (Fig. 10) operates on an *inertial* acceleration signal to generate a measure of the *linear* (or tangential) *relative* velocity in the direction of the P^1 axis (which is here "inertial about the vertical"). This relative velocity signal is then converted to an angular velocity signal (by division by r) which is used to torque the gyro with case input axis along P^2 so as to rotate the platform about P^2 to keep the P^1 axis level. Thus the P^1 channel attempts to generate $v_i{}^1 = v_R \sin (A + C)$, while generating $v_0{}^1 = v_0 \sin (A + C)_0$, and then; $r^{-1}v_0 \sin (A + C)_0$, which corresponds to just the first term of $\omega_{Pd}{}^2$ [expression (4.5)]. That is, as indicated by Fig. 10, the P^1 channel generates $v_0{}^1$ which is used both in the continuance of the level attitude of the P^1 axis and as an input to the computer which generates the guidance intelligence, V, C, λ, and ϕ. *However, an examination of expression* (4.5) *reveals that the torquer signal generated in the P^1 channel proper* (being $r^{-1}v_0 \sin (A + C)_0$) *is incomplete in that it does not include the term*

$$\omega_{EI} \cos A \cos \lambda,$$

needed due to the angular velocity of the earth. Computational generation of this signal is *not* indicated in Fig. 10, although it may be assembled from the variables of which the generations are indicated. Rather, the earth's rate torquing term in the P^1 channel, $\omega_{EI} \cos A \cos \lambda$, is inserted and canceled in the manner indicated, it being thus that its implementation is *not* here regarded as an error source. Corresponding explanations apply to the simultaneous operations in the P^2 leveling channel, involving the earth's rate torquing term, $\omega_{EI} \sin A \cos \lambda$. Accepting the symbol $\times$ for multiplication, the computer schematic is self-explanatory if it is understood that the "*tangent solver*" performs a rectangular to polar transformation of $v_0{}^1$ and $v_0{}^2$ to produce $v_0 = (v_R)_0$ and $(A + C)_0$, and that the scaling of the variables in the data processing is here ignored.

Expression (4.7) specifies the apparent angular velocity of the platform axis P^1 (or P^2) with respect to the instantaneous local meridian when the platform is "*inertial about the vertical.*" This is *equal* and *opposite* to the inertial angular velocity, about the vertical, of a *north oriented line* carried by the moving system over the rotating earth, that is, equal and opposite to $\omega_{Pd}{}^3$, as already employed. Consequently, for horizontal axes which are "inertial about the vertical" the magnitude of the angular velocity between the P^1 (or P^2) axis and the terrestrial meridians being crossed (that is, the north direction) is specified by expression (4.6). Thus, if the latitude λ, the radius r, and the velocity magnitude are available as an integral part of the closed-loop implementation, then $-\omega_{EI} \sin \lambda$ and $-\dfrac{v_R}{r} \sin C \tan \lambda$ may be computationally canceled from $\dfrac{dA}{dt} + \dfrac{dC}{dt}$ so that integration of

$$\frac{dC}{dt}$$

then supplies the terrestrial heading, $C(t)$. Other *present position* variables are generated by integrations of

$$\frac{d\lambda}{dt} = \frac{v_R}{r} \cos C \qquad \frac{d\phi}{dt} = \frac{v_R}{r} \sin C \sec \lambda$$

which were previously introduced (obtained by setting D equal to zero in the expressions following expression (2.23)). Other essential features of the system (Fig. 10) are the platform drift rates $\omega_D{}^2$ (about P^2, giving error in the P^1 channel), and $\omega_D{}^1$ (about P^1, giving error in the P^2 channel) and the *Coriolis corrections,* which are discussed in the following paragraph.

Having elected to characterize the two-channel system at the velocity level, as is indicated by Fig. 10, the matter of Coriolis corrections is examined by writing the total acceleration projections along the P^1 and P^2 axes in the expanded forms;

$$a_P{}^1 = \frac{dv_R}{dt} \sin (A + C) + v_R \cos (A + C)\left(\frac{dC}{dt} - \frac{v_R}{r} \sin C \tan \lambda\right) - 2\omega_{EI} v_R \cos (A + C) \sin \lambda = a_R{}^1 + a_c{}^1 \quad (4.8)$$

$$a_P{}^2 = \frac{dv_R}{dt} \cos (A + C) - v_R \sin (A + C)\left(\frac{dC}{dt} - \frac{v_R}{r} \sin C \tan \lambda\right) + 2\omega_{EI} v_R \sin (A + C) \sin \lambda = a_R{}^2 + a_c{}^2 \quad (4.9)$$

where the first two terms on the left in each expression are the *relative acceleration* projections ($a_R{}^1$ and $a_R{}^2$) in the directions of leveling axes P^1 and P^2. Expressions (4.8) and (4.9) are obtained from expressions (2.21) and (2.22) by resolving $a_P{}^1$ and $a_P{}^2$ (There they are the acceleration projections in the east and north directions.) through the angle A onto the current P^1 and P^2 axes, which are now "inertial about the vertical." On the other hand, to describe the required *relative velocity* projections (along P^1 and P^2) implementally generated by the *time integration* of signals within the respective channels, one begins with the actual input relative velocities $v_i^1 = v_R \sin (A + C)$, $v_i^2 = v_R \cos (A + C)$, and by time differentiation establishes what the integrator *inputs must be* if the *outputs* are to be the required relative velocity projections v_i^1 and v_i^2. Thus

$$\frac{dv_i^1}{dt} = \frac{dv_R}{dt} \sin (A + C) + v_R \cos (A + C)\left(\frac{dA}{dt} + \frac{dC}{dt}\right) = (a_R^1)_{RQ} \quad (4.10)$$

$$\frac{dv_i^2}{dt} = \frac{dv_R}{dt} \cos (A + C) - v_R \sin (A + C)\left(\frac{dA}{dt} + \frac{dC}{dt}\right) = (a_R^2)_{RQ} \quad (4.11)$$

which indicate that, without regard to component anomalies, the integrator outputs in the P^1 and P^2 channels must, respectively, be:

$$v_i^1 = \int (a_R^1)_{RQ}\, dt \quad (4.12)$$

$$v_i^2 = \int (a_R^2)_{RQ}\, dt. \quad (4.13)$$

However, of basic significance, when dA/dt [specified by expression (4.7)] is substituted into $(a_R^1)_{RQ}$ and $(Q_R^2)_{RQ}$, expressions (4.10) and (4.11), these become

$$(a_R^1)_{RQ} = \frac{dv_R}{dt} \sin (A + C) + v_R \cos (A + C) \times \left(\frac{dC}{dt} - \frac{v_R}{r} \sin C \tan \lambda - \omega_{EI} \sin \lambda\right) \quad (4.14)$$

$$(a_R^2)_{RQ} = \frac{dv_R}{dt} \cos (A + C) - v_R \sin (A + C) \times \left(\frac{dC}{dt} - \frac{v_R}{r} \sin C \tan \lambda - \omega_{EI} \sin \lambda\right) \quad (4.15)$$

which, because of the presence of $\omega_{EI} \sin \lambda$, are *not identical* to the a_R^1 and a_R^2 given, respectively, as the first two terms of expressions (4.8) and (4.9). Rather, $(a_R^1)_{RQ}$ and $(a_R^2)_{RQ}$ differ from the corresponding *total kinetic acceleration projections* $a_P^1 = a_R^1 + a_c^1$ and $a_P^2 = a_R^2 + a_c^2$ *only in that the terms involving* $\omega_{EI} \sin \lambda$ *are not accompanied by the coefficient* 2.

This is the genesis of the *half Coriolis correction* which is depicted within Fig. 10. Discussing the P^1 channel, the cardinal point in the current system is described as follows: input to the channel is regarded as the *relative* velocity $v_i^1 = v_R \sin(A + C)$ (where $v_i = v_R$), being a velocity which is *hypothetically* operated on by the *environmental* differentiation box to produce $(a_R^1)_{RQ}$. *Actual* kinetic acceleration impressed along P^1 is then accounted for by *environmentally* adding $(-\omega_{EI} v_i \cos(A + C) \sin\lambda)$, as is indicated in Fig. 10. Needless to state, there is *no physical implementation* involved in this environmental characterization.

Clearly, the desired output from the P^1 channel integrator (the physical component) is $v_i^1 = \int (a_R^1)_{RQ}\, dt = v_R \sin(A + C)$, where $(a_R^1)_{RQ}$ is as given by expression (4.14). On the other hand, the actual kinetic acceleration along P^1 is given by expression (4.8), that is, is a_P^1, as is schematically assembled in Fig. 10. Thus, as

$$\frac{d}{dt}(v_R \sin(A + C)) = (a_R^1)_{RQ} = a_P^1 + \omega_{EI} v_R \cos(A + C) \sin\lambda$$

the *required correction* which must be added to a_P^1 so that the sum becomes $(a_R^1)_{RQ}$ (the time integral of which is the desired v_i^1), is

$$(+\omega_{EI} v_i \cos(A + C) \sin\lambda),$$

being in magnitude *one-half* of the actual Coriolis acceleration impressed along the P^1 axis under the condition of relative motion referred to the earth. A similar examination of the P^2 channel reveals that the required correction therein is $(-\omega_{EI} v_i \sin(A + C) \sin\lambda)$. Thus, the required Coriolis corrections are here achieved by the interchannel cross-connections indicated in Fig. 10. Generation of these corrections involves multiplication of the velocity outputs by $\sin\lambda$ and ω_{EI}, which are available, respectively, from present position storage and a storage of the known magnitude, $\omega_{EI} = |\bar{\omega}_{EI}|$.

It is of interest to note that *simultaneous linear* descriptions of the *cross-connected* P^1 and P^2 leveling channels of Fig. 10 may be established under the assumption that the latitude λ is *constant* over the time interval of interest. For example, under the condition of constant latitude, it may be shown that the *velocity error* V_ϵ^1 in the P^1 channel is described by the linear differential equation:

$$\frac{d^3 V_\epsilon^1}{dt^3} + \frac{g}{r}\frac{d^2 V_\epsilon^1}{dt^2} + \left((\omega_{EI} \sin\lambda)^2 + \frac{g}{r}\right)\frac{dV_\epsilon^1}{dt} + \left(\frac{g}{r}\right)^2 V_\epsilon^1$$
$$= g\frac{d\omega_D^2}{dt} + \frac{(g)^2}{r}\omega_D^2 + (g\omega_{EI} \sin\lambda)\omega_D^1. \quad (4.16)$$

If the drift rates ω_D^1 and ω_D^2 are zero, this equation becomes

$$\frac{d^3 V_\epsilon^1}{dt^3} + (\omega_s)^2 \frac{d^2 V_\epsilon^1}{dt^2} + ((\omega_{EI} \sin\lambda)^2 + (\omega_s)^2)\frac{dV_\epsilon^1}{dt} + (\omega_s)^4 V_\epsilon^1 = 0$$

$$(\omega_s)^2 = \frac{g}{r}$$

of which the solutions depend only on the initial conditions imposed on the P^1 channel velocity error, $V_\epsilon^{\,1}(t)$.

5. Other Modes of Operation and Philosophies of Implementation

Other essential features and functions of vehicular inertial systems (implemented to generate directional reference and/or guidance intelligence) pertain to *erection* and *alignment* with respect to known or desired initial coordinated directions (in the relative coordinate frame of guidance). In the situation of a terrestrial guidance system which employs a directionally stabilized and controlled reference platform (axes P^i), it is usually required that a vertical (P^3) axis be erected to a geocentric or geographic vertical, while the consequently horizontal axes (P^1 and P^2) are aligned with respect to terrestrial directions, for example, the P^1 axis aligned to the east. This initial alignment is, of course, independent of the particular azimuth control (inertial about the vertical, P^1 slaved to the direction of motion, etc.) employed *after* erection and alignment. Other inertial guidance systems, not employing physical directional reference, must generate and/or store the computational equivalent of such physical erection and alignment.

In terrestrial inertial systems employing ponderable directional reference (platform systems), erection and/or alignment may be implemented by a systematic mode of operation which is identified by the term "*gyrocompassing*." In particular, consider the alignment of the P^1 axis to the eastward direction (see Fig. 3) *when the system is at rest relative to the earth*. It may be assumed that observation is sufficient to adjust the azimuth error ϵ_A to a relatively small value (two or three degrees) before the alignment system begins to function. Under this situation the fundamental activation in the gyrocompassing implementation of azimuth alignment is that *constant* torquing terms (here unscaled torquing signals), $\omega_c^{\,1} = 0$, $\omega_c^{\,2} = \omega_{EI} \cos \lambda$, and $\omega_c^{\,3} = \omega_{EI} \sin \lambda$, are applied, respectively, to the torquers of the P^1 and P^2 leveling gyros and the azimuth gyro *as though there is no azimuth error* ϵ_A. Differences between the required torquing signals and those actually applied, $\omega_c^{\,i}$, induce a tilt of the platform (if *not* already present), and consequently the generation of signals by the *leveling accelerometers* (along P^1 and P^2) due to sensing components of the gravitational acceleration $\bar{g}$. These *accelerometer signals* are processed and employed to torque the azimuth gyro so as to null the azimuth error ϵ_A by additional rotation of the platform about P^3 (and may also be employed to correct erection). An *idealized description* of this azimuth alignment mechanism is based on the P^1 gyro (case input axis along P^1) and the P^2 accelerometer (a description valid for small values of ϵ_A). For a *small* azimuth error ϵ_A, the torquing error to the P^1 gyro, which levels the P^2 accelerometer, is proportional to

$$(0 - \omega_{EI} \cos \lambda \sin \epsilon_A) \cong -(\omega_{EI} \cos \lambda)\epsilon_A,$$

where λ is *constant* (system at terrestrial rest). If now the signal from the P^2 accelerometer, $e_2 = -g\epsilon_v{}^2$ (here unscaled), is *negatively* applied *directly* to the azimuth gyro torquer (*without* preintegration), it is then easily shown that

$$\frac{d^2\epsilon_A}{dt^2} + g\,\frac{d\epsilon_A}{dt} + (g\omega_{EI} \cos \lambda)\epsilon_A = 0 \qquad (5.1)$$

of which the stable solutions depend only on the initial conditions $\epsilon_A(0)$ and $\dot{\epsilon}_A(0)$, imposed on $\epsilon_A(t)$, and are easily established.† Erection and alignment of a moving system may also be implemented. This involves a combination of the gyrocompassing mechanism and an external measurement of *relative velocity*. In this connection recall the second part of expression (3.33), and the statements which follow that expression.

Inertial guidance systems which are *fundamentally different* from those thus far explicitly considered are those which do *not* utilize a physical reference platform which is directionally isolated or controlled with respect to the transporting vehicle. Instead of being based on the physical implementation of directional reference, the inertial generation of guidance intelligence *may be implemented through computations performed with and on signals generated by inertial sensors which are fixed directly to the vehicle*. Such systems, which may be referred to as "*vehicle oriented inertial systems*" (VOIN systems), may employ three rectilinear accelerometers (or other rectilinear inertial sensors) orthogonally mounted parallel to the longitudinal, lateral, and nominally vertical axes, and two or three angular sensors with input axes parallel, respectively, to two or three of the same vehicle axes. Such an arrangement of vehicle oriented inertial sensors may be integrated within one package (quite similar to the stable element or platform of a platform system), or may be distributed in accord with the dictates of vehicle design. The generation of guidance intelligence is then, in theory, implemented by a *computer* (usually digital) of *sufficient capacity* so that *initial* conditions and *sensor signals* are thereafter processed to generate relative velocity, heading, present position, etc., *irrespective of vehicle attitude perturbations*. An explicit analytical characterization of a general VOIN system reveals mathematical complications in considerable excess of those which are encountered in the description of platform systems. On the other hand, while making more stringent demands of the vehicle borne computer and of the system analyst, the VOIN systems are endowed with considerable relative mechanical and fabricational simplicity, and would seem to show

† Actual implementation would involve adjustable gain parameters.

appreciable promise in the extraterrestrial domain (especially when employed in connection with stellar sensors).

It is fully appreciated, of course, that the fundamental kinematical and dynamical descriptions employed to characterize the environment of platform inertial systems (recall expressions (2.11), (2.19)–(2.25), and (4.2)–(4.6)) remain basically applicable to all vehicular inertial systems. Utilization of basic dynamical description in an implementation of VOIN systems is conceptually facilitated by an introduction of the concept of the "*phantom platform.*" A *phantom platform* is a *hypothetical* right-handed orthogonal triad of axes of which the *relative angular behavior* (in guidance coordinates) is *computationally extrapolated* from (vehicle fixed) sensor signals and a given set of initial directional conditions (the latter reflecting erection and alignment). That is, a *phantom platform* is mathematically generated within the computer by an iterated evaluation of the nine elements of a *direction cosine matrix* (which may be the *matric product* of several matrices) and reflects the directional behavior of a real platform *if* such *were present* and *stabilized* and *controlled* in a *selected manner*. The instantaneous (or digitally instantaneous) attitude of the real VOIN system sensor triad (fixed in relation to vehicle axes) is computationally reckoned against the *phantom platform* in a running generation of guidance intelligence and relative directional reference.

By way of example, suppose that a terrestrial VOIN system employs a phantom platform that is erected to a terrestrial vertical (geocentric or geographic) with the P^1 axis slaved to the east, and that the respective vehicle axes are also aligned along these directions at $t = 0$. The matric equation expressing vector projections in the vehicle frame ϕ_v, in terms of projections in the phantom platform frame ϕ_P, is

$$[v_v{}^i] = [a_j{}^i] \cdot [v_P{}^i]$$

[see expression (2.8)] where the direction cosine matrix at $t = 0$ is Kronecker's delta of order three. Here the computer must utilize the given initial conditions and the sensor signals, degraded by angular perturbations of the vehicle, to establish the rotation of the phantom platform relative to its initial inertial directions (under the selected phantom platform control philosophy), and must also keep up to date on the rotation of the vehicle triad relative to the phantom platform. There are here at least *two* direction cosine matrices the elements of which are explicitly related and evaluated by the operations of matric algebra applied to: the dynamical description of the environment of the phantom platform, the five or six actual sensor signals, and the initial conditions. That is, knowing the dynamical environment, the control philosophy, and relative initial directional conditions of the phantom platform, and having the sensor signals, the VOIN system computational generation of guidance intelligence may be implemented.

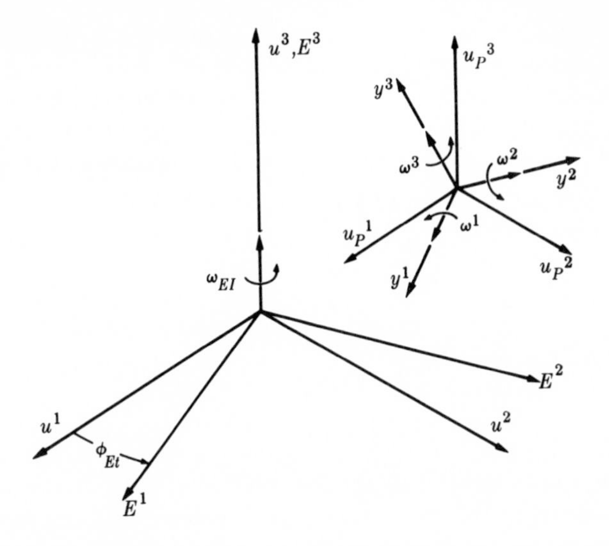

FIGURE 11. Equatorial-polar directional inertial axes; u^1, u^2, u^3, are phantom platform axes. Vehicle axes: y^1, y^2, y^3. Earth fixed axes: E^1, E^2, E^3.

In further cursory consideration of the VOIN system philosophy and its implementation, it is of particular interest to recapitulate the most direct conceptual approach to VOIN mechanization. VOIN implementations most readily visualized are those based on the *differential equations in the direction cosines* between *vehicle axes* and a *phantom platform* defined by *directional inertial axes* which remain respectively parallel to geocentric (equatorial-polar) directional inertial axes. That is, the control philosophy here applied to the phantom platform is one of hypothetical stabilization in the directional inertial space defined by the vernal equinox and the terrestrial polar axis. Right-handed orthogonal reference frames involved in this situation are depicted by Fig. 11, which includes the terrestrially fixed frame; ϕ_E (axes E^1, E^2, E^3). Direction cosines, $a_j{}^i = a_j{}^i(t)$, between the *directional inertial axes*; u^i (or $u_P{}^i$ which define the phantom platform), and the vehicle axes; y^i are conveyed by the matric equation;

$$\begin{bmatrix} y^1 \\ y^2 \\ y^3 \end{bmatrix} = \begin{matrix} & u^1 & u^2 & u^3 \\ y^1 & a_1{}^1 & a_2{}^1 & a_3{}^1 \\ y^2 & a_1{}^2 & a_2{}^2 & a_3{}^2 \\ y^3 & a_1{}^3 & a_2{}^3 & a_3{}^3 \end{matrix} \cdot \begin{bmatrix} u^1 \\ u^2 \\ u^3 \end{bmatrix}$$

where the u^i and y^i adjacent to the square matrix identify the direction cosines (for example, $a_3{}^2$ is the cosine of the angle between u^3 and y^2).

Realizing that the vehicle axes, y^i, rotate in an arbitrary manner relative to the directional inertial axes, $u_P{}^i$, while *angular rate sensors* with input axes respectively along the y^i may sense the inertial angular velocity projections; ω^1, ω^2, ω^3, one may employ some manipulations with unit vectors and the theorem of Coriolis to establish the nine simultaneous differential equations:

$$\frac{da_j{}^1}{dt} = \omega^3 a_j{}^2 - \omega^2 a_j{}^3$$

$$\frac{da_j{}^2}{dt} = \omega^1 a_j{}^3 - \omega^3 a_j{}^1$$

$$\frac{da_j{}^3}{dt} = \omega^2 a_j{}^1 - \omega^1 a_j{}^2$$

$$j = 1, 2, 3$$

Knowing the initial values, $a_j{}^i(0)$, the solutions; $a_j{}^i(t)$, of this system of differential equations (which is actually three independent systems) provide the *direction cosines* for *resolution* of signals from *rectilinear sensors* along the vehicle axes, y^i, onto the phantom platform axes, $u_P{}^i$. Navigation and guidance intelligence may then be generated in the phantom reference system (here being directional inertial space itself) and thereafter be transformed into the terrestrial system, axes E^i, which is of known behavior relative to the u^i axes. In general, the ω^i are variable. However, should it occur that these inertial angular velocities may be treated as *constants* (over short increments of computational time), then elementary state-space techniques may be employed to establish the *explicit solutions*:

$$a_j{}^1(t) = \left(\frac{(\omega^1)^2}{(\omega)^2} + \frac{(\omega^2)^2 + (\omega^3)^2}{(\omega)^2} \cos \omega t\right) a_j{}^1(0)$$
$$+ \left(\frac{\omega^1\omega^2}{(\omega)^2} - \frac{\omega^1\omega^2}{(\omega)^2} \cos \omega t + \frac{\omega^3}{\omega} \sin \omega t\right) a_j{}^2(0)$$
$$+ \left(\frac{\omega^1\omega^3}{(\omega)^2} - \frac{\omega^1\omega^3}{(\omega)^2} \cos \omega t - \frac{\omega^2}{\omega} \sin \omega t\right) a_j{}^3(0)$$

$$a_j{}^2(t) = \left(\frac{\omega^1\omega^2}{(\omega)^2} - \frac{\omega^1\omega^2}{(\omega)^2} \cos \omega t - \frac{\omega^3}{\omega} \sin \omega t\right) a_j{}^1(0)$$
$$+ \left(\frac{(\omega^2)^2}{(\omega)^2} + \frac{(\omega^1)^2 + (\omega^3)^2}{(\omega)^2} \cos \omega t\right) a_j{}^2(0)$$
$$+ \left(\frac{\omega^2\omega^3}{(\omega)^2} - \frac{\omega^2\omega^3}{(\omega)^2} \cos \omega t + \frac{\omega^1}{\omega} \sin \omega t\right) a_j{}^3(0)$$

$$a_j{}^3(t) = \left(\frac{\omega^1\omega^3}{(\omega)^2} - \frac{\omega^1\omega^3}{(\omega)^2} \cos \omega t + \frac{\omega^2}{\omega} \sin \omega t\right) a_j{}^1(0)$$

$$+\left(\frac{\omega^2\omega^3}{(\omega)^2} - \frac{\omega^2\omega^3}{(\omega)^2}\cos\omega t - \frac{\omega^1}{\omega}\sin\omega t\right)a_j^{\ 2}(0)$$

$$+\left(\frac{(\omega^3)^2}{(\omega)^2} + \frac{(\omega^1)^2 + (\omega^2)^2}{(\omega)^2}\cos\omega t\right)a_j^{\ 3}(0)$$

$$(\omega)^2 = (\omega^1)^2 + (\omega^2)^2 + (\omega^3)^2.$$

Functional configuration of a particular VOIN system based on the current philosophy is depicted by Fig. 12. The symbology in this illustration has been introduced in prior discussion.

Other important considerations in the engineering of vehicular inertial systems involve the application of stochastic and statistical techniques to

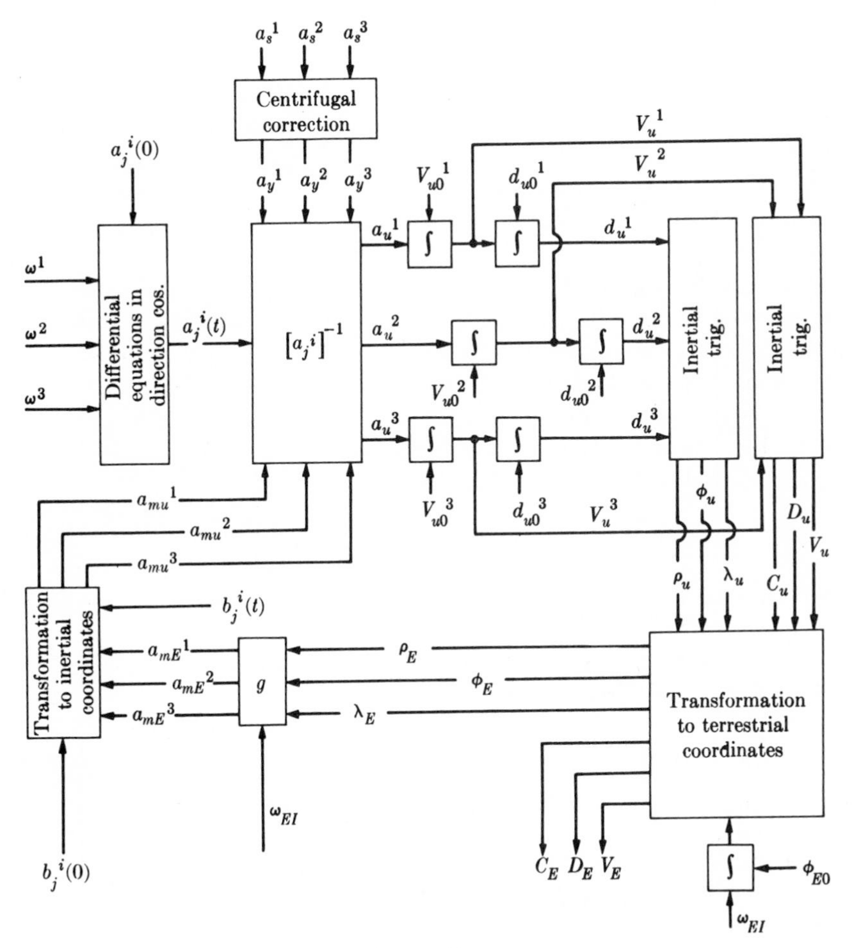

FIGURE 12.

the prediction of system performance and accuracy. These considerations belong to the general area of *random processes in automatic control*, of which there is an extensive literature. However, it may be noted here that a common criterion in guidance system evaluation is based on the concept of the "*circular probable error*," or CPE, which relates to the probability of a vehicle being guided to within a certain *radius* circumscribed about the intended destination. Due to random anomalies in guidance system and environment, the terminal points resulting from n repeated attempts to reach a destination from the *same starting point* will *not* be exactly reproduced, but will exhibit a random distribution (of some nature) about the destination. For a *coplanar situation*, and an *angularly homogeneous Gaussian distribution* of terminal points about the destination, it may be shown that the probability of a terminal point occurring within a radius R_c is

$$P_c = 1 - e^{-R_c^2/2\sigma^2} \tag{5.2}$$

where σ is the radial "*standard deviation*" of the distribution (has the same dimension as R_c), and is an over-all measure of a quality of the guidance system. If the radius R_c now encloses *one-half* of the terminal points, then $P_c = 0.5$, and expression (5.2) gives:

$$R_c = \text{CPE} = \sigma\sqrt{2 \log_e 2} \simeq 1.178\sigma. \tag{5.3}$$

That is, the "*circular probable error*" is the radius, about the destination (if there is no bias displacement), which encloses one half of the terminal points. In this connection, the main problem confronting the system designer is a preliminary evaluation of σ in terms of known anomalies (as opposed to subsequent verification by repeated duplications of actual guidance courses). A typical acceptable value of σ for a long range terrestrial guidance system is: $\sigma = 3$ kilometers.

BIBLIOGRAPHY

1. Baker, R. M. L., Jr., and Makemson, M. W., *Astrodynamics*, Academic, 1960.
2. Berman, A. I., *Astronautics*, Wiley, 1961.
3. Churchill, R. V., *Operational Mathematics*, McGraw-Hill, 1958.
4. Draper, C. S., Wrigley, W., and Hovorka, J., *Inertial Guidance*, Pergamon, 1960.
5. Laning, J. H., Jr., and Battin, R. H., *Random Processes in Automatic Control*, McGraw-Hill, 1956.
6. Leondes, C. T., *Computer Control Systems Technology*, McGraw-Hill, 1961.
7. McClure, C. L., *Theory of Inertial Guidance*, Prentice-Hall, 1960.
8. Moulton, F. R., *Differential Equations*, Macmillan, 1930.
9. Moulton, F. R., *Celestial Mechanics*, Macmillan, 1959.

10. Savant, C. J., Jr., Howard, R. C., Solloway, C. B., and Savant, C. A., *Principles of Inertial Navigation*, McGraw-Hill, 1961.
11. Savet, P. H., *Gyroscopes: Theory and Design*, McGraw-Hill, 1961.
12. Smart, W. M., *Celestial Mechanics*, Longmans, Green, 1953.
13. Webster, A. G., *The Dynamics of Particles and of Rigid, Elastic, and Fluid Bodies*, Hafner, 1949.
14. Whittaker, E. T., *Analytical Dynamics*, Dover, 1944.

CHAPTER IX

Computer Process Control

JOHN PESCHON

LUCAS PUN

SANJOY K. MITTER

CONTENTS

1. Introductory Comments

The expression "computer process control" is being used more and more frequently in the control literature to designate production, transportation, administration, etc., processes which are connected permanently—or on-line—to one or several computers programmed to perform a variety of information processing tasks in order to achieve more desirable process behavior. A few years ago, the meaning of computer process control was much narrower; it primarily referred to certain large production processes of the oil, chemical, steel, and electric utility industries relying on on-line computers to carry out fairly simple data logging, monitoring, and control tasks.

Any discussion of the subject of computer process control as it is being interpreted today remains of necessity superficial. The field of *computers* has become so vast that detailed understanding has become impossible even for the specialist. In addition to the general purpose digital and analog computers, a variety of special purpose, as well as hybrid, machines have been developed. The *processes* under consideration cover the whole range of industrial, commercial, and military activity. Mathematically speaking, these processes might be described by differential, difference, or stochastic equations, assuming that a satisfactory mathematical model can be found at all. Finally, the *control* tasks which the computer is assigned transcend those considered in the classical texts on automatic control. The general purpose digital computer is an information processing machine capable of a wide range of computation and decision operations carried out at high speed and with great accuracy. In an actual system, therefore, it would be a mistake to limit the computer's function to that of conventional controllers; the question which the designer should ask himself is:

How would a group of intelligent humans govern the process assuming that sufficient time were available to perform the required monitoring, computation, information, and rationally based decision tasks in order to ensure optimal performance?

After this question has been answered, the designer can proceed by exploring how these tasks must be reformulated to accord with the special characteristics of the computer, and deciding whether there is sufficient economic incentive to replace an operator or a group of operators by a machine. The important point is that modern computers are capable of a much greater *variety* of assignments than conventional controllers and that this should be taken into account if an economically sound design is to be evolved. A direct consequence of this observation is that the synthesis of computer-based systems not only requires knowledge of the modern theory of automatic control, but also of certain other scientific disciplines developed in order to comprehend and thereafter govern complex situations. Most notable among these are operations research, group dynamics, econometry, and—common sense.

There exist at the present time several hundred processes permanently connected to large digital or analog computers. In many of these installations results have been disappointing in that the savings expected were not, in fact, attained. There is little doubt that large computers are destined to play a major role in making industry and commerce benefit from automation. It is agreed, however, that their installation is economically justified only if imaginative use of their capabilities is made. *It does not suffice to place a computer next to a process to have computer process control;* many man-years of process analysis and system design are required to produce an economically viable installation. Due to the staggering complexity of the subject matter, the present chapter can only provide a broad discussion of trends illustrated by much simplified examples. A few of these examples correspond to systems which are in actual everyday operation. In most cases, however, they correspond to experimental systems which are expected to become operational in the late nineteen sixties. One should carefully distinguish between experimental and operational systems and acknowledge the fact that the latter require economic motivation and guaranties of reliability which may be very difficult to provide, particularly in the intellectually gratifying case of dynamic optimization.

1.1 Examples of Computer-Controlled Systems. Although the expression "computer process control" became widespread only after 1955 when the first general purpose digital computers were permanently connected to certain large industrial processes of the oil, chemical, steel, and electric utility industries, it should be noted that special purpose computers were already in operation before World War II. National telephone systems have relied for a long time on special purpose digital computers called "markers" to replace the manual operator in making and breaking connections between any two of millions of subscribers.

Certain fire-control systems which were operational during World War II employed special purpose analog computers to predict target position at the time of arrival of the shell on the basis of optical or radar measurements and to calculate the appropriate gun deflection.

In the early nineteen fifties, the electric utility industry, which had already developed remarkable control systems before the war, introduced special purpose analog computers to work out the most economic power setting of each of hundreds of interlinked generating units, taking into account their individual efficiencies as well as the cost of transporting electric power from production to consumption centers.

At about the same time, large-scale military systems such as the Continental Air Defense System came into being. Here, the defense weapons were directed with the help of a network of computers and telecommunication links so as to ensure optimal protection with the available resources in specific tactical situations.

Automobile traffic control systems comprising a centrally located analog or digital computer to direct the traffic lights at some of a city's intersections were introduced in 1952 to improve the flow of traffic. Airline traffic control systems capable of monitoring the positions of thousands of airliners, computing their routes to avoid in-flight collision, and shortening waiting time before landing, are presently being envisaged.

Long-range missiles naturally make use of highly sophisticated computer systems, both ground- and missile-based, to control the position and velocity coordinates during the powered part of the flight. The very stringent accuracy and reliability specifications of some of these systems have not been duplicated as yet in industrial and commercial applications.

1.2 The Process.

Definition and Boundaries. Computer process control is not a sharply defined subject; one reason for this is that the processes envisaged for control by computer vary widely, and frequently cannot be described by the deterministic mathematical models discussed in the previous chapters.

In order to illustrate this most important point, let us consider the major departments of a representative manufacturing company. There will be people concerned with market prediction, customer relations, accounting, inventory, etc., and there will be production machines. It is convenient for the purposes of this discussion to classify these activities into a three-level hierarchy, as shown in Fig. 1. The first or top level comprises the responsibilities of company management, such as decisions pertaining to investment, relations with labor,

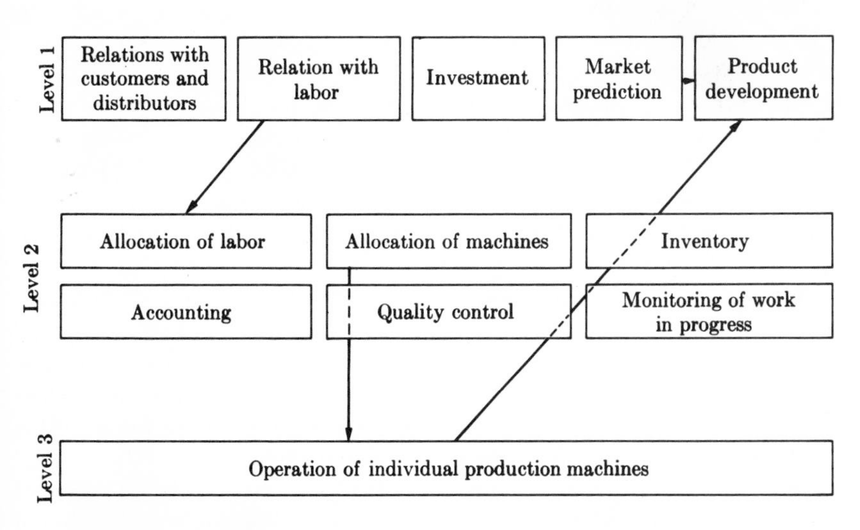

FIGURE 1. Classification of the subprocesses of a manufacturing company.

contract negotiation, market prediction, choice of new lines of product to be developed, etc. At the second level, available labor, material, and production equipment are procured and allocated by the executive staff so as to satisfy customer orders promptly and efficiently. The third and lowest level contains individual machines needed in the over-all production process. It is noted that the proportion of men to machines decreases sharply from the first to the third level: at the first level, there are practically no machines and decision is primarily based on intuition and common sense; at the third level, individual machines play a predominant role. In the manufacturing industries, automation naturally started at this level where controlling action can be automatically generated on the basis of fairly simple considerations pertaining to the process state and to a purely technical objective, such as zero steady-state error. At the second level, the automatic generation of controlling action became possible recently for certain activities, such as inventory control. Digital computers, rather than conventional analog control equipment, are generally required at this level. While at the first level machines are being used to collect and disseminate data, man remains responsible for evolving the proper correcting action.

A similar three-level pattern can be found in almost any undertaking involving a large number of men and machines, and the same comments can be made with regard to the utilization of machines for control. This three-level classification could be and in many countries has been extended upwards to include supervision by regional and national government. For the purposes of this discussion, it suffices to consider three levels of activity; this avoids political argument and circumvents the difficulty of our eventually attempting to optimize the universe by computer.

The three levels cannot function independently from each other and without taking into consideration the perturbing effects due to the "outside world." The body of policies evolved by management, the first level, is based on the state of the subsequent levels whose objectives must in turn be adjusted to fit these policies. Some of these relations are shown in Fig. 1: the allocation of labor at the second level depends on the labor policy postulated by management. Similarly, the choice of a new line of products depends on market prediction as well as on the characteristics of the available production machines. Digital computers are well suited to collect and interpret data and to strengthen coordination between departments by routing messages.

The outside world also influences the decisions taken at each level; at the top, a change in the nation's fiscal policy may provoke correcting action whereas at the third level, such action may be triggered by a change in the composition of raw material. These outside influences are perturbations or disturbances.

The operation of a manufacturing company, or of any other commercial or military entity involving a large number of men and machines, thus constitutes a single highly complex process which, for reasons of convenience, is subdivided into many interlinked *subprocesses* or departments. Effective control of any one subprocess requires that the relations with other subprocesses be accounted for. Control schemes which take into consideration these relations are referred to as "total" or "integrated." While at the present time, this terminology is ambitious, to say the least, it is likely that the highly automated industrial, commercial, and military systems of the future will make use of a hierarchy of interlinked computers each of which is assigned the task of monitoring and controlling the activities of one subprocess in accordance with the information received from adjacent computers.

The processes of the third level, which primarily comprise machines, are describable by deterministic mathematical models—arrived at either by analytical considerations or by experiment—and are susceptible of being controlled in accordance with the principles of the classical theory of automatic control. The processes of the second level, which comprise men as well as machines, are being characterized in a much more rudimentary and uncertain way by the deterministic and stochastic models of operations research. It is the scope of system engineering (see Chapter X) to automate routine decision at the second level. Mathematical techniques are available to assist the first level, but it would be unreasonable to assume that the activities of this level can be summarized by a mathematical model, since the human element of intuition, personal acquaintances, and original thought plays such a predominant role.

It has been argued that at each of the three levels, the decision processes taking place are conceptually similar in that controlling action is based on an assessment of the difference between the actual state and the desired state. This abstraction is correct, but the reader is cautioned against accepting that the principles of automatic control of demonstrated usefulness at the third level can be easily adapted to the first level.

What is important for the control engineer is the observation that processes of the third level, which are his primary concern, should not be treated separately from each other and from processes of the second and first levels. There is much evidence today that the utilization of computers at the third level, in particular digital computers, can only be economically justified if these relations are accounted for in the statement of the objective function and the treatment of the perturbations.

The present chapter is primarily concerned with the control of processes at the third level, of which the mathematical models are of the general form; see Chapter I, Section 3

$$\begin{aligned} \dot{\mathbf{x}} &= \mathbf{f}(\mathbf{x}, \mathbf{m}, \mathbf{u}) \\ \mathbf{y} &= \boldsymbol{\varphi}(\mathbf{x}) \end{aligned} \tag{1.1}$$

in the *dynamic* case and

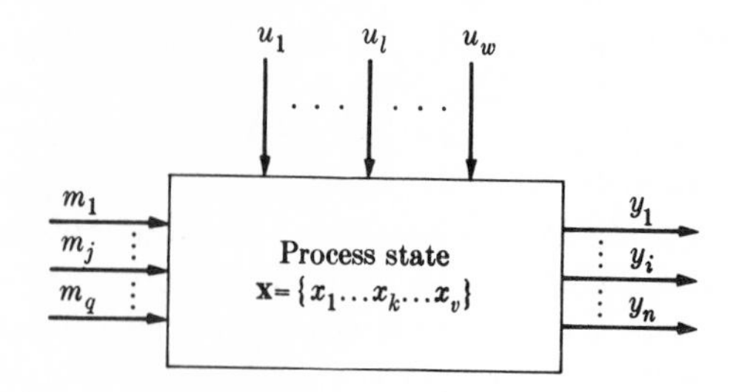

FIGURE 2. Mathematical model of a multivariable process. The x_k are state variables, the y_i are output variables, the m_j are actuating variables, and the u_l are disturbances.

$$
\begin{aligned}
0 &= \mathbf{f}(\mathbf{x}, \mathbf{m}, \mathbf{u}) \\
\mathbf{y} &= \boldsymbol{\varphi}(\mathbf{x})
\end{aligned}
\tag{1.2}
$$

in the *static* case. The notation will be that of Fig. 2.

As a result of the trend to operate machines at ever increasing efficiency, it is generally necessary to add to Eqs. (1.1) and (1.2) a set of constraints of the form

$$\mathbf{m}^L \leqslant \mathbf{m} \leqslant \mathbf{m}^H \tag{1.3}$$

as well as other constraints affecting $\mathbf{x}$, to be discussed later. The restriction (1.3) on $\mathbf{m}$ adds singularly to the difficulties of system synthesis.

The definition of a suitable *objective* to be satisfied by the control system is perhaps more difficult than the elaboration of a mathematical model, especially when it is impossible to consider the complex process as a whole. Subprocesses of the third level are generally controlled for reasons of convenience in such a way that a mathematically tractable function F of the state $\mathbf{x}$ is minimized or maximized.

The desirability of spending much effort on the elaboration of an accurate mathematical model and on the definition of a meaningful objective is emphasized throughout the literature on computer process control. It has been observed that the benefit derived through better process understanding frequently outweighs that resulting from actual control by computer. One of the major advantages of computer process control may thus be the requirement that classical processes be quantitatively assessed and that accepted design and operating practices be reconsidered as a result of this analysis!

2. Computer

The types of computers available for process control introduce almost as much variety as the process itself. In addition to the general purpose digital and analog machines, a large number of special purpose computers as well as various types of "hybrid" machines have become available for control applications. It is somewhat difficult to decide when a *controller* deserves the qualificative of *computer*, since such conventional gear as PID controllers are already capable of performing certain mathematical operations, namely multiplication by a constant (Proportional control), integration (Integral control), and differentiation (Derivative control). Relay networks have likewise been used for a long time to carry out logical operations and thus relieve the human operator from routine decision. PID controllers and switching networks are not normally considered to be computers although a sufficient number of them could perform most of the control tasks now envisaged for computers. Therefore, price per unit seems to be the only acceptable criterion: if it exceeds several thousand dollars, we may safely speak of a computer. Far more important than this somewhat immaterial question of terminology is the observation that no discontinuity of concept occurred when the first computers were introduced to control military and industrial processes and took over many of the functions previously performed by conventional gear.

Special purpose computers are based upon the same principles as general purpose machines, but are designed with a *specific* application in mind; they cannot be adapted easily to perform other tasks, primarily because their "program" is relatively fixed. *Hybrid* computers, of which there exist at least a dozen different types, were developed in order to combine in the same unit the chief advantages of the digital computer—accuracy, versatility, and memory capability—and of the analog computer—computing speed, ease of programming, and relatively low cost, [17].† Since the special purpose and the hybrid computers are derived from either or both the general purpose digital or the general purpose analog computer, our discussion will be limited to these two basic types of machines. It will be assumed that the reader is familiar with the rudiments of their principles of operation. The purpose of our discussion on computers will be to draw attention to certain factors which are particularly relevant to process control applications.

2.1 The General Purpose Digital Computer. The general purpose digital computer constitutes one of the most momentous inventions of all time. It makes possible the *processing* or transformation of *information*. The term "computer," which implies capability for calculation, is too narrow, since a variety of other information processing tasks—storage and retrieval of information, logical decision, adaptation, and learning, etc.—are possible.‡ As regards the capability for computation it is helpful to visualize the digital computer as a conventional desk calculator to which an automatic device designed to press the proper keys at the right time in accordance with a prerecorded "program" has been added, though the speed at which the "arith-

† Numbers in brackets refer to the bibliography at the end of this chapter.

‡ In the French language, the terms "machine à traiter l'information" or "ordinateur" are often preferred to "calculateur" for precisely this reason.

metic units" of modern computers performs the basic arithmetic operations of addition and multiplication has introduced a difference of *magnitude* as well as of *kind* in the type of computations one might attempt on a desk calculator.

2.2 Characteristics of Typical Digital Control Computers. Although in principle any sufficiently reliable general purpose digital computer developed for scientific computation or business data processing can be used as a control computer, at least a dozen machines have been developed especially for the control market. Most of these machines fall into the $100,000–300,000 range, and special care is taken to ensure high reliability, 99% of operating time being a commonly accepted figure. Ease of programming is not as important as in the case of the "scientific" computer, since program changes are less frequent.

The chief characteristics of the central part of a digital computer system—this is often called data processor—are computing speed and memory capacity. To define speed, it is customary in the computer industry to quote "add-time" and "access-time." This may suffice for a rough comparison of two data processors, but if a detailed study is to be made, it is necessary to find out what exactly the manufacturer understands by add-time and access-time; usually, the time required to add two randomly chosen numbers and to perform the ancillary operations of retrieval and storage is several times larger than the quoted add-time would lead one to believe. Moreover, it is advisable to find out how fast other arithmetic operations (substraction, multiplication, division, move, and test) can be effected.

The capacity refers to the number of "words" of specified length that can be stored in the fast-access memory, i.e., in the core or drum memory. As before, it is again advisable to inquire as to what exactly is meant by capacity, since word length, nature of the code, etc., determine to what extent the user can put to profit the stated capacity. Whereas speed is a relatively fixed quantity, the capacity can generally be adapted within certain limits to fit the customer's needs.

The following numbers provide an *order of magnitude* of the chief characteristics found in a large number of control computers:

add-time in μsec: 100;
access-time, assuming core storage, in μsec: 20;
word length, in bits: 30;
capacity, in words: 4000.

2.3 Input and Output Equipment. The price of a computer may vary by a factor of 2 depending on the nature and versatility of the "peripheral" equipment which permits the flow of information to take place between the process, the operators, and the computer. The main types of input and output equipment in process control applications are shown in Fig. 3.

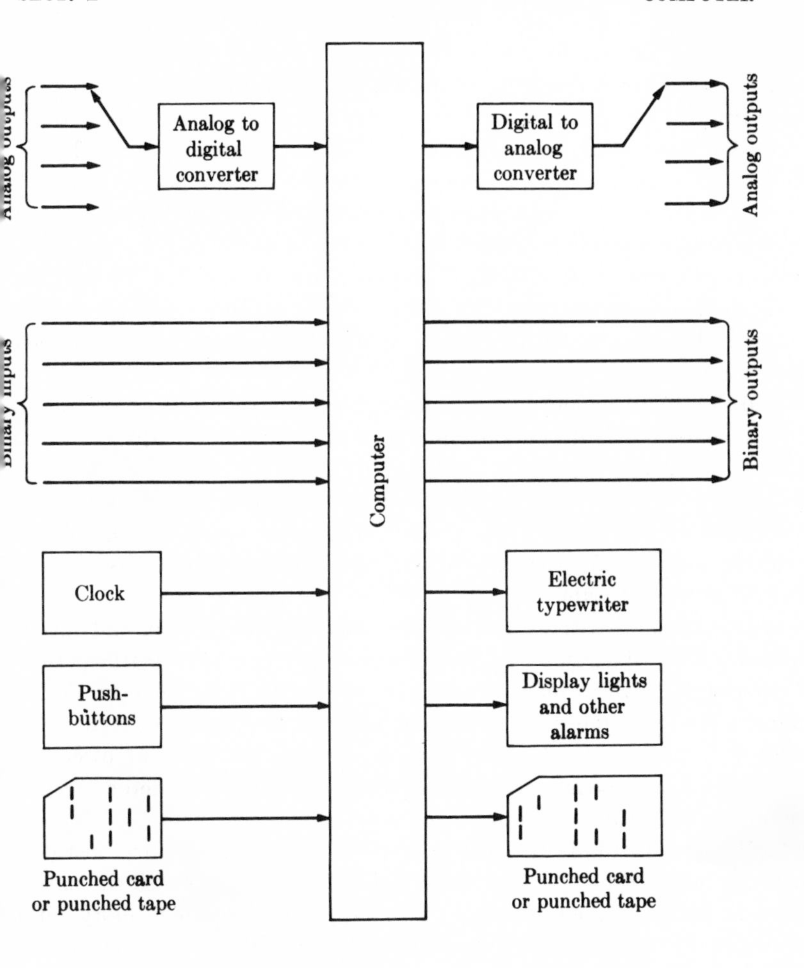

FIGURE 3. Principal inputs and outputs of digital process control computer.

The *analog*† *inputs*, which are assumed to be available under the form of electric voltages, are scanned at a rate compatible with the conversion speed of the analog to digital converter of which the coded output signals are accepted by the computer. There may be several hundred analog input lines; typical scanning rates are 20 lines per second.

† The adjective "analog," as opposed to "digital," is being used quite freely in the literature to denote any variable the magnitude of which is *not* given by a code. The outputs of pulse-frequency, pulse-amplitude, and pulse-position modulators are thus analog signals, whereas the outputs of pulse-code modulators are referred to as digital; in the majority of the computer-based systems, this is also equivalent to binary.

The *binary inputs* either consist of the status (open or closed) of process switches or of the coded signals available from digital process instruments.

In addition to the analog and binary inputs which characterize the state of the process, there may be push buttons, punched card, or punched tape readers to allow the operator to communicate with the computer.

On the output side, the computer provides the possibility of producing up to several hundred *analog outputs*. These signals are piecewise constant since, for reasons of operating safety, analog *holds* are usually inserted between the digital-to-analog converter and the process. If a computer failure were to occur, the process would thus remain in the state resulting from the last values stored in the holds.†

In addition to analog outputs, the computer may operate on-off devices in the process and inform the operator of abnormal conditions via display lights and other alarms.

Better process understanding is gained and operating records are established automatically by use of the electric typewriter, the card and/or paper punch which print out selected data in accordance with the instructions contained in the program.

It is emphasized that these are only the common types of input and output equipment. Extensive research is underway to produce more versatile peripheral equipment, such as machines capable of reading print directly, understanding a limited number of voice commands, and displaying the state of the process in a more comprehensive way. In a somewhat different direction, special equipment is being developed to permit computers of different designs to communicate with one another.

2.4 Programming [19]. The program of a digital computer consists of a set of prerecorded instructions which indicate with great detail the nature of the next partial computation and the precise location in the memory of the data required to perform this computation. The logical, information storage, and retrieval operations are likewise controlled by the program.

Until several years ago, the composition of a program was time-consuming and required a detailed knowledge of the machine's internal operation. The invention in the early fifties of the so-called automatic programming methods contributed much to the widespread utilization of computers by the non-specialist. Some of these methods make it possible for the user to write down the desired sequence of partial computations in a *language* which is almost clear English. The computer manufacturers, on the other hand, make available the programs corresponding to frequently used information processing and computation tasks. Automatic programming methods which have greatly aided scientific machine computation are not, unfortunately, as efficient as the

† These holds are servodriven potentiometers of which the output voltages change in a stepwise fashion at each sampling instant and remain constant in between.

conventional methods, and therefore should not be used when the same computation is to be repeated many times. Since, on the other hand, each process requires a different program, libraries are not of great help. The composition of an efficient program for process control applications thus remains a time-consuming task which may require several man-years of painstaking work. Much thought needs to be given to this task, since the success of a computer control system to a large extent rests on the proper utilization of the computer, that is, on the quality of the program.

In general, several different programs are contained in a process control computer to account for different situations, for example, emergencies. Transitions from one program to another (interrupts) can be provoked automatically, perhaps as a result of an abnormal condition signaled by a process instrument, or manually. Various other refinements, such as omission of a predetermined sequence of steps in the instruction program if certain conditions pertaining to the process state or to the computation itself are realized, may be used to increase speed. It is also customary to have the computer, at prescribed intervals of time, perform "test" computations where the correct results are known, to make certain that no essential part has failed.

At the present time, digital computers require extremely detailed instructions; their achievements are impressive only because of their capability to carry out very simple operations at very high speed. Significant research is underway to make possible more "intelligent" behavior, such as adaptation and learning, and the ability to act upon relatively superficial instructions. Success of this research depends more on imaginative methods of programming than on improved computing elements and systems.

2.5 The General Purpose Analog Computer. The electronic analog computer is based upon the observation that certain electronic components such as high-gain dc amplifiers, resistors, capacitors, etc., can be interconnected in such a way that the resulting network is described by precisely the mathematical equations of which the solution is sought. "Simulation" by these methods of linear, constant coefficient, differential equations is particularly straightforward, but many other types of equations (algebraic, nonlinear, time-varying, and partial differential) can be handled with the nonlinear and logical circuitry now available.

Although clearly the analog computer is conceptually much more limited than the highly versatile digital computer, its value for process control should not be underrated: in a number of specific situations, especially when high accuracy is not required, it surpasses the digital computer in speed at lower equipment and programming cost.

There is much evidence today that the control of complex processes will require the *simultaneous* utilization of analog and digital machines; analog computers appear to be well suited for the more conventional control tasks of the first level whereas digital computers are generally required for the second level. Linkage between the two will become desirable in an ever increasing number of situations.

2.6 Characteristics of a Typical Analog Control Computer. As before, it is difficult to define a "typical" machine, since *any* sufficiently reliable analog computer can be used to control a process. This covers an extremely wide range, from about $1000 for a low-accuracy ten-amplifier linear machine to $200,000 for a high-accuracy computer fitted with several hundred operational amplifiers, nonlinear and logical blocks, the possibility to accurately set the coefficient-potentiometers by tape-controlled servomechanism, etc. The characteristics given in the following correspond to the PC-12 which was specially designed by Electronic Associates Inc. for process control purposes.

The most outstanding feature of the PC-12 is its flexibility, obtained by use of *computing modules*, chosen so as to satisfy the computation needs in each individual case. Up to fifty solid-state modules, each of which consists of a computing component and a small patch panel attached to it, can be slipped into standard enclosures and connected to a single power supply. The manufacturer provides modules for multiplication by a constant, integration with respect to time, low-level amplification, multiplication or division of two variables, function generation, comparison of two variables, etc. Some of these modules are available in several grades of accuracy to satisfy computing needs at minimum cost. The program consists of interconnecting the individual patch panels by patch cords and special plugs; minor program changes can be effected easily to account for process alterations or modifications of the objective function. Module accuracies are usually of the order of 0.1%, which means that computing system accuracies are often better than 1%.

2.7 Input-Output Equipment and Programming. The analog computer accepts analog as well as on-off voltages from the process. The operator can change the nature of a computation by pressing push buttons on the computer console or by altering the settings of the coefficient-potentiometers. The outputs are generally dc analog voltages, although on-off signals are also obtained easily from commercially available relay blocks.

Whereas in the digital computer, information is processed *sequentially*, that is, one input line at a time, the analog computer acts upon all the inputs *simultaneously*. Though in general the computations are performed continuously, as in the case of a conventional controller, it is also possible to operate on a set of *sampled* process values, perhaps to predict the future state of the process by performing a "fast" simulation, and to produce a set of sampled actuating signals in accordance with the outcome of the fast simulation. An example of this will be given in Section 5.9.

Programming the analog computer consists in interconnecting the available electronic components in such a way that the resulting network is described by the equation to be solved or, more directly, by the *analog* of the mechanical, electrical, chemical, etc. process to be simulated.† Thus far, this operation has always been performed manually, which frequently led to "scaling" and "patching" errors. Digital computer programs have recently been developed to specify *optimum* patch diagrams and component values directly from the equations to be solved, which considerably reduces the drudgery of complex simulations [9].

2.8 Memories and Look-up Tables. Due to the high cost of computers, it is advisable to explore in each application if the desired system performance cannot be obtained by *storage* of the laws of control into a suitable memory, perhaps a nonlinear network or a magnetic drum. It is recalled here that the law of control relating the manipulating vector $\mathbf{m}$ to the process state $\mathbf{x}$ and the desired output $\mathbf{r}$ can generally be written in the form

$$\mathbf{m}(t) = \mathbf{g}[\mathbf{x}(t), \mathbf{r}(t), \mathbf{u}(t)] \tag{2.1}$$

or

$$\mathbf{m}[(l+1)T_s] = \mathbf{g}[\mathbf{x}(lT_s), \mathbf{r}(lT_s), \mathbf{u}(lT_s)] \tag{2.2}$$

T_s = constant sampling period.

The mathematical operations implied by Eqs. (2.1) and (2.2) are purely algebraic; they can be performed once and for all, either by hand calculation or by off-line machine computation, tabulated in a memory and retrieved for control when required. In order to avoid storing a prohibitive number of points, one may add simple interpolation equipment to the memory.

Example. Consider the classical second-order optimum relay system, of which the law of control is shown dotted in Fig. 4.

It may be sufficient to store a small number of points $M_1, M_2, \ldots, M_1', M_2', \ldots$, and to situate the actual operating point $\mathbf{P}$ with respect to the broken line $M_3'M_2'M_1'OM_1M_2M_3$. As long as $\mathbf{P}$ is located to the right of this line, m is positive. At the point Q, where the actual phase trajectory intersects the segment M_1M_2, a reversal of the relay polarity is provoked and nearly optimum performance is accomplished.

It is thus possible, in principle, to control a variety of static and dynamic processes by tabulating a sufficiently fine grid of points $\mathbf{x}$, $\mathbf{r}$, $\mathbf{u}$, and $\mathbf{m}$ and by retrieving the required actuating vector $\mathbf{m}$ corresponding to each "address" defined by the measured values of $\mathbf{x}$, $\mathbf{r}$, and $\mathbf{u}$. If, in a specific situation, the number of points to be stored becomes prohibitive, or if the plant parameters are subject to rapid change, a process computer may be more economic than an oversized memory. In still other cases, it may be best to store the law of control and to have a central computer upgrade the contents of the memory at periodic intervals of time to account for plant parameter and policy changes.

† Suppose that the process to be simulated consists of a cascade of transfer functions of the form $\alpha/(s+\beta)$. In this common situation, it is preferable to interconnect a cascade of integrators, each of which is provided with the required feedback path, rather than to start from the differential equation corresponding to the process.

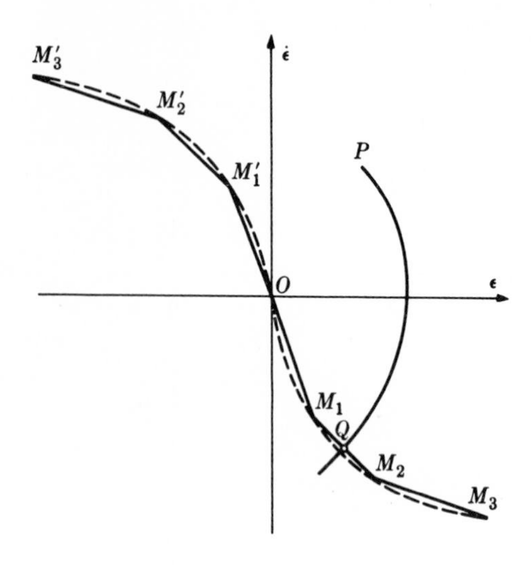

FIGURE 4. Law of control corresponding to optimum second-order relay system. The variables $\epsilon = r - y$ and $\dot{\epsilon} = \dfrac{d}{dt}(r - y)$ are the state variables.

2.9 Temporal Operation of On-Line Computers. In the majority of the situations where an analog computer is used for control, the actuating vector **m** is produced *continuously* on the basis of continuously available information on the process state **x**. In some analog systems and in the majority of the digital systems, the process state **x** is measured at discrete instants of time $0, T_s, 2T_s, \ldots, lT_s \ldots$ called sampling instants, and the required actuating vector **m** is made to change in a stepwise fashion at the instants $T_s, 2T_s, 3T_s, \ldots, (l + 1)T_s$.

The sum of the intervals Δ and δ which are required for data collection and computation, respectively, must be smaller than the sampling interval T_s. Data collection is generally not instantaneous since measurement of the process variables is performed sequentially and needs to be converted into a suitable code.

The time δ corresponding to each sampling period is not always constant, but may depend on the nature of the computation to be performed. The time required to solve a problem by means of successive iterations, for example, is a function of the numbers selected for the first iteration, i.e., of the process state. See Fig. 5.

The selection of a suitable sampling period T_s demands careful thought. If T_s is chosen too large, the disturbances occurring between consecutive samples are not accounted for, but sufficient time is available to perform detailed calculations on those disturbances actually observed. If, on the

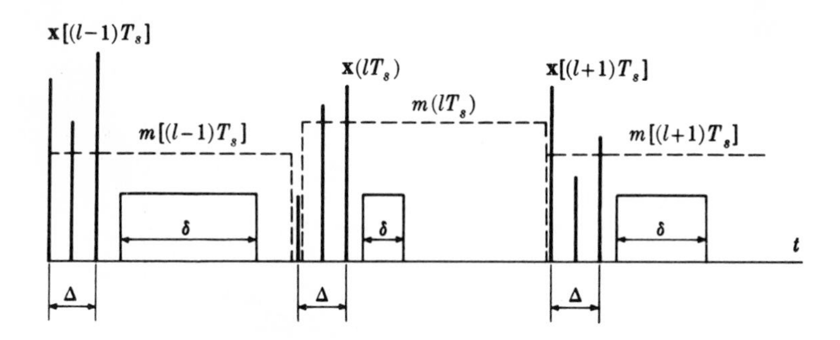

FIGURE 5. Temporal operation of sampled computer control system. Δ represents the time required for data collection and preparation; δ corresponds to actual computing time. The sum $\Delta + \delta$ must be smaller than the sampling period T_s.

other hand, T_s is chosen too small, most of the disturbances will be detected, but optimum control is impossible for lack of computation time within each cycle.

It is also possible to process measured data at irregular intervals of time, perhaps when a disturbance has been detected. If it should happen that several different disturbances, each requiring computer time, occur simultaneously, the machine can be programmed to treat these in their respective orders of priority.

3. Control

We agreed at the beginning of this chapter to take a rather wide view on the subject of computer process control by stressing the importance in the over-all system design of processes incorporating humans as well as machines. It is similarly desirable to interpret the expression "control" rather widely to include not only closed-loop, but also open-loop, as well as certain types of data processing systems. One justification for this is that most of the control computers installed at the present time are programmed to perform a variety of tasks pertaining to open- and closed-loop control and to data processing on a timeshared basis, with closed-loop control remaining a rather new and not yet fully proven application. Another justification is that a specific installation may at the beginning be purely open-loop and subsequently be made closed-loop after sufficient operating experience (and confidence) has been gained.

We shall exclude from our study the numerous situations where information is being processed in an entirely "off-line" fashion and will only consider those situations where a computer is permanently connected to a process, which is referred to as "on-line" operation.

Following closely the exposition given in Adriaenssens [1], we shall first discuss the data processing and open-loop control tasks of "data logging," "monitoring and alarm," "sequence control," and "dispatch of information." Separate sections will thereafter be devoted to the more critical and, for our purposes, more relevant subject of optimization by computer, which usually requires closed-loop control.

3.1 Data Logging. In this application, the measurements of the various process instruments are coordinated by the control computer and transformed into a "format" suitable for off-line data *reduction* by another computer. This involves the selection of the instants of time at which measurements are taken, fairly simple calculations such as are required to derive a nonmeasurable state variable from measurable process variables, and the production of punched cards, punched tape, or other operating records.

The chief purpose of data logging is to gather improved process understanding and to produce the *mathematical model* required before more sophisticated forms of control can be envisaged. Data logging installations are also used for "post-mortem" analysis and "operator surveillance"; if an abnormal condition or emergency arises in the operation of a large-scale process, it is very important to trace the causes by subsequent analysis of the evolution of the process state and the operators' interventions *before* the emergency materialized. This is accomplished conveniently by storage of the complete process history during a specified number of hours and by erasure from the memory of old data while new data are being introduced. The unwieldy masses of paper sharts of conventional analog recorders are thus avoided.

3.2 Monitoring and Alarm. Here, the computer scans the various process instruments in accordance with a predetermined sequence and compares their readings with internally stored low and high limits. If one such limit is exceeded, the computer sounds an alarm and thus informs the operator of an abnormal condition.

In addition to comparing each instrument reading to a predetermined limit the computer can *predict* the process evolution by extrapolating past samples and sound the alarm before the limits are transgressed. It is also possible to *adapt* the predetermined limits to operating conditions; excess values can thus be tolerated during short periods of time without leading to equipment damage.

3.3 Sequence Control. In this mode of operation, which is typical of open-loop control, the computer initiates a sequence of operations in accordance with an internally stored program. The next step of the sequence may be triggered after a specified interval of time has elapsed or when a stated set of process conditions is realized. Complex logical functions can thus be implemented without having to resort to expensive and cumbersome relay equipment. If a computer is used, it is frequently not necessary to store the complete program in detail: *interpolations* and other simple calculations eliminate the intermediate steps.

The applications of sequence control in industry are extremely important since they prevent equipment damage and inefficient process operation resulting from operator fatigue or negligence, and avoid uncoordinated and ill-timed operator intervention in case of emergency.

3.4 Dispatch of Information. In this application, the (digital) control computer gathers messages and data pertaining to the operation of subprocesses and distributes these to the proper departments at the proper time. Production data might thus be sent to the accounting department, whereas technical data would go to the engineering services. This substantially strengthens the links that should exist between the departments of the first, second, and third level. Dispatch of information, as well as some of the other applications discussed above, do not rely on sophisticated concepts of control and optimization. But the most valuable practical contribution of control computers may well be the reduction of chaos in the over-all process rather than the optimization of subprocesses in accordance with criteria the value of which is subject to question.

3.5 Regulation and Optimization. There are many ways in which the addition of an on-line computer can improve the response of a process to changes in reference input and disturbances and ensure more economic or otherwise more desirable operation. These two areas of application, which are broadly classified as regulation—or control in the conventional sense—and optimization, fall directly within the province of the control engineer

The techniques required to design computer-based regulation and optimization systems can be categorized according to the temporal behavior of the disturbances affecting the process. We distinguish between:

(1) step disturbances of which the mean time of occurrence is appreciably larger than the dominant time constant of the controlled process;

(2) step disturbances of which the mean time of occurrence is of the same order of magnitude as the dominant time constant of the controlled process;

(3) stationary and nonstationary random disturbances.

The detrimental effects of disturbances of the first kind can be minimized by the addition of a computer or controller of which the response time need not be fast. The resulting optimization is referred to as *static* since it is based exclusively upon consideration of the static process model (1.2).

Since disturbances of the second kind constantly prevent the process from attaining its objective, computers are required to improve the regulation capabilities of the system and to determine the optimum trajectory to be followed by the process state $\mathbf{x}$ between consecutive steady-state conditions. Since the design must be based upon consideration of the dynamic model (1.1), optimizations of this kind are referred to as *dynamic*. Whereas there are already several hundred computer systems capable of static optimization throughout the world, only a few dynamic optimization systems have been designed, largely for experimental and demonstration purposes.

If the disturbances are random, but stationary, it is usually possible to optimize an objective function of the form

$$J = \lim_{T \to \infty} \frac{1}{2T} \int_{-T}^{T} \mathbf{x}^T Q \mathbf{x}\, dt \qquad (3.1)$$

$Q = n \times n$ constant positive definite matrix

$\mathbf{x}^T =$ transpose of $\mathbf{x}$

by a straightforward extension of Wiener's theory of optimum linear filters. A control computer is not needed in this case, since the required system can be synthesized with linear analog networks; see, for example, Truxal [26], Chapter 8.

If the disturbances are random, but not stationary, or if the objective function (3.1) explicitly includes the parameter time, conventional compensating networks no longer suffice and a computer is required. Optimum stochastic systems are discussed in Chapters IV and VII and will not be mentioned further here.

Various types of computer-based systems capable of static optimization are reviewed in Section 4; dynamic optimization and control is discussed in Section 5. In both cases, it was judged preferable to outline briefly a relatively large number of systems rather than to present the details of a few selected examples. It is hoped that this presentation of the subject matter will emphasize the very broad range of potential control computer applications.

4. Static Optimization

Industrial processes comprise a large number of independent or single-variable feedback control systems, each of which forces an easily measurable

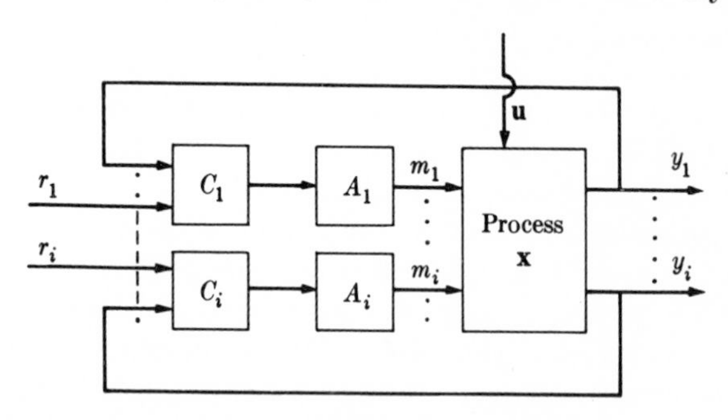

FIGURE 6. Conventional control of a multivariable industrial process by independent feedback systems, comprising actuators A_i and controllers C_i.

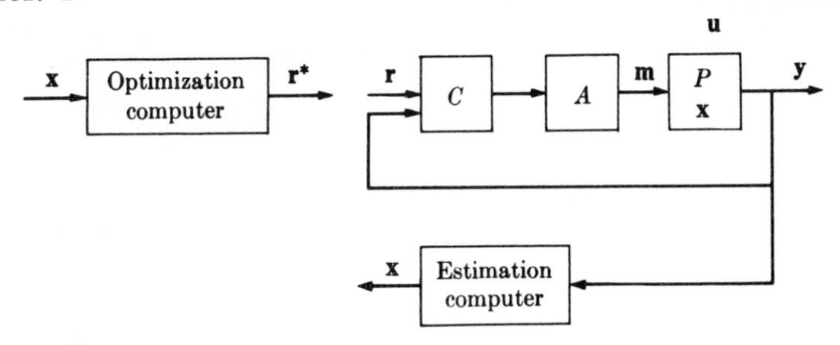

FIGURE 7. Early utilization of computers to estimate **x** and to calculate optimum settings **r***.

dependent variable y_i to be equal to the corresponding reference variable, or set-point r_i, as shown in Fig. 6.

It is the responsibility of the human operator to monitor the y_i and to adjust the r_i in such a way that some stated economic objective $F = F(\mathbf{x})$ be optimized, or approximately optimized, in spite of the (infrequent) disturbances **u** and subject to certain constraints affecting **m**. This task often exceeds the capabilities of the human operator for two reasons, namely:

(1) the objective function F generally comprises internal, that is nonmeasurable, process variables **x** which must be derived by calculation from **y**;
(2) the optimum set-points r_i are related in a complex manner to the internal variables x_k and thus to the objective function F.

Digital and analog computers were therefore systematically introduced during the last decade to assist the human operator in deriving the x_k from the measurable y_i and to indicate optimum set-points r_i on the basis of certain known properties of the process. Early computer control installations are thus represented by the diagram of Fig. 7, where, for simplicity, vector notation is used to designate the r_i, y_i, m_j, x_k, and u_l.

The system of Fig. 7 is open-loop as far as the estimation and optimization computers are concerned, since the human operator transfers the estimated values of **x** to the optimization computer and adjusts the r_i accordingly if the suggested values r_i* appear reasonable. Computer reliability thus is not a limiting factor in installations of this kind.

The next step, taken in 1959, was to automatically transfer information between the computers and the system, as shown by the closed-loop configuration of Fig. 8. The estimation and optimization computers of Fig. 7 have been merged in one block since both operations would normally be performed on the same machine. Note also that some of the disturbances **u**, those that are measurable, may be fed to the computer to facilitate optimization.

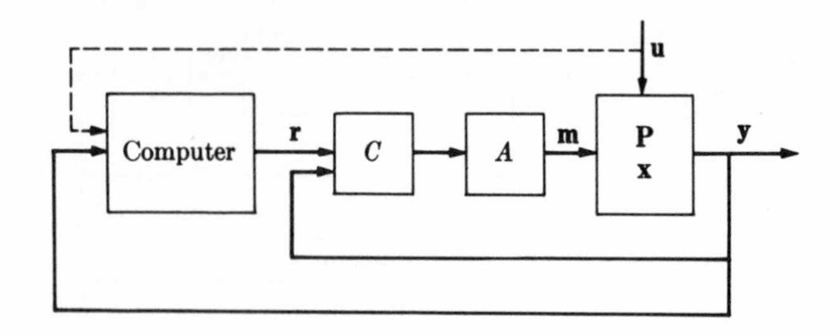

FIGURE 8. Closed-loop computer system for static optimization.

The mathematical techniques needed to design closed-loop systems for static optimization are not the same as those worked out for ordinary feedback controls, since temporal behavior and stability are immaterial. The system is admittedly closed-loop, but the "gain" of the outer path is deliberately kept so small that the state slowly evolves from one steady-state condition to the next. Reliability is not a major consideration either, since in the case of computer failure the process remains under the control of the inner loop.

Minimization of the cost F thus being the primary objective, static systems are designed in accordance with the mathematical methods of *operations research*. Since the control engineer is not, as a rule, familiar with this subject, a short discussion of linear and nonlinear programing which are among the most widely used methods of operations research, is given in the following.

4.1 Introduction to Linear Programming. In the hands of the operations researcher, linear and nonlinear programming are valuable mathematical methods to assist management in making rational and quantitatively based decisions regarding the operations under its control. In the hands of the control engineer, these same mathematical methods are programmed into a control computer, the function of which is to determine optimum set-points, either at regular intervals of time or whenever a disturbance has been detected.

The classical linear programming problem is formulated as follows; see, for example, Kaufmann [15].

Given N variables $z_1, \ldots, z_N$ constrained to be positive or zero and a linear objective function

$$F = \sum_{i=1}^{N} c_i z_i \tag{4.1}$$

$$c_i = \text{arbitrary known constant}$$

it is desired to minimize† F subject to M additional linearly independent constraints of the form

† Since F is usually a cost, we seek a *minimum*; if F were a profit, linear programming could easily be adapted to provide a *maximum*.

$$\sum_{i=1}^{N} a_{1i} z_i = b_1$$
$$\cdots\cdots\cdots\cdots \tag{4.2}$$
$$\sum_{i=1}^{N} a_{Mi} z_i = b_M$$

where the a_{ji} and b_j are also arbitrary known constants. For a meaningful solution to exist, it is required that $M < N$.

Example. Let $F = c_1 z_1 + c_2 z_2$

$$z_1 \geqslant 0, z_2 \geqslant 0 \tag{4.3}$$

and

$$a_{11} z_1 + a_{12} z_2 = b_1. \tag{4.4}$$

Equations (4.3) and (4.4) are graphically represented in Fig. 9; the minimum of F is seen to be located at either of the vertices A or B, since the permissible solutions are confined to the first quadrant.

In the classical applications of operations research, this is always the case, since F represents a total cost which, in a realistically formulated problem, must have a nonnegative minimum. It should be noted that at this minimum, either of the two variables z_i is zero (depending on c_1 and c_2), unless the line F = constant is parallel to the constraint (4.4); in this degenerate case, *any* point of Eq. (4.4) constitutes a solution. It can be shown that, generally speaking, $N - M$ variables must be zero at the minimum, which is located at one the vertices of the convex polyedron formed by the surfaces $z_i = 0$ and the M constraint surfaces (4.2).

It frequently happens in practical situations that some or all of the constraint equations (4.2) are replaced by inequalities of the form

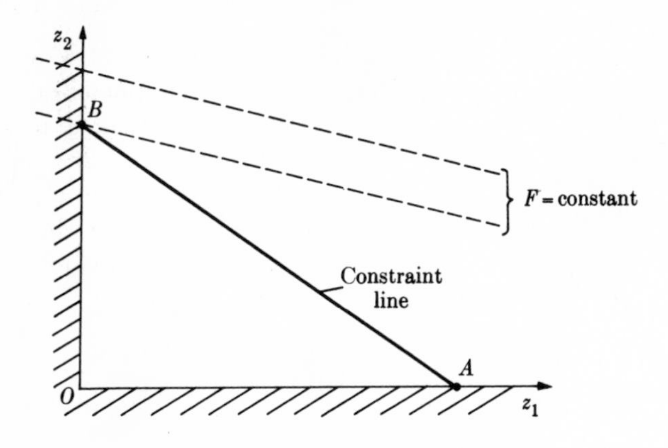

FIGURE 9. Graphical solution of the linear programming problem of the example.

$$\sum_{i=1}^{N} a_{1i} z_i \leqslant b_1 \tag{4.5}$$

$$\cdots\cdots\cdots\cdots$$

The addition of as many *auxiliary variables* z_k as there are inequalities permits this case to be treated as before. Inequality (4.5), for example, would thus be replaced by equality

$$\sum_{i=1}^{N} a_{1i} z_i + z_{N+1} = b_1. \tag{4.6}$$

The following typical example of application concerned with *production scheduling* in a steel plant is discussed in detail in Kaufmann [15].

There exist three rolling mills A, B, and C. The production schedule, established 1 month in advance, requires that p_j tons of 14 different grades of rolled product be produced ($j = 1, \ldots, 14$). The cost c_{ij} in \$/ton of the jth product in the ith mill and the production rate d_{ij} in tons/hour of the jth product in the ith mill are known. In addition, each of the 3 mills is constrained to operate no more than b_i hours/month. An exact solution is obtained by digital computer in a few minutes; this solution constitutes a saving of 6% as compared to the previous empirical schedule derived from experience.

In any realistic situation, the number N of variables is such that a solution can only be obtained by use of a digital computer. Since it is known that except in the degenerate case previously mentioned, the solution must lie at a vertex, one might attempt to calculate the value of F corresponding to each vertex located in the permissible region of the N-space and thereafter retain the minimum of the finite number of results thus obtained. This may still be prohibitive even for a modern digital computer, because the number of points to be tested is $\dfrac{N!}{M!\,(N-M)!}$. A convenient iterative procedure due to G. B. Dantzig (see, for example, Kaufmann [15]) reduces this number roughly to M and permits a computer solution to be envisaged for most practical situations.

Formulations (4.1) and (4.2) are particularly well suited to solve the classical operations research problem of the optimum *allocation of resources*, where the constraints are usually of the stated type. A variety of control processes can be statically optimized by use of a formulation which is *similar* to that of Eqs. (4.1), (4.2), and (4.5), as will be shown in the following.

We consider the *static* mathematical model

$$0 = \mathbf{f}(\mathbf{x}, \mathbf{m}, \mathbf{u}) \tag{4.7}$$

and we assume, for the time being, that Eq. (4.7) can be approximated by the linear model

$$0 = P\mathbf{x} + Q\mathbf{m} + S\mathbf{u} \tag{4.8}$$

for *large* variations of $\mathbf{x}$, $\mathbf{m}$, and $\mathbf{u}$. Moreover we assume that an objective function involving *some* of the x_i (and possibly m_j) has been defined and that some of the x_i are constrained to remain within the lower and upper bounds x_i^L and x_i^H. In any practical situation, *all* the actuating variables m_j are furthermore confined to the range m_j^L and m_j^H. It is desired to optimize the objective function

$$F = \sum \alpha_i x_i + \sum \beta_j m_j \tag{4.9}$$

subject to the constraints

$$x_i^L \leqslant x_i \leqslant x_i^H \tag{4.10}$$

$$m_j^L \leqslant m_j \leqslant m_j^H \qquad j = 1, \ldots, q \tag{4.11}$$

and to the static model (4.8).

It is convenient, though not necessary, to express the optimization problem solely in terms of the independent variables m_j. To this end, we make use of Eq. (4.8) to obtain,

$$\mathbf{x} = -P^{-1}Q\mathbf{m} - P^{-1}S\mathbf{u} \tag{4.12}$$

if P is a nonsingular matrix, and we rewrite (4.9), (4.10), and (4.11)

$$F = \sum_{i=1}^{N} c_i m_i + \varphi \tag{4.13}$$

$$m_j^L(\mathbf{u}) \leqslant \sum_{j=1}^{M} a_{ij} m_j \leqslant m_j^H(\mathbf{u}). \quad j = 1, \ldots, M \tag{4.14}$$

The quantities c_i, φ, and a_{ij} are defined for convenience of exposition. Their exact meaning will become clear in the example treated in the following.

Formulations (4.13) and (4.14) are similar to the original formulations (4.1) and (4.2) except that the constraint equations are *inequalities* and that the variables m_j are bounded by the generally nonzero m_j^L. It remains true that except in the degenerate case, the optimum is located at one of the vertices of the convex polyhedron defined by (4.14), but it can no longer be said that $N - M$ variables must be zero.† G. B. Dantzig's algorithm, though less efficient, remains applicable. The presumably known disturbances $\mathbf{u}$ enter into the objective function (4.13) as well as into the constraint equations (4.14), as a result of which the optimum vertex depends on the magnitude of the u_l. The task of the control computer, therefore, consists in finding the optimum vertex each time a change of disturbance has been detected.

Example. In order to illustrate the effect of a disturbance change, we consider the following hypothetical situation. Let

$$0 = -x + m_1 - m_2 - u \tag{4.15}$$

$$F = 2x - m_1 - \tfrac{1}{2}m_2 - u \tag{4.16}$$

$$-10 \leqslant x \leqslant 10 \tag{4.17}$$

$$-6 \leqslant m_1 \leqslant 6 \tag{4.18}$$

$$-12 \leqslant m_2 \leqslant 12. \tag{4.19}$$

† Also, as a result of this different formulation, it is no longer required that $M < N$.

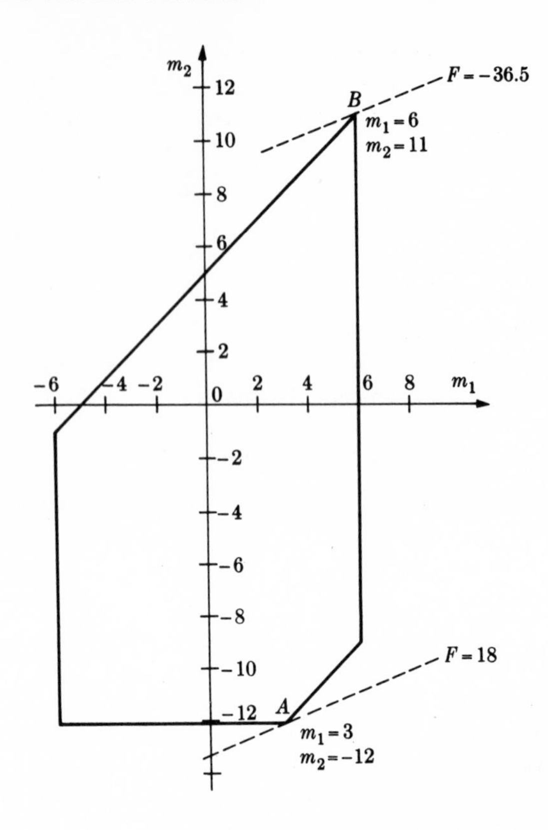

FIGURE 10. $\mu = 5$.

After elimination of the dependent variable x from Eqs. (4.16) and (4.17), the following equations result

$$F = m_1 - 2.5m_2 - 3u \tag{4.20}$$

$$\begin{gathered} -10 + u \leqslant m_1 - m_2 \leqslant 10 + u \\ -6 \leqslant m_1 \leqslant 6 \\ -12 \leqslant m_2 \leqslant 12. \end{gathered} \tag{4.21}$$

Equations (4.20) and (4.21) are plotted in Figs. 10 and 11 for $u = 5$ and $u = -5$. The optima—minima or maxima depending on the definition of F—are seen to be located at one vertex of a convex polygon which changes with the magnitude of u.

If it is unreasonable to approximate the process model (4.7) by the set of linear equations (4.8), the linear programming problem becomes much more difficult. An approximate solution, however, can be obtained as a result of iteration. The procedure consists in expanding the nonlinear process model

(4.7) about a *likely* operating point defined by the variables $\mathbf{m}^*$ and $\mathbf{x}^*$. Thus

$$0 = \mathbf{f}(\mathbf{x}, \mathbf{m}, \mathbf{u}) \approx \mathbf{f}(\mathbf{x}^*, \mathbf{m}^*, \mathbf{u}) + \sum \frac{\partial f_i}{\partial x_j}\, \delta x_j + \sum \frac{\partial f_i}{\partial m_j}\, \delta m_j \qquad (4.22)$$

where the $\partial f_i/\partial x_j$ and $\partial f_i/\partial m_j$ are evaluated at the point $\{\mathbf{m}^*, \mathbf{x}^*, u\}$. The increments δx_j and δm_j are thereafter allowed a range of variation compatible with the constraint equations (4.10) and (4.11) and a solution is sought for the *linearized* problem. If this solution, characterized by $\delta \mathbf{m}$, differs too much from the assumed point $\{\mathbf{m}^*, \mathbf{x}^*, \mathbf{u}\}$, new operating points are chosen until a reasonable fit is found. The successive points must be so selected that the iteration converges.

4.2 Nonlinear Model Optimization. (Nonlinear Programming). Let Eq. (4.7)

$$\mathbf{0} = \mathbf{f}(\mathbf{x}, \mathbf{m}, \mathbf{u})$$

be the (nonlinear) process model and consider the two sets of constraints (4.10) and (4.11) where, in the general nonlinear case, the upper and lower bounds

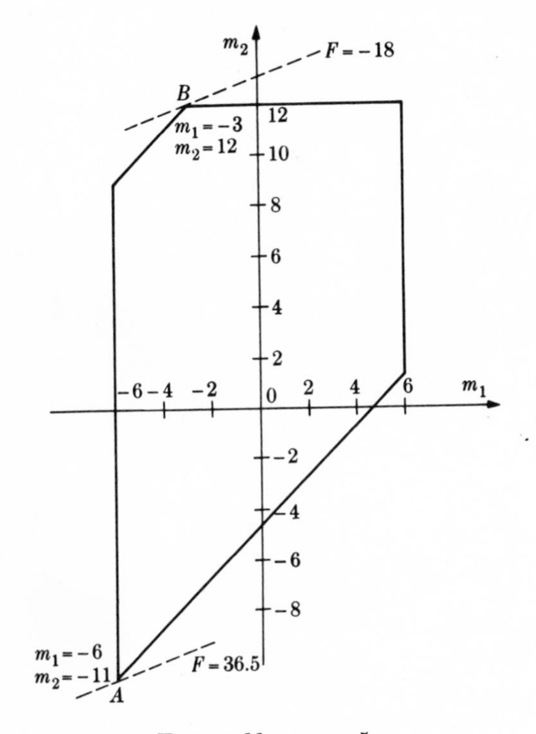

FIGURE 11. $u = -5$.

may not be constants, but may depend on $\mathbf{m}$ or $\mathbf{x}$. To find the optimum of the function

$$F = F(\mathbf{x}, \mathbf{m}, \mathbf{u}) \tag{4.23}$$

for a given $\mathbf{u}$.

In order to illustrate the difficulties arising from nonlinearity, we consider the hypothetical two-variable situation of Fig. 12, where two linear and two nonlinear constraint curves and contours of constant F are represented.

It is noted that a "local" maximum corresponding to $F = 6$ is situated in the permissible zone, whereas another maximum corresponding to $F = 13$ falls outside this zone. The optimum to be retained therefore occurs at point A, which is neither a vertex of the contour of constraints nor such that $\partial F/\partial m_1 = \partial F/\partial m_2 = 0$.

There exist several iterative computer procedures leading to this optimum by trial and error [14]. One of these procedures consists of selecting successive values of $m_1, m_2, \ldots$, in accordance with the sign and magnitude of the variation ΔF observed during the previous step until ΔF becomes sufficiently small. This iteration can be speeded up by proceeding along the line of "steepest ascent," i.e., by choosing the relative magnitude of the increments $\Delta m_1, \Delta m_2, \ldots$, so as to maximize the increment $\Delta F(\Delta m_1, \Delta m_2, \ldots)$.

4.3 Optimalizing Control. Optimalizing control, which was first described in the Western literature by Draper and Li [10], yields the static optimum operating point as a result of trial and error performed on the actual process and not on a model thereof. Let us assume that, in a specific situation, n independent outputs y_i are to be controlled by $n + \alpha$ available process

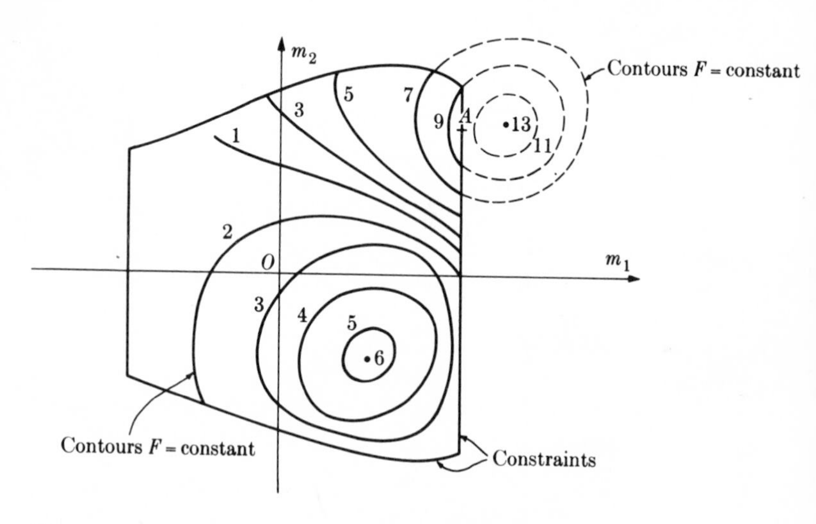

FIGURE 12. Diagram of the general two-variable nonlinear optimization problem.

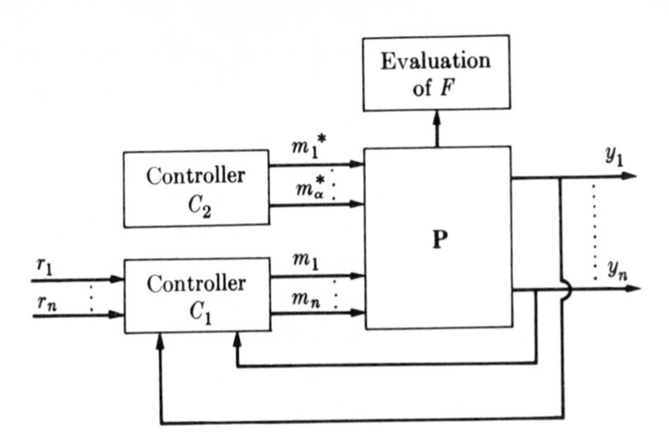

FIGURE 13. Diagram of a multivariable optimalizing system. Controller C_1 realizes the steady-state equilibrium $r_i = y_i$, $i = 1, \ldots, n$. Controller C_2 adjusts the remaining independent variables $m_1^*, \ldots, m_\alpha^*$ to optimize F.

inputs m_j. At least n of the actuating variables m_j are therefore needed to make y_i equal to r_i, $i = 1, \ldots, n$, but the remainder $m_1^*, m_2^*, \ldots, m_\alpha^*$ can be used to optimize the static objective function (4.23) subject to a constraint of the form

$$\mathbf{0} = \mathbf{f}(\mathbf{x}, \mathbf{r}, \mathbf{u}) \tag{4.24}$$

which accounts for the fact that some of the independent variables $\mathbf{x}$ are already related to the reference signals $\mathbf{r}$. Constraints of the form (4.10) and (4.11) are not considered in Draper and Li [10] and in subsequent papers on optimalizing control, although this could be done without great difficulty.

The procedure consists in performing a small change $\Delta m^*(0)$ and in observing the resulting change of F, $\Delta F(0)$. If a maximum of F is desired, the optimalizing controller is programmed in such a way that a positive $\Delta F(0)$ provokes a new increment $\Delta m^*(1)$ of the same sign as $\Delta m^*(0)$ and vice versa. If several actuating variables $m_1^*, m_2^*, \ldots, m_\alpha^*$ are available for optimization, their individual effects upon F are observed by provoking increments of each variable in sequence until finally F remains stationary. See Fig. 13. This signifies that the optimum operating point has been reached.† The set of constraints (4.23) does not need to be considered at all in this optimization scheme, since the trial and error process is performed on the actual plant, not on a model thereof. Constraints of the types (4.10) and (4.11) could be accounted for by scanning the permissible space of $\mathbf{m}^*$ only.

† Provided that the function F has only one maximum. If there were several maxima, the desired "maximum maximorum" would be determined by initiating several sequences of search with different initial conditions $\mathbf{m}^*(0)$. This complication, fortunately, is not of frequent occurrence in practice.

In addition to this *discrete* search technique which is identical in concept to the model search technique of Section 4.2, several other procedures based upon the use of periodic or random excitation of the $\mathbf{m}^*$ are available and will be found in Draper and Li [10].

A serious limitation of the concept of optimalizing control arises from the fact that the increments $\mathbf{\Delta m}^*$ do not provoke an instantaneous response ΔF as a result of the dynamics of the process and of the instrumentation needed to assess ΔF. Furthermore, process and instrument noise make it impossible to reach the exact optimum condition, since the small increments ΔF near the optimum can no longer be discerned, at least not in a straightforward manner.

Optimalizing control thus appears as a very attractive concept to attain optimum operation of fairly simple noise-free and fast-reacting (with respect to F) processes. If these conditions are not met, and this seems to be the case in many practical applications, it is preferable to construct a mathematical model and to determine the optimum either analytically or by search of the model.

4.4 Optimization by Memory. When the process is not subject to frequent parameter changes, and when all the disturbances are measurable, it is possible to store the optimum law of control, calculated off-line, in the controller. A well-known application of this concept is provided by the electric utility industry which is making extensive use of memories to set the power outputs of each of n interconnected power generating units so as to minimize total production cost subject to the constraint that a given customer area be supplied with power at the proper frequency [16].

Let $F_i = F_i(P_i)$ be the known cost-power curve of the ith generating unit and $P = \sum_{i=1}^{n} P_i$ be the power required by the customers. To minimize

$$F = \sum_{i=1}^{n} F_i \tag{4.25}$$

subject to the constraint

$$\sum_{i=1}^{n} P_i = P. \tag{4.26}$$

Minimization problems of this kind are best handled by the well-known method of the *Lagrangian multiplier*, which consists in optimizing the function

$$\mathcal{F} = F + \lambda P = \sum_{i=1}^{n} F_i + \lambda \sum_{i=1}^{n} P_i \tag{4.27}$$

$$\lambda = \text{Lagrangian multiplier.}$$

Thus:

$$\frac{\partial \mathcal{F}}{\partial P_i} = 0$$

or:

$$\frac{\partial F_i}{\partial P_i} = -\lambda. \qquad i = 1, \ldots, n \quad (4.28)$$

Equation (4.28) indicates that minimum operating cost F is attained when the incremental costs $\partial F_i/\partial P_i = \partial F_i/\partial P_i(P_i)$ are identical for each of the n-machines. This condition is satisfied *automatically* by storage of the known functions $P_i = P_i(\partial F_i/\partial P_i)$ in an analog or digital memory, as shown in Fig. 14 for $n = 2$.

If the consumers require more power than the sum $P_i + P_2$, the frequency f of the network will drop below the set frequency $f^{(d)}$ of 60 cps and an error ϵ develops. In response to ϵ, the nonlinear controllers generate the *desired* power outputs $P_1^{(d)}$ and $P_2^{(d)}$. The power regulators, not shown in Fig. 14, force the actual power outputs P_1 and P_2 to be equal to $P_1^{(d)}$ and $P_2^{(d)}$, respectively. A little reflexion shows that, at equilibrium, the incremental costs $\partial F_i/\partial P_i$ must be equal and that the frequency error ϵ is in fact the Lagrangian multiplier—λ.

Numerous refinements beyond the scope of this section are discussed in Kirchmayer [16]. In Carpentier [4], significant research toward the optimization of the power generation and distribution system of a whole country, in the presence of voltage, current, and power setting constraints, is reported. The determination of the optimum value of F in the presence of some thousand constraints takes a digital computer, programmed according to the theorem of Kuhn and Tucker, about a quarter of an hour.

5. Dynamic Control and Optimization

In principle, a control computer can be utilized to instrument any of the laws of control discussed in the previous chapters of this book. For reasons of economy, however, one should first examine if the desired law of control cannot be implemented by means of proven and less expensive conventional controllers; this is possible in a large number of practical situations. If the

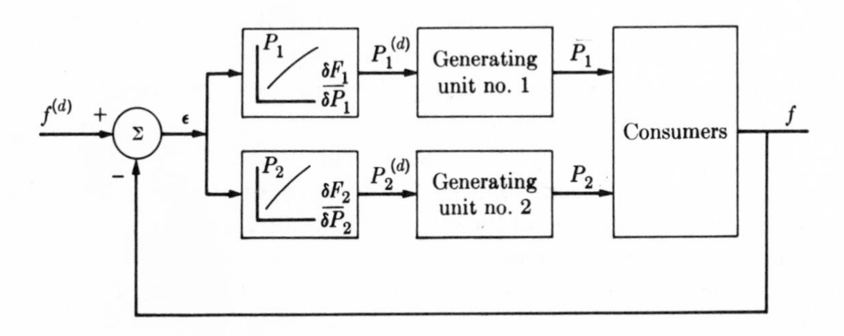

FIGURE 14. Optimization of two interlinked power generating units by storage of the law of control.

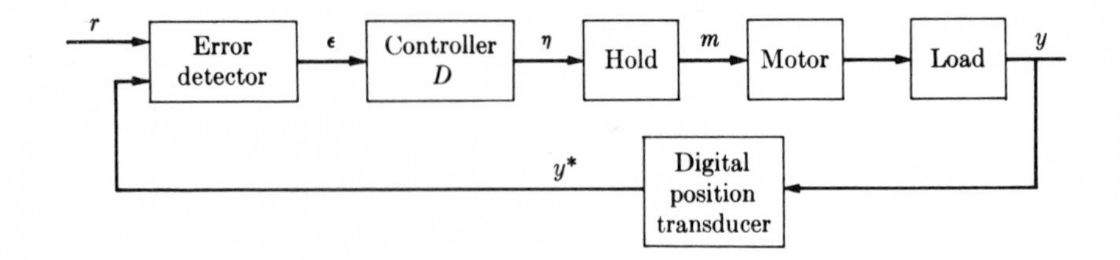

FIGURE 15. Diagram of a digital servomechanism.

purchase of a control computer of either the digital or analog type has already been justified for other reasons, perhaps static optimization, then the dynamic laws of control can often be added at little cost on a *timeshared basis*. There is some feeling that control computers, especially general purpose digital machines, may not be warranted for dynamic control and optimization alone except in a few very special situations.

In the present section, three classes of dynamic computer-based systems will be reviewed. In the first class, emphasis is placed on more efficient control in the conventional sense, i.e., improvement of steady-state accuracy and transient response to changes in set-points and disturbances. In the second class, the minimization of the cost associated with moving the process state between two consecutive equilibria by a *fixed* controller is sought (dynamic optimization). The last class, finally, allows satisfaction of this same objective by means of an *adaptive* controller. Computer control in the conventional sense, the first class, can be considered a proven technique; the second and third class remain experimental, no systematic industrial utilization having been reported as yet.

5.1 Digital Servomechanisms and Control Systems. In automatic *machine tool* applications, the accuracy capabilities of conventional analog position control systems (servomechanisms) are frequently exceeded. Servomechanisms incorporating digital position transducers, digital error comparators, and digital controllers were developed to permit the tool position $y(t)$ to track the reference input $r(t)$, contained on tape under the form of a binary code with the desired accuracy. The diagram corresponding to a digital (or sampled data) servomechanism fitted with a series controller D is shown in Fig. 15. The signals y^*, r, ϵ, and η are binary and therefore relatively immune to the perturbations limiting the accuracy of analog systems. The value of these signals changes at the sampling instants $0, T_s, 2T_s, \ldots, lT_s, \ldots$. The actuating variable m is analog and constant within one sampling interval.

As in the case of continuous control systems, it is possible and often preferable, to use a parallel rather than a series controller.

Proper adjustment of the parameters of the series or parallel controller permits satisfactory transient response to be achieved. It is recalled here that linear digital control systems can be designed so as to reach equilibrium in a *finite* number of sampling periods [20]. "Finite settling time" or "dead-beat" designs are frequently preferred to other designs which minimize the sum of the squared errors at the sampling instants. In either case, the series controller D must produce a (finite) sequence of samples

$$\eta(lT_s) = \alpha_0\epsilon(lT_s) + \alpha_1\epsilon[(l-1)T_s] + \cdots. \tag{5.1}$$

The law of control (5.1) can be instrumented easily with a drum memory followed by a simple arithmetic unit. In the case of a parallel controller connected to all the state variables, storage of past values of ϵ is unnecessary [13].

If a sufficiently large number of digital servomechanisms and other digital control systems are located in the same plant, a general purpose digital control computer may be more economic than as many digital controllers as there are systems.

Although digital instrumentation and control gear remains more expensive than comparable analog gear, there is a noticeable trend toward such equipment, even in those applications where high accuracy is not required. The reasons for this trend are that *coded* information can be transmitted, displayed, and processed more effectively than analog information. The major types of analog-to-digital and digital-to-analog conversion equipment are discussed in the Appendix to this chapter.

5.2 Noninteracting Control. The design procedures available to decouple the input and output variables of a multivariable process are discussed in detail in Chapter III, Section 3.8. The general subject of noninteraction (or invariance) is relevant to a discussion on computer process control for two reasons, namely the following.

(1) The series or parallel controller required for noninteraction generally cannot be instrumented conveniently by interconnection of conventional process controllers, although this is possible in relatively simple situations; see, for example, Chatterjee [6]. The analog computer is well suited to implement the required cross-coupled dynamic compensating network. Decoupling can also be achieved by means of a digital computer [18].

(2) Since the dynamic optimization of multivariable processes remains laborious except in simple cases, we frequently start out by *decoupling* the process and thereafter optimize each of the now independent loops. The resulting design is not, in general, optimal, since the true relations and constraints between state variables are ignored, but the *suboptimization* thus accomplished is expedient and more satisfactory than no optimization at all.

To familiarize the reader with the use of an analog computer for decoupling, we shall instrument the series compensating network discussed in Chapter III, Section 3.4, and reproduced below:

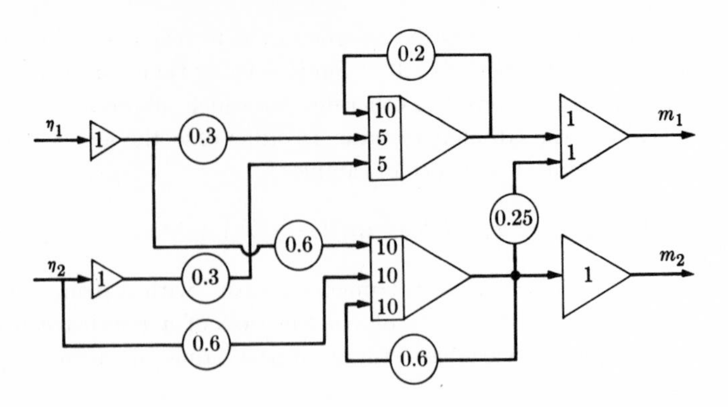

FIGURE 16. Analog computer diagram of the decoupling network (5.2). The symbols ▷ and ▹ represent integrators and summing amplifiers, respectively. Sign inversion is assumed to take place.

$$D(s) = \begin{bmatrix} -\dfrac{3(s+4)}{(s+2)(s+6)} & \dfrac{-6}{(s+2)(s+6)} \\ -\dfrac{6}{s+6} & \dfrac{6}{s+6} \end{bmatrix}. \tag{5.2}$$

In order to implement the transfer element $d_{11}(s)$, which, in addition to two poles, has a zero, it is convenient to perform a partial fraction expansion; this yields

$$d_{11}(s) = -3\left[\frac{\frac{1}{2}}{s+2} + \frac{\frac{1}{2}}{s+6}\right]. \tag{5.3}$$

The complete compensating network, which requires only two analog integrators, is shown in Fig. 16.

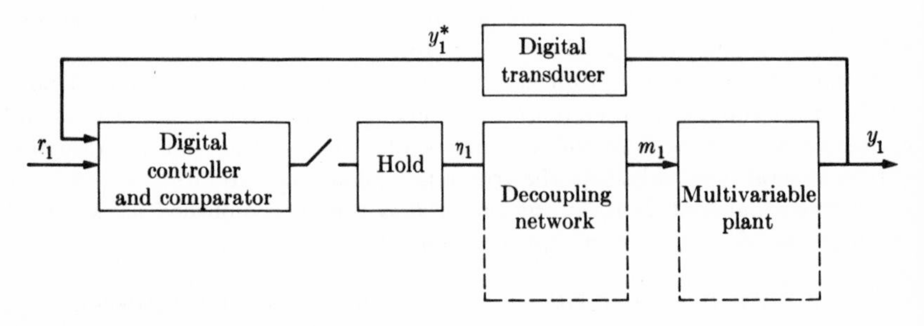

FIGURE 17. Closed-loop system configuration corresponding to the upper loop of the decoupled multivariable plant.

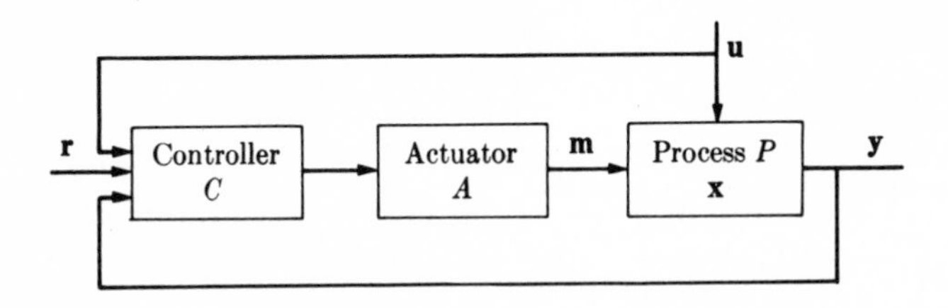

FIGURE 18. Diagram of a combined feedforward feedback system. The measured disturbance **u** is fed to the controller which generates an actuating vector **m** to cancel the effects of **u** upon **x** and **y**.

It is clear that other network configurations are possible and may be more appropriate in specific situations.

The plant considered in Chapter III, Section 3.4, can thus be decoupled by means of an analog computer programmed to satisfy Eq. (5.2). Other requirements, such as steady-state accuracy, optimum steady-state, and (suboptimum) dynamic performance are satisfied by use of additional controllers, either analog or digital. A possible *system* configuration utilizing a digital controller is thus shown in Fig. 17. The reference input r_1 of Fig. 17 may, in specific situations, be set at regular intervals of time by still another computer (not shown here) which is assigned the task of supervising and optimizing the whole process of which the plant considered in this section is only a part.

5.3 Feedforward. Feedforward is a commonly used procedure to cancel the static and dynamic effects of *measurable* disturbances upon the independent process variables.

This is accomplished by means of a controller programmed to generate an actuating vector **m** such that the effects of perturbations are compensated for, at least approximately, before they materialize. Feedback control alone may not be satisfactory, since correcting action starts only after the state variables have become affected. Feedforward, on the other hand, does not permit accurate disturbance cancellation under steady-state conditions because of incomplete knowledge of the process equations. It is for this reason that feedforward systems generally also include a feedback loop, as shown in Fig. 18.

In practice, it is often possible to improve the response time of the feedforward loop by addition of a second, third $\cdots$ actuator which directly acts upon those parts of the process located nearest to the output **y**. This is shown in Fig. 19.

The best configuration in each specific case depends more on the ease with which the successive parts of the process can be influenced by available actuators than on theoretical considerations. As an example of application of the concept of feedforward, we consider a mill stand where plate of non-

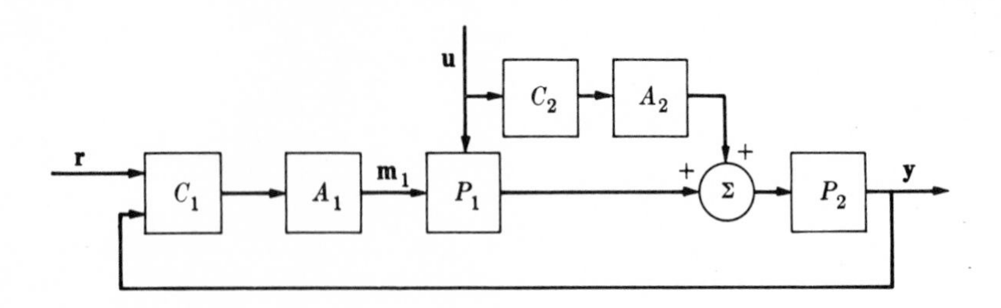

FIGURE 19. Combined feedforward feedback system; A_2 acts upon that part of the process, P_2, located nearest to the output.

uniform gauge—this is the disturbance u—enters the rollers at a known velocity v (see Fig. 20). The gauge of the outgoing product is determined by the spacing of the rollers e, and by the tension T. Since, for practical reasons, the actual gauge cannot be measured immediately after the product leaves the rollers, there is a pure time delay which precludes a fast-acting feedback control. Measurement of gauge variation at the input by g_1 and subsequent control of e and T on the basis of this measurement substantially improves product uniformity.

The analytical techniques to design the feedforward controller are straightforward. In the case of the system of Fig. 18, the following mathematical model

$$\mathbf{Y}(s) = P(s)\mathbf{M}(s) + P_u(s)\mathbf{U}(s) \tag{5.4}$$

is assumed to be known. If the dynamics of the actuator can be neglected, we seek the unknown transfer functions $C'(s)$ and $C''(s)$ of the two parts of the controller corresponding to feedback and feedforward, respectively, by writing that

$$\mathbf{M}(s) = C'(s)[\mathbf{R}(s) - \mathbf{Y}(s)] + C''(s)\mathbf{U}(s). \tag{5.5}$$

Combining Eqs. (5.4) and (5.5), it follows that

$$\mathbf{Y}(s) = P(s)C'(s)[\mathbf{R}(s) - \mathbf{Y}(s)] + P(s)C''(s)\mathbf{U}(s) + P_u(s)\mathbf{U}(s). \tag{5.6}$$

The effects of $\mathbf{U}(s)$ are completely canceled if $C''(s)$ is chosen such that

$$P(s)C''(s) + P_u(s) = \mathbf{0}. \tag{5.7}$$

Suitable transient response of the feedback loop is thereafter obtained by proper selection of $C'(s)$.

The analog computer is well suited to implement $C'(s)$ and $C''(s)$. If the process were highly nonlinear or contained time delays, a digital computer might be preferable. For example, in the case of the mill control previously discussed, it is necessary to delay the measurements of the gauge transducer g_1 until the exact time when the measured part of the plate enters the gap between the rollers. This then requires a pure time delay which can be

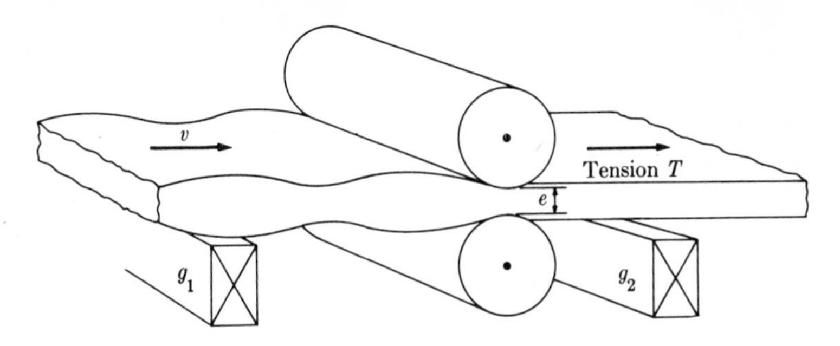

FIGURE 20. Gauge transducer g_1 permits "anticipatory" control of e and T_1 whereas g_2 eliminates possible calibration errors of the mathematical model.

instrumented much more easily on a digital computer. Another reason for preferring the digital computer in this application is that the same mill stand must process a large number of different grades and gauges of plate; therefore, it is necessary to store a mathematical model corresponding to each type of plate.

5.4 Optimum Control of Dynamic Processes. If the disturbances can be assumed to vary in a stepwise fashion, which is frequently the case in practice, the static optimization procedures of Section 4 provide optimum equilibrium points **r** for each set of disturbances. It is the function of dynamic optimization to determine the "best" trajectory to be followed by the process between consecutive set-points **r**. The "best" trajectory is usually defined such that the functional

$$J = \int_0^T F(\mathbf{x}, \mathbf{r}, \mathbf{m}, t)\, dt \tag{5.8}$$

is an extremum, subject to three sets of constraints, namely (1) the dynamic relations between process variables, for example

$$\dot{\mathbf{x}} = \mathbf{f}(\mathbf{x}, \mathbf{m}) \qquad \mathbf{x}(t)\big|_{t=0} = \mathbf{x}(0) \tag{5.9}$$

(2) the true constraints arising from the fact that some independent variables and all actuating variables have a restricted range of variation

$$\begin{aligned} \mathbf{m}^L \leqslant \mathbf{m} \leqslant \mathbf{m}^H \\ x_k{}^L \leqslant x_k \leqslant x_k{}^H \end{aligned} \tag{5.10}$$

for some of the x_k; (3) the condition that at some time $t = T$ the prescribed equilibrium position be, in fact, attained.†

† It sometimes happens that the state $\mathbf{x}$ at $t = T$ is not specified; see [21] or the example treated in Section 4 of Chapter VII.

The lower integration bound of Eq. (5.8) is arbitrarily set equal to zero in this discussion. The upper integration bound T may be fixed (including $T = \infty$), or else it may be desired to render T as short as possible, in which case (5.8) reduces to

$$J = \int dt = \text{minimum}. \tag{5.11}$$

In the case of a digital (sampled-data) system, the *discrete* versions of Eqs. (5.8) and (5.9) would need to be considered, i.e.,

$$J = \sum_{l=0}^{N} F[\mathbf{x}(lT_s), \mathbf{r}(lT_s), \mathbf{m}(lT_s), lT_s] \tag{5.12}$$

and

$$\mathbf{x}[(l+1)T_s] = \mathbf{f}[\mathbf{x}(lT_s), \mathbf{m}(lT_s)]. \tag{5.13}$$

The dynamic optimization problem thus defined is a typical *variational* problem, which can be approached by the Calculus of Variations, Dynamic Programming, the Principle of the Maximum, and, in the case of Eq. (5.11), by several direct solutions of the bang-bang problem. It is not the purpose of the present section to give an analytical account of these methods, since this has already been done in Chapter VII, but to examine briefly the computational requirements placed upon the optimum systems designed accordingly.

A few words need to be said about the *structure* or configuration of optimum systems. It was pointed out in Chapter I, Section 4, that in *advanced* systems, several compatible objectives $O_1, O_2, \ldots,$ could be defined and that, for reasons of convenience, structures of the first, second, . . . , *degree* could be considered. In Fig. 21, a first and a second degree structure are thus reproduced.

In the case of Fig. 21a, there is only one objective O_1 which can be satisfied optimally, or just adequately, depending on how much care is taken to design C. In the case of Fig. 21b, there are two compatible objectives O_1 and O_2; the controllers C_1 and C_2 can likewise be optimal or just adequate. In principle,

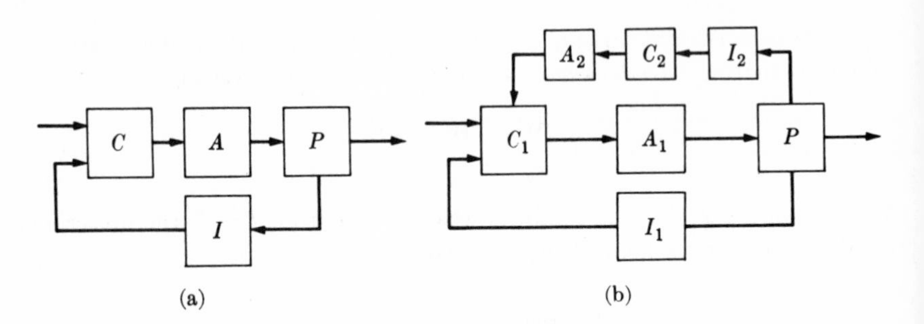

FIGURE 21. (a) First degree structure; (b) Second degree structure.

the variational methods to be reviewed in the following sections can be used to produce an optimum design of either or both of the two channels, though admittedly the mathematical difficulties may become excessive in the case of the second channel.

In what follows, we will primarily discuss the applicability of the variational methods to structures of the first degree. In Section 5.8, a structure of the second degree capable of optimum response to the first objective and of adequate response to the second objective is considered.

5.5 The Calculus of Variations. In its classical formulation, the Calculus of Variations yields that trajectory $x = x(t)$ which optimizes, maximizes or minimizes, the functional

$$J = \int_0^T F(x, \dot{x}; t)\, dt \tag{5.14}$$

for fixed T and given $x(0)$ and $x(T)$. The optimal trajectory satisfies the *Euler* equation

$$\frac{d}{dt}\frac{\partial F}{\partial \dot{x}} - \frac{\partial F}{\partial x} = 0 \tag{5.15}$$

which is a second-order ordinary differential equation of which the integration constants are determined by $x(0)$ and $x(T)$. Extensions to higher order situations, i.e.,

$$J = \int_0^T F(x, \dot{x}, \ddot{x}, \ldots; t)\, dt$$

with the boundary conditions

$$\begin{aligned} x(t)\big|_{t=0} &= x(0); \quad x(t)\big|_{t=T} = x(T) \\ \dot{x}(t)\big|_{t=0} &= \dot{x}(0); \quad \dot{x}(t)\big|_{t=T} = \dot{x}(T) \\ &\cdots\cdots\cdots\cdots\cdots \end{aligned}$$

exist; for example, see Weinstock [28].

The *classical* Calculus of Variations thus far has not been applied extensively to the synthesis of optimum controls for two reasons:

(1) The solution $x[x(0), x(T), t]$ of Eq. (5.15) is not suitable for instrumentation in a control system; what we seek is a solution of the form

$$m(t) = m[x(t), x(T), t] \tag{5.16}$$

which permits the desired $x(T)$ to be reached regardless of the perturbations that might occur en route. This point will be illustrated in the example treated in the following.

(2) The constraints (5.10) are not considered.

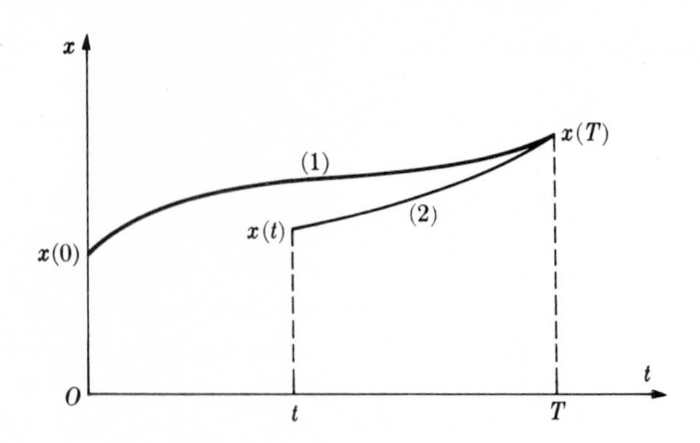

FIGURE 22. Optimal trajectory (1) $x = x[x(O), x(T), t]$, and (2) $x = [x(t), x(T), t]$.

Example. Consider

$$J = \int_0^T [(r - x)^2 + \dot{x}^2]\, dt$$

$$x(t)\big|_{t=0} = x(0); \quad x(t)\big|_{t=T} = x(T) \tag{5.17}$$

$$r = \text{constant}$$

and

$$\dot{x} + 2x = m. \tag{5.18}$$

There are no constraints on x, $\dot{x}$, and m. It is desired to minimize J. Equation (5.15) yields the condition

$$\ddot{x} - x = -r \tag{5.19}$$

which is integrated to provide a *mathematically* adequate solution of the form

$$\begin{aligned} x(t) &= C_0 e^t + C_1 e^{-t} + r \\ C_0 &= C_0[x(0), x(T)]; \quad C_1 = C_1[x(0), x(T)] \end{aligned} \tag{5.20}$$

as shown by curve 1 of Fig. 22.

For *control* purposes, however, it is preferable to consider the present state $x(t)$ which may have been displaced from the original trajectory (5.20) by disturbances and to generate that actuating signal $m(t)$ which moves x to $x(T)$ regardless of further perturbations; see curve 1 of Fig. 22. Integration of Eq. (5.19) between the bounds $x(t)$ and $x(T)$ rather than $x(0)$ and $x(T)$ and subsequent differentiation with respect to t yields the optimal slope

$$\dot{x}(t) = \frac{(r - x)\cosh(T - t)}{\sinh(T - t)} \tag{5.21}$$

at the present operating point. The desired actuating signal $m(t)$ is obtained by combination of Eqs. (5.18) and (5.21)

$$m(t) = \frac{r \cosh (T - t) + x[2 \sinh (T - t) - \cosh (T - t)]}{\sinh (T - t)} \tag{5.22}$$

in terms of r and $x(t)$.

The implementation of Eq. (5.22) requires a time-varying controller, unless $T \to \infty$, in which case m reduces to

$$m(t) = r + x. \tag{5.23}$$

It is known that a "quadratic" performance index† and a linear plant always yield a linear law of control of the form

$$m(t) = \beta r + \sum_{k=1}^{q} a_k x_k \tag{5.24}$$

where the "feedback coefficients" β and a_k depend in a known fashion on t, if T is finite, and are constants if T is infinite. In either case, a controller can be constructed with relative case.

In order to take into account the constraints (5.10), it is possible to add to the objective function (5.8) to be minimized a set of additional terms which grow very fast when (5.10) is violated. Suppose, for instance, that m_j must remain within the range $(-m_j^H, m_j^H)$, where m_j^H is a positive constant. If the exponent ρ in the objective function

$$J = \int_0^T F(x, \dot{x}, t)\, dt + \int_0^T \left(\frac{m_j}{m_j^H}\right)^\rho dt \tag{5.25}$$

$$\rho = \text{even integer}$$

is chosen to be much larger than unity, the Calculus of Variations yields a trajectory which does not (appreciably) violate the stated constraint.

Additional extensions of the classical calculus of variations to the constrained case and with a view on the utilization of control computers are discussed by Carter [5].

5.6 The Bang-Bang Problem. See Chapter V, Section 1 and Chapter VII, Section 2. If the reference signal were a step of amplitude r, the switching surfaces would be *stationary* and would need to be determined only once, either by hand calculation or by off-line machine computation. The coordinates of these switching surfaces could then be stored in the controller as discussed in Section 2.8. If $r(t)$ is not a step, the switching surfaces are (generally) not stationary and it may be more expedient to compute their coordinates on-line in each specific case by application of either of the analytical methods discussed in Chapters V and VII or by use of a fast model; see Section 5.9.

5.7 Dynamic Programming. See Chapter VII, Section 3, and Bellman [2]. Though originally developed to solve the operations research problem of

† The integrand of Eq. (5.14) is often referred to as performance index.

the optimum allocation of resources in multistage processes, Dynamic Programming has since been extended to include the variational problem defined by Eqs. (5.8) and (5.9) for fixed and for minimum T. It was stressed in Chapter VII that in its present form, Dynamic Programming is not only a computational algorithm, as suggested by the term "programming," but a body of knowledge which augments the classical Calculus of Variations.

A direct consequence of this observation is that it may be impossible, even for a very high speed digital computer, to master a specific control problem perfectly manageable by a much smaller machine (or even a passive network), depending on which result of Dynamic Programming is being instrumented. The applications record of Dynamic Programming in its "raw" form [see Eqs. (3.15) to (3.24) of Chapter VII] is expected to remain rather insignificant in the forseeable future, because the speed and memory capabilities of powerful machines are rapidly exceeded.† In its "manipulated" form, however, Dynamic Programming often does not demand great computational capability.

Example. It is desired to design a digital (sampled-data) controller which eliminates any initial perturbation $\mathbf{x}(0)$ of a linear single-input plant by minimizing a quadratic objective function of the form

$$J = \sum_{l=0}^{N} \mathbf{x}^T(lT_s)Q\mathbf{x}(lT_s) \tag{5.26}$$

$$N = \text{fixed}$$

$$x^T = \text{transpose of } x$$

$$Q = \text{given positive definite square matrix.}$$

It is shown in Kalman and Koepcke [13] with the help of Dynamic Programming that the optimum actuating signal $m(lT_s)$ at the lth sampling instant is linearly related to the actual state $\mathbf{x}(lT_s)$

$$m(lT_s) = \sum_{k=1}^{v} a_k x_k(lT_s) \tag{5.27}$$

$$a_k = a_k(lT_s).$$

If $N \to \infty$, which is a case of practical importance, the coefficients a_k relating $m(lT_s)$ and $\mathbf{x}(lT_s)$ are independent of l and implementation of the optimal controller only requires as many constant-gain feedback paths as there are state variables. If, on the other hand, N is finite, the a_k depend on l. Implementation in this case requires retrieval, at the lth sampling time, of the proper gain to be inserted into each feedback path. This is still less laborious than on-line computation of $m(lT_s)$ based upon the raw formulation of Dynamic Programming.

The resulting control system is shown in Fig. 23.

It should be mentioned that the example discussed here as well as the much more general linear case considered in Kalman and Koepcke [13] are

† The somewhat limited experience thus far available seems to indicate that, roughly speaking, dynamic systems of the fifth order represent an upper limit.

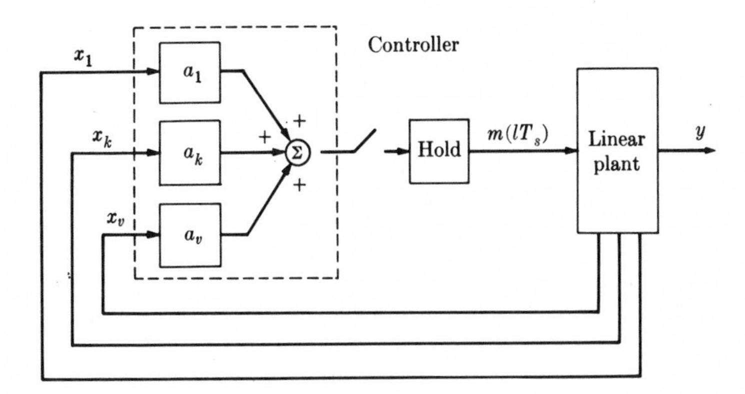

FIGURE 23. Optimum controller of a linear single-input plant to minimize a quadratic performance index.

particularly simple and could also be solved by straightforward application of the classical Calculus of Variations, as was previously done in Section 5.5. But it remains true that in each particular case, one should carefully explore whether results *derived from Dynamic Programming*, such as the pair of partial differential equations (3.36) of Chapter VII, might not alleviate the computational requirements placed upon the controller.

To summarize our discussion on Dynamic Programming, we may say that the optimum systems described in the literature thus far do not exploit the substantial advantages provided by this method, namely, inclusion of constraints and nonequivocal determination of the optimum optimorum when the Calculus of Variations yields several solutions, primarily because the computational requirements are such that there is hardly any economic incentive.

5.8 The Maximum Principle. See Chapter VII, Section 4. A major difficulty arising in the application of the Maximum Principle is the requirement of determining the vector $\tilde{\boldsymbol{\psi}}(t)$ or $\boldsymbol{\psi}(t)$. This necessitates the solution of a set of $2(v + 1)$ (or $2v$) ordinary differential equations in $\tilde{\boldsymbol{\psi}}$ and $\tilde{\mathbf{x}}$ (or $\boldsymbol{\psi}$ and $\mathbf{x}$), depending on whether the objective function is of the form (5.8) or (5.11). If the initial conditions $\tilde{\boldsymbol{\psi}}(0)$ (or $\boldsymbol{\psi}(0)$) were given, integration could be carried out in a straightforward fashion by either a digital or an analog computer. Unfortunately, this is never the case and the unknown initial conditions $\tilde{\boldsymbol{\psi}}(0)$ (or $\boldsymbol{\psi}(0)$) must be determined by trial and error. The procedure is to start by assuming a set of initial conditions $\tilde{\boldsymbol{\psi}}(0)$ (or $\boldsymbol{\psi}(0)$); since the final condition will probably not be satisfied at the end of the first trial, a new set of initial conditions is chosen, until the endpoint conditions, which may involve $\mathbf{x}(T)$ or $\boldsymbol{\psi}(T)$ or components of both, are satisfied. The computation speed of analog computers is often sufficient to permit a large number of trial runs in the

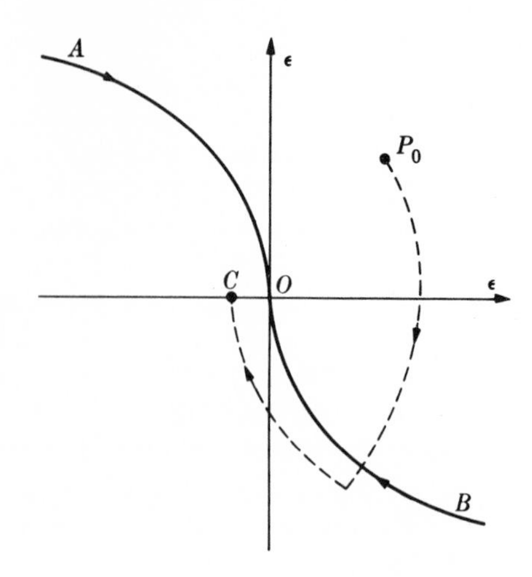

FIGURE 24. Stationary switching curve in $\{\epsilon, \epsilon\}$ plane. ϵ is the error $r - y$.

allotted time T_s; the major difficulty in high-order problems is to automatically select successive sets of initial conditions such that the iteration converges. The remarks of the previous section on the importance of carefully determining *which* results of the Maximum Principle should be instrumented and in terms of which process variables the actuating vector $\mathbf{m}$ should be expressed are equally valid here.

5.9 Control by Fast Model. If it is not possible or not practical to store the law of control relating $\mathbf{m}$ to $\mathbf{x}$ and $\mathbf{r}$ in the controller, the desired transient performance can still be obtained in certain cases by simulating the behavior of a fast model of the actual process and by *experimentally* adjusting the actuating vector $\mathbf{m}$ of the fast model until satisfactory performance is observed. The desired actuating vector thus obtained is thereafter used to control the actual process.

The use of a fast model to optimally control a relay system subjected to nonstationary polynomial input is discussed in Coales and Noton [7]. Since in this case the switching surfaces are not stationary, but dependent on the measured coefficients of the polynomial input, storage of the law of control is not practical.

In order to facilitate exposition, we assume that the input r is a step occurring at $t = 0$ and that the plant is linear and of the second order, in which case the switching surfaces reduce to a stationary curve. It is a well-known result that optimum, i.e., minimum time response, is accomplished if the polarity of the relay output m is changed once, at the precise moment when the state $\{\epsilon, \dot{\epsilon}\}$ crosses the switching curve AOB; see Fig. 24.

Since the differential equation of the plant is known, the method consists in resolving on a computer another differential equation obtained from that describing the plant by use of an accelerated time scale and in reversing the model drive signal at some arbitrary time τ_0; the initial conditions of the fast model are identical with those, $\epsilon(0)$ and $\dot{\epsilon}(0)$, of the actual process. The resulting model performance will in all likelihood not be optimal, and an improved value of the first reversal time τ_1 will be used in a second simulation. The initial conditions $\epsilon(1)$ and $\dot{\epsilon}(1)$ are those of the actual state as measured at the time when the second simulation commences. This iterative process is continued until a suitable value for τ has been found. Consecutive values of τ are selected on the basis of the sign and the magnitude of ϵ when $\dot{\epsilon} = 0$; see point C of Fig. 24. For example, if ϵ is negative, the actual system would exhibit overshoot because τ was chosen too large. In the following iteration, τ would therefore be made smaller until ϵ and $\dot{\epsilon}$ become zero simultaneously.†

If the system input r remained constant for $t > 0$, a single sequence of iterations yielding τ would suffice to optimally control the actual process. Since, in the situation discussed in Coales and Noton [7], r changes continuously, it is necessary to compute the reversal time continuously. In order for the system to operate without excessive limit cycles about equilibrium, the model must be many times faster than the process. Analog computers are often capable of the required high-speed operations.

Finally, it should be stressed that the concept of the fast model is applicable not only to the optimum control of relay systems, but, generally speaking, can also serve to improve the transient performance of a wide class of dynamic processes. The obvious limitation is the number of possible choices of $\mathbf{m}$; if this number exceeds the speed capabilities of the computer, the analytical approaches of Sections 5.5, 5.6, 5.7, or 5.8 are necessary.

6. Summary and Conclusions

Computer process control is not a sharply defined subject, but a broad area of applied research and development to utilize computers in estimating the state of the process and in implementing the laws of control derived from the theory of automatic control, operations research, and others; computer control systems thus differ by the nature of the process, in the type of the computer used and in the way the process is influenced. Computer control systems thus far have been designed from either the operations research (static optimization) or the automatic control (dynamic optimization) point of view. In the first case, improved economy of operation of complex

† The policy of adjusting τ is actually somewhat more complicated, as discussed in Coales and Noton [7]. Since no attempt is made to define an objective function for the iterative process other than eventual convergence, the design of the fast loop is not optimum, but just adequate.

man-machine systems is sought; in the second case, better satisfaction of the technical criteria of quality associated with the operation of relatively less complex processes primarily involving machines is the objective. These two points of view now converge, because past experience stresses the importance of considering complex processes as a single entity, particularly when the installation of a digital control computer is envisaged. If so, a host of routine decision tasks can often be added at little cost.

Three groups of tasks are thus handled by the control computer. These are, in increasing order of complexity:

(1) data logging, monitoring, sequence control, and dispatch of information;
(2) static optimization, either by operator guides or closed loop;
(3) dynamic control and optimization.

Although, generally speaking, process control by general-purpose analog or digital computer remains experimental, the first two tasks are already implemented in a sizable number of installations.

In spite of the fact that much progress was recently made to yield a better understanding of the variational problem with a view toward optimal dynamic control, widespread application is not likely to occur in the near future, because there appear to be relatively few practical situations where the utilization of a computer, especially of the general purpose digital type, is economically attractive.

Although it can be asserted that large digital and analog computers constitute the key to genuine automation and will eventually find extensive use, their present applications record is only moderately conclusive. The subject matter has definitely not yet been crystallized into handbook style design methodology. In order to accelerate the introduction of on-line computers into industry and commerce, it is necessary to find ways of predicting economic justification with greater confidence. Automatic control permits the temporal or frequency behavior of a system to be related to the known temporal or frequency behavior of its constituents. Success of computer process control requires that, in addition, the cost, labor-saving, reliability, maintainability, etc., characteristics of the constituents be linked to the corresponding characteristics of the system. This in turn allows economic benefit to be predicted with greater confidence. Such a design methodology, if it were available, would yield answers to the following questions.

Which processes are well suited for computer control? How accurate does the process model need to be? Which are the main process variables? By which model—deterministic or probabilistic, static or dynamic—should they be related? Which type of computer—digital, analog, hybrid—or which system of interlinked computers is required in a given case? Which mode of control is to be programed into the computer in order to fully exploit its capabilities?

APPENDIX

Digital Instrumentation and Conversion Equipment

A.1 Introduction. The object of using a computer for process control is to improve the efficiency of the process. To accomplish this, the relevant information from the plant must be fed into the computer, of which the output is used either to guide the plant operator where manual control is employed, or to control the process automatically. Plant variables—temperature, pressure, flow rate, etc.—are measured by transducers. The computing controller may be a digital or an analog computer, or a hybrid computing system. Analog-digital and digital-analog converters link the transducers to the computer and the computer back to the controlling actuators, since most transducers and actuators are analog devices and the controller is generally digital. Where a hybrid computer is used, i.e., a combination of analog and digital computing techniques, converters are again necessary to transmit the information from one to the other. These two fundamental conversion processes may be represented schematically as shown in Figs. 25a and 25b.

When designing instrumentation for computer control systems operating on-line, certain points must be borne in mind. For control, the computer must operate in real time, while for plant optimization, faster than real time operation may be required. Therefore the conversion equipment must be designed to have the necessary speed. Digital computers are inherently accurate; care must be taken not to lose this accuracy in the conversion equipment. The importance of reliability is well realized, but we should stress here that the reliability of on-line computers is far more critical than that of systems designed for off-line operation.

When specifying the equipment for the plant-to-computer and computer-to-plant links, the following points must be carefully considered.

(1) What type of transducer is necessary to obtain the plant information?

(2) What conversion equipment is required to match transducer output to computing controller input?

(3) Is the transducer located so far from the controller that special data transmission techniques are necessary?

(4) What conversion equipment is required to match the computer output to the actuator?

A.2 Transducers. Most of the transducers available today are of the analog type, although digital transducers do exist. A digital transducer is a measuring device that produces a numerical output signal representing the measured quantity. Most of them are analog devices which have a built-in analog-digital converter. Generally, the choice of a transducer depends on (1) balancing the transducer characteristic against desired system

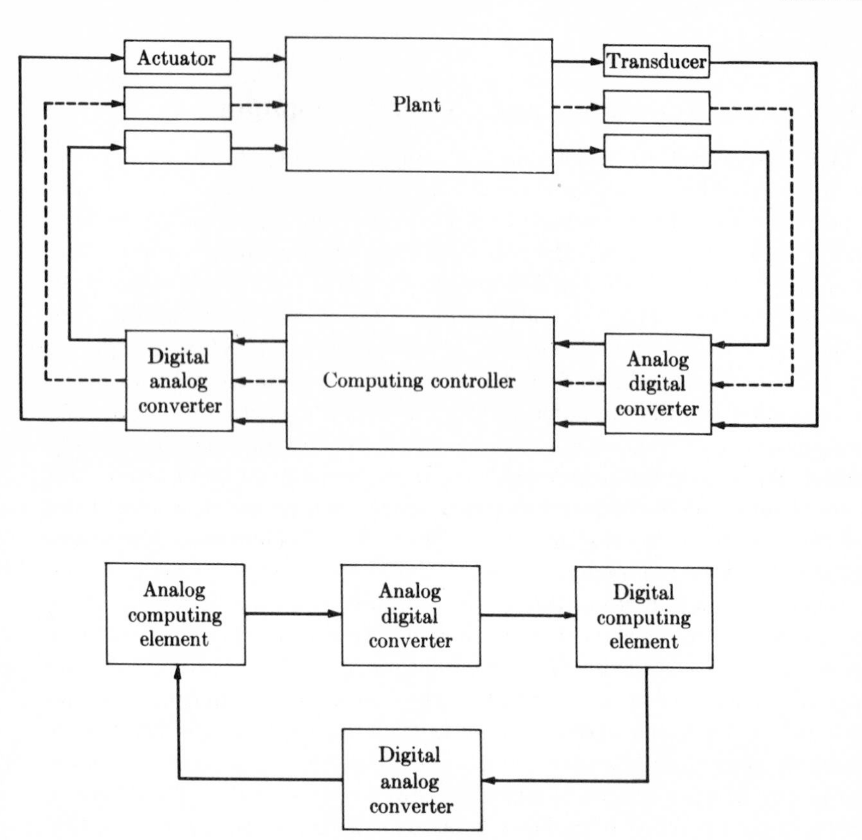

FIGURE 25. Fundamental conversion processes (analog-digital and digital-analog) for connecting (a) Plant to computing controller and back to plant via transducers and actuators; (b) Analog and digital computing elements.

performance, and (2) the input requirements of the controller. The different types of existing transducers have been surveyed in various publications.†

In the domain of digital transducers, several mechanical input devices with integral digital conversion are available for measuring angular displacement and linear motion. Angular displacement is measured by encoders which sense shaft position by means of coded disks and associated brushes. A typical example of a coded disk is shown in Fig. 26. Various methods of coding are used. One method is to photograph the pattern onto a glass disk so as to produce opaque and transparent areas. A light source (which may be pulsed or continuous) is placed on one side of the disk and, depending on the position of the shaft carrying the disk, light will be transmitted or absorbed,

† See, for example, Holzbock, W. G. [12].

giving high- or low-voltage outputs from a set of photocell detectors on the opposite side. Another convenient method is to make the pattern of electrically conducting and nonconducting areas and to detect the difference by means of brush contacts.

A.3 Telemetering. It is not always possible to place the computer near the plant. Economics, physical inaccessibility, or other factors may make it necessary to run long lines from the transducer to the computer. Frequently, it is found that there is a concentration of transducers in one part of an industrial plant, and in such cases it may be advantageous to do the analog-digital conversion locally, using pulse-code modulation techniques to transmit the data to the computer.

A.4 Nature of Transducer Output Signals.

Low-Level Analog Electrical Signals. This is a very large class and is the most difficult to treat because of the very low signal level (0 to ±10 mv).

High-Level Analog Electrical Signals. Some transducers, e.g., Honeywell Teletransmitter, have a transmitter combined with the transducer. These have standardized outputs in the range 0–5 mA or 0–5 v.

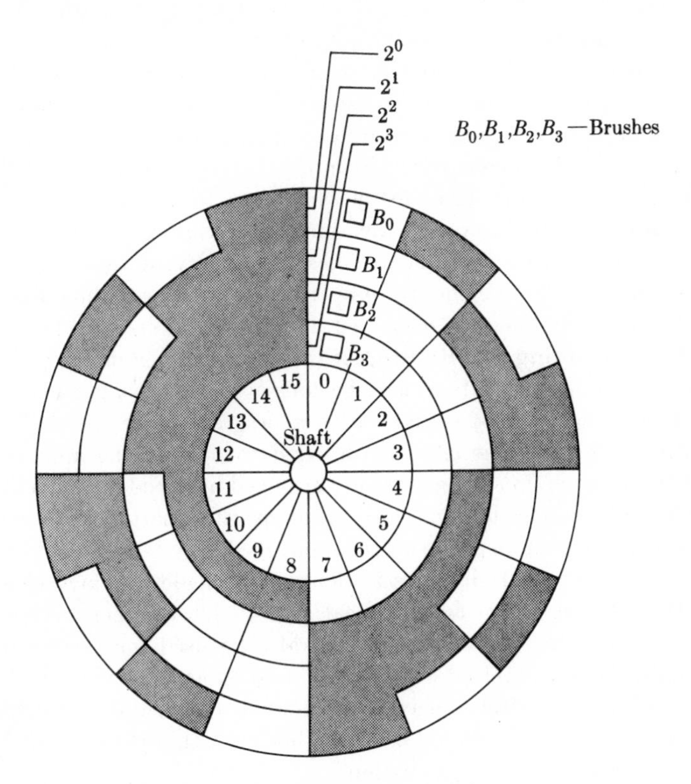

FIGURE 26. Diagram of a coding disk.

Analog Signals, e.g., frequency. Some transducers have outputs in the form of a frequency corresponding to the measured variable. Again, signals from radar or sonar are of pulse-time or frequency-modulated types.

Digital Signals. Signals in the form of a binary code (computer code) of sufficient level for the computer to handle.

Digital Signals. Signals in a code other than the binary, e.g., Gray, Binary Decimal, etc., as in shaft position encoders.

A.5 Organization of the Conversion Equipment Connecting Plant to Computer. A block diagram of the conversion equipment connecting the plant to the computer is shown in Fig. 27. The plant variables may be measured by either analog or digital transducers. Since the computer accepts the signals one at a time, suitable sampling and scanning operations must be carried out to route the information to it. This is done by the input selectors. Before analog-digital conversion can take place, the low-level analog signals must be amplified, this being done by the analog signal processor. Filtering of the low-level signals is also necessary.

A.6 Sampling and Filtering. Filtering is necessary for two reasons. The transducer may be located at a considerable distance from the computer and its signal may be seriously contaminated by noise in transmission. Also, as we shall explain later, since the analog signal is sampled it may be necessary to filter it in some way. It is known that a band-limited message can be transmitted by sampling at a rate two or more times the maximum message frequency f_m. The message can be completely recovered by passing the sampled message through an ideal low-pass filter with a cutoff frequency f_m. In practical systems, however, the signal spectrum is not band-limited and noise is necessarily introduced. These facts prevent the signal from being recovered with zero error. By proper choice of presampling and smoothing filters, the signal may be recovered with negligible error [23].

A.7 Scanning and Routing of Information. Referring to Fig. 27, the various scanning operations may be done according to a fixed clock signal, or a given input may be selected with a program order specifying the input address. This address must be decoded to operate the appropriate input selection switch. Decoding is usually achieved by decoding matrix techniques.

The address decoder sends a signal to operate a particular selection switch, of which the form depends on the input itself.

Where the input is digital, selection may be made with logic elements, such as the AND gate. For analog signals, the switch is either a relay or a semiconductor switch. A relay will generally be used for extremely low-level signals. (Mercury-wetted contacts are used to increase the life of the relay.) Semiconductor switches may be used when the analog signal level is high (100 mv or more). It should be noted, however, that the switching properties of these need careful examination.

A.8 Amplification and Signal Conditioning. Low-level amplifiers are necessary to bring the signals to a sufficiently high level for reasonably

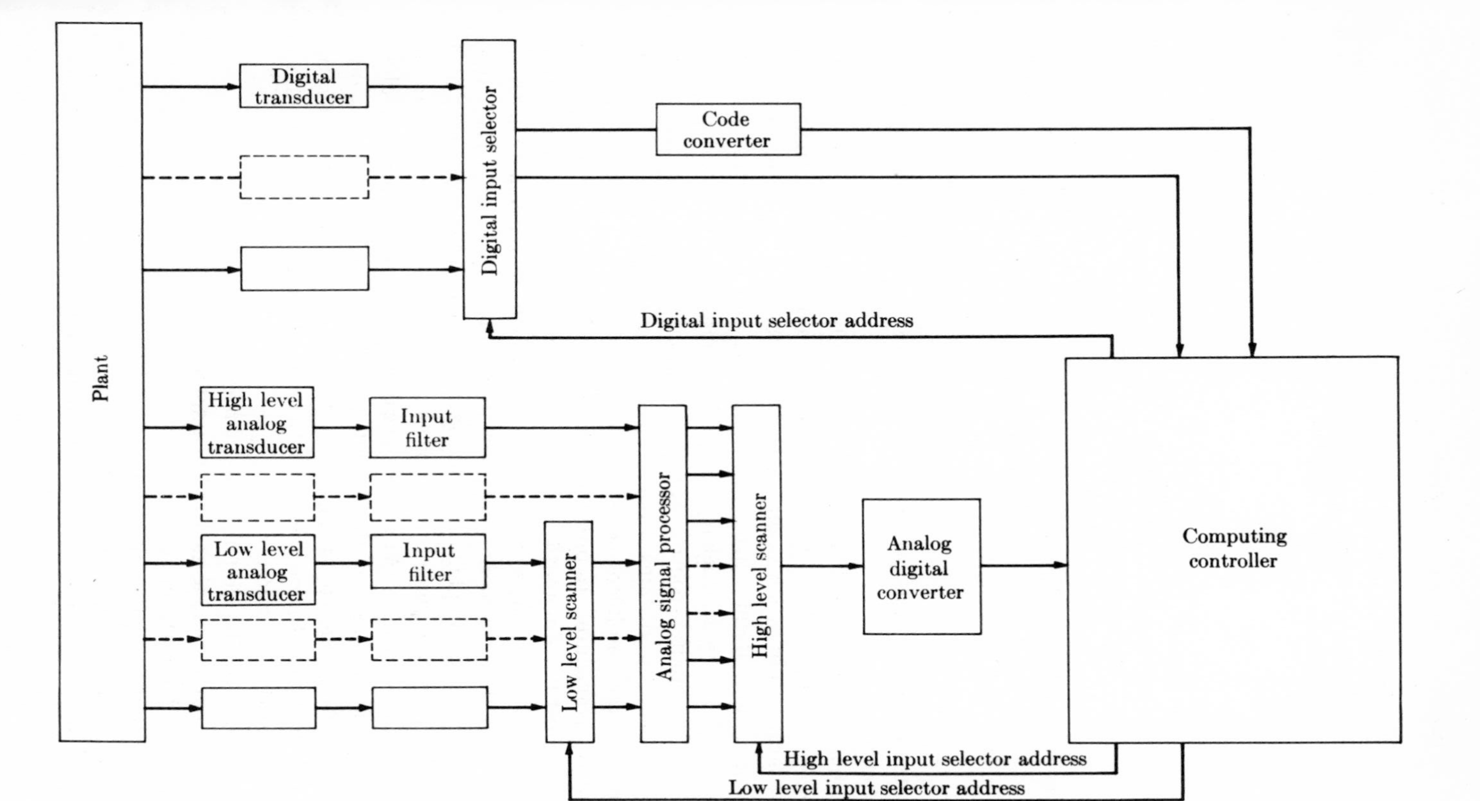

FIGURE 27. Block diagram of the conversion equipment connecting plant to computing controller.

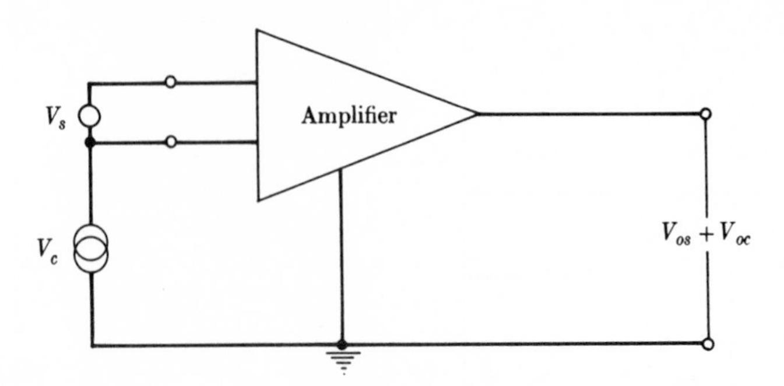

FIGURE 28. Differential and common mode input signals for a differential amplifier.

accurate digitizing in the analog-digital converter. Amplifications up to 1000 are typical.

Attenuation and gain changing are also usually necessary to allow proper scaling of the input channels to accept a wide range of input signal levels.

Low-level amplification is one of the most complex problems of on-line instrumentation. Besides drift, gain, stability, and nonlinearity, the most serious problem the designer has to face is "common-mode rejection."

In most computer control applications, amplification and conversion equipment is some distance from the measuring transducer so the ground potential at the amplifier and conversion equipment will be different from that at the transducer. In order to eliminate ground loops, the input of the amplifier must be "differential." In Fig. 28 V_s is the transducer voltage to be amplified and V_c is the voltage to ground which is common to both the terminals. V_c is termed the "common-mode voltage." Ideally, the output voltage V_0 of the amplifier should be insensitive to the common-mode voltage V_c. However, since the two parts of the differential amplifier are not exactly identical with respect to voltage gain and input resistance, a resultant error signal is produced at the output due to V_c. A figure of merit, often associated with a differential amplifier, is the "common-mode rejection ratio" K_{cm}. It is defined as the ratio between the differential gain and the common-mode gain of the amplifier.

If G_D = differential gain of the amplifier;
G_{cm} = common-mode gain of the amplifier;
V_s = differential input signal;
V_c = common-mode input signal;
V_{os} = output signal due to differential input;
V_{oc} = output signal due to common-mode input;

then,

$$K_{cm} = \frac{G_D}{G_{cm}} = \frac{V_{os}/V_s}{V_{oc}/V_c} \tag{A.1}$$

The higher K_{cm}, the better the amplifier, so far as common-mode signals are concerned. Contemporary designs of low-level differential amplifiers have common-mode rejection ratios of 10^6 to 10^7 at dc.

A.9 Analog-Digital Conversion. Once the signal has been amplified it must be converted into the appropriate digital form for introduction into the computer.

Analog-digital converters may be divided into two major groups according to the encoding process. In one group are those which depend upon a two-dimensional geometric pattern for quantization, while in the other are those which depend on a suitable arrangement of electronic circuitry for encoding. The former group may be referred to as geometric converters and the latter as electronic converters.

Comprehensive reviews of analog-digital converters already exist [3, 24]. In this section we shall describe the basic principles underlying their operation and indicate some trends in their development.

Geometric Converters. The operation of geometric converters is identical to that of coding wheels. Here we add a few words regarding the accuracies obtainable with such converters and indicate a further refinement of the basic device.

It is evident that as the resolution of geometric converters increases the area available for one of the least significant digits decreases, for a given over-all pattern size, so the precision engineering problems are increased. Consequently, one factor limiting the resolution of geometric converters is mechanical engineering practice [11]. Optical methods and etched circuit techniques are now being widely used to alleviate this problem, digit packings of 1000 per inch of track being achieved in present-day converters. In order to overcome the difficulty of producing a large number of small areas on one disk, it is possible to connect two disks through suitable reduction gearing. Work on problems associated with backlash and eccentricity has resulted in the adoption of nonlinear couplings, such as single-toothed gears, between the disks.

At present, geometric shaft position encoders are capable of resolutions up to 1 part in 2^{19}, by using two geared shafts. Patterns on one disk may be made to a resolution of 1 part in 2^{16}. Sampling rates of about 500 per second are possible with these encoders.

The fastest type of converter in this class accepts a voltage input, which becomes the displacement of the electron beam in a cathode-ray tube. A rectangular binary-coded mask is placed on the face of the tube so that a train of light is generated when the beam is deflected at right angles to the signal deflection. Alternatively, the pattern may be permanently photographed on the target of the tube to generate an electron pulse train. Sweep rates of a few million per second are possible, allowing independent conversions to be made at this rate with a suitably fast read-out mechanism. To achieve 10-digit accuracy, however, severe limitations are placed on the geometry of the tube and on the linearity of the wide-band input amplifiers. For a light-obstructing mask on the face of the tube, conversion speed is limited by the response time of the photocells to about 20,000 conversions per second.

In most of these devices, the digital code may be read from the pattern either serially or in parallel, depending on specific requirements. Codes available include the normal binary code, binary-coded decimal, and various forms of cyclic progressive, e.g., Gray, code. A cyclic progressive code is generally considered to be essential in geometric converters. Referring to the normal binary code pattern, (Fig. A26), it can be seen that very small positional differences between the read-out elements can cause large errors in the recorded value when the transition line between numbers happens to be under the read-out position. For the transition from 1000 to 0111, misalignment of the read-out device can give numbers bearing no relation to the true position of the variable. This is the worst case, but there can be ambiguity in the least significant two digits at every second transition. Transitions between adjacent numbers in the Gray code, however, involve a change in only one digit place and therefore misalignments can cause an uncertainty of only one level of quantization.

All-Electronic Converters. The basic principles underlying the design of electronic converters are:

(1) time-encoding;
(2) encoding by comparison;
(3) feedback encoding.

Time-Base Encoder. A block diagram of a time-base encoder is shown in Fig. 29a [22]. The conversion of the voltage signal to a time signal makes use of a saw-tooth voltage which sweeps upward at each conversion interval to an amplitude higher than that of the analog voltage input. From Fig. 29b it can be seen that the times t_1, t_2, t_3 necessary for the saw-tooth voltage to change from a fixed reference voltage to the analog voltage signal to be coded is directly proportional to the analog voltage at that instant. The time intervals t_1, t_2, t_3 are measured by a counting circuit. At the instant corresponding to point A in Fig. 29, the gate is opened to allow a set of pulses to flow into the binary counter. At the instant corresponding to point B, the gate is closed. Thus the counter starts at point A and stops at point B, where the sweep voltage is equal to the analog voltage being coded. The number of pulses from the clock pulse generator passing through the gate during the time interval is the number counted on the binary counter. Some time after that, e.g., at the point C, a pulse is generated to reset the counter to zero. Shortly thereafter, at the instant corresponding to the point A, the gate is opened again and the conversion cycle repeats.

The resolution of such a conversion device depends on the number of clock pulses contained in the full sweep interval. This number is inversely proportional to the size of the quantizing steps of the signal sample. If the frequency of the clock-pulse generator is so chosen that 128 pulses are generated during the full sweep interval, the resolution would be 1 part in 128. Since the maximum number of pulses in the full sweep interval is fixed, the number of pulses passing through the gate indicates not only the amplitude of the analog voltage being encoded, but also the exact time at which it is being measured. Since the signal may

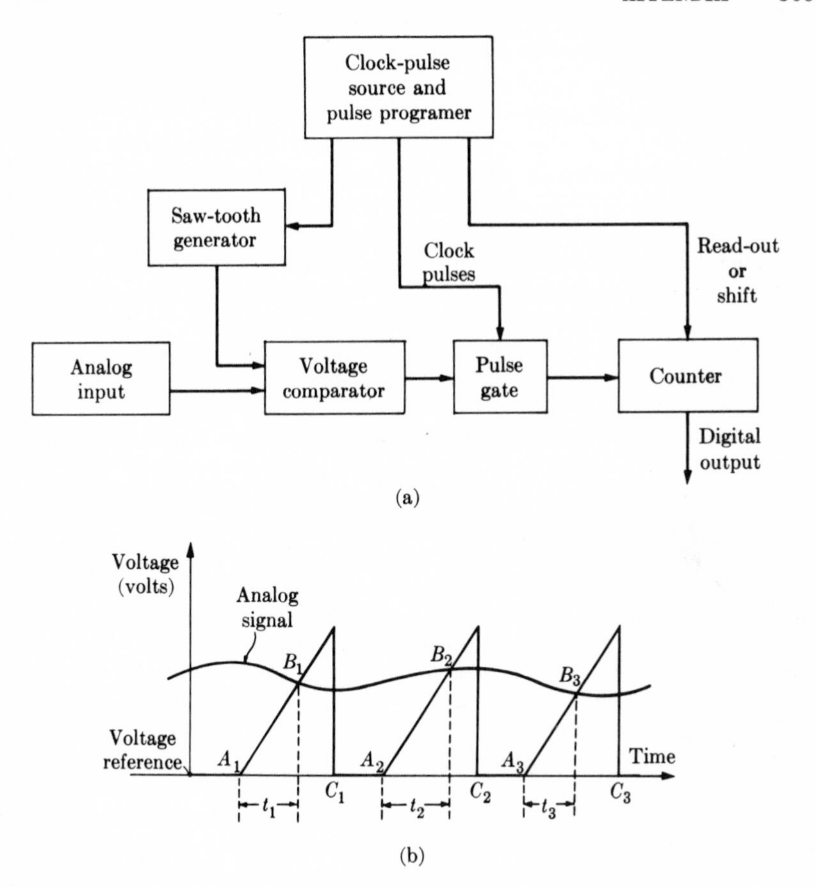

FIGURE 29. (a) Block diagram of time-base encoder. (b) Conversion of analog voltage into time duration.

fluctuate during a sweep interval, a temporary storage or clamping device is generally employed in order to sample the signal at precise intervals and to hold the voltage constant during the sweep period. By this means, the readings can be obtained at constant intervals. The accuracy of the time-base encoder is determined by the linearity of the sweep-signal waveform and the accuracy of the comparison circuit. The conversion time depends on the counting speed of the counter and the maximum number N to be coded. If the time required for reading and clearing the counter is t_r, the conversion time t_c is given by

$$t_c = \frac{N}{v_c} + t_r \tag{A.2}$$

where v_c = counting speed.

The highest operating speed of a practical counter is about 5 mc/sec; it usually takes a minimum of 1 μsec to read and reset the counter. Thus the lowest conversion time which can be attained is

$$t_c = \frac{N + 5}{5} \mu \text{ sec} \tag{A.3}$$

For instance, if the maximum number to be encoded is of two decimal digits, then 7 bits are required in the binary code and the lowest conversion time would be 26.6 μsec. If the maximum number to be coded is of three decimal digits, 10 bits are required in binary notation and the conversion time would not be less than 205.8 μsec. The time-base encoder offers the advantage of simplicity of circuitry, ease of construction, and extremely simple logic circuits. The accuracy depends primarily on the drift of the comparator and the slope and linearity of the sweep generator. Accuracies of the order of 0.1% have been attained with such a converter.

Encoding by Comparison. A block diagram of a typical encoder using the principle of comparison is shown in Fig. 30 [24].

The operation of this type of converter is based on comparing the input voltage with a locally generated voltage which is varied by a control circuit until the two voltages agree. The state of the local voltage generator at the time of agreement is read out in digital form and thus furnishes the desired number. One method of operation is as follows. The most significant source S_n is turned on first by the control circuit and the voltage to be converted compared with S_n in the comparator. If the input voltage is greater than S_n, S_n is left on; if less, S_n is turned off. The control circuit then switches on the next most significant source S_{n-1}. Again, if the input signal is greater than S_{n-1}, it is left on and if less, S_{n-1} is switched off and so on. If a source is left on, a "1" is read out and if it is switched off, a "0" is read out.

As an example, let us consider a 4-digit binary coder capable of handling inputs ranging from 0 to 15 v. The most significant source S_3 is $2^3 = 8$ v. The next is 4 v, the following is 2v, and the least significant source, 1 v. For an input of 9 v, agreement is reached when the most and least significant sources are on, causing an output read-out of 1001.

Encoders of the comparison type are limited in accuracy by the accuracy of the trial voltage and the voltage comparison circuit. When the trial voltages are

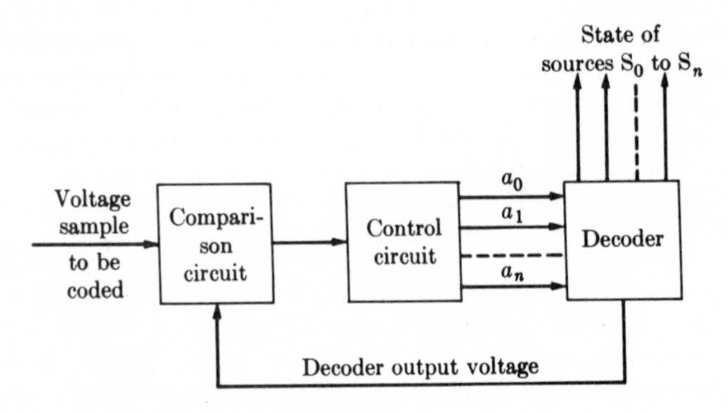

FIGURE 30. Block diagram of comparison type coder.

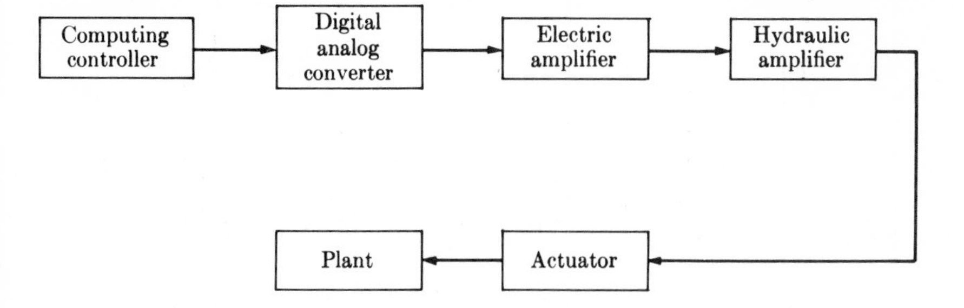

FIGURE 31. Typical link connecting computing controller back to the plant.

obtained from voltage dividers, the conversion accuracy also depends upon the stability and accuracy of the reference voltage and the resistors of the voltage dividers. The conversion speed of this type is usually faster than that of time-base encoding.

Recent Developments in Analog-Digital Conversion. Recent developments in analog-digital conversion appear to be following two trends:

(1) development of very high speed converters;
(2) low-level converters.

In the field of high-speed converters, conversion times of 25 μsec and sampling rates of 5×10^6 samples per second have recently been achieved [8]. Direct conversion of low-level analog signals (0—10 mv) is also being attempted. This eliminates the complicated problem of dc amplification. A magnetic core device which converts the low-level signals to a corresponding time duration has recently been developed [27].

Connection between Computer Output and Process. A typical link connecting the computing controller back to the plant is shown in Fig. 31. We shall examine the various elements of the link.

A.10 Digital-Analog Conversion.

If the computing controller is a digital computer, the signals from it have to be converted into a suitable analog form for the actuator. This conversion is necessary since most of the actuating devices are analog.

Digital-analog converters may be broadly divided into two types:

(1) those which convert the binary number into an equivalent electrical signal;
(2) those which convert the binary number into an equivalent physical motion.

Converters of Type (1). The method consists of using the numerical representation to switch electrical sources into a network in accordance with the number to be decoded. The principles involved in the design of the various possible network configurations are more or less the same. We shall describe one scheme to illustrate these principles. A simplified diagram of a decoder of this type is shown in Fig. 32 [24]. When the jth digit is One, switch S_j is closed and the current

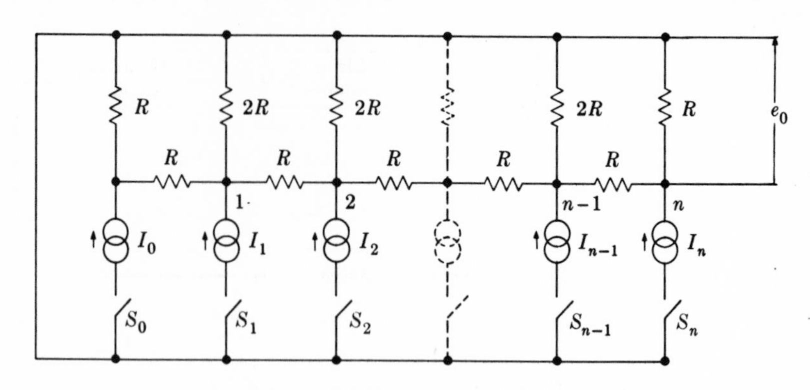

FIGURE 32. Voltage decoder with ladder network.

source I_j contributes to the output voltage e_0. When the jth digit is Zero, switch S_j is open and I_j does not contribute to the output. All current sources I_0 to I_n are of equal magnitude I and, by definition, a current source has infinite impedance. It follows then that the presence of absence of all the other sources does not affect the loading of I_j when S_j is closed; the only loading on I_j is that represented by the resistive network consisting of R and $2R$. The configuration is so arranged that the load on every interior stage ($j = 1$ to $j = n - 1$) is $2R$ looking to the left of node j, $2R$ looking to the right of node j, and $2R$ looking up. The load on every interior stage is, therefore

$$\frac{1}{R_L} = \frac{1}{2R} + \frac{1}{2R} + \frac{1}{2R} = \frac{3}{2R} \tag{A.4}$$

or

$$R_L = \frac{2R}{3}. \tag{A.5}$$

It may be shown that each source j sets up between its node j and ground a voltage which is given by $E = \dfrac{2R}{3} I$

Further,
$$e_0 = \frac{E_0}{2^n} + \frac{E_1}{2^{n-1}} + \cdots + \frac{E_n}{2^0}. \tag{A.6}$$

But,
$$E_j = \frac{2R}{3} I_j \text{ where } I_j = 0 \text{ or } I.$$

If the number to be decoded is given by

$$p = a_n 2^n + a_{n-1} 2^{n-1} + \cdots + a_0 2^0 \tag{A.7}$$

we may write:

$$e_0 = \frac{2}{3} RI \left(\frac{a_0}{2^n} + \frac{a_1}{2^{n-1}} + \cdots + \frac{a_n}{2^0} \right)$$

$$= \frac{2}{3} RI \frac{1}{2^n} p. \tag{A.8}$$

Therefore the output voltage is a linear function of the number to be decoded.

Incremental Position Decoder. In an incremental position decoder the number is first converted into a train of pulses. These pulses may then be used to drive a quantized electromechanical transducer. The number of pulses in the train is a measure of the digital number, and each pulse represents one position increment.

An incremental feedback decoder is shown in Fig. 33.

A.11 Amplification. The command signal generated in a computing controller, after being converted into the correct form in the digital-analog converter, may require several stages of amplification before it can actuate the final mechanism.

On-off control is the simplest form of amplification. A low-power signal can energize a relay capable of handling a much higher power level, and relays may be cascaded to achieve high gains. Electronic amplifiers, both tube type and transistor type, may be used to raise the computer output signal to a level capable of operating relays, solenoids, electric motors, etc.

Another important element for electronic amplification is the thyratron and its modern form, the semiconductor-controlled rectifier.

When reliability and the ability to withstand shock and vibration are essential, magnetic amplifiers are often preferred to electron tube amplifiers.

Electric motors are also used. They not only amplify, but at the same time convert the signal into a mechanical form.

Hydraulic amplifier systems are efficient, extremely compact, fast, and capable of high torque output.

A.12 Actuation. The whole range of final plant variables—temperature, pressure, liquid level, flow-rate, machined shape, humidity, etc.—can be controlled by liquid flow, linear or angular displacement, or a rate of displacement. As flow is regulated by the motion of a valve or pump, so the final controlled output is a movement or a rate of movement of an actuating

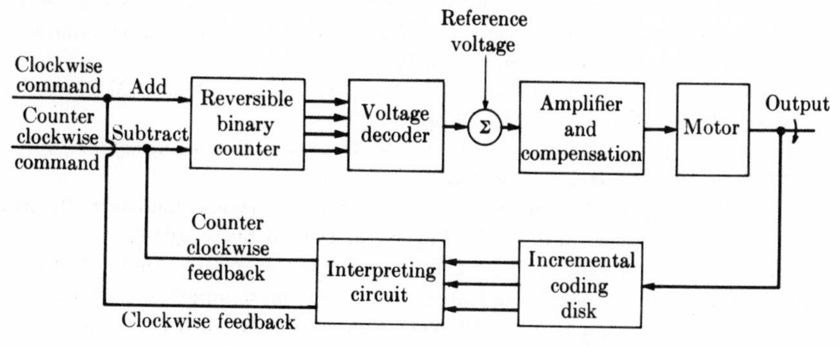

FIGURE 33. Block diagram of incremental feedback decoder servo.

element. The only obvious exception occurs when electric power is modulated and even here the final control is often by means of a displacement.

Liquid or gas flow may be used to control many physical and chemical processes. For liquids under pressure valve motion can act as the passive actuating element. Pumps can be used to actively control the flow. Electric motors are most widely used to control displacement and speed.

Where linear displacement involves large forces and high performance requirements, hydraulic or pneumatic devices are often preferred as actuators because of their direct linear motion output and their compactness and high response characteristics.

In some processes, actuation is carried out by the controlled flow of electric power rather than by mechanical motion or fluid flow.

Although actuators today are mostly analog devices, more and more attention is being paid to direct digital actuation. Thus the signal from the digital computer may be used to actuate the process without undergoing digital-analog conversion, although some amplification may be necessary. One such device exists commercially—the power stepping motor [25]. These motors respond to any source of pulses where the frequency of the pulses is proportional to the desired motor speed and the number of pulses is proportional to the desired angular displacement. Motors with speeds up to 100,000 steps/min and torque outputs to 3000 in.-lb have been built. Another type of digital actuator is a cylinder with a piston whose stroke varies as 2^n.

BIBLIOGRAPHY

1. Adriaenssens, G. A., *Applications Industrielles des Calculateurs Numeriques*, IBM-Belgium, 1962, 50 pp.
2. Bellman, R., *Adaptive Control Processes: a Guided Tour*. Princeton, 1961. 256 pp.
3. Bower, G. C., "Analog to digital converters," Control Eng. (April, 1959).
4. Carpentier, J., "Contribution à l'Etude du Dispatching Economique," Electricité de France (February 15, 1952), 78 pp.
5. Carter, L. V. P., "Optimization Techniques," TN 18.048. IBM Nordiska Laboratorier (June 12, 1961), 28 pp.
6. Chatterjee, H. K., "Multivariable Process Control," *Proceedings of the IFAC. Moscow, 1960*, Butterworths, 1961.
7. Coales, J. F., and Noton, A. R. M., "An on-off servomechanism with predicted change-over," Proc. IEE Paper No. 1895 M (July, 1956).
8. Crocker, C., and Prager, M., "A Technique for Converting Analog Voltages to Digital Codes at Sampling Rates above 5 Million Samples per Second with Accuracies of Seven Bits," IRE Natl. Convention Record, Globecom (May, 1961).

9. Debroux, A., *et al.*, "Code Apache destiné a la Programmation d'un Problème Analogique au moyen d'un Calculateur Digital," Rapport CETIS 30, Euratom (September, 1961).
10. Draper, C. S., and Li, Y. T., "Principles of Optimalizing Control Systems and an Application to the Internal Combustion Engine," ASME Publication (1951).
11. Herring, G. J., *Analogue-to-Digital Conversion Techniques: Progress in Automation*, Butterworths, 1960.
12. Holzbock, W. G., *Instruments for Measurement and Control*, Reinhold, 1955.
13. Kalman, R. E., and Koepcke, R. W., "Optimal Synthesis of Linear Sampling Control Systems Using Generalized Performance Indexes," ASME Paper No. 58-IRD-6, 7 pp.
14. Karlin, S., *Mathematical Methods and Theory in Games, Programming, and Economics*, Vol. 1, Addison-Wesley, 1959.
15. Kaufmann, A., *Méthodes et Modèles de la Recherche Opérationnelle*, Dunod, 1962, 534 pp.
16. Kirchmayer, L. K., "Optimalizing Computer Control in the Electric Utility Industry," *Proceedings of the IFAC, Moscow, 1960*, Butterworths, 1961.
17. Korn, G. A., "The impact of hybrid analog digital techniques on the analog computer art." Proc. Inst. Radio Engrs. 1077–1087 (May, 1962).
18. Nishida, F., "Synthesis of Multivariable Control Systems by Means of Sampled Data Compensations," *Proceedings of the IFAC, Moscow, 1960*, Butterworths, 1961.
19. Orchard-Hays, W., "The evolution of programming systems." Proc. Inst. Radio Engrs. 283–295 (January, 1961).
20. Ragazzini, J. R., and Franklin, F. G., *Sampled Data Control Systems*, McGraw-Hill, 1958.
21. Rozonoer, L. I., "The maximum principle of L. S. Pontriagin in optimal system theory, I, II, III," Automation and Remote Control Nos. 10, 11, and 12 (1959).
22. Slaughter, D. W., "An analog-to-digital converter with an improved linear sweep generator," IRE Natl. Convention Record Part 7, 7–12 (1953).
23. Spilker, J. J., "Theoretical bounds on the performance of sampled-data communication systems," IRE Trans. on Circuit Theory (1960).
24. Susskind, A. K., *Notes on Analog/Digital Conversion Techniques*, Technology and Wiley.
25. Thomas, A., and Fleischauer, F., "The power stepping motor—a new digital actuator," Control Eng. 74–81 (October, 1957).
26. Truxal, J. G., *Automatic Feedback Control System Synthesis*, McGraw-Hill. 1955, 675 pp.
27. van Praag, V. A., Stanks, William, and van Minders, David, "Magnetic core converts voltage to pulse duration," Control Eng. (1961).
28. Weinstock, R., *Calculus of Variations*, McGraw-Hill, 1952.

CHAPTER X

Systems Engineering: its Principles, Practices, and Prospects

ROY C. AMARA

CONTENTS

1. Introduction

Control systems are becoming increasingly larger and complex. Missile, process control, and adaptive systems may be cited as examples. In addition, it is not uncommon to find that a control system represents but a single unit in a much larger system incorporating digital computer and communication elements. An air defense, an air traffic control, or a passenger space reservation system are representative examples. Such systems, composed of large numbers of closely interacting and diverse components, are designated *information* systems.

The extension of engineering and scientific methods for the planning and design of large systems to achieve proper balance, performance, and economy is increasingly being referred to as systems engineering [3–5].† It is not an entirely new discipline—telephone systems have been designed by the application of some of its principles for many years—but the activities which it encompasses and the techniques that are utilized have undergone rapid development in recent years. In particular is this true for the planning and design of large information systems which have become so complex that their development and understanding are impractical without the use of adequate theory. In the following sections such information systems will be used as convenient vehicles for the development and presentation of the principal ideas.

The existence of large systems and their continued growth stems from the increasing complexity of business, industrial, and military operations. When large numbers of components—computers, input-output devices, communication lines, and control devices—are connected to form systems, problems of interaction and proper balance arise which subordinate the design problems of the individual components. Not only must the components be mutually compatible, but the assemblage must also be compatible with the system environment.

Since the systems engineer is concerned with the planning and design of large aggregates of components, his primary interest centers upon the properties of a system which stem from its organization and structure as well as from its purely physical properties. These are essentially problems of organized complexity, and it is here that the essence of the difference between systems engineering and other engineering disciplines comes to focus [14]. In *common* with other engineering activities, systems engineering is primarily concerned with *design* rather than *analysis*. In *contrast* with other engineering disciplines, the basic technical subject for systems engineering is mathematics rather than physics, particularly those branches of mathematics applicable to a description of relationships between many interacting elements such as linear graph theory, topology, matrix algebra, and linear programing.

† Numbers in brackets refer to the bibliography at the end of this chapter.

The similarities and differences of systems engineering and operations research should also be noted. Both systems engineering and operations research employ tools stemming from the use of the scientific method, and pursue multidisciplinary approaches in their studies. The essence of the difference is that operations research is concerned with the analysis of systems in being, primarily from the standpoint of procedural changes; in contrast, systems engineering is concerned with the design of equipment for systems yet to be. At various stages of the design process, the activities of each may appear identical. For example, equipment changes cannot be considered independently of procedural changes; also, in evaluating technical performance, in establishing merit criteria, and in constructing models, the same tools may be employed.

2. Characteristics of Large-Scale Information Systems

Large-scale information systems are the objects of prime interest, and, therefore, it is important to define their principal characteristics as precisely as possible [5]. Of course the best way to do this is to provide examples; this is done subsequently. An appreciation of the basic characteristics will serve to determine the approaches and tools that are to be most useful in planning and design.

First, the systems of interest are large and complex—large in the number of inputs and outputs, in the number of functions to be performed and, of course, in cost. Large is a relative term and should perhaps be clarified somewhat in the context of the extent of interaction that exists among system elements. Largeness is accompanied by or implies complexity, in particular when a change in one variable produces a change in many other variables. The control engineer is familiar with strongly interacting or coupled multivariable systems. He also has considerable experience with simple and multiple loop feedback systems in which the emphasis is on the interactions and feedback of information for processing and control. In either case, signal processing might be used as a term common to both.

A second distinguishing feature of a large-scale information system is the nature of the primary inputs. These are almost always statistical and time-distributed in the manner of telephone calls, demands for passenger space, or arrival of signals on a radar screen. This means that the loading of a system may be analyzed only in statistical terms and that measures of performance will involve the use of probability distributions. In addition, of course, special attention must usually be given to alternative methods for handling situations in which peak loads may occur.

A third common feature of considerable importance is that the systems under consideration are man-machine. Although the emphasis is on equipment systems, the final performance will always be dependent on the interaction of man and machines operating together. Of particular interest will be the determination of the proper boundaries separating machine from human functions. In no case will it be expected that the division of functions will be such that human beings perform all operations or that no human beings are involved at all.

Finally, in the most general case, the systems under consideration are subject to the influence of a rational agent seeking to reduce the effectiveness of the system. Normally, control, communication, and computer systems, that is, information systems, are influenced by natural disturbances such as noise, random failure, atmospheric effects, and so on. Here, in addition, the systems under consideration, in particular for military applications, may be subjected to jamming of communication links or partial destruction of any of its elements. As will be demonstrated subsequently, such effects introduce a new class of problem into the design process.

Many examples of large-scale systems (information and otherwise) may be cited to illustrate some of the properties above. A multivariable control system for a steel rolling mill may be considered large-scale in this context even though the total number of inputs is not excessively large. This is because the inputs are *closely* interacting (thickness, tension between stands, rolling speed, etc.), and each of these has superimposed significant disturbances and fluctuations. A military message-switched global communications network represents perhaps an even more graphic illustration of a large-scale system, since the competitive aspects, i.e., noise, jamming, destruction, become extremely important. In this case, the large number of possible message inputs, describable only in statistical terms and operating in an environment where the interface between man and machine poses critical problems, makes this an even more appropriate illustration. Finally, systems in which the emphasis is strictly on the data processing functions, may be drawn from many business, accounting, inventory control, or information retrieval applications.

However, the most interesting and significant large-scale systems of the future will be composed of aggregates of control, communication, and computing elements. An air traffic control system is an outstanding example of this rapidly emerging class of information systems. The inputs here may be considered aircraft position and velocity vectors as functions of time, together with descriptions of the environment in which the aircrafts are operating. Communication, radar, and navigation networks as well as systems for data collection are superimposed. The objective, of course, is the safe, efficient, and flexible control of each aircraft from origin to destination.

Other composite examples may be drawn from missile systems, military command and control systems, passenger space reservation systems, nuclear blast detection networks, and oceanographic data sensing networks. Even casual reflection will show that such systems incorporate all of the essential features by which large-scale systems may be characterized.

3. Elements of Design Process and Design Methodology

It would be fortunate indeed if the process and methodology of systems engineering could be reduced to a series of explicit, well-defined steps. This is not possible, and perhaps may never be, since the most useful approaches for attacking the major system problems are necessarily indirect and iterative. The number of variables involved is too large, the interactions between them too complex, and the number of alternatives too varied to permit direct synthesis by strictly analytical methods. Instead, the methods to be described will require the judicious application of one or more different techniques at each step. Furthermore, the procedure will be cyclic in the sense that gradual refinement is introduced as initial hypotheses and approximations are compared with the results of evaluations.

In spite of the difficulty of presenting the steps of the systems engineering process in a completely ordered fashion, it is possible to outline the main steps in such a way that the interlocking feedback loops between the major steps are made evident. To do this, the following discussion is divided into three principal parts: determination of requirements, system design, and system evaluation (Fig. 1). As has been previously emphasized, these steps are combined to produce the end result by successive approximations. The first "requirement—design—evaluation" cycle is followed by more sharply defined requirements which in turn produce variations of the design. As this iteration continues, an increasingly detailed design emerges.

3.1 Requirements. The first, and often most neglected, step in the systems engineering process is the translation of the user's goals into system requirements that can be stated in technical terms. In fact, this is the process

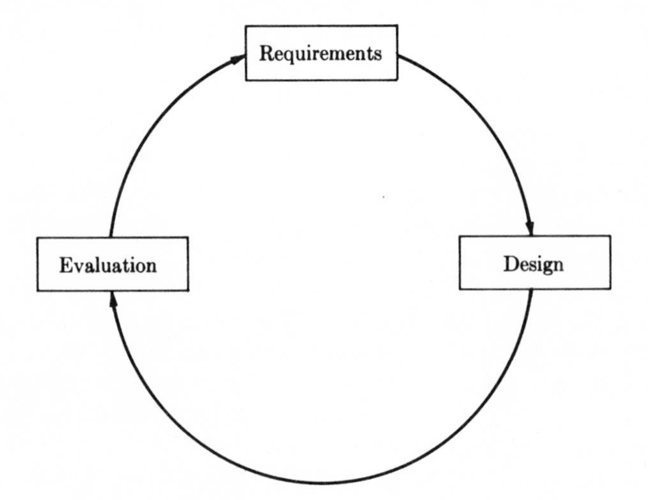

FIGURE 1. Elements of the systems engineering process.

by which the relationships of the system to the external world are defined. A precise description of the inputs and the desired outputs provides one simple basis for doing this.

There are at least two distinct aspects here. First, the user has certain goals: to control passenger space on airplanes, to handle messages in a communications network; to organize, store, and retrieve information for reference purposes; and so on. Secondly, these goals must be achieved within an environment over which the user (and the system engineer) may not be able or willing to exercise control. Both of these aspects must be carefully included in a statement of system requirements.

In stating the user's objectives in technical terms, a variety of factors must be considered. For example, the nature (analog, digital, deterministic, random, etc.) of the input and output signals must be specified; the volume and expected variation of items, messages, planes, checks, etc., must be determined; and the rates at which inputs and outputs are to be processed must be specified. But of greatest importance is the realistic determination of the essential performance parameters of the system. Among the most important of these are accuracy, response or delay time, and reliability. If the inputs are physical items such as checks, sales slips, etc., both the tolerable error rate and reject rate must also be specified since trade-offs between the two are often possible.

For most systems, response or delay time represents one of the most critical parameters since it is extremely cost-sensitive over its most interesting range. Because of the statistical nature of the input and processing times, such delays must necessarily be stated as distribution functions if they are to be meaningful. Finally, a system parameter that has assumed preponderant importance because of the enormous number of components in present and proposed systems is reliability. Such indices as mean time between failures and mean time to repair must be carefully defined if vague notions of the user about "24 hour operation," "failure-proof," etc., are to be made realistic.

In dealing with the environment, statistical considerations nearly always enter into the description. For example, all information systems are coupled to human users at the input and output. The number of people attempting to make phone calls, to make plane reservations, or to deposit checks, within a given time period can usually be described mathematically by a Poisson distribution. Often more elaborate mathematical models are necessary in defining external boundary conditions. For example, in military systems, the environment includes the belligerent action of an enemy. In a communications network, the probability of failure (not necessarily independent) of links and nodes must be included. Also, any security or priority restrictions must be known and specified.

In short, the generation of requirements provides the framework upon which the remainder of the system engineering process is based. To assure balance, economy, and proper performance in the resulting system, each requirement must be considered carefully, and ultimately its cost sensitivity must be determined by iteration through several design and evaluation cycles. The tools for requirement generation are simple, involving primarily the application of statistical techniques to operations analysis. In addition, the models for analysis often tend to be verbal rather than strictly mathematical.

3.2 Design. The design step itself is, of course, the central and key step in the system engineering process. Starting from a knowledge of requirements, the objective is to find that configuration of functional elements that, translated into physical terms, meets the requirements as economically and efficiently as possible. To do this, a number of promising alternative solutions must be considered. In most cases, it is necessary to develop the design of several competing systems to the point where cross comparisons between them can be made.

Two distinct phases can be identified in the design process. The first is designated configurative design; the second is designated functional design.

Perhaps the most basic and pervasive decisions are made at the stage in which the configuration of the system is determined. This is because the subsequent design effort is restricted in large part by the boundary conditions imposed by the over-all system structure. As such, this phase offers one of the outstanding opportunities for creative engineering.

Many factors enter into the choice of the proper configuration. The identification of the principal functions, the determination of their proper sequence, and the relative merits of centralization versus decentralization are but a few. In addition, the manner in which the system is to be sectionalized is also of considerable importance. It has previously been pointed out that one of the basic problems in systems engineering is the resolution of the complex interactions that exist within the system. Often, due to analytical and conceptual difficulties, it is not possible to treat these interactions *in toto.* Also, from a practical standpoint, it is almost always necessary to divide large systems into smaller sub-systems, for which the detail design can proceed as independently as possible. Both of these considerations compel the systems engineer to seek to subdivide the system along boundaries of minimum interaction. Failure to do this can result in serious design difficulties because of the inability to take into account important interactions between sub-systems.

As has been previously pointed out, the configurative design of a system involves the making of some of the most basic system decisions, and yet it is perhaps the area in which there is the greatest need for the development of improved analytical tools. Basic to all of these is the ability to model the essential elements of the system by using equations, block diagrams, and flow diagrams. In such instances, principles from flow and linear graph theory appear to be useful. In others, for example the design of communication networks, linear programing formulations can effect considerable assistance in determining the structure of the network. Also, the work in partitioning of networks by Kron [7] and others [10] may ultimately prove useful in this connection. In the main, however, heavy reliance must still be placed on trial-and-error methods followed by evaluation and direct comparison of alternatives.

While the configurative system alternatives are being analyzed, a parallel system activity designated functional design must be started. The building blocks here are the principal system functions that must be performed to effect the transformation of the inputs to the required outputs. The requirements themselves, generated earlier, should not normally impose a firm need for a particular type of equipment to perform a given function. During this phase, each function must be assigned to specific equipment. The equipment may be "off-the-shelf" with respect to availability and performance characteristics. Or, the equipment may represent a composite of characteristics achievable from the present or projected state of the art. Thus, fairly detailed engineering knowledge is required by the systems engineer in those areas of the particular system application. It is not only necessary to maintain close contact with equipment suppliers, it is also necessary to be familiar with the state of development of components and subsystems. Such intimate firsthand knowledge is required for two reasons. First, the equipment is often used in a manner not originally considered or intended; secondly, the systems engineer should be in a position to influence the development of components in subsystems in consideration of the over-all user requirements and those of over-all system performance.

The functional design of a system incorporates the essence of well-known engineering practices. As such, many practical considerations of availability, flexibility, and cost must enter into the selection of equipments. However, what is particularly important is that in the design of information systems, a relatively new range of disciplines must be encompassed by the systems engineer. Many of these stem from the field of digital computer-related or communication sciences: logical design, programing, coding theory, switching theory, information theory, and control theory. These disciplines form the nucleus of the skills with which the systems engineer must be familiar in order to understand both the potentialities and limitations of the equipments that are to be used.

3.3 Evaluation. Ideally, if direct means were available for generating optimum system designs from requirements, the evaluation stage would assume a secondary role in the systems engineering process. Since this is emphatically not the case, evaluation becomes the handle by which the system engineering process is refined, improved, and made meaningful. In fact, it is from the work in evaluation of systems that the greatest opportunities exist for developing analytical tools that may be applied directly to the design process. This is because design by iteration or successive analysis—the state in which the systems engineering process finds itself today—can provide the basis for synthesis procedures.

The objective of evaluation is to ascertain the performance of the system with respect to requirements. However, this is not all. It also provides the basis by which comparisons between alternatives can be made. But most importantly, it yields information concerning the sensitivity of the output to changes in requirements or boundary conditions. It is through such a sensitivity analysis that the successive cycles of iteration evolve into a progressively improved design.

Many analytical disciplines and tools come to focus in the evaluation stage. Application of queuing theory is basic to understanding the behavior of systems involving randomly occurring demands. Such critical parameters as loading, and waiting and delay times may be determined in this manner. Reliability estimates may be made in a similar manner by application of well-known statistical concepts. If a prototype or experimental system exists, evaluation may involve actual performance measurements using principles from the design of experiments. In many instances, however, the design is stopped short of prototype production, and experimentation must be done not with the actual component configurations, but with their representations. Simulation thus emerges as a valuable tool for analysis, and indirectly for synthesis. Simulation can provide useful checks to results that can be determined only approximately analytically. However, it is not a cure-all, and it must be used judiciously since the attendant costs are high. The relationships between parameters are obtained only after considerable time and effort. Also, interpretation of results may often be difficult.

4. Illustrative Examples

Up to this point the description of the background and process of systems engineering has necessarily been general. Perhaps more than in any other engineering discipline, it is necessary to make more tangible the principles and practices of systems engineering by the use of detailed examples. It is the purpose of this section to describe two specific examples that will serve to illustrate the methods and techniques described above. The examples have been chosen to illustrate two aspects of systems engineering. In the first, the emphasis is on the wide variety of systems decisions that must be made during the design process. For this, an airlines space reservation system is used as the vehicle. In the second, the emphasis is on the application of promising analytical techniques for a systems engineering problem; here the vehicle is a global military communication network.

4.1 Airline Passenger Space Reservation System. An airline passenger space reservation system represents an almost ideal vehicle for illustrating the essential features of an information system. The design of such a system brings to focus in a unique way the fundamental systems engineering decisions that must be made. Frequent reference will be made throughout the following specific discussion to the principal steps in the systems engineering process.

The structure and operation of an automatic space reservation system embodies computing, communication, and control elements. In the following it will be assumed that the general objectives of such a system are: (1) to provide accurate, timely, and reliable information about the availability of seats in all scheduled aircraft; and (2) to maintain an accurate, up-to-the-minute inventory of all seats. The closely related problems of maintaining records of passenger names, addresses, and of performing other specialized information functions bear directly on both these problems; these functions are not, for simplicity, included in the present discussion.

A little reflection will show that the problem of collecting, maintaining, and disseminating airline availability and inventory information is a serious one. Many reservations are made or changed far from the originating point and many are changed at the last minute. Furthermore, an aircraft seat is a highly perishable commodity whose value is reduced abruptly to zero if the aircraft takes off with empty seats. On the one hand, the difference between say 70% and 80% of the seats filled may spell the difference between profit and loss for a system; on the other hand, a single oversold seat on a flight will result in customer dissatisfaction and possible consumer-induced government pressure. The number of inputs may be very large (perhaps over 1000 agent sets); they are distributed over a wide geographical area (United States or possibly worldwide); demand is statistical, much in the nature of telephone calls; and the operation of the system depends heavily on the delicate interplay of men and machines (agents, telephones, input sets, communication links, etc.). These include all of the distinguishing features of a (nonmilitary) large-scale information system.

The design of a nationwide passenger space reservation system involves making a host of major system decisions. Among these are those concerned with the achievement of the required reliability by use of element and subsystem backup, the achievement of the proper transaction response time by the assignment of adequate service capacity, and the achievement of the necessary accuracy by incorporation of error control procedures. In addition, a variety of practical problems relating to system structure must be considered. Included in these are the method of storing inventory (leg or segment), the design of the agent set, and the degree to which off-line processing operations are to be integrated with real-time on-line functions.

But perhaps the central problem of design is that of selecting the basic system configuration. In this case, the alternatives relate to the method of interconnecting the geographically distributed agent sets to the system

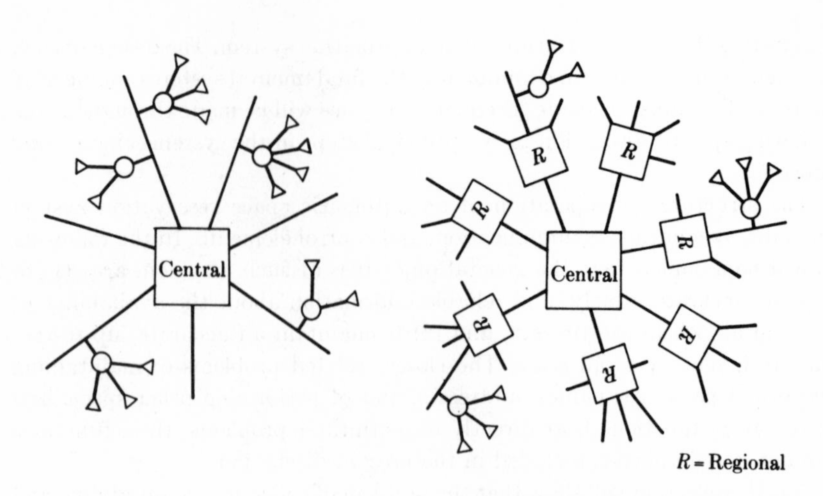

FIGURE 2. Basic configurations. (a) Centralized configuration; (b) Decentralized configuration.

inventory. In similar systems, this problem may be stated in terms of centralization versus decentralization (Fig. 2). Each alternative normally has its share of advantages and disadvantages. A centralized structure may offer economies at the risk of reduced flexibility and reliability over a decentralized pattern. The selection of the proper configuration within these extremes involves complicated considerations of reliability, cost, and response time.

The following example demonstrates how the ultimate decision for one particular airline system was determined by the adoption of a singularly clever arrangement of communication and data processing facilities.

The initial plans for a nationwide airline passenger space reservation system were made on the basis of a *regional* system. In this case the United States was divided into four to six regions within each of which was located a data processor. Each regional (or availability) processor would contain only that information that would enable the agent to determine whether he could sell up to four seats, a maximum to which he was limited by the agent set. Each regional processor would in turn be connected to a central (or inventory) processor where the exact system inventory for all flights was kept.

Using this scheme, the regional processors would be required to know only whether the number of available seats was greater than four, or lay between zero and four, or were zero. When an agent booked or canceled seats on the basis of information from the regional processor, the latter would immediately transfer the transaction data to the central processor. In return, when the number of seats available (as stored in the central processor) fell below a predetermined level, all regional processors were informed of the status change immediately.

The basic structure of the communication network was that of multiple stars (see Fig. 2b). Generally, each agent set was connected to the regional processors by teletype lines; regional processors were connected to the central processor by telephone lines.

Although the foregoing system was capable of meeting the performance requirements adequately, it possessed serious drawbacks with respect to cost and maintainability. Specifically, the presence of complex processing equipment in a number of localities created gross inefficiencies in view of the 24-hour staffing requirement. In addition, the necessity for providing duplicate facilities at all regional centers made it practically impossible to load equipment satisfactorily.

The final solution that provided the required performance and flexibility at reduced cost was based on a novel method for achieving centralization [13]. In this case, the number of processors was sharply reduced by installing the central processor in triplicate; all other processors were eliminated. This provided a high degree of reliability at satisfactory load. However, the key feature of the proposed system was provided by the extensive communication network required to interconnect agent sets and processors. Briefly, the network has the following general structure (Fig. 3).

Emanating from a central processing and switching center are two complete loops, one for westward traffic, the other for eastward traffic. Each loop is composed of a number of high-speed full-duplex point-to-point connections in tandem. Each station on the double loop has facilities for connecting agent sets directly into the high-speed lines, or through line buffers fed from low-speed teletype lines. Also, each station has facilities (four channel terminating sets complete with modulating and demodulating equipment) for interrupting the eastward and westward channels.

In principle, the method of operation is as follows. Messages arriving at a station may be classified as origin, transit, or destination. If the message is

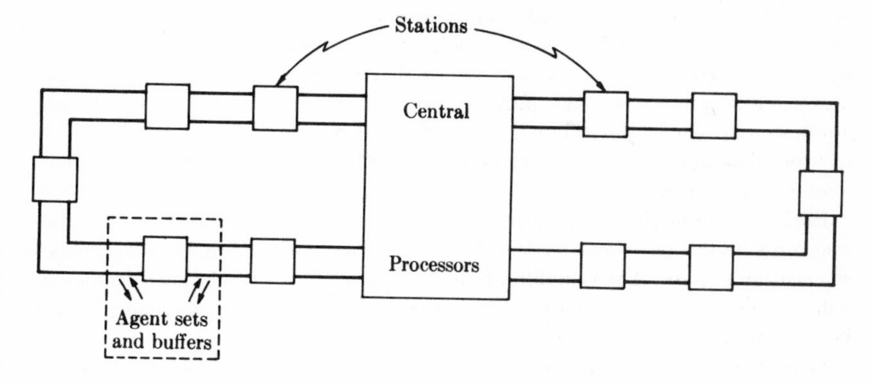

FIGURE 3. Central processor and high-speed loops.

originating at the station, the outgoing channel is seized and the message is transmitted. If the message is destined for the station or is in transit, it may be passed directly to outgoing lines or to the agent set, or stored temporarily. Transit traffic is assumed to have priority over originating traffic. Although messages may travel to the center in either direction along a loop, normally the shortest route is chosen. The alternate route is used only if this route is unavailable. As a result, good efficiency is obtained by the reasonably even distribution of traffic.

This "free-flow" party line system offers several outstanding advantages over the regional scheme employing the centralized star configuration. First and foremost, traffic computations indicate that the average delay is low even with high loading. Second, the system exhibits excellent flexibility in the manner in which various types and priorities of traffic may be handled at each station. Finally, the double loop two-way feature provides the system with the ability to withstand equipment and line malfunctions, by resorting to automatic fallback procedures that insure communication in one direction or the other, and for each loop independently.

Many other examples of the kinds of systems, problems, and considerations that enter into the planning and design of such an information system may be described in detail. However, at this point it may be more appropriate to enumerate a few of these areas briefly in order to provide further indication of the wide variety of problems encompassed in the system design process [9].

Time Versus Space Redundancy [1]. When some interference exists on a particular communications link without causing complete paralysis of communications, it is possible to decrease the error rate by the use of time redundancy. This is simply done by designing extended message formats that have a greater chance of survival against interference. The use of special error-correcting or error-detecting codes are particular cases in point.

But the use of time redundancy is only one variable over which the system designer may exercise control. Often, either because the interferences are of such nature that the use of time redundancy is inappropriate, or because its use will not permit desired results to be achieved, resort must be made to the use of space redundancy. In this case, use is made of that special property of the network which allows point-to-point communication to be achieved by virtue of using alternate message routes. Thus the properties of the network as a whole may be utilized in achieving a given over-all error rate in the face of severe interference over any particular communication link.

Both the use of time and space redundancy considerations entered into planning and design decisions for the digital data network of the passenger space reservation system. A reasonably optimum balance in the use of both techniques will prevent the use of either beyond the range within which diminishing returns become predominant.

Storage of Flight Information on Leg or Segment Basis. A central inventory may be organized by flight leg, in which case a booking will require access to several addresses to make up the flight segment which constitutes the booking. On the other hand, it is possible to have the inventory tallies organized according to flight segment. In this case, only one address is required at the time of the booking (of one segment); a subsequent program bringing other overlapping flight segments up to date is, then necessary, however. Storing flight segment data, in addition to flight leg data, is, of course, less economical in terms of the storage required, but it may possibly lead to shorter program time.

This simple example illustrates how the system designer is faced many times with a host of decisions that involve trade-offs between program complexity, storage capacity, cost, and response time. Many of these decisions cannot be made in final form until the full influence of each on the others is ascertained and evaluated.

Transaction Data Flow. The data flow from transactions themselves may be organized in various ways. Each booking or availability message has an origin that must be remembered in order to get the answer back to the proper place. The remembering of the origin can be accomplished in two ways; it can be done by holding the connection between the agent set and the computer; or, it can be done by associating with the booking message at origin an address which is utilized at the time of response to re-establish the connection between the computer and the agent set. The first method, where the connection is held, is the simplest, but it is very inefficient since it blocks the communications line not only during the periods of transmission, but also during the periods of waiting. If excessive communications capacities are available, this inefficiency may be of no particular consequence. However, with a fully addressed mode of operation, the communications lines are used more efficiently, although part of the channel capacity is now taken up by the transmission of addresses. The use of address messages adds to the complexity of the terminal equipment which must now be capable of interpreting the addresses.

This is still another example of the trade-offs which must be considered before final systems decisions are made.

A Simplified Model of a Booking and Cancellation Pattern. Shown in Fig. 4 is a diagrammatic representation of an extremely simplified booking/cancellation pattern. It has been used for the assessment of certain message volumes in a problem in which no alternate ways of determining the required answers were known. It will be assumed that only single bookings are made on a particular flight leg. The states indicated by the nodes are the number of seats sold. The probability that a booking is made is b_1, or $b_2, \ldots, b_{58}$, or b_{59}, depending on the number of seats sold. The probability that a cancellation is made is correspondingly

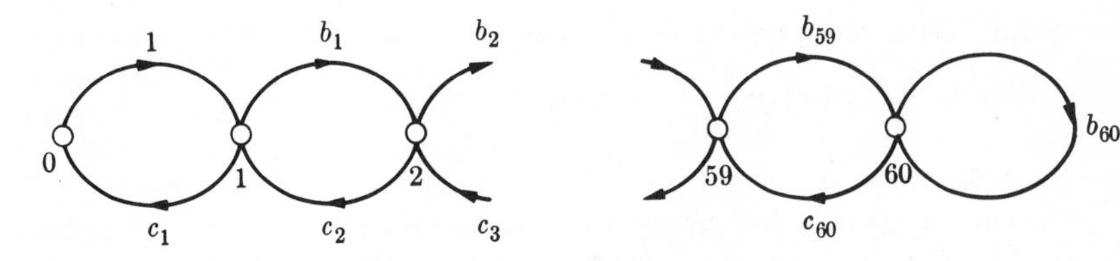

FIGURE 4. Booking/cancellation representation.

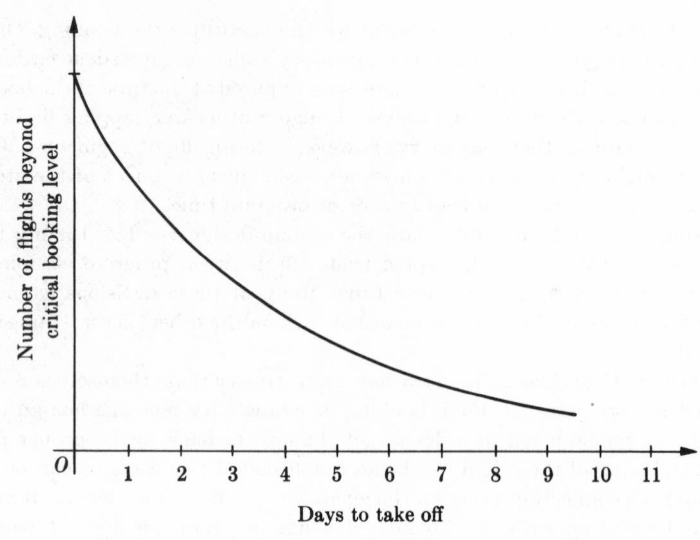

FIGURE 5. Critical booking level versus days to take-off.

$c_1, c_2, \ldots, c_{59}$, or c_{60}. If the flight is profitable, one assumes reasonably that the probability of a booking exceeds that of a cancellation. The state of a chain, as it is called, tends to move progressively from the left toward the right. This is an illustration of a stochastic process which is accessible to further analysis by known mathematical means.

Estimation of Drum Storage Capacity. In the design of the passenger space reservation system, the problem arose of estimating the amount of drum storage required at the central inventory computer. In the scheme used, flight tallies are stored on a drum on an exception basis. That is to say, initially when a flight has a low booking level, the corresponding seat tally is stored on magnetic tape. When the flight reaches a certain critical level, the tally is transferred to a drum. The question now arises concerning the number of flight tallies that must be provided for the drum storage. In other words, how many flights are at any time beyond the critical booking level? The answer may be obtained by studying the plot generated on the basis of available operating data (Fig. 5). The data were averaged over a 14-day period during the peak season before being used.

The area under this curve represents the required number of drum storage positions. With the data, it turned out that the curve could reasonably well be approximated by the function $N = Aq^n$, where N is the number of flights beyond the critical booking level, n is the number of days to take-off, and A and q are constants. With this approximation, the number of storage positions required can be calculated simply as $\dfrac{A}{1-q}$.

Returning once again to the principal example involving the determination of the basic system configuration, it is seen that the more satisfactory solution was, in practice, determined largely by successive trial and evaluation.

System considerations involving over-all configuration and structure are normally resolved in this manner. Adequate tools and concepts for more straightforward approaches are rare, and are only now in the process of development.

Such approaches will be introduced in the final illustration of a system design problem. The vehicle in this instance will be a global communications network. In contrast with the first illustration, the emphasis here will be on the use of very precise analytical tools for providing system solutions.

4.2 Global Military Communications Network. Communication networks may be classified in many ways. Circuit switched networks (represented by standard telephone circuits) operate so that each link in a route must be available simultaneously before end-to-end communication takes place. In contrast, message switched networks (represented by standard teletype or store-and-forward circuits) operate so that each message is forwarded as soon as the first link is available; the message is then stored at the first relay node until the second link in the route is available, and so on.

For simplicity, the example that follows deals only with the design and utilization of circuit switched networks [1]. In particular, its purpose is to outline a number of techniques applicable to *allocated* circuit switched networks. In an allocated circuit switched network, user traffic demands are converted and stated (at the outset) in terms of the *required number of circuits or trunks between each node pair*. Such allocated circuit networks find applicability in both commercial and military environments where fixed point-to-point communication is desired.

Problems in the design and utilization of allocated circuit switched networks have been previously treated by linear programing methods, particularly by Kalaba and Juncosa [6]. A significant aspect of the communication network problem that has not been treated in detail is that of design and utilization in the face of probabilistic demands or network resources [2]. Efficient network design and utilization may be viewed as an attempt to achieve as economical a match as possible between the demands that are imposed and the network resources that are brought to bear to satisfy these demands. Mismatches may then occur because either demands or network resources (or both) change. Continued efficient utilization then depends heavily on adjustments that may be made in response to these changes.

It is important to review first a few basic definitions. For convenience, a general network diagram is shown in Fig. 6. Nodes A, B, etc. can act as origins, relays, and destinations. Links AB, BE, FI, etc., are composed of a number of channels. A route is a sequence of connected links. A link may contribute channels to two or more circuits passing through it.

Three sets of network parameters are assumed to be given: network configuration, user demands, and network degradation (or element failure) matrices.

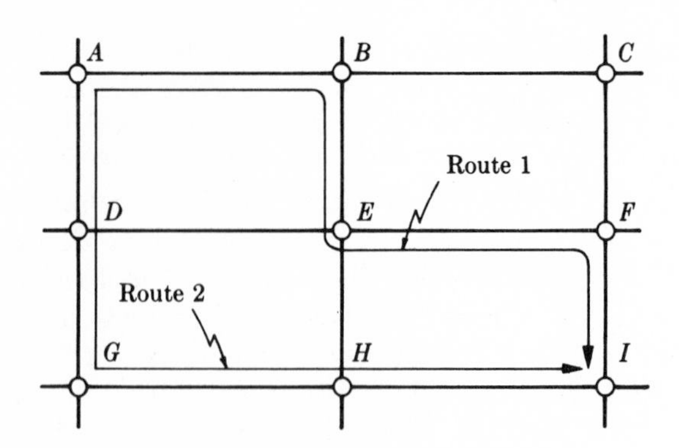

FIGURE 6. General network diagram.

Network Configuration. The number of nodes and their locations (distance from each other) are determined and fixed. The connectivity of the network is also specified. The network of Fig. 6 is drawn as a grid only for convenience; no such connectivity restriction is implied.

User Demand. The demand matrix is specified. Demands are given in terms of the number of required channels between each origin-destination pair. The measure of demand is thus assumed to be "number of channels." Demands are all for nonswitched service.

Network Degradation. The network is subject to physical destruction of links and nodes. The probability of link failure can be characterized by an $n \times n$ (n equal number of nodes) link matrix that specifies the probability of survival of each link in the network. Similarly, an $n \times 1$ (or $1 \times n$) node survivability matrix is also assumed to be given.

Two sets of network parameters must be determined: link capacities and restoral doctrine.

Link Capacity. The measure of capacity is also "number of channels." Any value of capacity is allowed between any node pair subject only to the following restriction for the entire network: the total number of "channel miles" must not exceed some preset value, say D.

Restoral Doctrine. Routes between each origin-destination pair requiring service are to be determined on an allocated basis, both initially and after degradation of the network (that is, after links and nodes fail). The selected routes remain fixed during each period in which the network suffers no additional degradation.

As stated, the problem contains all the essential features of a large-scale system defined earlier. The number of inputs (and outputs), representing messages flowing between network users, is large; the describing parameters of these inputs are statistical (arrival times, holding times, delays); the operation of the network depends heavily on the interplay between users and network facilities in dealing with such characteristics as message priorities, multiple address traffic, etc.; and finally, the system (network) is subject to both man-made and natural degradation. In fact, in this case, it is this last feature that provides the problem with its unique system characteristics.

The statement of the problem must be accompanied by the choice of suitable merit criteria. That is, the measure by which the performance of the network is to be judged must be selected. Since the network is subject to degradation to which the restoral doctrine must be responsive, it is natural to examine criteria based on the *expected* number of completed circuits—the expected number being obtained over all possible network configurations resulting from link or node failure. For example, for a network with a total of l links, each with a probability of survival less than unity, the total number of configurations is $U = 2^l$. This is true whether the nodes are perfectly reliable or not. Using the data provided by the link and node degradation matrices, it is then possible to compute directly the probability of occurrence of each possible network configuration, $p(u)$, where $u = 1, 2, \ldots, U$. For convenience, the merit criterion may be normalized by using the expected fractional demands satisfied for each node pair over all possible configurations. Thus, the network performance ratio, ρ, becomes:

$$\rho = \sum_u \left(\frac{\sum_{i,j} \begin{pmatrix}\text{number of circuits completed}\\ \text{between nodes } i \text{ and } j \text{ in } u\text{th}\\ \text{network configuration}\end{pmatrix}}{\sum_{i,j} \begin{pmatrix}\text{number of circuits desired}\\ \text{between nodes } i \text{ and } j\end{pmatrix}} \right) \times \begin{pmatrix}\text{probability of}\\ u\text{th network}\\ \text{configuration}\end{pmatrix}.$$

The problem may now be succinctly stated as follows: given a network connectivity pattern, a user demand matrix, and link and node survivability matrices, specify the link capacities, and the restoral doctrine for maximizing the expected number of allocated circuits for all origin-destination pairs subject only to the restriction that the total number of channel miles be less than a preset maximum value.

As stated, the problem may be formulated precisely in linear programing terms. In doing this, it is useful to define the principal network parameters as follows:

a_{ij} = the number of circuits desired between nodes i and j;
d_{ij} = distance between nodes i and j;
$p(u)$ = probability of occurrence of uth network configuration, where $u = 1$ represents the network with no link or node failures;
$c_{ij}{}^u$ = number of channels in the link between nodes i and j in the uth network configuration;
x^u_{ijk} = the number of circuits in link ij destined for node k in the uth network configuration;
ρ = system performance ratio.

The a_{ij} reflect the users' demands on the network; d_{ij} represents the channel mile distance between nodes i and j. For a network with l links, $U = 2^l$ possible network configurations; the probability of occurrence of each of these configurations is determined from the basic link and node failure probabilities and is designated $p(u)$. Link capacity $c_{ij}{}^u$ is equal to c_{ij} where link ij exists. Otherwise a zero value is used for $c_{ij}{}^u$ and this means that no direct link exists between nodes i and j in the uth configuration; in all such cases, x^u_{ijk} or x^u_{jik} is also zero. Finally, ρ is a probabilistic performance ratio expressing the fractional part of completed circuits averaged over all possible network configurations.

The linear program is then to maximize

$$\rho = \sum_u p(u) \left\{ \frac{\sum_{i,j} x^u_{ijj}}{\sum_{i,j} a_{ij}} \right\} \qquad \begin{array}{l} u = 1, 2, \ldots, U \\ i, j = 1, 2, \ldots, n \end{array}$$

subject to the following restrictions:

$$(1) \qquad \sum_k x^u_{jik} - \sum_k x^u_{kij} \leqslant a_{ij} \qquad \text{for all } u \text{ and all } i, j$$

$$(2) \qquad \sum_k x^u_{ijk} + \sum_k x^u_{jik} - c^u_{ij} \leqslant 0 \qquad \text{for all } u \text{ and all } i, j \text{ where } i < j$$

$$(3) \qquad \sum_{\substack{i,j \\ i<j}} c_{ij} d_{ij} \leqslant D \qquad \text{for all } i, j$$

$$(4) \qquad x^u_{ijk} \geqslant 0 \qquad \text{for all } i, j, k, \text{ and } u, \text{ but } i \neq j, i \neq k$$

$$(5) \qquad c_{ij} \geqslant 0 \qquad \text{for all } i, j \text{ where } i < j.$$

In the objective function, x^u_{ijj} denotes the number of circuits in link ij, terminating at node j (that is, completed) in the uth configuration. The first restriction states that for each configuration, the total number of circuits destined for node j, leaving node i, minus the total number destined for j entering node i, cannot exceed the demand between i and j. The second restriction states that for each configuration, the total number of circuits cannot exceed the available link capacity. The third restriction is that the total number of channel miles not exceed a maximum value D. The fourth and fifth restrictions are the nonnegative conditions. A solution of the linear program yields c_{ij}, the initial link capacities required, and the x^u_{ijk}. From the set of the x^u_{ijk} a corresponding network restoral doctrine for each network configuration may be easily constructed by methods described by Kalaba and Juncosa.

The foregoing example has been treated in considerable detail to illustrate how even very complex system problems may often be formulated and stated in precise analytical terms. This does not, however, mean that such formulations lead necessarily to tractable solutions. On the contrary, in the case illustrated above, it can be shown that for networks of eight to ten nodes the linear programing formulation becomes hopelessly large even for modern day computing machines.

What is the value, then, of these formulations? First, and most important, they provide insight into the structure of large-scale problems that is extremely difficult to obtain in any other way. Secondly, and equally important, they provide a reference against which less precise and less efficient methods may be compared. In other words, in the progression through successive design cycles, the exact solutions yield an end point in the accuracy-versus-complexity sensitivity relationship.

Finally, a word about implementation. The system design is not complete, of course, until methods for implementation of resulting doctrines are sought. Whether exact or approximate design and control methods are employed, these implementation methods must satisfy the following three conditions:

(1) they must permit knowledge of the status of the network to be disseminated to proper control points in the network;

(2) they must permit restoral solutions to be computed or selected;

(3) they must permit knowledge of proper restoral switching instructions to be disseminated to each node.

A wide variety of alternatives, both on-line and off-line, may be considered and evaluated. This, indeed, involves a marriage between computers and communication networks for real-time control and adaptation in the face of a continuously changing environment.

5. The Future of Systems Engineering

Current research activity in the control engineering field points toward the increasing combination of computer and control technologies, particularly in the extension of the concept of adaptive control to more and more elaborate systems. Similarly, considerable effort is being devoted to the planning and design of global communication networks in which real-time operation is strongly dependent on decisions provided by digital computers. At the same time, the use of geographically distributed data gathering devices, interconnected to regional or centralized decision making centers for the purposes of control of passenger space, air traffic, inventories, etc., are growing rapidly in business, industry and government.

In a very real sense, then, the era in which computers, control systems, and communication networks are being employed to operate in a highly integrated and interdependent fashion is practically here. During the next decade the enormous advances that will be made in their application will leave few areas untouched. Included in these will be the fields of merchandising, medicine, law, education, banking, and many others. Much of this activity will require that systems engineering continuously develop improved tools for planning and designing systems in which enormous quantities of data must be stored and organized in such a fashion that it may be consulted, distributed, and made available in short time to a large number of geographically distributed users. In most of these cases, no new technologies are required for implementation; the principal steps that remain are to design systems that can be proved to be economically justifiable. A few examples will serve to illustrate the major ideas [12].

Consider the practice of law. In the not too distant future, each practicing attorney might have in his office a means for direct access to a huge national repository of all the laws, rulings, regulations, and procedures that he needs. Direct queries may be made through an input-output device and communication network. At the central repository would be the capability for automatically searching, organizing, and distributing in a few seconds the equivalent results of dozens of trained searchers. This would enable the lawyer to devote a substantially larger fraction of time to the more complex intellectual tasks, and it would speed up a substantial fraction of legal practice.

The doctor also needs assistance in the performance of his daily tasks. The data of each patient's entire history, the results of all tests, symptoms, and complaints—all this may be stored in a central (that is, functionally) repository. Such a system can be organized to give the doctor, on request, key portions of the equivalent of many consultations with other physicians. It will give statistical probabilities of the relative efficiencies of various treatments. All this can be automatically provided by the machine, triggered by the specific detailed data that the physician introduced about his patient. Again the system will both raise the intellectual effort of the users and provide more rapid, more complete consultative aid.

It is difficult to find a better example for the use of communication, control, and computing facilities than air traffic control. It is clear that as the volume and speed of planes increases, the unaided human being cannot integrate all of the changing dynamic split-second facts to make decisions leading to the smoothest, safest use of available traffic space. Automatic predictions will have to be made concerning the alternatives for various contingencies. To do this, an enormous amount of data on the number of planes, spatial spread, etc., must be collected, organized, collated, and processed quickly, accurately, and reliably.

There is still another class of information systems for which technology is now in the early stages of development. It is important because it will influence the direction in which systems engineering must proceed if it is to cope successfully with new problems in the next decade. These systems stem from the exciting developments in recent years toward increasing the capabilities of man and computer to perform increasingly higher level information processing functions. In particular, reference is made to the enormous growth and activity in artificial intelligence, self-organizing machines, and man-machine systems [8, 11]. Included in the principal areas of artificial intelligence are learning and problem-solving activities. Self-organizing machines may be composed of variable networks, of which the elements are to be organized by the equipment to meet criteria of success in the environment in which they operate. In a more restricted area, self-adaptive systems are usually employed in feedback control systems for automatically modifying internal network parameters to optimize, stabilize, or otherwise improve performance. Intensive efforts are being made to extend the range of tasks assigned to machines so that man-machine can operate as an integrated problem solver, each performing those tasks for which it is best suited.

There is no doubt that developments in artificial intelligence, self-organizing devices and man-machine systems will result in more complex and powerful systems. It behooves systems engineers to understand the properties and limitations of these elements; but beyond this, there is a more immediate impact to the systems engineering process. This is, that the application of computers to a field of activity outside the fields that primarily employ mathematics and logic for their theories, causes that field to undergo greater formalization. For example, efforts to apply computers to medical diagnosis have already fostered useful standardization of terminology. Language translation has initiated exciting work on the theory of the structure of language. Thus, new areas of activity are open to the systems engineer providing opportunities for identifying, understanding, and organizing the basic elements of a new field.

APPENDIX

Annotated List of Tools and Techniques for the Systems Engineer

In outlining briefly those tools and techniques that show most promise and utility for the systems engineer, it is assumed that a core covering engineering, mathematics, and economic fundamentals has been previously acquired. Included in these is a basic knowledge of the theoretical and equipment aspects of computers (digital, analog, etc.), control systems (continuous, multivariable, sampled data, etc.), and communication networks (voice, teletype, facsimile, etc.). Also, it is assumed that a fundamental knowledge is included of probability and statistics (quality control, design of experiments, etc.), and mathematics dealing with relationships between aggregates (matrix algebra, set theory, linear graph theory, etc.). Finally, a knowledge of engineering economy and the methods of assessing and evaluating equipment and operational costs is presumed.

To this core must be added a wide variety of techniques drawn from many fields, a few of which are enumerated in the following.

(1) Modeling (symbolic representations; flow charts; computer simulation; Monte Carlo methods). A model is a representation of a system under study. The representation may be completely in symbolic form or in the form of flow charts and block diagrams. The objective is to depict or describe functional relationships so that such relationships may be examined under a variety of conditions with respect to suitably selected merit criteria. These models achieve their utility from the fact that it is generally easier to examine and manipulate symbols or flow charts than the system elements themselves.

In many cases the mathematical model becomes unsolvable for the complex system; in other cases the required simplifying assumptions make the results only marginally applicable to the real problem. Simulation, using computer and Monte Carlo techniques, is then often employed to study system behavior. In this case a stochastic model of a real situation is set up and then sampling experiments are performed on the model. It should be emphasized that simulation yields only an empirical form of knowledge; in this sense, it is inferior to mathematical models that lead directly to functional relationships.

(2) System Dynamics (linear operators; state diagrams; stability criteria). Flow graph representations are limited to static systems exhibiting constant inputs. More generally the dynamics of a system must be considered in which the variables are subject to both internal and external changes. Accordingly, techniques for specifying input-output relationships, linear stationary operators, frequency and time-domain representations, state diagrams for probabilistic systems, and stability criteria must be studied.

(3) Optimization (linear programing; queuing theory; information theory; game theory). At some time in the design process, the systems engineer is concerned with the evaluation and selection of these alternatives that achieve optimum trade-off (in some sense) among the principal variables. A number of analytical tools may be employed to examine the essential relationships between the variables in an effort to find optima. Four principal techniques are selected for brief mention.

(a) Linear Programing. Although the fundamental relationships among system variables are usually nonlinear when considered over their entire range, piecewise linearity may often be advantageously assumed. The ability to handle a large number of interacting variables by the methods of linear programing represents one of the most valuable tools for analysis of the technical and economic aspects of a system.

(b) Queuing Theory. Congestion theory is a formal body of knowledge designed to deal with complex problems of organization and planning in the face of randomly fluctuating demand of some service to be performed. Since one of the principal features of an information system is the statistical nature of inputs and outputs, the application of queuing theory to system design assumes prime importance.

(c) Information Theory. The common thread for the system under consideration is information. A basic understanding of the fundamental nature and relationships existing among such variables as information rate, channel capacity and bandwidth, error rate, etc., is therefore necessary. A large body of knowledge exists based on the work of Wiener, Shannon, and many others.

(d) Game Theory. Still another promising technique for the systems engineer is game theory. This discipline deals with systems in which two or more decision makers are in competition. Extensive applications have already been made to military and industrial operations research problems. Although these applications have so far been limited, a wider impact of the technique on social sciences, operations research, and systems engineering is expected.

BIBLIOGRAPHY

1. Amara, R. C., "Computer design and control of probabilistic communication networks," IRE Trans. on Commun. Systems (March, 1963).
2. Dantzig, G. B., "Linear programing under uncertainty," Management Sci. 197–206 (April-July, 1955).
3. Eckman, D. P., *Systems: Research and Design*, Wiley, 1961.
4. Flagle, C. D., Huggins, W. H., and Roy, R. H., *Operations Research and Systems Engineering*, Johns Hopkins, 1960.
5. Goode, H. H., and Machol, R. E., *Systems Engineering*, McGraw-Hill, 1957.
6. Kalaba, R. E., and Juncosa, M. L., "Optimum design and utilization of communication networks," Management Sci. 33–44 (October, 1956).
7. Kron, G., "A method of solving very large physical systems in easy stages," Proc. Inst. Radio Engrs. 680–686 (April, 1954).
8. Licklider, J. C. R., "Man-computer symbiosis," IRE Trans. on Human Factors in Electronics 4–11 (March, 1960).
9. Meisling, T. H., "Technical and Managerial Problems Arising in the Design of Information Handling Systems," Paper presented before the Integrated Data Processing Committee of S.I.T.A., Paris, December, 1959.

Significant contributions to the range of systems problems described were made by various members of the Systems Engineering Laboratory at Stanford Research Institute. Chief among these were Dr. Oliver Whitby, and Messrs. Bonnar Cox and David Nee.

10. Ponstein, J., "Matrix description of networks," J. Src. Ind. and Appl. Math. 233–267 (June, 1961).
11. Proc. Inst. Radio Engrs., Special Issue on Computers (January, 1961).
12. Ramo, S., "The Coming Technological Society," an address to the First Engineering Assembly at Stanford University, May 25, 1961.
13. Unk, J. M., "Communication networks for digital information," IRE Trans. on Communication Systems 207–214 (December, 1960).
14. Wiesner, J. B., "Communication sciences in a university environment," IBM Journal 268–275 (October, 1958).

Index

Printed in the United States of America